The Council of State Government

STATE DIRECTORY

Directory III—
Administrative Officials 2011

The Council of State Governments
2760 Research Park Drive
Lexington, KY 40511-8482

Contact the Publication Sales Department at
1-800-800-1910 or sales@csg.org to order:

Directory I—Elective Officials 2011,

Directory II—Legislative Leadership, Committees and Staff 2011,

Directory III—Administrative Officials 2011

or mailing lists of state government officials.

Since 1933, The Council of State Governments has served our nation's state leaders by providing a forum for "sharing capitol ideas." As the only state services organization spanning all three branches of government, CSG offers a unique look into the issues shaping state policy and legislation from the national and regional perspectives. This unique arrangement contributes to a strong national presence for CSG, creating unparalleled opportunities to network, collaborate and form problem-solving partnerships.

The Council of State Governments Officers

President **Gov. Brian Schweitzer**, Mont. ▪ *President-Elect* **Gov. Luis Fortuño**, P.R.

Chair **Rep. Bob Godfrey**, Conn. ▪ *Vice Chair* **Sen. Gary Stevens**, Alaska

The Council of State Governments

David Adkins, Executive Director CEO

2760 Research Park Drive ▪ P.O. Box 11910 ▪ Lexington, KY 40578-1910 ▪ (859) 244-8000 ▪ Fax: (859) 244-8001 ▪ www.csg.org

Eastern Office	**Midwestern Office**	**Southern Office**	**Western Office**	**Washington Office**
Wendell M. Hannaford, Director	*Michael H. McCabe, Director*	*Colleen Cousineau, Director*	*Kent Briggs, Director*	*Christopher Whatley, Director*
100 Wall Street, 20th Floor	701 East 22nd Street, Suite 110	P.O. Box 98129	1107 9th Street, Suite 730	444 N. Capitol Street, N.W., Suite 401
New York, NY 10005	Lombard, IL 60148	Atlanta, GA 30359	Sacramento, CA 95814	Washington, DC 20001
(212) 482-2320	(630) 925-1922	(404) 633-1866	(916) 553-4423	(202) 624-5460
Fax: (212) 482-2344	Fax: (630) 925-1930	Fax: (404) 633-4896	Fax: (916) 446-5760	Fax: (202) 624-5452
www.csgeast.org	www.csgmidwest.org	www.slcatlanta.org	www.csgwest.org	www.csg.org

Editorial Staff

Kelley Arnold ▪ Jessica Clay ▪ Eric Lancaster ▪ Heather Perkins

*Special thanks to the CSG regional offices
and the clerks and secretaries of the legislature for each state.*

Table of Contents

How to Use This Directory

This annual directory provides basic information about elected and appointed officials with primary responsibility in more than 110 state government functions. The directory includes names, addresses, telephone, fax and e-mail addresses. The information is organized alphabetically by function (e.g., Labor) and by state and U.S. jurisdiction name. Generally, there is one entry per function for each state or U.S. jurisdiction. State names and jurisdictions are not listed if there is not a corresponding entry for a given section.

CSG collected the information for the 2011 directory between March and May 2011. The data contained in this volume was compiled through one of three methods. First, national associations were given the opportunity to provide a roster for the directory. For those categories that did not have rosters provided, the information was gathered through two other methods. Each state and territory was sent a survey requesting updated information for their administrative officials. If states did not respond to the surveys, CSG staff collected the updated information from state-sponsored Web sites or phone calls to state offices.

Party Abbreviations

D	Democrat
R	Republican
REFORM	Reform
C	Covenant
I	Independent
L	Libertarian
S	Statehood
ICM	Independent Citizen Movement
DFL	Democratic-Farmer-Labor
NP	Nonpartisan
P	Progressive
NPP	New Progressive Party
PDP	Popular Democratic Party
PIP	Puerto Rican Independent Party
RA	Rural Alaskan
TRIBAL	Delegate representing a Native American tribe
U	Unenrolled

Adjutant General

The executive or administrative head of the state's military service.

ALABAMA
Maj. Gen. Perry G. Smith
Adjutant General
National Guard
P.O. Box 3711
Montgomery, AL 36109
P: (334) 271-7200
F: (334) 271-7366

ALASKA
Brigadier Thomas H. Katkus
Acting Adjutant General
Department of Military &
Veterans Affairs
P.O. Box 5800
Camp Denali
Fort Richardson, AK 99505
P: (907) 428-6003
F: (907) 428-6019

AMERICAN SAMOA
Hon. Fepulea'i A.
  Ripley Jr.
Attorney General
Office of the Attorney General
American Samoa Government
Executive Office Building,
Utulei
Pago Pago, AS 96799
P: (684) 633-4163
F: (684) 633-1838

ARIZONA
Maj. Gen. Hugo E. Salazar
Adjutant General
Department of Emergency &
Military Affairs
5636 East McDowell Road
Phoenix, AZ 85008
P: (602) 267-2710
F: (602) 267-2715

ARKANSAS
Maj. Gen. William D.
  Wofford
Adjutant General
Military Department
Camp Robinson
North Little Rock, AR 72199
P: (510) 212-5001
F: (510) 212-5009
E: william.d.wofford
  @ar.ngb.army.mil

CALIFORNIA
Brigadier Mary J. Kight
Adjutant General
Military Department
9800 Goethe Road
P.O. Box 269101
Sacramento, CA 95826
P: (916) 854-3500
F: (916) 854-3671

COLORADO
Brig. Gen. H. Michael
  Edwards
Adjutant General
Department of Military Affairs
6848 South Revere Parkway
Englewood, CO 80112
P: (720) 250-1500
F: (720) 250-1509

CONNECTICUT
Maj. Gen. Thaddeus Martin
Adjutant General
Military Department
Governor William A. O'Neill
State Armory
360 Broad Street
Hartford, CT 06105
P: (860) 524-4953
F: (860) 524-4953

DELAWARE
Maj. Gen. Francis D. Vavala
Adjutant General
National Guard
First Regiment Road
Wilmington, DE 19808
P: (302) 326-7001
F: (302) 326-7029
E: frank.vavala
  @de.ngb.army.mil

DISTRICT OF COLUMBIA
Maj. Gen. Errol R. Schwartz
Commanding General
National Guard
National Guard Armory
2001 East Capitol Street, SE
Washington, DC 20003
P: (202) 685-9790

FLORIDA
Maj. Gen. Emmett R. Titshaw
Adjutant General
Department of Military Affairs
P.O. Box 1008
St. Augustine, FL 32084
P: (904) 823-0101
F: (904) 823-0149
E: emmett.titshaw
  @fl.ngb.army.mil

GEORGIA
Maj. Gen. William T.
  Nesbitt
Adjutant General
Department of Defense
P.O. Box 1970
Marietta, GA 30061
P: (678) 569-6001

GUAM
Maj. Gen. Benny M. Paulino
Adjutant General
National Guard
430 Army Drive
Building 300
Barrigada, GU 96913
P: (671) 735-0400
E: benny.paulino
  @gu.ngb.army.mil

HAWAII
Maj. Gen. Darryl D.M. Wong
Adjutant General
Department of Defense
3949 Diamond Head Road
Honolulu, HI 96816
P: (808) 733-4246
F: (808) 733-4499

IDAHO
Maj. Gen. Gary L. Sayler
Adjutant General
Military Division
4040 West Guard Building 600
Boise, ID 83705
P: (208) 422-5242
F: (208) 422-6179

ILLINOIS
Maj. Gen. William L. Enyart
Adjutant General
National Guard
1301 North MacArthur
Boulevard
Springfield, IL 62702
P: (217) 761-3500
F: (217) 761-3736

INDIANA
Maj. Gen. R. Martin
  Umbarger
Adjutant General
Adjutant General's Office
2002 South Holt Road
Indianapolis, IN 46241
P: (317) 247-3300
F: (317) 247-3540

KANSAS
Maj. Gen. Lee E.
  Tafanelli (R)
Adjutant General
Adjutant General's Department
2800 South Topeka Boulevard
Topeka, KS 66611
P: (785) 274-1001
F: (913) 274-1682

KENTUCKY
Maj. Gen. Edward W. Tonini
Adjutant General
Department of Military Affairs
100 Minuteman Parkway
Frankfort, KY 40601
P: (502) 607-1240
F: (502) 607-1558

LOUISIANA
Maj. Gen. Bennett C.
  Landreneau Jr.
Adjutant General
National Guard
Building 305, F Street
Camp Beauregard
Pineville, LA 71360
P: (318) 290-3858

MAINE
Maj. Gen. John W. Libby
Adjutant General
Department of Defense,
Veterans & Military Affairs
Camp Keyes
Augusta, ME 04333
P: (207) 626-4271
F: (207) 626-4509

MARYLAND
Maj. Gen. James Adkins
Adjutant General
Military Department
5th Regiment Armory
29th Division Street
Baltimore, MD 21201
P: (410) 576-6097
F: (410) 576-6079
E: bruce.tuxill
  @md.ngb.army.mil

MASSACHUSETTS
Maj. Gen. Joseph C.
  Carter Jr.
Adjutant General
Headquarters, National Guard
50 Maple Street
Milford, MA 01757
P: (508) 233-6552
F: (508) 233-6554

Adjutant General

MICHIGAN
Maj. Gen. George J. Vadnais
Adjutant General
Department of Military &
Veterans Affairs
3411 North Martin Luther King
Lansing, MI 48906
P: (517) 481-8083
F: (517) 481-8125

MINNESOTA
Maj. Gen. Richard Nash
Adjutant General
Department of Military Affairs
Veterans Services Building, 4th
Floor
20 West 12th Street, #115
St. Paul, MN 55155
P: (651) 268-8924
F: (651) 282-4541

MISSISSIPPI
Maj. Gen. Bill A. Freeman
Adjutant General
National Guard
P.O. Box 5027
Jackson, MS 39296
P: (601) 313-6232
F: (601) 313-6251

MISSOURI
Brigadier Stephen L. Danner
Adjutant General
National Guard
2302 Militia Drive
Jefferson City, MO 65101
P: (573) 638-9500
F: (573) 638-9722

MONTANA
Brigadier John E. Walsh
Adjutant General
Department of Military Affairs
P.O. Box 4789
Fort Harrison, MT 59636
P: (406) 324-3000
F: (406) 841-3011
E: john.walsh
@mt.ngb.army.mil

NEBRASKA
Brigadier Judd Lyons
Adjutant General
National Guard
1300 Military Road
Lincoln, NE 68508
P: (402) 309-7100
F: (402) 309-7147

NEVADA
Brigadier William R. Burks
Adjutant General
National Guard
2460 Fairview Drive
Carson City, NV 89701
P: (775) 887-7302
F: (775) 887-7315

NEW HAMPSHIRE
Maj. Gen. William N.
Reddel III
Adjutant General
National Guard
4 Pembroke Road
Concord, NH 03301
P: (603) 225-1200
F: (603) 225-1257

NEW JERSEY
Maj. Gen. Glenn K. Rieth
Adjutant General
Department of Military and
Veterans Affairs
P.O. Box 340
Trenton, NJ 08625
P: (609) 530-6957
F: (609) 530-7191
E: glenn.rieth
@njdmava.state.nj.us

NEW MEXICO
Maj. Gen. Kenny C. Montoya
Adjutant General
Military Affairs Department
47 Bataan Boulevard
East Frontage Road
Santa Fe, NM 87508
P: (505) 474-1200

NEW YORK
Maj. Gen. Patrick A. Murphy
Adjutant General
Division of Military & Naval
Affairs
330 Old Niskayuna Road
Latham, NY 12110
P: (518) 786-4502
F: (518) 786-4325

NORTH CAROLINA
Maj. Gen. Gregory A. Lusk
Adjutant General
National Guard
4105 Reedy Creek Road
Raleigh, NC 27607
P: (919) 664-6101
F: (919) 664-6400

NORTH DAKOTA
Maj. Gen. David A.
Sprynczynatyk
Adjutant General
National Guard
Fraine Barracks
P.O. Box 5511
Bismarck, ND 58506
P: (701) 333-2001
F: (701) 333-2017
E: david.sprynczynatyk
@us.army.mil

OHIO
Maj. Gen. Deborah A.
Ashenhurst
Adjutant General
National Guard
2825 West Dublin Granville
Road
Columbus, OH 43235
P: (614) 336-7070
F: (614) 336-7074

OKLAHOMA
Maj. Gen. Myles L. Deering
Adjutant General
National Guard
3501 Military Circle
Oklahoma City, OK 73111
P: (405) 228-5201
F: (405) 228-5524
E: myles.deering
@us.army.mil

OREGON
Maj. Gen. Raymond F. Rees
Adjutant General
Office of the Adjutant General
Military Department
P.O. Box 14350
Salem, OR 97309
P: (503) 584-3991
F: (503) 584-3962
E: raymond.f.rees
@state.or.us

PENNSYLVANIA
Maj. Gen. Stephen M. Sischo
Adjutant General
Department of Military &
Veterans Affairs
Building S-0-47, Room 200
Fort Indiantown Gap
Annville, PA 17003
P: (717) 861-8500
F: (717) 861-8314

PUERTO RICO
Maj. Gen. Antonio J.
Vicens-Gonzalez
Adjutant General
National Guard
P.O. Box 9023786
San Juan, PR 00901
P: (787) 721-3131
F: (787) 723-6360

RHODE ISLAND
Maj. Gen. Robert T. Bray
Adjutant General
National Guard
Joint Force Headquarters
645 New London Avenue
Cranston, RI 02920
P: (401) 275-4102
F: (401) 275-4338

SOUTH CAROLINA
Maj. Gen. Robert
Livingston Jr.
Adjutant General
National Guard
One National Guard Road
Columbia, SC 29201
P: (803) 806-4217
F: (803) 803-4468

SOUTH DAKOTA
Maj. Gen. Tim Reisch
Adjutant General
Department of Military &
Veterans Affairs
Soliders & Sailors Memorial
Building
425 East Capitol Avenue
Pierre, SD 57501
P: (605) 773-3269
F: (605) 773-5380

TENNESSEE
Maj. Gen. Terry M. Haston
Adjutant General
Military Department
Houston Barracks
P.O. Box 41502
Nashville, TN 41502
P: (615) 313-3001
F: (615) 313-3100

TEXAS
Maj. Gen. Jose S. Mayorga
Adjutant General
Adjutant General's Department
2200 West 35th Street
P.O. Box 5218
Austin, TX 78703
P: (512) 782-5006
F: (512) 465-5578

U.S. VIRGIN ISLANDS
Mr. Renaldo Rivera
Adjutant General
National Guard
4031 LaGrande Princess, Lot 1B
Christiansted, VI 00820
P: (340) 712-7710
F: (340) 712-7711
E: renaldo.rivera
    @vi.ngb.army.mil

UTAH
Maj. Gen. Brian L. Tarbet
Adjutant General
Army National Guard
12953 South Minuteman Drive
Draper, UT 84020
P: (801) 432-4401
F: (801) 432-4677
E: btarbet2@NTLGUARD.MNE1

VERMONT
Maj. Gen. Michael D. Dubie
Adjutant General
Office of the Adjutant General
Camp Johnson
789 Vermont National Guard
Road
Colchester, VT 05446
P: (802) 338-3124
F: (802) 338-3425
E: michael.dubie
    @vt.ngb.army.mil

VIRGINIA
Maj. Gen. Daniel E.
    Long Jr.
Adjutant General
National Guard
202 North 9th Street, Fourth
Floor
9th Street Office Building
Richmond, VA 23219
P: (804) 371-2526
F: (804) 371-0073

WASHINGTON
Maj. Gen. Timothy J.
    Lowenberg
Adjutant General
Military Department
Camp Murray, Building 1
Tacoma, WA 98327
P: (253) 512-8000
F: (253) 512-8497

WEST VIRGINIA
Mr. James A. Hoyer
Adjutant General
Army National Guard
1703 Coonskin Drive
Charleston, WV 25311
P: (304) 561-6316
F: (304) 561-6327

WISCONSIN
Maj. Gen. Donald Dunbar
Adjutant General
Department of Military Affairs
P.O. Box 8111
Madison, WI 53708
P: (608) 242-3001
F: (608) 242-3111
E: donald.p.dunbar
    @ng.army.mil

WYOMING
Maj. Gen. Edward L. Wright
Adjutant General
Military Department
5500 Bishop Boulevard
Cheyenne, WY 82009
P: (307) 772-5234
F: (307) 772-5010
E: ed.boenisch
    @wy.ngb.army.mil

Administration

Umbrella agency of administration that coordinates administrative services provided to state agencies.

Information provided by:

National Association of State Chief Administrators
Marcia Stone
Association Director
2760 Research Park Drive
P.O. Box 11910
Lexington, KY 40578
P: (859) 244-8181
F: (859) 244-8001
mstone@csg.org
www.nasca.org

ALABAMA
Mr. David Perry
Director
Department of Finance
State Capitol
600 Dexter Avenue, Suite N-105
Montgomery, AL 36130
P: (334) 242-7160
F: (334) 353-3300
E: david.perry
    @finance.alabama.gov

ALASKA
Ms. Becky Hultberg
Commissioner
Department of Administration
P.O. Box 110200
Juneau, AK 99811
P: (907) 465-5671
F: (907) 465-2135
E: becky.hultberg
    @alaska.gov

ARIZONA
Mr. Scott Smith
Director
Department of Administration
100 North 15th Avenue, Suite 401
Phoenix, AZ 85007
P: (602) 542-1500

ARKANSAS
Mr. Richard Weiss
Administrator
Department of Finance & Administration
P.O. Box 2485
Little Rock, AR 72203
P: (501) 682-2242
F: (501) 682-1029
E: richard.weiss
    @dfa.state.ar.us

CALIFORNIA
Mr. Fred Klass
Chief Operating Officer
Department of General Services
State Capitol, Room 1145
Sacramento, CA 95814
P: (916) 445-4923
F: (916) 445-7997
E: david.botelho@dof.ca.gov

COLORADO
Ms. Kathy Nesbitt
Executive Director
Department of Personnel & Administration
Suite 1600, 633 17th Street
Denver, CO 80202
P: (303) 866-6559

CONNECTICUT
Mr. Martin W. Anderson
Commissioner
Department of Administrative Services
165 Capitol Avenue
Room 491
Hartford, CT 06106
P: (860) 713-5100
F: (860) 713-7481
E: martin.anderson@ct.gov

Mr. Donald J. DeFronzo
Commissioner
Department of Administrative Services
165 Capitol Avenue
Hartford, CT 06106
P: (860) 713-5100

DELAWARE
Ms. Ann Shepard Visalli
Director
Office of Management & Budget
Haslet Armory
122 William Penn Street
Dover, DE 19901
P: (302) 739-4204
F: (302) 739-5661
E: Ann.Visalli@state.de.us

FLORIDA
Mr. Jack Miles
Secretary
Department of Management Services
4050 Esplande Way, Suite 280
Tallahassee, FL 32399
P: (850) 488-2786
F: (850) 922-6149

GEORGIA
Mr. Sid Johnson
Commissioner
Department of Administrative Services
200 Piedmont Avenue, 1804 West Tower
Atlanta, GA 30334
P: (404) 656-5514

HAWAII
Mr. Bruce Coppa
State Comptroller
Department of Accounting & General Services
P.O. Box 119
Honolulu, HI 96810
P: (808) 586-0400
F: (808) 586-0775
E: bruce.a.coppa@hawaii.gov

IDAHO
Ms. Teresa Luna
Director
Department of Administration
650 West State Street, Room 100
P.O. Box 83720
Boise, ID 83720
P: (208) 332-1827
F: (208) 334-2307
E: teresa.luna
    @adm.idaho.gov

ILLINOIS
Mr. James P. Sledge
Director
Department of Central Services Management
JRTC 100 W. Randolph, Suite 4-500
Chicago, IL 60601
P: (312) 814-2648

INDIANA
Mr. Robert Wynkoop
Commissioner
Department of Administration
402 West Washington Street, Room W478
Indianapolis, IN 46204
P: (317) 234-232-3185

IOWA
Mr. Mike Carroll
Director
Department of Administrative Services
1305 East Walnut Street
Hoover Building, 3rd Floor
Des Moines, IA 50319
P: (515) 281-3273

KANSAS
Mr. Dennis Taylor
Secretary
Department of Administration
Suite 500, 1000 Southwest Jackson
Topeka, KS 66612
P: (785) 296-4278

KENTUCKY
Ms. Lori Flanery
Cabinet Secretary
Department of Finance & Administration
Room 383, Capitol Annex
Frankfort, KY 40601
P: (502) 564-4240
F: (502) 564-5856
E: Lori.Flanery@ky.gov

LOUISIANA
Mr. Paul Rainwater
Commissioner of Administration
Division of Administration
1201 North Third Street
Claiborne Building
Baton Rouge, LA 70802
P: (225) 342-7000

MAINE
Mr. H. Sawin Millett Jr.
Commissioner
Department of Administration
78 State House Station
Augusta, ME 04333
P: (207) 624-7800
F: (207) 624-7804

MARYLAND
Mr. Alvin Collins
Secretary
Department of General Services
301 West Preston Street, Suite 1401
Baltimore, MD 21201
P: (410) 767-4960
E: alvin.collins
    @dgs.state.md.us

MASSACHUSETTS
Mr. Jay Gonzalez
Secretary
Office for Administration & Finance
State House, Room 373
Boston, MA 02133
P: (617) 727-2040
E: jay.gonzalez@state.ma.us

MICHIGAN
Mr. John Nixon
Director
Department of Technology,
Management & Budget
320 South Walnut Street
P.O Box 30026
Lansing, MI 48909
P: (517) 241-5150

MINNESOTA
Mr. Spencer Cronk
Commissioner
Department of Administration
50 Sherburne Avenue
200 Administration Building
St. Paul, MN 55155
P: (651) 201-2555
F: (651) 297-7909
E: Spencer.Cronk
@state.mn.us

MISSISSIPPI
Mr. Kevin J. Upchurch
Executive Director
Department of Finance &
Administration
P.O. Box 267
Jackson, MS 39201
P: (601) 359-3402
F: (601) 359-2405
E: kupchurch
@dfa.state.ms.us

MISSOURI
Mr. Kelvin Simmons
Commissioner
Office of Administration
Room 125, State Capitol
Building
P.O. Box 809
Jefferson City, MO 65102
P: (573) 751-1851
F: (573) 751-7258
E: comofc@oa.mo.gov

MONTANA
Hon. Janet Kelly
Director
Department of Administration
125 North Roberts Street
Room 155, Mitchell Building
Helena, MT 59620
P: (406) 444-3033
F: (406) 444-6194
E: jakelly@mt.gov

NEBRASKA
Mr. Carlos Castillo
Director
Department of Administrative
Services
State Capitol, Room 1315
Lincoln, NE 68509
P: (402) 471-2331
E: carlos.castillo
@email.state.ne.us

NEVADA
Mr. Andrew K. Clinger
Director
Department of Administration
Balsdel Building
209 East Musser Street, Room
200
Carson City, NV 89701
P: (775) 684-0222
F: (775) 684-0260
E: aclinger
@budget.state.nv.us

NEW HAMPSHIRE
Ms. Linda M. Hodgdon
Commissioner
Department of Administrative
Services
25 Capitol Street, Room 120
State House Annex
Concord, NH 03301
P: (603) 271-3201
F: (603) 271-6600
E: linda.hodgdon@nh.gov

NEW JERSEY
Mr. David Ridolfino
Director & Chief Financial
Officer
Department of the Treasury
P.O. Box 211
Trenton, NJ 08625
P: (609) 633-2826

Hon. Andrew P.
     Sidamon-Eristoff
State Treasurer
Department of the Treasury
State House
P.O. Box 002
Trenton, NJ 08625
P: (608) 292-6748
F: (609) 984-3888

NEW MEXICO
Mr. Ed Burckle
Cabinet Secretary
General Services Department
P.O. Drawer 26110
Santa Fe, NM 87502
P: (505) 827-2000

NEW YORK
Ms. RoAnn M. Destito
Commissioner
Office of General Services
41st Floor, Corning Tower
Empire State Plaza
Albany, NY 12242
P: (518) 474-3899

NORTH CAROLINA
Mr. Moses Carey Jr.
Secretary
Department of Administration
116 West Jones Street, Suite
5106
Raleigh, NC 27699
P: (919) 807-2341
F: (919) 733-9420
E: m.carey@ncesc.gov

NORTH DAKOTA
Ms. Pam Sharp
Director
Office of Management &
Budget
600 East Boulevard Avenue
Department 110
Bismarck, ND 58505
P: (701) 328-2680
F: (701) 328-3230
E: psharp@nd.gov

OHIO
Mr. Bob Blair
Director
Department of Administrative
Services
30 East Broad Street, Suite 4040
Columbus, OH 43215
P: (614) 466-6511
F: (614) 644-8151
E: robert.blair
@das.state.oh.us

OKLAHOMA
Mr. John Richard
Director
Department of Central Services
10801 East Apple Valley Road
Oklahoma City, OK 73151
P: (405) 521-2124
F: (405) 521-6403
E: john_richard
@dcs.state.ok.us

OREGON
Mr. Michael Jordan
Director
Department of Administrative
Services
155 Cottage Street, Northeast,
U20
Salem, OR 97301
P: (503) 373-0914

Ms. Kris Kautz
Acting Agency Director
Department of Administrative
Services
155 Cottage St. Northeast, U20
Salem, OR 97301
P: (503) 378-5967
E: Kristine.M.Kautz
@das.state.or.us

PENNSYLVANIA
Ms. Kelly Logan
Secretary
Office of Administration
Finance Building
Harrisburg, PA 17102
P: (717) 787-9945

Ms. Sheri Phillips
Secretary
Department of General Services
515 North Office Building
Harrisburg, PA 17125
P: (717) 787-5996

Ms. Kelly Powell Logan
Secretary
Governor's Office of
Administration
613 North Street, Room 207
Finance Building
Harrisburg, PA 17120
P: (717) 787-9945

RHODE ISLAND
Mr. Richard Licht
Department of Administration
One Capitol Hill
Providence, RI 02908
P: (401) 222-2280

SOUTH CAROLINA
Ms. Eleanor Kitzman
Executive Director
Budget & Control Board
1200 Senate Street, Suite 600
Columbia, SC 29201
P: (803) 734-2320
F: (803) 734-2117

SOUTH DAKOTA
Mr. Paul Kinsman
Commissioner
Bureau of Administration
500 East Capital Avenue
Pierre, SD 57501
P: (605) 773-3688
F: (605) 773-3887

Administration

TENNESSEE
Mr. Steven Cates
Commissioner
Department of General Services
312 8th Avenue, North
24th Floor
Nashville, TN 37243
P: (615) 741-9270

TEXAS
Mr. Terry Keel
Executive Director
Facilities Commission
1711 San Jacinto
Austin, TX 78701
P: (512) 463-3446
E: terry.keel
    @tfc.state.tx.us

UTAH
Ms. Kimberly Hood
Executive Director
Administrative Services
3120 State Office Building
Salt Lake City, UT 84010
P: (801) 538-3215
F: (801) 538-3844
E: vschoenfeld@utah.gov

VERMONT
Mr. Jeb Spaulding
Secretary of Administration
Agency of Administration
109 State Street
Montpelier, VT 05609
P: (802) 828-3322
E: jeb.spaulding
    @state.vt.us

VIRGINIA
Mr. Richard F. Sliwoski
Director
Department of General Services
1100 Bank Street, Suite 420
Richmond, VA 23219
P: 804-786-3311
F: 804-371-8305
E: richard.sliwoski
    @dgs.virginia.gov

WASHINGTON
Ms. Joyce Turner
Director
Department of General
Administration
P.O. Box 41000
Olympia, WA 98504
P: (360) 902-7300
E: joyce.turner@ga.wa.gov

WEST VIRGINIA
Mr. Robert Ferguson
Cabinet Secretary
Department of Administration
Building 1, Room E-119
1900 Kanawha Boulevard, East
Charleston, WV 25305
P: (304) 558-4331
F: (304) 558-2999
E: secretary.
    administration@wv.gov

WISCONSIN
Mr. Michael D. Huebsch
Secretary
Department of Administration
10th Floor, 101 East Wilson
Street
Madison, WI 53703
P: (608) 266-1741

WYOMING
Mr. Christopher Boswell
Director
Department of Administration &
Information
700 West 21st Street
Cheyenne, WY 82002
P: (307) 777-6414
E: cboswe@wyo.gov

Aging

Develops and strengthens services for the aged and conducts or promotes research into their problems.

ALABAMA
Ms. Irene B. Collins
Commissioner
Department of Senior Services
770 Washington Avenue
RSA Plaza, Suite 470
Montgomery, AL 36130
P: (334) 242-5743
F: (334) 242-5594
E: Irene.collins
@adss.alabama.gov

ALASKA
Mr. William Streur
Commissioner
Department of Health and
Social Services
3601 C Street
Suite 902
Anchorage, AK 99503
P: (907) 465-3030
F: (907) 465-3068
E: william.streur
@alaska.gov

AMERICAN SAMOA
Mr. Taesalialii F. Lutu
Director
Territorial Administration on
Aging
American Samoa Government
Pago Pago, AS 96799
P: (684) 633-1251
F: (684) 633-2533

ARIZONA
Ms. Melanie K. Starns
Assistant Director
Division of Aging & Adult
Services
Department of Economic
Security
1789 West Jefferson, No. 950A
Phoenix, AZ 85007
P: (602) 542-4446
F: (602) 542-6575
E: mstarns@azdes.gov

ARKANSAS
Ms. Krista Hughes
Assistant Director
Division of Aging & Adult
Services
P.O. Box 1437
700 Main Street, 5th Floor, S530
Little Rock, AR 72203
P: (501) 682-2441
F: (501) 682-8155

COLORADO
Mr. Todd Coffey
SUA Director
Division of Aging & Adult
Services
Department of Human Services
1575 Sherman Street, 10th Floor
Denver, CO 80203
P: (303) 866-2636
F: (303) 866-2696
E: Todd.Coffey@state.co.us

Ms. Jeanette Hensley
Director
Division of Aging & Adult
Services
Department of Human Services
1575 Sherman Street, 10th Floor
Denver, CO 80203
P: (303) 866-2636
F: (303) 866-2696
E: Jeanette.Hensley
@state.co.us

CONNECTICUT
Ms. Pamela Giannini
Director
Bureau of Aging, Community &
Social Work Services
Department of Social Services
25 Sigourney Street
Hartford, CT 06106
P: (860) 424-5277
F: (860) 424-4957
E: pamela.giannini
@po.state.ct.us

DELAWARE
Mr. Guy Perrotti
Director
Division of Services for Aging
& Adults with Physical
Disabilities
1901 North DuPont Highway
Main Building Annex, 1st Floor,
Room 109
New Castle, DE 19720
P: (302) 255-9354
F: (302) 255-4445
E: Guy.perrotti@state.de.us

DISTRICT OF COLUMBIA
Mr. Clarence Brown
Director
Office on Aging
One Judiciary Square
441 4th Street, Northwest, 9th
Floor
Washington, DC 20001
P: (202) 724-5622
F: (202) 724-4979
E: Clarence.brown@dc.gov

GEORGIA
Ms. Jean O'Callaghan
Interim Director
Division of Aging Services
2 Peachtree Street, Northwest,
9th Floor
Atlanta, GA 30303
P: (404) 657-5258
F: (404) 657-5285

GUAM
Mr. Arthur U. San Agustin
Senior Citizens Administrator
Division of Senior Citizens
Government of Guam
P.O. Box 2816
Hagaina, GU 96932
P: (671) 735-7382
F: (671) 735-7416
E: chiefdsc
@dphss.govguam.net

HAWAII
Ms. Noemi Pendleton
Director
Executive Office on Aging
No. 1 Capitol District
250 South Hotel Street, Suite
406
Honolulu, HI 96813
P: (808) 586-0100
F: (808) 586-0185
E: eoa@doh.hawaii.gov

IDAHO
Ms. Kim Toryanski
Administrator
Commission on Aging
3380 Americana Terrace, No.
120
P.O. Box 83720
Boise, ID 83720
P: (208) 334-3833
F: (208) 334-3033
E: ktoryanski
@aging.idaho.gov

ILLINOIS
Mr. Charles D. Johnson
Director
Department on Aging
421 East Capitol Avenue
Springfield, IL 62701
P: (217) 785-2870
F: (217) 785-4477
E: Charles.Johnson
@aging.state.il.us

INDIANA
Ms. Faith Laird
Director
Division of Aging
402 West Washington Street,
Room W454
P.O. Box 7083
Indianapolis, IN 46207
P: (317) 232-1731
F: (307) 232-7867
E: Faith.Laird@fssa.IN.gov

IOWA
Mr. John McCalley
Director
Department of Elder Affairs
Jessie Parker Building
510 East 12th Street, Suite 2
Des Moines, IA 50319
P: (515) 725-3301
F: (515) 725-3300
E: john.mccalley@iowa.gov

KANSAS
Mr. Martin Kennedy
Secretary
Department of Aging
New England Building
503 South Kansas Avenue
Topeka, KS 66603
P: (785) 296-5222
F: (785) 296-0256

KENTUCKY
Ms. Deborah Anderson
Commissioner
Department for Aging &
Independent Living
Cabinet for Health & Family
Services
275 East Main Street, 3W-F
Frankfort, KY 40621
P: (502) 564-6930
F: (502) 564-4595
E: Deborah.anderson2@ky.gov

MAINE
Ms. Diana Scully
Director
Office of Elder Services
442 Civic Center Drive
11 State House Station
Augusta, ME 04333
P: (207) 287-9200
F: (207) 287-9230
E: Diana.scully@maine.gov

Aging

MARYLAND
Ms. Gloria Lawlah
Secretary
Department of Aging
301 West Preston Street, Suite 1007
Baltimore, MD 21201
P: (410) 767-1100
F: (410) 333-7943
E: ggl@ooa.state.md.us

MASSACHUSETTS
Ms. Ann Hartstein
Secretary
Executive Office of Elder Affairs
One Ashburton Place
Boston, MA 02108
P: (617) 222-7451
F: (617) 727-6944

MICHIGAN
Ms. Sharon Gire
Executive Director
Office of Services to the Aging
P.O. Box 30676
7109 West Saginaw, First Floor
Lansing, MI 48909
P: (517) 373-8230
F: (517) 373-4092
E: OSADirector@michigan.gov

MINNESOTA
Ms. Jean Wood
Director
Board on Aging
Department of Human Services
P.O. Box 64976
St. Paul, MN 55164
P: (651) 431-2500
F: (651) 431-7453
E: jean.wood@state.mn.us

MISSISSIPPI
Mr. Dan George
Interim Director
Council on Aging
Division of Aging & Adult Services
750 North State Street
Jackson, MS 39202
P: (601) 359-4925
F: (601) 359-4370

Mr. Wayne Parker
Director
Council on Aging
Division of Aging & Adult Services
3750 I-55 North Frontage Road
Jackson, MS 39211
P: (601) 987-3083
F: (601) 987-3085
E: wparker@mdps.state.ms.us

MISSOURI
Ms. Connie Boeckman
Interim Division Director
Division of Senior Services
Department of Health & Senior Services
P.O. Box 570
Jefferson City, MO 65102
P: (573) 526-3626
F: (573) 751-8687

MONTANA
Mr. Charles Rehbein
Aging Services Bureau Chief
Office on Aging
Senior & Long Term Care Division
111 Sanders Street, P.O. Box 4210
Helena, MT 59604
P: (406) 444-7788
F: (406) 444-7743
E: crehbein@mt.gov

NEBRASKA
Ms. Sarah Briggs
Director
Health & Human Services - State Unit on Aging
P.O. Box 95044
301 Centennial Mall, South
Lincoln, NE 68509
P: (402) 471-2307
F: (402) 471-4619
E: Sarah.briggs
@nebraska.gov

NEVADA
Ms. Carol Sala
Administrator
Division for Aging Services
Department of Health & Human Services
3416 Goni Road, Building D-132
Carson City, NV 89706
P: (775) 687-4210 Ext. 226
F: (775) 687-4264
E: csala@aging.nv.gov

NEW JERSEY
Ms. Patricia A. Polansky
Assistant Commissioner
Division of Aging & Community Services
Department of Health & Senior Services
240 West State Street, P.O. Box 807
Trenton, NJ 08625
P: (609) 292-4027
F: (609) 943-3343
E: patricia.polansky
@doh.state.nj.us

NEW MEXICO
Mr. Michael Spanier
Secretary
Aging & Long-Term Services Department
2550 Cerrillos Road
Santa Fe, NM 87505
P: (505) 476-4755
F: (505) 476-4750

NEW YORK
Mr. Michael Burgess
Director
Office for the Aging
Two Empire State Plaza
Albany, NY 12223
P: (518) 474-7012
F: (518) 474-1398
E: mike.burgess
@ofa.state.ny.us

NORTH CAROLINA
Mr. Dennis W. Streets
Director
Division of Aging & Adult Services
Department of Health & Human Services
2101 Mail Service Center, 693 Palmer Dr.
Raleigh, NC 27699
P: (919) 733-3983
F: (919) 733-0443
E: dennis.streets
@ncmail.net

NORTH DAKOTA
Ms. Linda Wright
Director
Aging Services Division
Department of Human Services
1237 West Divide Avenue, Suite 6
Bismarck, ND 58501
P: (701) 328-4601
F: (701) 328-4061
E: sowril@nd.gov

NORTHERN MARIANA ISLANDS
Mr. Melvin Faiao
Acting Director
Commonwealth of the Northern Mariana Islands
Office on Aging
P.O. Box 502178
Saipan, MP 96950
P: (670) 233-1320
F: (670) 233-1327

OKLAHOMA
Mr. Lance A. Robertson
Director
Aging Services Division
Department of Human Services
2401 Northwest 23rd Street, Suite 40
Oklahoma City, OK 73107
P: (405) 521-2281
F: (405) 521-2086
E: lance.robertson
@okdhs.org

OREGON
Mr. James Toews
Assistant Director
Seniors & People with Disabilities
Department of Human Services
500 Summer Street, Northeast, E02
Salem, OR 97301
P: (503) 945-6478
F: (503) 373-7823
E: james.d.toews
@state.or.us

PENNSYLVANIA
Mr. John Michael Hall
Secretary
Department of Aging
555 Walnut Street, 5th Floor
Harrisburg, PA 17101
P: (717) 783-1550
F: (717) 772-3382
E: johhall@state.pa.us

PUERTO RICO
Ms. Rossana Lopez Leon
Executive Director
Governor's Office for Elderly Affairs
P.O. Box 191179
San Juan, PR 00919
P: (787) 721-5710
F: (787) 721-6510
E: rlopez@ogave.gobierno.pr

RHODE ISLAND
Ms. Corinne Calise Russo
Director
Department of Elderly Affairs
Benjamin Rush Building, #55
35 Howard Avenue
Cranston, RI 02920
P: (401) 462-0501
F: (401) 462-0503
E: crusso@dea.state.ri.us

SOUTH CAROLINA
Mr. Tony Kester
Interim Director
Bureau of Senior Services
1301 Gervais Street, Suite 200
Columbia, SC 29201
P: (803) 734-9900
F: (803) 734-9886
E: kester@aging.sc.gov

SOUTH DAKOTA
Ms. Marilyn Kinsman
Administrator
Office of Adult Services &
Aging
Department of Social Services
700 Governors Drive
Pierre, SD 57501
P: (605) 773-3656
F: (605) 773-6834
E: marilyn.kinsman
   @state.sd.us

TENNESSEE
Mr. Mike Hann
Executive Director
Commission on Aging &
Disability
Andrew Jackson Building
500 Deaderick Street, No. 825
Nashville, TN 37243
P: (615) 741-2056
F: (615) 741-3309
E: Mike.Hann@state.tn.us

TEXAS
Mr. Chris Traylor
Commissioner
Department of Aging &
Disability Services
701 West 51st Street
P.O. Box 149030
Austin, TX 78714
P: (512) 438-3011
F: (512) 438-4220

U.S. VIRGIN ISLANDS
Ms. Eva Williams
Administrator
Senior Citizen Affairs
Administration
Department of Human Services
3011 Golden Rock, Christiansted
St. Croix, VI 00820
P: (340) 772-9811
F: (340) 772-9849
E: dhssca@yahoo.com

UTAH
Mr. Nels Holmgren
Director
Division of Aging & Adult
Services
Department of Human Services
195 North 1950 West
Salt Lake City, UT 84116
P: (801) 538-3921
F: (801) 538-4395
E: nholmgren@utah.gov

VERMONT
Ms. Joan Senecal
Commissioner
Department of Disabilities,
Aging & Independent Living
Division of Disability and Aging
Service
103 South Main Street, Weeks
Building
Waterbury, VT 05671
P: (802) 241-2401
F: (802) 241-2325
E: Joan.Senecal
   @ahs.state.vt.us

VIRGINIA
Ms. Linda Nablo
Commissioner
Department for the Aging
1610 Forest Avenue, Suite 100
Richmond, VA 23229
P: (804) 662-9333
F: (804) 662-7035
E: linda.nablo
   @vda.virginia.gov

WEST VIRGINIA
Ms. Sandra Vanin
Commissioner
Bureau of Senior Services
1900 Kanawha Boulevard, East
3003 Town Center Mall
Charleston, WV 25305
P: (304) 558-3317
F: (304) 558-5609
E: svanin@boss.state.wv.us

WISCONSIN
Ms. Donna McDowell
Director
Bureau of Aging & Disability
Resources
One West Wilson Street, Room
450
P.O. Box 7851
Madison, WI 53707
P: (608) 266-3840
F: (608) 267-3203
E: mcdowdb@dhfs.state.wi.us

WYOMING
Ms. Ginny Mahoney
Administrator
Aging Division
Department of Health
6101 Yellowstone Road, Suite
259B
Cheyenne, WY 82002
P: (307) 777-7986
F: (307) 777-5340

Agriculture

Enforces agriculture laws and administers agricultural programs in the state.

ALABAMA
Hon. John McMillan (R)
Commissioner
Department of Agriculture & Industries
Richard Beard Building
P.O. Box 3336
Montgomery, AL 36109
P: (334) 240-7100
F: (334) 240-7190

ALASKA
Ms. Franci Havemeister
Director
Division of Agriculture
Department of Natural Resources
1800 Glenn Highway, Suite 12
Palmer, AK 99645
P: (907) 761-3867
F: (907) 745-7112

AMERICAN SAMOA
Turituri Manupo
Director
Department of Agriculture
American Samoa Government
Executive Office Building, Utulei
Pago Pago, AS 96799
P: (684) 699-1497
F: (684) 699-4031

ARIZONA
Mr. Donald Butler
Director
Department of Agriculture
1688 West Adams
Phoenix, AZ 85007
P: (602) 542-0990
F: (602) 542-5420

ARKANSAS
Mr. Richard Bell
Secretary
Agriculture Department
No. 1 Natural Resources Drive
Little Rock, AR 72205
P: (501) 683-4851
F: (501) 683-4852

CALIFORNIA
Ms. Karen Ross
Secretary
Department of Food & Agriculture
1220 N Street, Suite 400
Sacramento, CA 95814
P: (916) 654-0433

COLORADO
Mr. John Salazar
Commissioner
Department of Agriculture
700 Kipling Street, Suite 4000
Lakewood, CO 80215
P: (303) 239-4100

CONNECTICUT
Mr. Steven Reviczky
Commissioner
Department of Agriculture
165 Capitol Avenue
Hartford, CT 06106
P: (860) 713-2500

DELAWARE
Mr. Ed Kee
Secretary
Department of Agriculture
2320 South DuPont Highway
Dover, DE 19901
P: (302) 698-4500
F: (302) 697-4463

FLORIDA
Hon. Adam H. Putnam (R)
Commissioner
Department of Agriculture & Consumer Services
The Capitol, PL10
Tallahassee, FL 32399
P: (850) 488-3022
F: (850) 922-4936

GEORGIA
Mr. Gary Black
Commissioner
Department of Agriculture
19 Martin Luther King Jr. Drive, SW
204 Agricultural Building
Atlanta, GA 30334
P: (404) 656-3600
F: (404) 656-3600

GUAM
Mr. Paul C. Bassler
Director
Department of Agriculture
163 Dairy Road
Mangilao, GU 96913
P: (671) 734-3942
F: (671) 734-6569

IDAHO
Ms. Celia R. Gould
Director
State Department of Agriculture
P.O. Box 790
Boise, ID 83701
P: (208) 332-8503
F: (208) 332-2170

ILLINOIS
Mr. Tom Jennings
Director
Department of Agriculture
State Fairgrounds
P.O. Box 19281
Springfield, IL 62794
P: (217) 782-2172
F: (217) 785-4505

INDIANA
Mr. Joseph Kelsay
Director
State Department of Agriculture
One North Capitol, Suite 600
Indianapolis, IN 46204
P: (317) 232-8770
F: (317) 232-1362

IOWA
Mr. Bill Northey
Secretary
Department of Agriculture & Land Stewardship
Wallace Building
502 East 9th Street
Des Moines, IA 50319
P: (515) 281-5322
F: (515) 281-6236

KANSAS
Mr. Dale Rodman
Secretary
Department of Agriculture
109 Southwest 9th Street, 4th Floor
Topeka, KS 66612
P: (785) 296-3556

KENTUCKY
Mr. Richie Farmer
Commissioner
Department of Agriculture
32 Fountain Place
Frankfort, KY 40601
P: (502) 564-6099
F: (502) 564-5016
E: richie.farmer@ky.gov

LOUISIANA
Dr. Michael G. Strain
Commissioner
Department of Agriculture & Forestry
P.O. Box 631
Baton Rouge, LA 70821
P: (225) 922-1234
F: (225) 923-4880
E: commissioner
   @ldaf.state.la.us

MAINE
Mr. Walter E. Whitcomb
Commissioner
Department of Agriculture, Food & Rural Resources
28 State House Station Deering Building
AMHI Complex
Augusta, ME 04333
P: (207) 287-3419

MARYLAND
Mr. Earl F. Hance
Secretary
Department of Agriculture
50 Harry S. Truman Parkway
Annapolis, MD 21401
P: (410) 841-5880
F: (410) 841-5914
E: hanceef@mds.state.md.us

MASSACHUSETTS
Mr. Scott J. Soares
Commissioner
Department of Agricultural Resources
251 Causeway Street, Suite 500
Boston, MA 02114
P: (617) 626-1701
F: (617) 626-1850

MICHIGAN
Mr. Keith Creagh
Director
Department of Agriculture & Rural Development
525 West Allegan Street
P.O. Box 30017
Lansing, MI 48909
P: (517) 373-1052

MINNESOTA
Mr. Dave Frederickson
Commissioner
Department of Agriculture
Freeman Office Building
625 Robert Street North
St. Paul, MN 55155
P: (651) 201-6219

MISSISSIPPI
Dr. Lester Spell Jr.
Commissioner
Department of Agriculture & Commerce
P.O. Box 1609
Jackson, MS 39201
P: (601) 359-1100
F: (601) 354-6290

MISSOURI
Dr. Jon Hagler
Director
Department of Agriculture
P.O. Box 630
Jefferson City, MO 65102
P: (573) 751-5617
F: (573) 751-1784

MONTANA
Mr. Ron De Yong
Director
Department of Agriculture
P.O. Box 200201
Helena, MT 59620
P: (406) 444-3144
F: (406) 444-5409
E: agr@mt.gov

NEBRASKA
Mr. Greg Ibach
Director
Department of Agriculture
P.O. Box 94947
Lincoln, NE 68509
P: (402) 471-2341
F: (402) 471-6876

NEVADA
Mr. Jim Barbee
Acting Director
Department of Agriculture
405 South 21st Street
Sparks, NV 89431
P: (775) 353-3600

NEW HAMPSHIRE
Ms. Lorraine Merrill
Commissioner
Department of Agriculture,
Markets & Food
P.O. Box 2042
Concord, NH 03302
P: (603) 271-3551
F: (603) 271-1109

NEW JERSEY
Mr. Douglas H. Fisher
Secretary of Agriculture
Department of Agriculture
P.O. Box 330
John Fitch Plaza
Trenton, NJ 08625
P: (609) 292-3976
F: (609) 292-3978

NEW MEXICO
Mr. Tom Bagwell
Director/Secretary
Department of Agriculture
MSC 3189 Box 30005
Las Cruces, NM 88003
P: (575) 646-3007

NEW YORK
Mr. Darrel J. Aubertine
Commissioner
Department of Agriculture &
Markets
10B Airline Drive
Albany, NY 12235
P: (518) 457-8876

NORTH CAROLINA
Mr. Steve Troxler
Commissioner
Department of Agriculture &
Consumer Services
1001 Mail Service Center
Raleigh, NC 27699
P: (919) 707-3000
F: (919) 733-1141

NORTH DAKOTA
Mr. Doug Goehring
Commissioner
Department of Agriculture
600 East Boulevard Avenue
Department 602
Bismarck, ND 58505
P: (701) 328-2231
F: (701) 328-4567
E: ndda@nd.gov

OHIO
Mr. James J. Zehringer
Director
Department of Agriculture
8995 East Main Street
Reynoldsburg, OH 43068
P: (614) 466-2732

OKLAHOMA
Mr. Jim Reese
Secretary
Department of Agriculture,
Food & Forestry
P.O. Box 528804
Oklahoma City, OK 73152
P: (405) 521-3864

OREGON
Ms. Katy Coba
Director
Department of Agriculture
635 Capitol Street, Northeast
Salem, OR 97301
P: (503) 986-4552
F: (503) 986-4750

PENNSYLVANIA
Mr. George Greig
Secretary
Department of Agriculture
2301 North Cameron Street
Harrisburg, PA 17110
P: (717) 783-6985

PUERTO RICO
Mr. Javier Rivera Aquino
Secretary
Department of Agriculture
1309 Fernandez Guncos Avenue
Pda. 19 1/2, Floor 2
San Juan, PR 00908
P: (787) 722-0871
F: 723-8512

RHODE ISLAND
Mr. Kenneth Ayars
Chief
Division of Agriculture, DEM
235 Promenade Street, Room
370
Providence, RI 02908
P: (401) 222-2781 Ext. 4500
F: (401) 222-6047

SOUTH CAROLINA
Mr. Hugh E. Weathers
Commissioner
Department of Agriculture
Wade Hampton Office Building
P.O. Box 11280
Columbia, SC 29211
P: (803) 734-2190
F: (803) 734-2192

SOUTH DAKOTA
Mr. Walt Bones
Secretary
Department of Agriculture
523 East Capitol
Pierre, SD 57501
P: (605) 773-5436

TENNESSEE
Mr. Julius Johnson
Commissioner
Department of Agriculture
Melrose Station
P.O. Box 40627
Nashville, TN 37204
P: (615) 837-5100
F: (615) 837-5333

TEXAS
Mr. Todd Staples
Commissioner
Department of Agriculture
P.O. Box 12847
Capitol Station
Austin, TX 78711
P: (512) 463-7476
F: (512) 463-1104

U.S. VIRGIN ISLANDS
Mr. Louis Petersen
Commissioner
Department of Agriculture
Estate Lower Love
Kingshill
St. Croix, VI 00850
P: (340) 778-0991
F: (340) 778-7977

UTAH
Mr. Leonard Blackham
Commissioner
Department of Agriculture &
Food
P.O. Box 146500
Salt Lake City, UT 84114
P: (801) 538-7101
F: (801) 538-7126

VERMONT
Mr. Chuck Ross
Secretary
Agency of Agriculture, Food &
Markets
116 State Street
Montpelier, VT 05620
P: (802) 828-1619

VIRGINIA
Mr. Matthew J. Lohr
Commissioner
Department of Agriculture &
Consumer Services
102 Governor Street
Richmond, VA 23218
P: (804) 786-3501
F: (804) 371-2945

WASHINGTON
Mr. Daniel Newhouse
Director
State Department of Agriculture
P.O. Box 42560
Olympia, WA 98504
P: (360) 902-1887
F: (360) 902-2092
E: newhouse@agr.wa.gov

WEST VIRGINIA
Mr. Gus R. Douglass
Commissioner
Department of Agriculture
1900 Kanawha Boulevard East
Charleston, WV 25305
P: (304) 558-2201
F: (304) 558-2203
E: douglass@ag.state.wv.us

Agriculture

WISCONSIN
Mr. Ben Brancel
Secretary
Department of Agriculture,
Trade & Consumer Protection
2811 Agriculture Drive
P.O. Box 8911
Madison, WI 53708
P: (608) 224-5012

WYOMING
Mr. Jason Fearneyhough
Director
Department of Agriculture
2219 Carey Avenue
Cheyenne, WY 82002
P: (307) 777-6569
F: (307) 777-6593

Alcohol and Substance Abuse

Plans, establishes and administers programs for the prevention, treatment, and rehabilitation of alcohol and/or drug and other abusers.

ALABAMA
Ms. Tammy Peacock
Associate Commissioner
Division of Substance Abuse
Services
100 North Union Street
P.O. Box 301410
Montgomery, AL 36130
P: (334) 242-3952
F: (334) 242-0725
E: kent.hunt@mh.alabama.gov

ALASKA
Ms. Melissa Witzler-Stone
Director, Behavioral Health
Division of Behavioral Health
3601 C Street, Suite 934
Anchorage, AK 99503
P: (907) 269-3410
F: (907) 269-8166
E: melissa.stone@alaska.gov

AMERICAN SAMOA
Ms. Leilua Stevenson
Director
Department of Human & Social
Services
American Samoa Government
P.O. Box 997534
Pago Pago, AS
P: (684) 633-7506
F: (684) 633-7449

ARIZONA
Dr. Laura Nelson
Acting Deputy Director
Division of Behavioral Health
Services
Department of Health Services
150 North 18th Avenue, Suite 200
Phoenix, AZ 85007
P: (602) 364-4566
F: (602) 364-4570
E: nelsonla@azdhs.gov

ARKANSAS
Mr. Joe Hill
Director
Office of Alcohol & Drug
Prevention
305 South Palm Street
Little Rock, AR 72205
P: (501) 682-9867
F: (501) 686-9035
E: Joe.Hill@arkansas.gov

CALIFORNIA
Ms. Renee Zito
Director
Department of Alcohol & Drug
Programs
1700 K Street
Sacramento, CA 95811
P: (916) 445-1943
F: (916) 323-5873

COLORADO
Ms. Joscelyn Gay
Deputy Executive Director
Division of Behavioral Health
Services
1575 Sherman Street
Denver, CO 80203
P: (303) 866-2806
F: (303) 866-2362
E: joscelyn.gay@state.co.us

CONNECTICUT
Ms. Patricia Rehmer
Commissioner
Department of Mental Health &
Addiction Services
410 Capitol Avenue
P.O. Box 341431
Hartford, CT 06134
P: (860) 418-7000
F: (860) 418-6691
E: Pat.Rehmer
   @po.state.ct.us

DELAWARE
Ms. Kevin Huckshorn
Director
Division of Substance Abuse &
Mental Health
Department of Health & Social
Services
1901 North DuPont Highway
New Castle, DE 19720
P: (302) 255-9398
F: (302) 255-4427
E: Kevin.Huckshorn
   @state.de.us

DISTRICT OF COLUMBIA
Ms. Tori Fernandez Whitney
Senior Deputy Director
Addiction Prevention &
Recovery Administration
1300 First Street, Northeast
Washington, DC 20002
P: (202) 727-8857
F: (202) 727-0092
E: tori.whitney@dc.gov

FLORIDA
Mr. David A. Sofferin
Assistant Secretary for
Substance Abuse & Mental
Health
Department of Children &
Families
1317 Winewood Boulevard
Tallahassee, FL 32399
P: (850) 414-9063
F: (850) 487-2239
E: david_sofferin
   @dcf.state.fl.us

GEORGIA
Dr. Frank E. Shelp
Commissioner
Department of Behavioral
Health & Developmental
Disabilities
2 Peachtree Street, Northwest
24th Floor
Atlanta, GA 30303
P: (404) 463-7946
F: (770) 408-5480

GUAM
Mr. Paca Remengesau
Supervisor
Department of Mental Health &
Substance Abuse
Drug & Alcohol Branch
J&G Commercial Center
Hagatna, GU 96910
P: (671) 475-5439
F: (671) 477-7782

HAWAII
Mr. Keith Y. Yamamoto
Division Chief
Alcohol & Drug Abuse Division
601 Kamokila Boulevard, Room 360
Kapolei, HI 96707
P: (808) 692-7507
F: (808) 692-7521
E: kyamamoto
   @mail.health.state.hi.us

IDAHO
Ms. Bethany Gadzinski
Bureau Chief
Bureau of Substance Use
Disorders
3rd Floor, Pete T. Cenarrusa
Building
450 West State Street
Boise, ID 83720
P: (208) 334-5756
F: (208) 332-7305
E: gadzinsb@dhw.idaho.gov

ILLINOIS
Ms. Theodora Binion-Taylor
Director
Division of Alcoholism &
Substance Abuse
James R. Thompson Center
100 West Randolph Street, Suite
5-600
Chicago, IL 60601
P: (312) 814-2300
F: (312) 814-3838
E: DHSASA4@dhs.state.il.us

INDIANA
Ms. Gina Eckart
Director
Division of Mental Health &
Addiction
Family & Social Services
Administration
402 West Washington Street,
Room W353
Indianapolis, IN 46204
P: (317) 232-7860
F: (317) 233-3472
E: gina.eckart@fssa.in.gov

IOWA
Ms. Julie McMahon
Division Director
Health Promotion & Chronic
Disease Prevention
Lucas State Office Building
321 East 12th Street
Des Moines, IA 50319
P: (515) 281-3733
F: (515) 242-6384
E: jmcmahon
   @idph.state.ia.us

KANSAS
Mr. Deborah Stidham
Director
Addiction & Prevention
Services
915 Southwest Harrison
Docking State Office Building,
9th Floor
Topeka, KS 66612
P: (785) 296-6807
F: (785) 296-7275

Alcohol and Substance Abuse

LOUISIANA
Mr. Peter Calamari
Interim Assistant Secretary
Office of Behavioral Health
Department of Health &
Hospitals
P.O. Box 4049
Baton Rouge, LA 70821
P: (225) 342-2540
F: (225) 342-5066
E: pete.calamari@la.gov

MAINE
Mr. Guy R. Cousins
Director
Office of Substance Abuse
41 Anthony Avenue
#11 State House Station
Augusta, ME 04333
P: (207) 287-2595
F: (207) 287-4334
E: guy.cousins@maine.gov

MARYLAND
Ms. Renata J. Henry
Deputy Secretary
Behavioral Health &
Disabilities
201 West Preston Street
Baltimore, MD 21201
P: (410) 767-3167
E: rhenry@dhmd.state.md.us

MASSACHUSETTS
Mr. Michael Botticelli
Assistant Commissioner for
Substance Abuse Services
Department of Public Health
250 Washington Street
Boston, MA 02108
P: (617) 624-5111
F: (617) 624-5261

MICHIGAN
Ms. Cynthia Kelly
Acting Deputy Director
Mental Health & Substance
Abuse Administration
Capitol View Building
201 Townsend Street
Lansing, MI 48913
P: (517) 373-3740

MINNESOTA
Ms. Carol Falkowski
Director
Chemical Health Division
Department of Human Services
P.O. Box 64977
St. Paul, MN 55164
P: (651) 431-2460
F: (651) 431-7449
E: carol.falkowski
   @state.mn.us

MISSISSIPPI
Mr. Herbert Loving
Director
Division of Alcohol & Drug
Abuse
Robert E. Lee State Office
Building
239 North Lamar Street, 11th
Floor
Jackson, MS 39201
P: (601) 359-1288
F: (601) 359-6295
E: hloving@msdmh.org

MISSOURI
Mr. Mark G. Stringer
Director
Division of Alcohol & Drug
Abuse
1706 East Elm Street
P.O. Box 687
Jefferson City, MO 65102
P: (573) 751-4122
F: (573) 751-8224
E: mark.stringer@dmh.mo.gov

MONTANA
Ms. Joan Cassidy
Chief
Chemical Dependency Services
Addictive & Mental Disorders
Division
555 Fuller Ave., P.O. Box
202905
Helena, MT 59620
P: (406) 444-6981
F: (406) 444-4435
E: jcassidy@mt.gov

NEBRASKA
Dr. Scot L. Adams
Director
Division of Behavioral Health
Department of Health & Human
Services
301 Centennial Mall South, 3rd
Floor
Lincoln, NE 68509
P: (402) 471-8553
F: (402) 471-9449
E: scot.adams@nebraska.gov

NEVADA
Ms. Deborah Harris
Chief
Bureau of Child, Family &
Community Wellness
State Health Division
4150 Technology Way
Carson City, NV 89706
P: (775) 684-5958
F: (775) 684-4245
E: daharris@health.nv.gov

NEW HAMPSHIRE
Mr. Joseph P. Harding
Director
Alcohol, Tobacco and Other
Drug Services
Department of Health & Human
Services
105 Pleasant Street
Concord, NH 03301
P: (603) 271-6104
F: (603) 271-6116
E: jharding
   @dhhs.state.nh.us

NEW JERSEY
Ms. Raquel Mazon-Jeffers
Director
Division of Addiction Services
P.O. Box 362
120 South Stockton Street, 3rd
Floor
Trenton, NJ 08625
P: (609) 292-5760

NEW MEXICO
Ms. Sidonie Squier
Secretary
Human Services Department
P.O. Box 2348
Santa Fe, NM 87504
P: (505) 827-7750
F: (505) 827-3185

NEW YORK
Ms. Arlene Gonzalez-Sanchez
Commissioner
Office of Alcoholism &
Substance Abuse Services
1450 Western Avenue
Albany, NY 12203
P: (518) 473-3460
F: (518) 457-5474

NORTH CAROLINA
Mr. Steve Jordan
Director
Division of Mental Health,
Developmental Disabilities &
Substance Abuse Services
Department of Health & Human
Services
3001 Mail Service Center
Raleigh, NC 27699
P: 9919) 733-7011
F: (919) 508-0951
E: steve.jordan@dhhs.nc.gov

NORTH DAKOTA
Mr. Don Wright
Unit Administrator
Division of Mental Health &
Substance Abuse Services
1237 West Divide Avenue, Suite
1C
Bismarck, ND 58501
P: (701) 328-8920
F: (701) 328-8969
E: dwright@nd.gov

**NORTHERN MARIANA
ISLANDS**
Mr. Joseph P. Villagomez
Secretary of Public Health
Department of Public Health
P.O. Box 500409
Saipan, MP 96950
P: (670) 236-8201
F: (670) 234-8930
E: jkvsaipan@aol.com

OHIO
Mr. Orman Hall
Director
Department of Alcohol & Drug
Addiction Services
280 Plaza
280 North High Street, 12th
Floor
Columbus, OH 43215
P: (614) 466-3445
F: (614) 728-4936
E: INFO@ada.ohio.gov

OKLAHOMA
Ms. Caletta McPherson
Deputy Commissioner,
Substance Abuse Services
Department of Mental Health &
Substance Abuse Services
1200 Northeast 13th Street
P.O. Box 53277
Oklahoma City, OK 73152
P: (405) 522-3908
F: (405) 522-3650

OREGON
Mr. Richard L. Harris
Assistant Director
Addictions & Mental Health
Division
Department of Human Services
500 Summer Street, Northeast,
E86
Salem, OR 97301
P: (503) 945-9708
F: (503) 373-7327
E: Richard.Harris
   @state.or.us

PENNSYLVANIA
Ms. Robin Rothermel
Director
Bureau of Drug & Alcohol
Programs
02 Kline Plaza
Harrisburg, PA 17104
P: (717) 783-8200
F: (717) 787-6285

RHODE ISLAND
Dr. Craig S. Stenning
Director
Department of Behavioral
Healthcare, Developmental
Disabilities and HospitalsÊ
Barry Hall
14 Harrington Road
Cranston, RI 02920
P: (401) 462-2339
F: (401) 462-6636
E: cstenning@mhrh.ri.gov

SOUTH CAROLINA
Mr. Bob Toomey
Director
Department of Alcohol & Other
Drug Abuse Services
101 Executive Center Drive,
Suite 215
Columbia, SC 29210
P: (803) 896-5555
F: (803) 896-5557
E: btoomey@daodas.sc.gov

SOUTH DAKOTA
Mr. Gilbert Sudbeck
Director
Division of Alcohol & Drug
Abuse
Division of Alcohol & Abuse
Services
C/o 500 East Capitol
Pierre, SD 57501
P: (605) 773-3123
F: (605) 773-7076
E: gib.sudbeck@state.sd.us

TENNESSEE
Mr. E. Douglas Varney
Commissioner
Department of Mental Health &
Developmental Disabilities
Cordell Hull Building, 3rd Floor
425 Fifth Avenue, North
Nashville, TN 37243
P: (615) 532-6500
F: (615) 532-6514
E: Doug.Varney@tn.gov

TEXAS
Mr. Michael D. Maples
Assistant Commissioner for
Mental Health Substance Abuse
Services
Mental Health & Substance
Abuse Services
1100 West 49th Street
P.O.Box 149347
Austin, TX 78714
P: (512) 206-5968
F: (512) 206-5718
E: mike.maples
    @dshs.state.tx.us

UTAH
Ms. Lana Stohl
Director
Division of Substance Abuse &
Mental Health
Department of Human Services
195 North 1950 West
Salt Lake City, UT 84116
P: (801) 538-3939
F: (801) 538-4696
E: lstohl@utah.gov

VERMONT
Ms. Barbara Cimaglio
Deputy Commissioner of
Alcohol & Drug Abuse
Programs
Division of Alcohol & Drug
Abuse Programs
Department of Health
108 Cherry Street, P.O. Box 70
Burlington, VT 05402
P: (802) 951-1258
F: (802) 651-1573
E: Barbara.Cimaglio
    @ahs.state.vt.us

VIRGINIA
Mr. James Stewart
Commissioner
Department of Behavioral
Health & Developmental
Services
1220 Bank Street
P.O. Box 1797
Richmond, VA 23218
P: (804) 786-3921
F: (804) 371-6638
E: jim.stewart
    @dbhds.virginia.gov

WEST VIRGINIA
Ms. Kimberly A. Walsh
Deputy Commissioner
Bureau for Behavioral Health &
Health Facilities
350 Capitol Street, Room 350
Charleston, WV 25301
P: (304) 356-4798
E: Kimberly.A.Walsh@wv.gov

WISCONSIN
Ms. Joyce Bohn Allen
Director
Division of Mental Health &
Substance Abuse Services
1 West Wilson Street, Room 850
P.O. Box 7851
Madison, WI 53707
P: (608) 266-1351
F: (608) 266-2579
E: joyce.allen
    @wisconsin.gov

WYOMING
Ms. Chris Newman
Interim Administrator
Mental Health & Substance
Abuse Division
Department of Health
6101 Yellowstone Road, Room
220
Cheyenne, WY 82002
P: (307) 777-8763
F: (307) 777-5580
E: chris.newman
    @health.wyo.gov

Alcoholic Beverage Control

Administers and enforces the laws governing the manufacturing, distribution, and dispensing of alcoholic beverages.

ALABAMA
Mr. Mac Gipson
Administrator
Alcoholic Beverage Control Board
2715 Gunter Park Drive West
Montgomery, AL 36101
P: (334) 271-3840
F: (334) 277-2150

ALASKA
Ms. Shirley Gifford
Director
Alcoholic Beverage Control Board
Department of Public Safety
5848 East Tudor Road
Anchorage, AK 99507
P: (907) 269-0350
F: (907) 272-9412

ARIZONA
Mr. Alan Everett
Director
Department of Liquor Licenses & Control
800 West Washington Street, 5th Floor
Phoenix, AZ 85007
P: (602) 542-9052
F: (602) 542-5707

ARKANSAS
Mr. Michael W. Langley
Director
Alcoholic Beverage Control Division
1515 West 7th Street, Suite 503
Little Rock, AR 72201
P: (501) 682-1105
F: (501) 682-2221
E: michael.langley
   @dfa.state.ar.us

CALIFORNIA
Mr. Jacob Appelsmith
Director
Department of Alcoholic Beverage Control
3927 Lennane Drive, Suite 100
Sacramento, CA 95834
P: (916) 419-2500
F: (916) 419-2516
E: jacob.appelsmith
   @abc.ca.gov

COLORADO
Ms. Laura K. Harris
Division Director
Liquor Enforcement Division
Department of Revenue
1881 Pierce Street, Suite 108A
Lakewood, CO 80214
P: (303) 205-2300
F: (303) 205-2341
E: lharris
   @spike.dor.state.co.us

CONNECTICUT
Mr. William M. Rubenstein
Commissioner
Department of Consumer Protection
165 Capitol Avenue
Hartford, CT 06106
P: (860) 713-6050
F: (860) 713-7243
E: william.rubenstein
   @ct.gov

DELAWARE
Mr. John H. Cordrey
Commissioner
Alcoholic Beverage Control
Carvel State Office Building
820 North French Street, 3rd Floor
Wilmington, DE 19801
P: (302) 577-5222
F: (302) 577-3204
E: john.cordrey@state.de.us

DISTRICT OF COLUMBIA
Mr. Fred Moosally
Director
Alcoholic Beverage Regulation Administration
2000 14th Street Northwest, Suite 400S
Washington, DC 20002
P: (202) 442-4423
F: (202) 442-9563
E: fred.moosally@dc.gov

FLORIDA
Mr. John R. Powell
Director
Division of Alcoholic Beverages & Tobacco
1940 North Monroe Street
Tallahassee, FL 32399
P: (850) 413-7973
F: (850) 922-5175
E: john.powell
   @dbpr.state.fl.us

GEORGIA
Mr. Howard A. Tyler
Division Director
Alcohol & Tobacco Division
1800 Century Center Boulevard, Northeast
Suite 4235
Atlanta, GA 30345
P: (404) 417-4900
F: (404) 417-4901
E: howard.tyler@dor.ga.gov

HAWAII
Mr. Eric K. Honma
Director
Kauai Department of Liquor Control
County of Kauai
4444 Rice Street, Suite 120
Lihue, Kauai, HI 96766
P: (808) 241-6580
F: (808) 241-6585
E: ehonma@kauaigov.com

Mr. Greg I. Nishioka
Administrator
Honolulu Liquor Commission
711 Kapiolani Boulevard, Suite 600
Honolulu, HI 96813
P: (808) 768-7301
F: (808) 591-2700
E: gnishioka@honolulu.gov

Mr. Franklyn L. Silva
Director
Maui Department of Liquor Control
County of Maui
2145 Kaohu Street, Suite 105
Wailuku, HI 96793
P: (808) 243-7753
F: (808) 243-7558
E: liquor@mauicounty.gov

Mr. Gerald Takase
Director
Department of Liquor Control
Hilo Lagoon Center
101 Aupuni Street, Suite 230
Hilo, HI 96720
P: (808) 961-8218
F: (808) 961-8684

IDAHO
Mr. Jeffrey R. Anderson
Executive Director
State Liquor Division
1199 Shoreline Lane, Suite 100
P.O. Box 6537
Boise, ID 83707
P: (208) 334-2600
E: janderson
   @lottery.idaho.gov

ILLINOIS
Ms. Gloria L. Materre
Executive Director
Liquor Control Commission
100 West Randolph Street, Suite 7-801
Chicago, IL 60601
P: (312) 814-2206
F: (312) 814-2241

INDIANA
Mr. Alex Huskey
Chair
Alcohol & Tobacco Commission
State Excise Police
302 West Washington, Room E-114
Indianapolis, IN 46204
P: (317) 232-2430
F: (317) 234-1520
E: ahuskey@atc.in.gov

IOWA
Mr. Stephen Larson
Administrator
Alcoholic Beverages Division
1918 Southeast Hulsizer Avenue
Ankeny, IA 50021
P: (515) 281-7402
F: (515) 281-7385
E: larson@iowabd.com

KANSAS
Mr. Tom Groneman
Director
Alcoholic Beverage Control Division
915 Southwest Harrison, Room 214, North
Docking State Office Building
Topeka, KS 66625
P: (785) 296-7015
F: (785) 296-7185
E: tom_groneman
   @kdor.state.ks.us

KENTUCKY
Mr. Tony Dehner
Commissioner
Department of Alcoholic
Beverage Control
1003 Twilight Trail, Suite A-2
Frankfort, KY 40601
P: (502) 564-4850
F: (502) 564-1442
E: tony.dehner@ky.gov

LOUISIANA
Mr. Troy Hebert
Commissioner
Office of Alcohol & Tobacco
Control
Department of Revenue
8549 United Plaza, Suite 220
Baton Rouge, LA 70809
P: (225) 925-4054
F: (225) 925-3975
E: thebert@rev.state.la.us

MAINE
Mr. Dan Gwadosky
Director
Bureau of Alcoholic Beverages
& Lottery Operations
8 State House Station
Augusta, ME 04333
P: (207) 287-3721
F: (207) 287-6769
E: dgwadosky@maine.gov

MARYLAND
Hon. Peter Franchot (D)
Comptroller
Office of the Comptroller
L.L. Goldstein Treasury
Building
P.O. Box 466
Annapolis, MD 21404
P: (410) 260-7801
F: (410) 974-3808
E: pfrachot
    @comp.state.md.us

Mr. George F. Griffin
Director
Department of Liquor Control
16650 Crabbs Branch Way
Rockville, MD 20855
P: (240) 777-1922
F: (240) 777-1962
E: george.griffin
    @montgomerycountymd.gov

MASSACHUSETTS
Ms. Kim Gainsboro
Chair
Alcoholic Beverage Control
Commission
239 Causeway Street, Suite 200
Boston, MA 02114
P: (617) 727-3040
F: (617) 727-1510

MICHIGAN
Ms. Nida R. Samona
Chair
Liquor Control Commission
7150 Harris Drive
P.O. Box 30005
Lansing, MI 48909
P: (517) 322-1353
F: (517) 322-5188
E: nrsamon@michigan.gov

MISSISSIPPI
Ms. Alice Gorman
Deputy Commissioner
State Tax Commission,
Alcoholic Beverage Control
Division
P.O. Box 22828
Jackson, MS 39225
P: (601) 923-7411
F: (601) 923-7423
E: agorman@mstc.state.ms.us

MISSOURI
Mr. Lafayette Lacy
State Supervisor
Division of Alcohol & Tobacco
Control
1738 East Elm Street, Lower
Level
P.O. Box 837
Jefferson City, MO 65102
P: (573) 751-4092
F: (573) 526-4540
E: lafayette.lacy
    @dps.mo.gov

MONTANA
Mr. John Flynn
Bureau Chief
Liqour Control Division
Department of Revenue
P.O. Box 1712
Helena, MT 59624
P: (406) 444-6900
F: (406) 444-3696
E: jflynn@state.mt.gov

NEBRASKA
Mr. Hobert Rupe
Executive Director
Liquor Control Commission
301 Centennial Mall, South, 5th
Floor
P.O. Box 95046
Lincoln, NE 68509
P: (402) 471-2571
F: (402) 471-2814

NEVADA
Ms. Claudi Olivares
Liquor Tax Examiner
Department of Taxation
1550 East College Parkway,
Suite 115
Carson City, NV 89706
P: (775) 684-2122
F: (775) 684-2020
E: colivares
    @tax.state.nv.us

NEW HAMPSHIRE
Mr. Joseph W. Mollica
Chair
State Liquor Commission
P.O. Box 503
Concord, NH 03301
P: (603) 230-7005

NEW JERSEY
Mr. Jerry Fischer
Director
Division of Alcoholic Beverage
Control
140 East Front Street, 5th Floor
P.O. Box 087
Trenton, NJ 08625
P: (609) 984-3230
F: (609) 633-6078
E: jerry.fischer
    @lps.state.nj.us

NEW MEXICO
Mr. Gary Tomada
Director
Alcohol & Gaming Division
2550 Cerrillos Road, 2nd Floor
P.O. Box 25101
Santa Fe, NM 87505
P: (505) 476-4550
F: (505) 476-4595
E: gary.tomada@state.nm.us

NEW YORK
Mr. Dennis Rosen
Chair
State Liquor Authority
Alfred E. Smith Building
80 South Swan Street, Suite 900
Albany, NY 12210
P: (518) 474-0810
F: (518) 402-4015

NORTH CAROLINA
Mr. Michael Herring
Chief Administrator
Alcoholic Beverage Control
Commission
3322 Garner Road
4307 Mail Service Center
Raleigh, NC 27699
P: (919) 779-0700
F: (919) 662-3583
E: herringm@ncabc.com

NORTH DAKOTA
Mr. Kevin Schatz
Supervisor, Alcoholic Beverages
Alcoholic Beverages Tax
Office of State Tax Commission
500 East Boulevard Avenue,
Dept. 127
Bismarck, ND 58505
P: (701) 328-3657
F: (701) 328-1283
E: kschatz@nd.gov

OHIO
Mr. Bruce D. Stevenson
Superintendent
Division of Liquor Control
6606 Tussing Raod
Reynoldsburg, OH 43068
P: (614) 644-2472
F: (614) 644-2480
E: webliqr@com.state.oh.us

OKLAHOMA
Mr. A. Keith Burt
Director
Alcoholic Beverage Laws
Enforcement Commission
4545 North Lincoln Boulevard,
Suite 270
Oklahoma City, OK 73105
P: (405) 521-3484
F: (405) 521-6578
E: akburt
    @mhs.oklaosf.state.ok.us

OREGON
Mr. Philip D. Lang
Chair
Liquor Control Commission
9079 Southeast McLoughlin
Boulevard
Portland, OR 97222
P: (503) 872-5242
F: (503) 872-5266
E: pdavidlang@msn.com

Alcoholic Beverage Control

PENNSYLVANIA
Mr. Patrick J.
  Stapleton III
Chair
Liquor Control Board
Room 517
Northwest Office Building
Harrisburg, PA 17124
P: (717) 787-2696
F: (717) 772-3714
E: pstapleton@state.pa.us

PUERTO RICO
Mr. Alberto Pratts
Director
Bureau of Alcoholic Beverages
& Licenses
Treasury Department
P.O. Box 9024140
San Juan, PR 00902
P: (787) 721-5245
F: (787) 722-6749

RHODE ISLAND
Ms. Maria D'Alessandro
Deputy Director &
Superintendent
Commercial Licensing &
Racing & Athletics
Department of Business
Regulation
1511 Pontiac Avenue
Cranston, RI 02920
P: (401) 462-9506
F: (401) 462-9645

SOUTH CAROLINA
Ms. Dana Krajack
Administrator, Regulatory
Division
Alcoholic Beverage Licensing
Department of Revenue
301 Gervais Street, P.O. Box 125
Columbia, SC 29214
P: (803) 898-5172
F: (803) 898-5907
E: krajackd@sctax.org

SOUTH DAKOTA
Mr. David Wiest
Interim Secretary of Revenue &
Regulation
Department of Revenue &
Regulation
445 East Capital Avenue
Pierre, SD 57501
P: (605) 773-3311
F: (605) 773-5129

TENNESSEE
Ms. Danielle Elks
Executive Director
Alcoholic Beverage
Commission
226 Capitol Boulevard, Room
300
Nashville, TN 37243
P: (615) 741-1602
F: (615) 741-0847

TEXAS
Mr. Alan Steen
Administrator
Alcoholic Beverage
Commission
5806 Mesa Drive
P.O. Box 13127
Austin, TX 78711
P: (512) 206-3217
F: (512) 206-3203
E: alan.steen
  @tabc.state.tx.us

UTAH
Mr. Dennis Kellen
Director
Department of Alcoholic
Beverage Control
1625 South 900 West
Salt Lake City, UT 84130
P: (801) 977-6800
F: (801) 977-6888
E: dkellen@utah.gov

VERMONT
Mr. Michael J. Hogan
Commissioner
Department of Liquor Control
13 Green Mountain Drive
Montpelier, VT 05620
P: (802) 828-2345
F: (802) 828-2803
E: mike.hogan@state.vt.us

VIRGINIA
Mr. J. Neal Insley
Chair
Alcohol Beverage Control
Board
2901 Hermitage Road
P.O. Box 27491
Richmond, VA 23261
P: (804) 213-4406
F: (804) 213-4411
E: abcboard
  @abc.virginia.gov

WASHINGTON
Ms. Sharon Foster
Chair
State Liquor Control Board
3000 Pacific Avenue, Southeast
P.O. Box 43080
Olympia, WA 98504
P: (360) 664-1600
F: (360) 586-3190

WEST VIRGINIA
Mr. Ronald M. Moats
Acting Commissioner
Alcohol Beverage Control
Administration
322 70th Street, Southeast
Charleston, WV 25304
P: (304) 558-2481
F: (304) 558-0081
E: ronald.m.moats@wv.gov

WISCONSIN
Ms. Barbara Brandt
Chief of Special Investigations
Department of Revenue
2135 Rimrock Road
P.O. Box 8933, Mail Stop 6-40
Madison, WI 53708
P: (608) 266-2776
E: Barbara.Brandt
  @wisconsin.gov

WYOMING
Mr. Greg Cook
Division Administrator
Liquor Distribution Division
Herschler Building
122 West 25th Street, 2nd West
Cheyenne, WY 82002
P: (307) 777-6448
F: (307) 777-7722
E: gcook@wy.gov

Arbitration and Mediation

Promotes the settlement of a variety of labor disputes.

ALABAMA
Mr. Jim Bennett
Commissioner
Department of Labor
P.O. Box 303500
Montgomery, AL 36130
P: (334) 242-3460
F: (334) 240-3417
E: jbennett
   @alalabor.alabama.gov

ALASKA
Mr. Click Bishop
Commissioner
Department of Labor &
Workforce Development
P.O. Box 21149
Juneau, AK 99802
P: (907) 465-2700
F: (907) 465-2784
E: commissioner.labor
   @ak.gov

AMERICAN SAMOA
Lt. Col. Evelyn Vaiautolu
   Langford
Director
Department of Human
Resources
American Samoa Government
Pago Pago, AS 96799
P: (684) 644-4485
F: (684) 633-1139

ARIZONA
Ms. Laura L. McGrory
Director
Industrial Commission
800 West Washington Street
Phoenix, AZ 85007
P: (602) 542-4411
F: (602) 542-7889
E: lmcgrory@ica.state.az.us

ARKANSAS
Mr. James L. Salkeld
Director
Department of Labor
10421 West Markham Street
Suite 100
Little Rock, AR 72205
P: (501) 682-4541
F: (501) 682-4535
E: james.salkeld
   @arkansas.gov

CALIFORNIA
Ms. Annie Song-Hill
Presiding Mediator
State Mediation & Conciliation
Service
1515 Clay Street, Suite 2206
Oakland, CA 94612
P: (510) 873-6465
F: (510) 873-6475

COLORADO
Ms. Ellen Golombek
Executive Director
Department of Labor &
Employment
633 17th Street, Suite 201
Denver, CO 80202
P: (303) 318-8000
F: (303) 318-8048
E: egolombek@state.co.us

CONNECTICUT
Mr. Glenn Marshall
Commissioner
Department of Labor
200 Folly Brook Boulevard
Wethersfield, CT 06109
P: (860) 263-6505
F: (860) 263-6529
E: glenn.marshall@ct.gov

DELAWARE
Mr. John McMahon
Secretary of Labor
Department of Labor
4425 North Market Street, 4th
Floor
Wilmington, DE 19802
P: (302) 761-8000
F: (302) 761-6621
E: john.mcmahon@state.de.us

DISTRICT OF COLUMBIA
Ms. Lisa Maria Mallory
Acting Director
Department of Employment
Services
4058 Minnesota Avenue,
Northeast
Washington, DC 20019
P: (202) 724-7000
F: (202) 673-6993
E: does@dc.gov

FLORIDA
Ms. Stephanie Williams Ray
Chair
Public Employees Relations
Commission
Room 150
4050 Esplanade Way
Tallahassee, FL 32399
P: (850) 488-8641
F: (850) 488-9704
E: stephanie.ray
   @perc.myflorida.com

GEORGIA
Hon. Mark Butler (R)
Commissioner
Department of Labor
148 International Boulevard
Northeast
Atlanta, GA 30303
P: (404) 232-7300
F: (404) 656-2683
E: mark.butler
   @dol.state.ga.us

GUAM
Mr. Tony Lamorena
Director
Civil Service Commission
P.O. Box 1356
Hagatna, GU 98932
P: (671) 647-1855
F: (671) 647-1867

Ms. Leah Beth Naholowaa
Director
Department of Labor
Government of Guam
P.O. Box 9970
Tamuning, GU 96931
P: (671) 647-6510
F: (671) 674-6517

HAWAII
Mr. Dwight Y. Takamine
Director
Department of Labor &
Industrial Relations
830 Punchbowl Stree, Room
321
Honolulu, HI 96813
P: (808) 586-8865
F: (808) 586-9099

IDAHO
Mr. Roger B. Madsen
Director
Department of Labor
317 West Main Street
Boise, ID 83735
P: (208) 332-3579
F: (208) 334-6430
E: rmadsen@cl.idaho.gov

ILLINOIS
Mr. John F. Brosnan
Executive Director
Labor Relations Board
160 North LaSalle Street, Suite
S-400
Chicago, IL 60601
P: (312) 793-6400
F: (312) 793-6989

INDIANA
Ms. Lori A. Torres
Commissioner
Department of Labor
Indiana Government
Center-South
402 West Washington Street,
Room W-195
Indianapolis, IN 46204
P: (317) 232-2655
F: (317) 974-2001
E: ltorrcs@dol.in.gov

IOWA
Mr. David Neil
Commissioner
Division of Labor Services
1000 East Grand Avenue
Des Moines, IA 50319
P: (515) 281-3447
F: (515) 281-4698
E: dave.neil@iwd.iowa.gov

KENTUCKY
Ms. Jodie M. Craig
Program Coordinator
Labor-Management Relations &
Mediation
1047 U.S. Highway 127 South
Suite 4
Frankfort, KY 40601
P: (502) 564-3202
F: (502) 696-1897
E: jodie.craig@ky.gov

LOUISIANA
Mr. Curt Eysink
Executive Director
Workforce Commission
1001 North 23rd Street
Baton Rouge, LA 70802
P: (225) 342-3111
F: (225) 342-3778
E: ceysink@lwc.la.gov

MAINE
Ms. Laura Boyett
Acting Commissioner
Department of Labor
P.O. Box 259
Augusta, ME 04332
P: (207) 287-3787
F: (207) 623-7934
E: luara.l.boyett@maine.gov

MASSACHUSETTS
Ms. Susan Jeghelian
Executive Director
Office of Dispute Resolution
100 Morrissey Boulevard
McCormack Building, Room
627
Boston, MA 02125
P: (617) 287-4047
F: (617) 287-4049
E: susan.jeghelian@umb.edu

Arbitration and Mediation

MICHIGAN
Ms. Ruthanne Okun
Director
Bureau of Employment
Relations
Cadillac Place, Suite 2-750
3026 West Grand Boulevard
Detroit, MI 48202
P: (313) 456-3519
F: (313) 456-3511
E: okunr@michigan.gov

MINNESOTA
Mr. Steven Hoffmeyer
Commissioner
Bureau of Mediation Services
1380 Energy Lane, Suite 2
St. Paul, MN 55108
P: (651) 649-5421
F: (651) 643-3013
E: steven.hoffmeyer
@state.mn.us

MISSOURI
Mr. William F. Ringer
Chair
Labor & Industrial Relations
Commission
3315 West Truman Boulevard,
Room 214
P.O. Box 599
Jefferson City, MO 65102
P: (573) 751-2461
F: (573) 751-7806
E: lirc@labor.mo.gov

MONTANA
Hon. Janet Kelly
Director
Department of Administration
125 North Roberts Street
Room 155, Mitchell Building
Helena, MT 59620
P: (406) 444-3033
F: (406) 444-6194
E: jakelly@mt.gov

NEBRASKA
Ms. Annette Hord
Administrator
Commission of Industrial
Relations
P.O. Box 94864
Lincoln, NE 68509
P: (402) 471-2934
F: (402) 471-6597
E: annette.hord
@nebraska.gov

NEVADA
Mr. Seaton J. Curran
Chair
Local Government
Employee-Management
Relations Board
Department of Business &
Industry
2501 East Sahara Avenue, Suite
203
Las Vegas, NV 89104
P: (702) 486-4504
F: (702) 486-4355
E: emrb@business.nv.gov

NEW HAMPSHIRE
Mr. George N. Copadis
Commissioner of Labor
Department of Labor
95 Pleasant Street
Concord, NH 03301
P: (603) 271-3171
F: (603) 271-6852
E: gcopadis
@labor.state.nh.us

NEW JERSEY
Mr. Harold Wirths
Commissioner
Department of Labor &
Workforce Development
P.O. Box 110
Trenton, NJ 08625
P: (609) 292-2323
F: (609) 633-9271
E: hal.wirths
@dol.state.nj.us

NEW MEXICO
Ms. Celina Bussey
Secretary
Department of Workforce
Solutions
401 Broadway Northeast
Albuquerque, NM 87103
P: (505) 841-8405
F: (505) 841-8491

NEW YORK
Ms. Colleen C. Gardner
Commissioner
Department of Labor
W. Averell Harriman State
Office Campus
Building 12
Albany, NY 12240
P: (518) 457-9000
F: (518) 485-6297
E: colleen.gardner
@labor.state.ny.us

NORTH CAROLINA
Hon. Cherie K. Berry (R)
Commissioner
Department of Labor
1101 Mail Service Center
Raleigh, NC 27699
P: (919) 733-0359
F: (919) 733-7640
E: commissioners.office
@nclabor.com

NORTH DAKOTA
Mr. Tony Weiler
Commissioner of Labor
Department of Labor
600 East Boulevard Avenue
Department 406
Bismarck, ND 58505
P: (701) 328-2660
F: (701) 328-2031
E: tjweiler@nd.gov

**NORTHERN MARIANA
ISLANDS**
Mr. Gil M. San Nicolas
Secretary
Department of Labor
Caller Box 10007
Saipan, MP 96950
P: (670) 322-9834
F: (670) 322-2633

OHIO
Mr. Bob Blair
Director
Department of Administrative
Services
30 East Broad Street, Suite 4040
Columbus, OH 43215
P: (614) 466-6511
F: (614) 644-8151
E: robert.blair
@das.state.oh.us

OKLAHOMA
Hon. Mark Costello
Commissioner of Labor
Department of Labor
3017 North Stiles, Suite 100
Oklahoma City, OK 73105
P: (405) 521-6100
F: (405) 521-6018

OREGON
Mr. Paul B. Gamson
Chair
Employment Relations Board
Old Garfield School Building,
Suite 400
528 Cottage Street, Northeast
Salem, OR 97301
P: (503) 378-8039
F: (503) 373-0021
E: paul.gamson@state.or.us

PENNSYLVANIA
Ms. Julia Hearthway
Acting Secretary
Department of Labor & Industry
651 Boas Street, Room 1700
Harrisburg, PA 17121
P: (717) 787-5279
F: (717) 787-8826

PUERTO RICO
Mr. Miguel Romero
Director
Department of Labor & Human
Resources
P.O. Box 191020
San Juan, PR 00919
P: (787) 754-5353
F: (787) 756-1149

RHODE ISLAND
Mr. Charles J. Fogarty
Director
Department of Labor & Training
1511 Pontiac Avenue
Cranston, RI 02920
P: (401) 462-8000
F: (401) 462-8872
E: director-dlt@dlt.ri.gov

SOUTH CAROLINA
Ms. Catherine Templeton
Director
Department of Labor, Licensing
& Regulation
P.O. Box 11329
Columbia, SC 29211
P: (803) 896-4390
F: (803) 896-4393
E: templetonc@llr.sc.gov

SOUTH DAKOTA
Ms. Pamela S. Roberts
Secretary
Department of Labor
700 Governors Drive
Pierre, SD 57501
P: (605) 773-3101
F: (605) 773-4211
E: pamela.roberts
@state.sd.us

TENNESSEE
Ms. Karla Davis
Commissioner
Department of Labor &
Workforce Development
Andrew Johnson Tower
710 James Robertson Parkway
Nashville, TN 37243
P: (615) 741-6642
F: (615) 741-5078
E: karla.davis@state.tn.us

TEXAS
Mr. Larry E. Temple
Executive Director
Workforce Commission
101 East 15th Street
Austin, TX 78778
P: (512) 463-0735
F: (512) 475-2321
E: larry.temple
 @twc.state.tx.us

U.S. VIRGIN ISLANDS
Mr. Albert Bryan Jr.
Commissioner of Labor
Department of Labor
2203 Church Street,
Christiansted
St. Croix, VI 00820
P: (340) 773-1994
F: (340) 773-0094
E: abryan@vidol.gov

UTAH
Ms. Sherrie M. Hayashi
Commissioner
Labor Commission
160 East 300 South, 3rd Floor
P.O. Box 146600
Salt Lake City, UT 84114
P: (801) 530-6848
F: (801) 530-6390
E: shayashi@utah.gov

VERMONT
Mr. Timothy J. Noonan
Executive Director
Labor Relations Board
133 State Street
Monpelier, VT 05633
P: (802) 828-2700
F: (802) 828-2392
E: tim.noonan@state.vt.us

VIRGINIA
Mr. Courtney Malveaux
Commissioner
Department of Labor & Industry
13 South 13th Street
Richmond, VA 23219
P: (804) 786-2377
F: (804) 371-6524
E: courtney.malveaux
 @doli.virginia.gov

WASHINGTON
Ms. Judy Schurke
Director
Department of Labor &
Industries
P.O. Box 44001
Olympia, WA 98504
P: (360) 902-4203
F: (360) 902-4202
E: scju235@lni.wa.gov

WEST VIRGINIA
Mr. David W. Mullins
Commissioner
Division of Labor
Bureau of Commerce
Capitol Complex, Building 6,
Room B-749
Charleston, WV 25305
P: (304) 558-7890
F: (304) 558-3797
E: david.w.mullins@wv.gov

WISCONSIN
Mr. Manny Perez
Secretary
Department of Workforce
Development
P.O. Box 7946
Madison, WI 53707
P: (608) 267-9692
F: (608) 266-1784
E: manuel.perez
 @dwd.wisconsin.gov

Archives

Identifies, acquires, preserves and makes available state government records of continuing historical and research value.

ALABAMA
Dr. Ed C. Bridges
Director
Department of Archives & History
624 Washington Avenue
P.O. Box 300100
Montgomery, AL 36130
P: (334) 242-4441
E: ed.bridges
@archives.alabama.gov

ALASKA
Mr. Glenn Cook
Deputy Director
Division of Libraries, Archives & Museums
Dept. of Education & Early Development
P.O. Box 110571
Juneau, AK 99811
P: (907) 465-2912
F: (907) 465-2151
E: glenn.cook@alaska.gov

ARIZONA
Dr. Melanie Sturgeon
Division Director
State Library, Archives & Public Records
History & Archives Division
1901 West Madison
Phoenix, AZ 85009
P: (602) 926-3729
F: (602) 256-7982
E: services@lib.az.us

ARKANSAS
Ms. Wendy Richter
State Historian
History Commission
One Capitol Mall
Little Rock, AR 72201
P: (501) 682-6900
E: wendy.richter
@arkansas.gov

CALIFORNIA
Ms. Nancy Zimmelman Lenoil
Chief
State Archives
1020 O Street
Sacramento, CA 95814
P: (916) 653-0401
F: (916) 653-7134
E: nancy.lenoil@sos.ca.gov

COLORADO
Mr. Terry Ketelsen
State Archivist
State Archives
Division of Information Technologies
1313 Sherman Street, Room 1B-20
Denver, CO 80203
P: (303) 866-4900
F: (303) 866-2257

CONNECTICUT
Mr. Mark H. Jones
State Archivist
State Library & Archives
231 Capitol Avenue
Hartford, CT 06106
P: (860) 757-6511
F: (860) 757-6542
E: mjones@cslib.org

DELAWARE
Mr. Stephen M. Marz
Director
Public Archives
121 Duke of York Street
Dover, DE 19901
P: (302) 744-5000
F: (302) 739-8436

DISTRICT OF COLUMBIA
Mr. Clarence Davis
Public Records Administrator
Public Records/Archives
1300 Naylor Court, Northwest
Washington, DC 20001
P: (202) 671-1105
F: (202) 671-6076
E: clarence.davis@dc.gov

FLORIDA
Ms. Judith Ring
Director
State Library & Archives
Department of State, R.A. Gray Building
500 South Bronough Street
Tallahassee, FL 32399
P: (850) 245-6600
F: (850) 488-4894
E: jring@dos.state.fl.us

GEORGIA
Mr. David W. Carmichael
Director
The Georgia Archives
5800 Jonesboro Road
Morrow, GA 30260
P: (678) 364-3700
F: (678) 364-3856

GUAM
Ms. Sylvia Flores
Director
Department of Chamorro Affairs
Barracks 13-6 Seagull Avenue
Tiyan
212 Aspinall Avenue
Hagatna, GU 96932
P: (671) 475-4279
F: (671) 475-4227

Ms. Teresita L.G. Kennimer
Acting Territorial Librarian & Director
Public Library System
254 Martyr Street
Hagatna, GU 96910
P: (671) 475-4754
F: (671) 477-9777

HAWAII
Ms. Susan E. Shaner
State Archivist
Department of Accounting & General Services
Kekauluohi Bldg., Iolani Palace Grounds
364 S. King Street
Honolulu, HI 96813
P: (808) 586-0310
F: (808) 586-0330

IDAHO
Mr. Rod House
State Archivist
State Archives
2205 Old Penitentiary Road
Boise, ID 83712
P: (208) 514-2316
F: (208) 334-2626
E: rod.house@ishs.idaho.gov

ILLINOIS
Mr. David A. Joens
Director
State Archives
Margaret Cross Norton Building
Capitol Complex
Springfield, IL 62756
P: (217) 782-4682
F: (217) 524-3930

INDIANA
Mr. Jim Corridan
Director/State Archivist
Commission on Public Records
402 West Washington Street, Room W472
Indianapolis, IN 46204
P: (317) 232-3380
F: (317) 233-1713
E: jcorridan@icpr.IN.gov

IOWA
Mr. Jerome Thompson
Interim Administrator
Historical Society of Iowa
Capitol Complex
East 6th & Locust Street
Des Moines, IA 50319
P: (515) 281-4221
F: (515) 242-6498
E: Jerome.Thompson@Iowa.gov

KANSAS
Ms. Pat Michaelis
Division Director
State Historical Society
Library & Archives
6425 Southwest 6th Avenue
Topeka, KS 66615
P: (785) 272-8681 Ext. 270
F: (785) 272-8682
E: pmichaelis@kshs.org

KENTUCKY
Ms. Barbara Teague
State Archivist & Records Administrator
Department for Libraries & Archives
Public Records Division
300 Coffee Tree Road
Frankfort, KY 40601
P: (502) 564-8300 ext.249
F: (502) 564-5773
E: barbara.teague@ky.gov

LOUISIANA
Dr. Florent Hardy Jr.
State Archivist
State Archives
Office of the Secretary of State
3851 Essen Lane
Baton Rouge, LA 70809
P: (225) 922-1200
F: (225) 922-0433
E: florent.hardy
@sos.louisiana.gov

MAINE
Mr. Dave Cheever
State Archivist
State Archives
84 State House Station
Augusta, ME 04333
P: (207) 287-5790
F: (207) 287-6935
E: david.cheever@maine.gov

MARYLAND

Dr. Edward C. Papenfuse
State Archivist & Commissioner
of Land Patents
State Archives
350 Rowe Boulevard
Annapolis, MD 21401
P: (410) 260-6401
F: (410) 974-2525
E: edp@mdsa.net

MASSACHUSETTS

Dr. John D. Warner Jr.
Archivist of the Commonwealth
State Archives
Secretary of the Commonwealth
220 Morrissey Boulevard
Boston, MA 02125
P: (617) 727-2816
F: (617) 288-8429
E: john.warner
    @sec.state.ma.us

MICHIGAN

Mr. Mark Harvey
State Archivist
Archives of Michigan
Library & Historical Center
702 W. Kalamazoo Street
Lansing, MI 48913
P: (517) 373-1415
E: HarveyM@michigan.gov

MINNESOTA

Mr. Robert Horton
State Archivist
State Archives
Historical Society
345 W. Kellogg Boulevard
St. Paul, MN 55102
P: (651) 259-3240
F: (651) 296-9961
E: robert.horton@mnhs.org

MISSISSIPPI

Mr. H.T. Holmes
State Historic Preservation
Officer
Department of Archives &
History
P.O. Box 571
Jackson, MS 39205
P: (601) 576-6850
F: (601) 576-6975

MISSOURI

Mr. John Dougan
State Archivist
State Archives
600 West Main Street
P.O. Box 1747
Jefferson City, MO 65102
P: (573) 751-3280
F: (573) 526-7333
E: archref@sos.mo.gov

MONTANA

Jodie Foley
State Archivist
Historical Society, Research
Center
225 North Roberts
P.O. Box 201201
Helena, MT 59620
P: (406) 444-7482
E: jofoley@mt.gov

NEBRASKA

Ms. Andrea Faling
Associate Director
Historical Society, Library &
Archives Division
1500 "R" Street
P.O. Box 82554
Lincoln, NE 68501
P: (402) 471-4785
F: (402) 471-3100
E: andrea.faling
    @nebraska.gov

NEVADA

Mr. Jeffrey M. Kintop
Assistant Administrator for
Archives and Records
State Library & Archives
Department of Cultural Affairs
100 North Stewart Street
Carson City, NV 89701
P: (775) 684-3410
F: (775) 684-3371
E: jkintop
    @nevadaculture.org

NEW HAMPSHIRE

Mr. Brian N. Burford
Director & State Archivist
Division of Archives & Records
Management
Department of State
71 South Fruit Street
Concord, NH 03301
P: (603) 271-2236
F: (603) 271-2272
E: bburford@sos.state.nh.us

NEW JERSEY

Mr. Joseph Klett
Deputy Director for Archives
Division of Archives & Records
Management
225 W. State Street, Level 2
P.O. Box 307
Trenton, NJ 08625
P: (609) 292-9507
F: (609) 292-9105
E: joseph.klett
    @sos.state.nj.us

NEW MEXICO

Ms. Sandra Jaramillo
State Records Administrator
State Records Center &
Archives
1205 Camino Carlos Rey
Santa Fe, NM 87507
P: (505) 476-7911
F: (505) 476-7893
E: sandra.jaramillo
    @state.nm.us

NEW YORK

Ms. Christine Ward
Assistant Commissioner, State
Archives
Education Department
Cultural Education Center
Albany, NY 12230
P: (518) 473-7091
F: (518) 473-7058
E: cward@mail.nysed.gov

NORTH CAROLINA

Dr. Jeffrey J. Crow
State Historic Preservation
Officer
Division of Archives & History
4610 Mail Service Center
Raleigh, NC 27699
P: (919) 807-7280
F: (919) 733-8807
E: jeff.crow@ncdcr.gov

NORTH DAKOTA

Ms. Ann B. Jenks
State Archivist
State Historical Society
612 East Boulevard Avenue
Bismarck, ND 58505
P: (701) 328-2666
F: (701) 328-3710
E: ajenks@nd.gov

NORTHERN MARIANA ISLANDS

Mr. Herbert S. Del Rosario
Archivist
CNMI Archives
P.O. Box 501250
Saipan, MP 96950
P: (670) 234-5498 x.1110
F: (670) 234-1270
E: herbertr@nmcnet.edu

OHIO

Mr. Burt Logan
Director
Historical Society
1982 Velma Avenue
Columbus, OH 43211
P: (614) 297-2350
F: (614) 297-2352
E: blogan@ohiohistory.org

OKLAHOMA

Ms. Jan Davis
Administrator
Archives & Records
Department of Libraries
200 Northeast 18th Street
Oklahoma City, OK 73105
P: (405) 522-3191
E: jdavis
    @oltn.odl.state.ok.us

OREGON

Ms. Mary Beth Herkert
State Archivist
State Archives
Secretary of State
800 Summer Street, Northeast
Salem, OR 97310
P: (503) 378-5196
F: (503) 373-0953
E: mary.e.herkert
    @state.or.us

PENNSYLVANIA

Ms. Barbara Franco
Executive Director
Historical & Museum
Commission
300 North Street
Harrisburg, PA 17120
P: (717) 787-2891
F: (717) 783-9924

RHODE ISLAND

Ms. R. Gwenn Stearn
State Archivist & Public Records
Administrator
State Archives
337 Westminster Street
Providence, RI 02903
P: (401) 222-2353
F: (401) 222-3199
E: statearchives@sos.ri.gov

Archives

SOUTH CAROLINA
Mr. Eric Emerson
State Historic Preservation
Officer
Department of Archives &
History
8301 Parklane Road
Columbia, SC 29223
P: (803) 896-6100
F: (803) 896-6167
E: eemerson
   @scdah.state.sc.us

SOUTH DAKOTA
Ms. Chelle Somsen
State Archivist
State Historical Society
Cultural Heritage Center
900 Governors Drive
Pierre, SD 57501
P: (605) 773-5521
F: (605) 773-6041
E: chelle.somsen
   @state.sd.us

TENNESSEE
Mr. Charles A. Sherrill
State Librarian & Archivist
State Library & Archives
403 7th Avenue, North
Nashville, TN 37243
P: (615) 741-7996
F: (615) 532-9293
E: Chuck.Sherrill@tn.gov

TEXAS
Ms. Peggy D. Rudd
Director & Librarian
State Library & Archives
Commission
1201 Brazos Street
P.O. Box 12927
Austin, TX 78711
P: (512) 463-5460
F: (512) 463-5436
E: prudd@tsl.state.tx.us

U.S. VIRGIN ISLANDS
Ms. Susan Laura Lugo
Territorial Librarian for the
Archives
Division of Libraries, Archives
& Museums
1122 King Street
St. Croix, VI 00820
P: (304) 773-5715
F: (304) 773-5327

UTAH
Ms. Patricia
   Smith-Mansfield
Director
Division of State Archives &
Records Service
346 South Rio Grande
Salt Lake City, UT 84101
P: (801) 531-3850
F: (801) 531-3854
E: pmansfie@utah.gov

VERMONT
Mr. D. Gregory Sanford
State Archivist
Archives & Records
Administration
Secretary of State Office
1078 U.S. Route 2, Middlesex
Montpelier, VT 05633
P: (802) 828-2369
F: (802) 828-3710
E: gsanford@sec.state.vt.us

VIRGINIA
Ms. Sandra Treadway
Director
The Library of Virginia
800 East Broad Street
Richmond, VA 23219
P: (804) 692-3500
E: sandra.treadway
   @lva.virginia.gov

WASHINGTON
Mr. Jerry Handfield
State Archivist
Office of the Secretary of State
State Archives
P.O. Box 40238
Olympia, WA 98504
P: (360) 586-1492
E: archives@sos.wa.gov

WEST VIRGINIA
Mr. Joe Geiger
Director, Archives & History
Division of Culture & History
The Culture Center, Capitol
Complex
1900 Kanawha Boulevard, East
Charleston, WV 25305
P: (304) 558-0230
F: (304) 558-2779
E: Joe.N.Geiger@wv.gov

WISCONSIN
Mr. Peter Gottlieb
Director & State Archivist
Historical Society
Library-Archives Division
816 State Street, Room 422
Madison, WI 53706
P: (608) 264-6480
F: (608) 264-6486
E: pgottlieb@whs.wisc.edu

WYOMING
Mr. Roger Joyce
State Archivist
Department of State Parks &
Cultural Resources
State Archives Division
2301 Central Avenue
Cheyenne, WY 82002
P: (307) 777-7020
F: (307) 777-7044
E: rjoyce@state.wy.us

Attorney General

The chief legal officer of the state who represents the state or its offices in all litigation.

ALABAMA
Hon. Luther Strange (R)
Attorney General
Office of the Attorney General
500 Dexter Avenue
Montgomery, AL 36130
P: (334) 242-7300

ALASKA
Hon. John J. Burns
(appointed)
Attorney General
Office of the Attorney General
P.O. Box 110300
Diamond Courthouse
Juneau, AK 99811
P: (907) 465-2133
F: (907) 465-2075
E: attorney.general
@alaska.gov

AMERICAN SAMOA
Hon. Fepulea'i A.
Ripley Jr.
(appointed)
Attorney General
Office of the Attorney General
American Samoa Government
Executive Office Building,
Utulei
Pago Pago, AS 96799
P: (684) 633-4163
F: (684) 633-1838

ARIZONA
Hon. Tom Horne (R)
Attorney General
Office of the Attorney General
1275 West Washington Street
Phoenix, AZ 85007
P: (602) 542-5025
F: (602) 542-4085

ARKANSAS
Hon. Dustin McDaniel (D)
Attorney General
Office of the Attorney General
323 Center Street, Suite 200
Little Rock, AR 72201
P: 501) 682-2341
F: (501) 682-8084

CALIFORNIA
Hon. Kamala Harris (D)
Attorney General
Office of the Attorney General
1300 I Street, Suite 1740
Sacramento, CA 95814
P: (916) 445-9555

COLORADO
Hon. John Suthers (R)
Attorney General
Office of the Attorney General
1525 Sherman Street
Denver, CO 80203
P: (303) 866-4500
F: (303) 866-5691
E: attorney.general
@state.co.us

CONNECTICUT
Hon. George C. Jepsen (D)
Attorney General
Office of the Attorney General
55 Elm Street
Hartford, CT 06141
P: (860) 808-5318
E: Jepsen
@senatedems.state.ct.us

DELAWARE
Hon. Joseph R.
Biden III (D)
Attorney General
Office of the Attorney General
Carvel State Office Building
820 North French Street
Wilmington, DE 19801
P: (302) 577-8400
E: Attorney.General
@state.de.us

DISTRICT OF COLUMBIA
Hon. Irvin Nathan
(appointed)
Acting Attorney General
Office of the Attorney General
441 4th Street Northwest
Washington, DC 20001
P: (202) 727-3400
F: (202) 347-8922

FLORIDA
Hon. Pam Bondi (R)
Attorney General
Office of the Attorney General
The Capitol, PL 01
Tallahassee, FL 32399
P: (850) 414-3300
F: (954) 712-4826

GEORGIA
Hon. Sam S. Olens (R)
Attorney General
Office of the Attorney General
40 Capitol Square, Southwest
Atlanta, GA 30334
P: (404) 656-3300
F: (404) 657-8733

GUAM
Hon. Leonardo Rapadas
Attorney General
Office of the Attorney General
287 West O'Brien Drive
Hagatna, GU 96910
P: (671) 475-3324
F: (671) 472-2493

HAWAII
Hon. David Louie
(appointed)
Attorney General
Office of the Attorney General
425 Queen Street
Honolulu, HI 96813
P: (808) 586-1500
F: (808) 586-1239

IDAHO
Hon. Lawrence Wasden (R)
Attorney General
Office of the Attorney General
700 West State Street
P.O. Box 83720
Boise, ID 83720
P: (208) 334-2400
F: (208) 854-8071

ILLINOIS
Hon. Lisa Madigan (D)
Attorney General
Office of the Attorney General
James R. Thompson Center
100 West Randolph Street
Chicago, IL 60601
P: (312) 814-3000

INDIANA
Hon. Greg Zoeller (R)
Attorney General
Office of the Attorney General
Indiana Government Center
South
302 West Washington Street
Indianapolis, IN 46204
P: (317) 232-6201
F: (317) 232-7979
E: Constituent@atg.in.gov

IOWA
Hon. Tom Miller (D)
Attorney General
Office of the Attorney General
Hoover State Office Building
1305 East Walnut
Des Moines, IA 50319
P: (515) 281-5164
F: (515) 281-4209

KANSAS
Hon. Derek Schmidt (R)
Attorney General
Office of the Attorney General
120 Southwest 10th Avenue
2nd Floor
Topeka, KS 66612
P: (785) 296-2215
F: (785) 296-6296

KENTUCKY
Hon. Jack Conway (D)
Attorney General
Office of the Attorney General
700 Capitol Avenue
Capitol Building, Suite 118
Frankfort, KY 40601
P: (502) 696-5300
F: (502) 564-2894
E: attorney.general
@ag.ky.gov

LOUISIANA
Hon. James D. Caldwell (D)
Attorney General
Office of the Attorney General
1885 North 3rd Street
P.O. Box 94005
Baton Rouge, LA 70804
P: (225) 326-6705
F: (225) 326-6797
E: executive@ag.state.la.us

MAINE
Hon. William J.
Schneider (R)
Attorney General
Office of the Attorney General
State House Station 6
Augusta, ME 04333
P: (207) 626-8800

MARYLAND
Hon. Douglas F. Gansler (D)
Attorney General
Office of the Attorney General
200 Saint Paul Place
Baltimore, MD 21202
P: (410) 576-6300
F: (410) 576-6404
E: oag@oag.state.md.us

Attorney General

MASSACHUSETTS
Hon. Martha Coakley (D)
Attorney General
Office of the Attorney General
One Ashburton Place
Boston, MA 02108
P: (617) 727-2200

MICHIGAN
Hon. Bill Schuette (R)
Attorney General
Office of the Attorney General
P.O. Box 30212
525 West Ottawa Street
Lansing, MI 48909
P: (517) 373-1110

MINNESOTA
Hon. Lori Swanson (DFL)
Attorney General
Office of the Attorney General
State Capitol, Suite 102
St. Paul, MN 55155
P: (651) 296-3353
F: (651) 297-4193
E: attorney.general
    @state.mn.us

MISSISSIPPI
Hon. Jim Hood (D)
Attorney General
Office of the Attorney General
550 High Street, Suite 1200
P.O. Box 220
Jackson, MS 39205
P: (601) 359-3680
E: msag05@ago.state.ms.us

MISSOURI
Hon. Chris Koster (D)
Attorney General
Office of the Attorney General
207 West High Street
P.O. Box 899
Jefferson City, MO 65102
P: (573) 751-3321
F: (573) 751-0774

MONTANA
Hon. Steve Bullock (D)
Attorney General
Department of Justice
215 North Sanders, Third Floor
Helena, MT 59620
P: (406) 444-2026
F: (404) 444-3549
E: contactdoj@mt.gov

NEBRASKA
Hon. Jon C. Bruning (R)
Attorney General
Office of the Attorney General
State Capitol
P.O. Box 98920
Lincoln, NE 68509
P: (402) 471-2682
F: (402) 471-3297

NEVADA
Hon. Catherine Cortez
    Masto (D)
Attorney General
Office of the Attorney General
Old Supreme Court Building
100 North Carson Street
Carson City, NV 89701
P: (775) 684-1100
F: (775) 684-1108
E: aginfo@ag.state.nv.us

NEW HAMPSHIRE
Hon. Michael A. Delaney
    (appointed)
Attorney General
Office of the Attorney General
Department of Justice
33 Capitol Street
Concord, NH 03301
P: (603) 271-1202
F: (603) 271-2110
E: michael.a.delaney
    @doj.nh.gov

NEW JERSEY
Hon. Paula T. Dow
    (appointed)
Attorney General
Office of the Attorney General
P.O. Box 080
Trenton, NJ 08625
P: (609) 292-4925

NEW MEXICO
Hon. Gary K. King (D)
Attorney General
Office of the Attorney General
P.O. Drawer 1508
Santa Fe, NM 87504
P: (505) 827-6000
F: (505) 827-5826

NEW YORK
Hon. Eric T.
    Schneiderman (D)
Attorney General
Office of the Attorney General
Department of Law
The Capitol, 2nd Floor
Albany, NY 12224
P: (518) 474-7330

NORTH CAROLINA
Hon. Roy A. Cooper III (D)
Attorney General
Office of the Attorney General
Department of Justice
P.O. Box 629
Raleigh, NC 27602
P: (919) 716-6400
F: (919) 716-6750

NORTH DAKOTA
Hon. Wayne Stenehjem (R)
Attorney General
Office of the Attorney General
State Capitol, Department 125
600 East Boulevard Avenue
Bismarck, ND 58505
P: (701) 328-2210
F: (701) 328-2226
E: wstenehjem@nd.gov

**NORTHERN MARIANA
ISLANDS**
Hon. Edward T. Buckingham
Attorney General
Office of the Attorney General
Administration Building
P.O. Box 10007
Saipan, MP 96950
P: (670) 664-2341
F: (670) 664-2349

OHIO
Hon. Mike DeWine (R)
Attorney General
Office of the Attorney General
State Office Tower
30 East Broad Street
Columbus, OH 43266
P: (614) 466-4320

OKLAHOMA
Hon. Scott Pruitt (R)
Attorney General
Office of the Attorney General
313 Northeast 21st Street
Oklahoma City, OK 73105
P: (405) 521-3921

OREGON
Hon. John R. Kroger (D)
Attorney General
Office of the Attorney General
Justice Building
1162 Court Street, Northeast
Salem, OR 97301
P: (503) 378-4732

PENNSYLVANIA
Hon. William H.
    Ryan Jr. (R)
Acting Attorney General
Office of the Attorney General
16th Floor, Strawberry Square
Harrisburg, PA 17120
P: (717) 787-3391
F: (717) 787-5211

PUERTO RICO
Hon. Guillermo Somoza
    Colombani
Attorney General
Office of the Attorney General
G.P.O. Box 902192
San Juan, PR 00902
P: (787) 721-2900

RHODE ISLAND
Hon. Peter F. Kilmartin (D)
Attorney General
Office of the Attorney General
150 South Main Street
Providence, RI 02903
P: (401) 274-4400

SOUTH CAROLINA
Hon. Alan Wilson (R)
Attorney General
Office of the Attorney General
Rembert C. Dennis Office
Building
P.O. Box 11549
Columbia, SC 29211
P: (803) 734-3970

SOUTH DAKOTA
Hon. Marty J. Jackley (R)
Attorney General
Office of the Attorney General
1302 East Highway 14,
Suite 1
Pierre, SD 57501
P: (605) 773-3215
F: (605) 773-4106
E: atghelp@state.sd.us

TENNESSEE
Hon. Robert E. Cooper Jr.
    (appointed)
Attorney General
Office of the Attorney General
500 Charlotte Avenue
Nashville, TN 37243
P: (615) 741-5860

TEXAS
Hon. Greg Abbott (R)
Attorney General
Office of the Attorney General
Capitol Station
P.O. Box 12548
Austin, TX 78711
P: (512) 463-2100
E: greg.abbott
    @oag.state.tx.us

U.S. VIRGIN ISLANDS
Hon. Vincent Frazer
    (appointed)
Attorney General
Office of the Attorney General
Department of Justice, G.E.R.S.
Complex
488-50C Kronprinsdens Gade
St. Thomas, VI 00802
P: (340) 774-5666
F: (340) 774-9710

UTAH
Hon. Mark L. Shurtleff (R)
Attorney General
Office of the Attorney General
350 North State Street, Suite
230
P.O. Box 142320
Salt Lake City, UT 84114
P: (801) 538-1191
F: (801) 538-1121
E: MSHURTLEFF@utah.gov

VERMONT
Hon. William H. Sorrell (D)
Attorney General
Office of the Attorney General
109 State Street
Montpelier, VT 05609
P: (802) 828-3173
F: (802) 828-3187

VIRGINIA
Hon. Ken T.
    Cuccinelli II (R)
Attorney General
Office of the Attorney General
900 East Main Street
Richmond, VA 23219
P: (804) 786-2071

WASHINGTON
Hon. Rob McKenna (R)
Attorney General
Office of the Attorney General
1125 Washington Street,
Southeast
P.O. Box 40100
Olympia, WA 98504
P: (360) 753-6200
F: (360) 664-0228

WEST VIRGINIA
Hon. Darrell V.
    McGraw Jr. (D)
Attorney General
Office of the Attorney General
State Capitol Complex, Building
1
Room E-26
Charleston, WV 25305
P: (304) 558-2021
F: (304) 558-0140

WISCONSIN
Hon. J.B. Van Hollen (R)
Attorney General
Office of the Attorney General
State Capitol, Suite 114 East
P.O. Box 7857
Madison, WI 53707
P: (608) 266-1221

WYOMING
Hon. Greg Phillips (D)
    (appointed)
Attorney General
Office of the Attorney General
State Capitol Building
Cheyenne, WY 82002
P: (307) 777-7841

Hon. Bruce A. Salzburg
    (appointed)
Attorney General
Office of the Attorney General
State Capitol Building
Cheyenne, WY 82002
P: (307) 777-7841
F: (307) 777-6869

Auditor

Determines that governmental funds are handled appropriately and assesses how effectively government organizations are achieving their purposes.

Information provided by:

National Association of State Auditors, Comptrollers & Treasurers
Kinney Poynter
Executive Director
449 Lewis Hargett Circle
Suite 290
Lexington, KY 40503
P: (859) 276-1147
F: (859) 278-0507
kpoynter@nasact.org
www.nasact.org

ALABAMA
Mr. Ronald L. Jones
Chief Examiner
Department of Examiners of Public Accounts
50 North Ripley Street, Room 3201
Montgomery, AL 36104
P: (334) 242-9200
F: (334) 353-1436
E: ron.jones
    @examiners.alabama.gov

Hon. S. Samantha Shaw (R)
State Auditor
Office of the State Auditor
State Capitol, Room S-101
600 Dexter Avenue
Montgomery, AL 36130
P: (334) 242-7010
F: (334) 242-7650
E: sam.shaw
    @auditor.alabama.gov

ALASKA
Hon. Pat Davidson
Legislative Auditor
Division of Legislative Audit
P.O. Box 113300
Juneau, AK 99811
P: (907) 465-3830
F: (907) 465-2347
E: pat_davidson
    @legis.state.ak.us

AMERICAN SAMOA
Hon. Robert Dantini
Territorial Auditor
Territorial Audit Office
Executive Office Building
AP Lutali - 2nd Floor
Pago Pago, AS 96799
P: (684) 633-5191
F: (684) 633-1039
E: auditor.tao
    @americansamoa.gov

ARIZONA
Hon. Debra K. Davenport
Auditor General
Office of the Auditor General
2910 North 44th Street, Suite 410
Phoenix, AZ 85018
P: (602) 553-0333
F: (602) 553-0051
E: ddavenport@azauditor.gov

ARKANSAS
Mr. Roger Norman
Legislative Auditor
Division of Legislative Audit
172 State Capitol
Little Rock, AR 72201
P: (501) 683-6600
F: (501) 683-8605
E: roger.norman
    @arklegaudit.gov

CALIFORNIA
Hon. Elaine M. Howle
State Auditor
Bureau of State Audits
555 Capitol Mall, Suite 300
Sacramento, CA 95814
P: (916) 445-0255
F: (916) 323-0913
E: elaineh@bsa.ca.gov

COLORADO
Hon. Sally W. Symanski
State Auditor
Office of the State Auditor
Legislative Service Building
200 East 14th Avenue
Denver, CO 80203
P: (303) 866-2051
F: (303) 866-3060
E: sally.symanski
    @state.co.us

CONNECTICUT
Hon. John C. Geragosian (D)
State Auditor
Office of the Auditors of Public Accounts
State Capitol
210 Capitol Avenue
Hartford, CT 06106
P: (860) 240-5300
F: (860) 240-8655
E: john.geragosian
    @cga.ct.gov

Hon. Robert M. Ward
State Auditor
Office of the Auditors of Public Accounts
State Capitol
210 Capitol Avenue
Hartford, CT 06106
P: (860) 240-5300
F: (860) 240-8655
E: robert.ward@cga.ct.gov

DELAWARE
Hon. R. Thomas
    Wagner Jr. (R)
Auditor of Accounts
Office of the Auditor of Accounts
401 Federal Street, Suite 1
Dover, DE 19901
P: (302) 739-4241
F: (302) 739-6707
E: r.thomas.wagner
    @state.de.us

DISTRICT OF COLUMBIA
Hon. Deborah Kay Nichols
Auditor
Office of the Auditor
717 14th Street, Northwest, Suite 900
Washington, DC 20005
P: (202) 727-3600
F: (202) 724-8814
E: Deborah.Nichols@dc.gov

FLORIDA
Hon. David W. Martin
Auditor General
Office of the Auditor General
111 West Madison Street, Room 236
Tallahassee, FL 32399
P: (850) 488-0840
F: (850) 488-6975
E: davidmartin
    @aud.state.fl.us

GEORGIA
Hon. Russell W. Hinton
State Auditor
Department of Audits & Accounts
270 Washington Street, Southwest
Suite 4-114
Atlanta, GA 30334
P: (404) 656-2174
F: (404) 651-9448
E: hintonrw@audits.ga.gov

GUAM
Hon. Doris Flores Brooks
Public Auditor
Office of the Public Auditor
DNA Building, Suite 401
238 Archbishop Flores Street
Hagatna, GU 96910
P: (671) 475-0390
F: (671) 472-7951
E: dfbrooks@guamopa.org

HAWAII
Hon. Marion M. Higa
State Auditor
Office of the Auditor
465 South King Street, Room 500
Honolulu, HI 96813
P: (808) 587-0800
F: (808) 587-0830
E: mmhiga
    @auditor.state.hi.us

IDAHO
Mr. Don Berg
Audit Division Manager
Office of the Legislative Audits
Legislative Services Office
P.O. Box 83720
Boise, ID 83720
P: (208) 342-2475
F: (208) 334-2125
E: berg@lso.idaho.gov

Mr. Rakesh Mohan
Director
Office of Performance Evaluations
954 West Jefferson Street
10th Street Entrance, 2nd Floor
Boise, ID 83720
P: (208) 332-1470
F: (208) 332-1471
E: rmohan@ope.idaho.gov

ILLINOIS
Hon. William G. Holland
Auditor General
Office of the Auditor General
Iles Park Plaza
740 East Ash Street
Springfield, IL 62703
P: (217) 782-3536
F: (217) 785-8222
E: oag22@mail.state.il.us

INDIANA
Mr. Bruce Hartman
State Examiner
State Board of Accounts
302 West Washington Street
Room E-418
Indianapolis, IN 46204
P: (317) 232-2524
F: (317) 232-4711
E: bhartman@sboa.in.gov

IOWA
Hon. David A. Vaudt (R)
Auditor of State
Office of the Auditor of State
State Capitol
1007 East Grand Avenue
Des Moines, IA 50319
P: (515) 281-5835
F: (515) 242-6134
E: david.vaudt
   @auditor.state.ia.us

KANSAS
Mr. Scott Frank
Legislative Post Auditor
Legislative Division of Post
Audit
800 Southwest Jackson Street
Suite 1200
Topeka, KS 66612
P: (785) 296-3792
F: (785) 296-4482
E: scott.frank@lpa.ks.gov

KENTUCKY
Hon. Crit Luallen (D)
Auditor of Public Accounts
Office of the Auditor of Public
Accounts
209 St. Clair Street
Frankfort, KY 40601
P: (502) 564-5841
F: (502) 564-2912
E: Crit.Luallen
   @auditor.ky.gov

MAINE
Hon. Neria R. Douglass (D)
State Auditor
Department of Audit
66 State House Station
Augusta, ME 04333
P: (207) 624-6250
F: (207) 624-6273
E: neria.r.douglass
   @maine.gov

MARYLAND
Hon. Bruce A. Myers
Legislative Auditor
Office of Legislative Audits
301 West Preston Street, Room
1202
Baltimore, MD 21201
P: (410) 946-5900
F: (410) 946-5998
E: bmyers@ola.state.md.us

MASSACHUSETTS
Hon. Suzanne M. Bump (D)
Auditor of the Commonwealth
Office of the Auditor of the
Commonwealth
State House, Room 229
Boston, MA 02133
P: (617) 727-2075
F: (617) 727-2383
E: suzanne.bump
   @sao.state.ma.us

MICHIGAN
Hon. Thomas H. McTavish
Auditor General
Office of the Auditor General
201 North Washington Square
Suite 600, Victor Center
Lansing, MI 48913
P: (517) 334-8050
F: (517) 334-8079
E: tmctavish
   @audgen.michigan.gov

MINNESOTA
Mr. James Nobles
Legislative Auditor
Office of the Legislative Auditor
Centennial Office Building
658 Cedar Street, 1st Floor South
St. Paul, MN 55155
P: (651) 296-4710
F: (651) 296-4712
E: james.nobles@state.mn.us

Hon. Rebecca Otto (DFL)
State Auditor
Office of the State Auditor
525 Park Street, Suite 400
St. Paul, MN 55103
P: (615) 296-2551
F: (615) 296-4755
E: rebecca.otto@state.mn.us

MISSISSIPPI
Mr. Max Arinder
Executive Director
Joint Committee on
Performance
Evaluation & Expenditure
Review
P.O. Box 1204
Jackson, MS 39215
P: (601) 359-1226
F: (601) 359-1420
E: arinder@peer.state.ms.us

Hon. Stacey E.
   Pickering (R)
State Auditor
Office of the State Auditor
P. O. Box 956
Jackson, MS 39205
P: (601) 576-2640
F: (601) 576-2650
E: stacey.pickering
   @osa.ms.gov

MISSOURI
Hon. Tom Schweich (R)
State Auditor
Office of the State Auditor
State Capitol, Room 224
Jefferson City, MO 65102
P: (573) 751-4824
F: (573) 751-6539
E: tom.schweich
   @auditor.mo.gov

MONTANA
Hon. Tori M. Hunthausen
Legislative Auditor
Legislative Audit Division
Room 160, State Capitol
Building
P.O. Box 201705
Helena, MT 59620
P: (406) 444-3122
F: (406) 444-9784
E: thunthausen@mt.gov

NEBRASKA
Hon. Mike Foley (R)
State Auditor
Office of the Auditor of Public
Accounts
2303 State Capitol
Lincoln, NE 68509
P: (402) 471-2111
F: (402) 471-3301
E: mike.foley@nebraska.gov

NEVADA
Hon. Paul V. Townsend
Legislative Auditor
Legislative Counsel Bureau
Audit Division
401 South Carson Street
Carson City, NV 89701
P: (775) 684-6815
F: (775) 684-6435
E: townsend@lcb.state.nv.us

NEW HAMPSHIRE
Mr. Jeffry A. Pattison
Legislative Budget Assistant
Office of Legislative Budget
Assistant
State House, Room 102
107 North Main Street
Concord, NH 03301
P: (603) 271-2389
F: (603) 271-1097
E: jeff.pattison
   @leg.state.nh.us

NEW JERSEY
Mr. Matthew Boxer
State Comptroller
Office of the State Comptroller
P.O. Box 024
Trenton, NJ 08625
P: (609) 984-2888
F: (609) 292-2017
E: matthew.boxer
   @osc.state.nj.us

Hon. Stephen Eells
State Auditor
Office of the State Auditor
P.O. Box 067
Trenton, NJ 08625
P: (609) 292-3700
F: (609) 633-0834
E: seells@njleg.org

Auditor

NEW MEXICO
Hon. Hector H. Balderas (D)
State Auditor
Office of the State Auditor
2540 Camino Edward Ortiz,
Suite A
Santa Fe, NM 87507
P: (505) 827-3500
F: (505) 827-3512
E: hector.balderas
@osa.state.nm.us

Mr. Charles Sallee
Deputy Director for Program
Evaluation
Legislative Finance Committee
416 Capitol Building
Santa Fe, NM 87503
P: (505) 986-4550
F: (505) 986-4644
E: charles.sallee
@nmlegis.gov

NEW YORK
Hon. Mark Pattison
Executive Deputy Comptroller
Office of the State Comptroller
633 3rd Avenue, 21st Floor
New York, NY 10017
P: (518) 474-4040
F: (518) 474-3004
E: mpattison
@osc.state.ny.us

NORTH CAROLINA
Hon. Beth Wood (D)
State Auditor
Office of the State Auditor
2 South Salisbury Street
20601 Mail Service Center
Raleigh, NC 27699
P: (919) 807-7500
F: (919) 807-7647
E: Beth_Wood@ncauditor.net

NORTH DAKOTA
Mr. Allen H. Knudson
Legislative Budget Analyst &
Auditor
Legislative Council
State Capitol Building
Bismarck, ND 58501
P: (701) 328-2916
F: (701) 328-3615
E: aknudson@nd.gov

Hon. Robert R. Peterson (R)
State Auditor
Office of the State Auditor
State Capitol Building
600 East Boulevard Avenue, 3rd
Floor
Bismarck, ND 58505
P: (701) 328-2241
F: (701) 328-1406
E: rpeterso@nd.gov

**NORTHERN MARIANA
ISLANDS**
Mr. Michael S. Pai
Public Auditor
Office of the Public Auditor
P.O. Box 501399
Saipan, MP 96950
P: (670) 322-6481
F: (670) 322-7812
E: mpai@opacnmi.com

OHIO
Hon. David A. Yost (R)
Auditor of State
Office of Auditor of State
88 East Broad Street, 5th Floor
P.O. Box 1140
Columbus, OH 43216
P: (614) 466-4514
F: (614) 466-4490
E: contactus
@auditor.state.oh.us

OKLAHOMA
Hon. Gary Jones (R)
State Auditor & Inspector
Office of the State Auditor &
Inspector
2300 North Lincoln Boulevard
State Capitol Building, Room
100
Oklahoma City, OK 73105
P: (405) 521-3495
F: (405) 521-3426
E: gjones@sai.ok.gov

OREGON
Mr. Gary Blackmer
Director
Division of Audits
255 Capitol Street, Northeast
Suite 500
Salem, OR 97310
P: (503) 986-2355
F: (503) 378-4829
E: gary.blackmer
@state.or.us

PENNSYLVANIA
Mr. Philip R. Durgin
Executive Director
Legislative Budget & Finance
Committee
400 Finance Building
Harrisburg, PA 17120
P: (717) 783-1600
F: (717) 787-5487
E: pdurgin
@lbfc.legis.state.pa.us

Hon. Jack Wagner (D)
Auditor General
Department of the Auditor
General
406 Finance Building
Harrisburg, PA 17120
P: (717) 787-2543
F: (717) 783-4407
E: auditorgen
@auditorgen.state.pa.us

RHODE ISLAND
Mr. Dennis Hoyle
Acting Auditor General
Office of the Auditor General
88 Waybossett Street
Providence, RI 02903
P: (401) 222-2435
F: (401) 222-2111
E: dennis.hoyle@oag.ri.gov

SOUTH CAROLINA
Mr. Thomas J. Bardin Jr.
Director
Legislative Audit Council
133 Elmwood Avenue
Suite 315
Columbia, SC 29201
P: (803) 253-7612
F: (803) 253-7639
E: tbardin@lac.sc.gov

Hon. Richard H. Gilbert Jr.
Interim State Auditor
Office of the State Auditor
1401 Main Street, Suite 1200
Columbia, SC 29201
P: (803) 253-4160
F: (803) 343-0723
E: rgilbert@osa.state.sc.us

SOUTH DAKOTA
Mr. Martin Guindon
Auditor General
Department of Legislative Audit
427 South Chapelle
C/O 500 East Capitol
Pierre, SD 57501
P: (605) 773-3595
F: (605) 773-6454
E: marty.guindon
@state.sd.us

TENNESSEE
Mr. Justin P. Wilson
Comptroller of the Treasurer
Office of the Comptroller of the
Treasury
505 Deaderick Street, Suite
1500
Nashville, TN 37243
P: (615) 741-2501
F: (615) 741-7328
E: justin.wilson@tn.gov

TEXAS
Hon. John Keel
State Auditor
Office of the State Auditor
1501 North Congress Avenue,
Suite 4-22Y
P.O. Box 12067
Austin, TX 78701
P: (512) 936-9500
F: (512) 936-9400
E: eguzman@sao.state.tx.us

U.S. VIRGIN ISLANDS
Mr. Steven G.
Van Beverhoudt
Inspector General
Office of the Inspector General
2315 Kronprindsens Gade #75
Charlotte Amalie
St. Thomas, VI 00802
P: (340) 774-3388
F: (340) 774-3381
E: svanbeverhoudt@viig.org

UTAH
Hon. Auston G. Johnson (R)
State Auditor
Office of the State Auditor
East Office Building, Suite E310
P.O. Box 142310
Salt Lake City, UT 84114
P: (801) 538-1360
F: (801) 538-1383
E: austonjohnson@utah.gov

Mr. John Schaff
Auditor General
Office of the Legislative Auditor
General
130 State Capitol
Salt Lake City, UT 84114
P: (801) 538-1033
F: (801) 538-1063
E: jschaff@utah.gov

VERMONT
Hon. Thomas M. Salmon (D)
State Auditor
Office of the State Auditor
132 State Street
Montpelier, VT 05633
P: (802) 828-2281
F: (802) 828-2198
E: tom.salmon@state.vt.us

VIRGINIA
Hon. Walter J. Kucharski
Auditor of Public Accounts
Office of the Auditor of Public
Accounts
P.O. Box 1295
Richmond, VA 23218
P: (804) 225-3350
F: (804) 225-3357
E: walter.kucharski
    @apa.virginia.gov

Mr. Glen Tittermary
Director
Joint Legislative Audit &
Review Commission
General Assembly Building,
Suite 1100
Richmond, VA 23219
P: (804) 371-4589
F: (804) 371-0101
E: gtittermary
    @jlarc.virginia.gov

WASHINGTON
Mr. Keenan Konopaski
Legislative Auditor
Joint Legislative Audit &
Review Committee
1300 Quince Street, Southeast
Olympia, WA 98504
P: (360) 786-5281
E: keenan.konopaski
    @leg.wa.gov

Hon. Brian Sonntag (D)
State Auditor
Office of the State Auditor
P.O. Box 40021
Olympia, WA 98504
P: (360) 902-0370
F: (360) 753-0646
E: sonntagb@sao.wa.gov

WEST VIRGINIA
Mr. Aaron Allred
Legislative Auditor
Legislative Auditor's Office
State Capitol Complex
Building 1, E-132
Charleston, WV 25305
P: (304) 347-4880
F: (304) 347-4815
E: aaron.allred
    @wvlegislature.gov

WISCONSIN
Hon. Janice L. Mueller
State Auditor
Legislative Audit Bureau
22 East Mifflin Street, Suite 500
Madison, WI 53703
P: (608) 266-2818
F: (608) 267-0410
E: janice.mueller
    @legis.wisconsin.gov

WYOMING
Mr. Michael Geesey
Director
Department of Audit
Herschler Building
3rd Floor, East Wing
Cheyenne, WY 82002
P: (307) 777-5312
F: (307) 777-5341
E: mgeesey
    @wyaudit.state.wy.us

Banking

Administers laws regulating the operation of banking institutions in the state.

ALABAMA
Mr. John D. Harrison
Superintendent
Banking Department
P.O. Box 4600
Montgomery, AL 36130
P: (334) 242-3452
F: (334) 242-3500
E: john.harrison
　@banking.alabama.gov

ALASKA
Ms. Lori L. Hovanec
Director
Department of Commerce,
Community & Economic
Development
Division of Banking &
Securities
P.O. Box 110807
Juneau, AK 99811
P: (907) 465-2521
F: (907) 465-2549
E: lori.hovanec@alaska.gov

AMERICAN SAMOA
Mr. Lolo M. Moliga
President
Development Bank of American
Samoa
P.O. Box 9
Pago Pago, AS 96799
P: (684) 633-4565
F: (684) 633-1163

ARIZONA
Mr. Lauren W. Kingry
Superintendent
Department of Financial
Institutions
2910 North 44th Street, Suite
310
Phoenix, AZ 85018
P: (602) 771-2800
F: (602) 381-1225

ARKANSAS
Ms. Candace Franks
Commissioner
Securities Department
400 Hardin, Suite 100
Little Rock, AR 72211
P: (501) 324-9019
F: (501) 324-9028
E: cfranks
　@banking.state.ar.us

CALIFORNIA
Mr. William S. Haraf
Commissioner
Department of Financial
Institutions
45 Fremont Street, Suite 1700
San Francisco, CA 94105
P: (415) 263-8507
F: (415) 288-8830
E: wharaf@dfi.ca.gov

CONNECTICUT
Mr. Howard F. Pitkin
Commissioner
Department of Banking
260 Constitution Plaza
Hartford, CT 06103
P: (860) 240-8100
F: (860) 240-8178
E: howard.pitkin@ct.gov

DELAWARE
Mr. Robert A. Glen
Commissioner
Office of State Bank
Commissioner
555 East Lockerman Street,
Suite 210
Dover, DE 19901
P: (302) 739-4235
F: (302) 739-3609

DISTRICT OF COLUMBIA
Mr. William P. White
Commissioner
Department of Insurance,
Securities & Banking
810 First Street, Northeast, Suite
70
Washington, DC 20002
P: (202) 727-8000
F: (202) 535-1196

GEORGIA
Mr. Rob Braswell
Commissioner
Department of Banking &
Finance
2990 Brandywine Road, Suite
200
Atlanta, GA 30341
P: (770) 986-1628
F: (770) 986-1654
E: robertb@dbf.state.ga.us

GUAM
Mr. John Camacho
Banking & Insurance
Commissioner
Department of Revenue &
Taxation
Regulatory Division
P.O. Box 23607 GMF
Barrigada, GU 96921
P: (671) 635-1817
F: (671) 633-2643

HAWAII
Ms. Iris Ikeda Catalani
Commissioner
Division of Financial
Institutions
King Kalakaua Building
335 Merchant Street, Room 221
Honolulu, HI 96813
P: (808) 586-2820
F: (808) 586-2818

IDAHO
Mr. Gavin M. Gee
Director
Department of Finance
800 Park Boulevard, Suite 200
Boise, ID 83712
P: (208) 332-8010
F: (208) 332-8097
E: ggee@finance.idaho.gov

ILLINOIS
Mr. Manuel Flores
Director
Division of Banking
122 South Michigan Avenue,
Suite 1900
Chicago, IL 60603
P: (312) 793-3000
F: (312) 793-0756

INDIANA
Mr. David Mills
Director
Department of Financial
Institutions
30 South Meridian Street, Suite
300
Indianapolis, IN 46204
P: (317) 233-9460
F: (317) 232-7655
E: DaMills@dfi.IN.gov

IOWA
Mr. James M. Schipper
Superintendent
Division of Banking
200 East Grand Avenue, Suite
300
Des Moines, IA 50309
P: (515) 281-4014
F: (515) 281-4862
E: jschipper
　@idob.state.ia.us

KANSAS
Mr. Ed Splichal
Commissioner
Office of the State Banking
Commissioner
700 Jackson, Suite 300
Topeka, KS 66603
P: (785) 296-2266
F: (785) 296-0168

KENTUCKY
Mr. Charles A. Vice
Commissioner
Department of Financial
Institutions
1025 Capital Center Drive, Suite
200
Frankfort, KY 40601
P: (502) 573-3390
F: (502) 573-0086
E: charles.vice@ky.gov

LOUISIANA
Mr. John P. Ducrest
Commissioner
Office of Financial Institutions
8660 United Plaza Boulevard,
2nd Floor
P.O. Box 94095
Baton Rouge, LA 70804
P: (225) 925-4660
F: (225) 925-4548
E: jducrest@ofi.la.gov

MAINE
Mr. Lloyd P. LaFountain III
Superintendent
Bureau of Financial Institutions
Bureau of Financial Institutions
36 State House Station
Augusta, ME 04333
P: (207) 624-8570
F: (207) 624-8590
E: lloyd.p.lafountain.III
　@maine.gov

MARYLAND
Mr. Mark Kaufman
Commissioner of Financial
Regulation
Department of Labor, Licensing
& Regulation
500 North Calvert Street, Room
402
Baltimore, MD 21202
P: (410) 230-6100
F: (410) 333-0475
E: mkaufman
　@dllr.state.md.us

MASSACHUSETTS
Mr. David Cotney
Commissioner
Division of Banks
1000 Washington Street,
10th Floor
Boston, MA 02118
P: (617) 956-1500
F: (617) 956-1599

MICHIGAN
Mr. R. Kevin Clinton
Commissioner
Office of Financial & Insurance
Regulation
P.O. Box 30220
Lansing, MI 48909
P: (517) 373-0220
F: (517) 373-4978

MINNESOTA
Mr. Mike Rothman
Commissioner of Commerce
Department of Commerce
85 7th Place East, Suite 500
St. Paul, MN 55101
P: (651) 296-6025
F: (651) 297-1959
E: commerce.commissioner
@state.mn.us

MISSISSIPPI
Mr. John S. Allison
Commissioner
Department of Banking &
Consumer Finance
501 North West Street
901 Woolfolk Building, Suite A
Jackson, MS 39202
P: (601) 359-1031
F: (601) 359-3557
E: john.allison@dbcf.ms.gov

MISSOURI
Mr. Richard J. Weaver
Commissioner
Division of Finance
Truman State Office Building,
Room 630
P.O. Box 716
Jefferson City, MO 65102
P: (573) 751-3242
F: (573) 751-9192
E: finance@dof.mo.gov

MONTANA
Ms. Melanie Griggs
Commissioner
Division of Banking &
Financial Institutions
301 South Park, Suite 316
P.O. Box 200546
Helena, MT 59620
P: (406) 841-2920
F: (406) 841-2930
E: mgriggs@mt.gov

NEBRASKA
Mr. John Munn
Director
Department of Banking &
Finance
P.O. Box 95006
Lincoln, NE 68509
P: (402) 471-2171
E: john.munn@nebraska.gov

NEVADA
Mr. Steven W. Kondrup
Administrator
Financial Institutions Division
Department of Business &
Industry
2785 East Desert Inn Road, Suite
180
Las Vegas, NV 89121
P: (702) 486-4120
F: (702) 486-4563
E: skondrup@fid.state.nv.us

NEW HAMPSHIRE
Mr. Ronald A. Wilbur
Commissioner
Banking Department
53 Regional Drive, Suite 200
Concord, NH 03301
P: (603) 271-3561
F: (603) 271-1090
E: Commissioner
@banking.state.nh.us

NEW JERSEY
Mr. Thomas B. Considine
Commissioner
Department of Banking &
Insurance
20 West State Street
P.O. Box 325
Trenton, NJ 08625
P: (609) 292-7272
F: (609) 663-3601
E: commissioner
@dobi.state.nj.us

NORTH CAROLINA
Mr. Joseph A. Smith Jr.
Commissioner of Banks
Banking Commission
316 West Edenton Street
4309 Mail Service Center
Raleigh, NC 27699
P: (919) 733-3016
F: (919) 733-6918
E: jsmith@nccob.org

NORTH DAKOTA
Mr. Robert J. Entringer
Commissioner
Department of Financial
Institutions
2000 Schafer Street, Suite G
Bismarck, ND 58501
P: (701) 328-9933
F: (701) 328-0290
E: rentring@nd.gov

**NORTHERN MARIANA
ISLANDS**
Mr. Sixto Igisomar
Acting Secretary
Department of Commerce
Caller Box 10007
Saipan, MP 96950
P: (670) 664-3064
F: (670) 664-3067

OHIO
Mr. Charles J. Dolezal
Superintendent
Division of Financial
Institutions
Department of Commerce
77 South High Street
Columbus, OH 43215
P: (614) 728-8400
F: (614) 728-0380

OKLAHOMA
Mr. Mick Thompson
Commissioner
State Banking Department
2900 North Lincoln Boulevard
Oklahoma City, OK 73105
P: (405) 521-2782
F: (405) 522-2993
E: rmt1@onenet.net

OREGON
Mr. David C. Tatman
Division Administrator
Division of Finance &
Corporate Securities
350 Winter Street, Northeast,
Room 410
Salem, OR 97301
P: (503) 378-4140
F: (503) 947-7862
E: dcbs.dfcsmail
@state.or.us

PENNSYLVANIA
Mr. Glenn E. Moyer
Secretary of Banking
Department of Banking
17 North 2nd Street, Suite 1300
Harrisburg, PA 17101
P: (717) 787-2665
F: (717) 787-8773
E: ra-pabanking@state.pa.us

PUERTO RICO
Mr. Alfredo Padilla
Commissioner of Financial
Institutions
Office of the Commissioner of
Financial Institutions
Commonwealth of Puerto Rico
P.O. Box 11855
San Juan, PR 00910
P: (787) 723-3131
F: (787) 723-4042
E: comisionado
@ocif.gobierno.pr

SOUTH CAROLINA
Ms. Paige H. Parsons
Senior Assistant State Treasurer,
Internal Auditor
Office of the State Treasurer
1200 Senate St., Wade Hampton
Bldg.
P.O. Box 11778
Columbia, SC 29211
P: (803) 734-9822
F: (803) 734-2690
E: paige.parsons@sto.sc.gov

SOUTH DAKOTA
Mr. Bret Afdahl
Director
Division of Banking
Department of Revenue &
Regulation
217 1/2 West Missouri Avenue
Pierre, SD 57501
P: (605) 773-3421
F: (866) 326-7504
E: drr.banking.info
@state.sd.us

TENNESSEE
Mr. Greg Gonzales
Commissioner
Department of Financial
Institutions
414 Union Street, Suite 1000
Nashville, TN 37219
P: (615) 741-2236
F: (615) 253-6306
E: Greg.Gonzales@tn.gov

TEXAS
Mr. Charles G. Cooper
Commissioner
Department of Banking
2601 North Lamar Boulevard
Austin, TX 78705
P: (512) 475-1323
F: (512) 475-1313
E: executive
@banking.state.tx.us

Banking

U.S. VIRGIN ISLANDS
Mr. John McDonald
Director
Division of Banking &
Insurance
#18 Kongens Gade
St. Thomas, VI 00802
P: (340) 774-7166
F: (340) 774-9458

UTAH
Mr. G. Edward Leary
Commissioner
Department of Financial
Institutions
324 South State Street, Suite
201
P.O. Box 146800
Salt Lake City, UT 84114
P: (801) 538-8761
F: (801) 538-8894
E: ELEARY@utah.gov

VERMONT
Mr. Steve Kimbell
Commissioner
Department of Banking,
Insurance, Securities & Health
Care Administration
89 Main Street
Montpelier, VT 05620
P: (802) 828-3301
F: (802) 828-3306
E: steve.kimbell
    @state.vt.us

VIRGINIA
Mr. E. Joseph Face Jr.
Director
Bureau of Financial Institutions
1300 East Main Street, Suite
800
P.O. Box 640
Richmond, VA 23218
P: (804) 371-9657
F: (804) 371-9416
E: joe.face
    @scc.virginia.gov

WASHINGTON
Mr. Scott Jarvis
Director
Department of Financial
Institutions
P.O. Box 41200
Olympia, WA 98504
P: (360) 902-8700
F: (360) 586-5068
E: confsec@dfi.wa.gov

Ms. Gloria McVey
Acting Director of Banks
Division of Banks
Department of Financial
Institutions
P.O. Box 41200
Olympia, WA 98504
P: (360) 902-8704
F: (360) 753-6070
E: banks@dfi.wa.gov

WEST VIRGINIA
Ms. Sara M. Cline
Commissioner
Division of Banking
One Players Club Drive, Suite
300
Charleston, WV 25311
P: (304) 558-2294
F: (304) 558-0442
E: scline@wvdob.org

WISCONSIN
Mr. Michael Mach
Administrator
Division of Banking
345 West Washington Avenue
P.O. Box 7876
Madison, WI 53707
P: (608) 261-7578
F: (608) 267-6889
E: Mike.Mach
    @dfi.wisconsin.gov

WYOMING
Mr. Jeffrey C. Vogel
Commissioner
Division of Banking
Herschler Building, 3rd Floor,
East
122 West 25th Street
Cheyenne, WY 82002
P: (307) 777-7797
F: (307) 777-5341
E: jvogel
    @wyaudit.state.wy.us

Borders Management

Oversees and regulates the flow of transportation and immigration over state and international borders.

ALABAMA
Mr. Spencer Collier
Director
Department of Homeland Security
P.O. Box 304115
Montgomery, AL 36130
P: (334) 353-3050
E: director@dhs.alabama.gov

AMERICAN SAMOA
Hon. Fepulea'i A.
  Ripley Jr.
Attorney General
Office of the Attorney General
American Samoa Government
Executive Office Building, Utulei
Pago Pago, AS 96799
P: (684) 633-4163
F: (684) 633-1838

FLORIDA
Mr. Gerald M. Bailey
Commissioner
Department of Law Enforcement
2331 Phillips Road
P.O. Box 1489
Tallahassee, FL 32302
P: (850) 410-7001
E: GeraldBailey
  @fdle.state.fl.us

GEORGIA
Mr. Vance Smith Jr.
Commissioner
Department of Transportation
One Georgia Center
600 West Peachtree Street, Northwest
Atlanta, GA 30308
P: (404) 631-1000
F: (404) 631 1846

GUAM
Mr. Dennis Santo Tomas
Director
Customs & Quarantine Agency
Building 13-16, 17 Mariner Drive, Tiyan
Barrigada, GU 96932
P: (671) 475-6202
F: (671) 475-6227

KANSAS
Colonel Ernest E. Garcia
Superintendent
Highway Patrol
122 Southwest 7th Street
Topeka, KS 66603
P: (785) 296-6800
F: (785) 296-3049

MASSACHUSETTS
Colonel Marian McGovern
Superintendent
State Police
470 Worcester Road
Framingham, MA 01702
P: (508) 820-2300
F: (617) 727-6874

MINNESOTA
Ms. Ramona Dohman
Commissioner
Department of Public Safety
Bremer Tower, Suite 1000
445 Minnesota Street
St. Paul, MN 55101
P: (651) 201-7160
F: (651) 297-5728
E: Mona.Dohman@state.mn.us

MISSOURI
Mr. John M. Britt
Director
Department of Public Safety
P.O. Box 749
Jefferson City, MO 65102
P: (573) 751-4905
F: (573) 751-5399

MONTANA
Hon. Steve Bullock (D)
Attorney General
Department of Justice
215 North Sanders, Third Floor
Helena, MT 59620
P: (406) 444-2026
F: (404) 444-3549
E: contactdoj@mt.gov

NEW HAMPSHIRE
Mr. John J. Barthelmes
Commissioner
Department of Safety
James H. Hayes Safety Building
33 Hazen Drive
Concord, NH 03305
P: (603) 271-2791
F: (603) 271-3903
E: john.barthelmes
  @dos.nh.gov

NORTH DAKOTA
Ms. Debbie LaCombe
State Director
Homeland Security Division
Fraine Barracks Lane, Building 35
P.O. Box 5511
Bismarck, ND 58504
P: (701) 328-8100
F: (701) 328-8181
E: dlacombe@nd.gov

SOUTH CAROLINA
Mr. Robert J. St. Onge Jr.
Secretary of Transportation
Department of Transportation
Silas N. Pearman Building
955 Park Street
Columbia, SC 29201
P: (803) 737-2314
F: (803) 737-2038

U.S. VIRGIN ISLANDS
Mr. Kenn Hobson
Executive Director
Port Authority
P.O. Box 301707
St. Thomas, VI 00803
P: (340) 774-1629
F: (340) 774-0025

UTAH
Mr. Richard A. Clasby
Director
Motor Carriers Division
Department of Transportation
4501 South 2700 West, P.O. Box 148240
Salt Lake City, UT 84114
P: (801) 965-4156
F: (801) 965-4847
E: RCLASBY@utah.gov

VIRGINIA
Mr. Jerry A. Bridges
Executive Director
Port Authority
600 World Trade Center
Norfolk, VA 23510
P: (757) 683-2103
F: (757) 683-8500
E: jbridges
  @portofvirginia.com

WASHINGTON
Maj. Gen. Timothy J.
  Lowenberg
Adjutant General
Military Department
Camp Murray, Building 1
Tacoma, WA 98327
P: (253) 512-8000
F: (253) 512-8497

Budget

Collects and analyzes budget requests and supporting materials and prepares the executive budget documents.

ALABAMA
Mr. David Perry
Director
Department of Finance
State Capitol
600 Dexter Avenue, Suite N-105
Montgomery, AL 36130
P: (334) 242-7160
F: (334) 353-3300
E: david.perry
@finance.alabama.gov

ALASKA
Ms. Karen Rehfeld
Director
Office of Management &
Budget
P.O. Box 110020
Juneau, AK 99811
P: (907) 465-4660
F: (907) 465-3640
E: karen.rehfeld@alaska.gov

ARKANSAS
Mr. Richard Weiss
Administrator
Department of Finance &
Administration
P.O. Box 2485
Little Rock, AR 72203
P: (501) 682-2242
F: (501) 682-1029
E: richard.weiss
@dfa.state.ar.us

CALIFORNIA
Ms. Ana J. Matosantos
Director of Finance
Department of Finance
915 L Street
Sacramento, CA 95814
P: (916) 445-4141

COLORADO
Mr. Henry Sobanet
Director
Office of State Planning &
Budgeting
200 East Colfax, Room 111
Denver, CO 80203
P: (303) 866-3317
F: (303) 866-3044
E: henry.sobanet
@state.co.us

CONNECTICUT
Mr. Benjamin Barnes
Secretary
Office of Policy & Management
450 Capitol Avenue
Hartford, CT 06106
P: (860) 418-6500
F: (860) 418-6487
E: benjamin.barnes@ct.gov

Ms. Brenda L. Sisco
Acting Secretary
Office of Policy & Management
450 Capitol Avenue
Hartford, CT 06106
P: (860) 418-6500
E: brenda.sisco@ct.gov

DELAWARE
Ms. Ann Shepard Visalli
Director
Office of Management &
Budget
Haslet Armory
122 William Penn Street
Dover, DE 19901
P: (302) 739-4204
F: (302) 739-5661
E: Ann.Visalli@state.de.us

DISTRICT OF COLUMBIA
Dr. Natwar M. Gandhi
Chief Financial Officer
Office of the Chief Financial
Officer
1350 Pennsylvania Avenue,
Northwest
Room 203
Washington, DC 20004
P: (202) 727-2476
F: (202) 727-1643
E: ocfo@dc.gov

FLORIDA
Mr. Jerry McDaniel
Director
Office of Policy & Budget
The Capitol
400 South Monroe Street
Tallahassee, FL 32399
P: (850) 487-1880

GEORGIA
Ms. Debra Dlugolenski
Director
Office of Planning & Budget
270 Washington Street,
Southwest
Suite 8057 A
Atlanta, GA 30334
P: (404) 656-3820
F: (404) 656-7198
E: debbie.dlugolenski
@opb.state.ga.us

HAWAII
Hon. Kalbert K. Young
Director of Finance
Department of Budget &
Finance
P.O. Box 150
Honolulu, HI 96810
P: (808) 586-1518
F: (808) 586-1976
E: HI.BudgetandFinance
@hawaii.gov

IDAHO
Mr. Wayne Hammon
Administrator
Division of Financial
Management
700 West Jefferson, First Floor
P.O. Box 83720
Boise, ID 83720
P: (208) 334-3900
F: (208) 334-2438
E: wayne.hammon
@dfm.idaho.gov

ILLINOIS
Mr. David Vaught
Director
Office of Management &
Budget
108 State House
Springfield, IL 62706
P: (217) 782-4520
F: (217) 524-1514
E: BureauBudget.OMB
@illinois.gov

INDIANA
Mr. Adam Horst
Director
State Budget Agency
200 West Washington Street,
Room 212
Indianapolis, IN 46204
P: (317) 233-5707
F: (317) 233-3323
E: ahorst@sba.in.gov

KANSAS
Mr. Steve Anderson
Director of the Budget
Division of the Budget
1000 Southwest Jackson, Suite
504
Topeka, KS 66612
P: (785) 296-3011
F: (785) 296-0231
E: steve.anderson
@budget.ks.gov

KENTUCKY
Ms. Mary Lassiter
State Budget Director
Office of State Budget Director
702 Capitol Avenue
Room 284, Capitol Annex
Frankfort, KY 40601
P: (502) 564-7300
F: (502) 564-6684

LOUISIANA
Mr. Ray Stockstill
Director
Office of Planning & Budget
Division of Administration
P.O. Box 94095
Baton Rouge, LA 70804
P: (225) 342-7005
F: (225) 342-7220
E: Ray.Stockstill@la.gov

MAINE
Ms. Dawn J. Lopatosky
State Budget Officer
Bureau of the Budget
3rd Floor, Burton M. Cross
Building
58 State House Station
Augusta, ME 04333
P: (207) 624-7810
E: dawna.lopatosky
@maine.gov

MARYLAND
Ms. T. Eloise Foster
Secretary
Department of Budget &
Management
45 Calvert Street, 1st Floor
Annapolis, MD 21401
P: (410) 260-7041
E: efoster@dbm.state.md.us

MASSACHUSETTS
Mr. Jay A. Gonzalez
Secretary of Administration and
Finance
Executive Office for
Administration & Finance
State House, Room 373
Boston, MA 02133
P: (617) 727-2040
F: (617) 727-2779

MICHIGAN
Mr. John Nixon
Director
Department of Technology,
Management & Budget
320 South Walnut Street
P.O Box 30026
Lansing, MI 48909
P: (517) 241-5150

MINNESOTA
Mr. Jim Schowalter
Commissioner
Management & Budget
658 Cedar Street, Suite 400
St. Paul, MN 55155
P: (651) 201-8010
F: (651) 296-7714
E: James.Schowalter
@state.mn.us

MISSISSIPPI
Mr. Kevin J. Upchurch
Executive Director
Department of Finance &
Administration
P.O. Box 267
Jackson, MS 39201
P: (601) 359-3402
F: (601) 359-2405
E: kupchurch
@dfa.state.ms.us

MONTANA
Mr. David Ewer
Budget Director
Office of Budget & Program
Planning
State Capitol, Room 277
P.O. Box 200802
Helena, MT 59620
P: (406) 444-3616
F: (406) 444-4670
E: dewer@mt.gov

NEBRASKA
Mr. Gerry A. Oligmueller
State Budget Administrator
Department of Administrative
Services
Room 1320, State Capitol
P.O. Box 94664
Lincoln, NE 68509
P: (402) 471-2526
F: (402) 471-8074
E: gerry.oligmueller
@nebraska.gov

NEVADA
Mr. Andrew K. Clinger
Director
Division of Budget & Planning
Balsdel Building
209 East Musser Street, Room
200
Carson City, NV 89701
P: (775) 684-0222
F: (775) 684-0260
E: aclinger
@budget.state.nv.us

NEW HAMPSHIRE
Ms. Linda M. Hodgdon
Commissioner
Department of Administrative
Services
25 Capitol Street, Room 120
State House Annex
Concord, NH 03301
P: (603) 271-3201
F: (603) 271-6600
E: linda.hodgdon@nh.gov

NEW JERSEY
Ms. Charlene Holzbaur
State Comptroller
Office of Management &
Budget
33 West State Street
P.O. Box 221
Trenton, NJ 08625
P: (609) 292-6746
F: (609) 633-8179
E: charlene.holzbaur
@treas.state.nj.us

NEW MEXICO
Ms. Duffy Rodriguez
Deputy Secretary for Budget &
Policy
State Budget Division
Bataan Memorial Building,
Suite 190
407 Galisteo Street
Santa Fe, NM 87501
P: (505) 827-3640
F: (505) 827-3861
E: duffy.rodriguez
@state.nm.us

NEW YORK
Mr. Robert L. Megna
Budget Director
Division of the Budget
State Capitol
Albany, NY 12224
P: (518) 474-0580

NORTH CAROLINA
Mr. Andy Willis
State Budget Director
Office of State Budget &
Management
116 West Jones Street
Raleigh, NC 27603
P: (919) 807-4700
E: andy.willis@osbm.nc.gov

NORTH DAKOTA
Ms. Sheila Peterson
Director
Fiscal Management Division
600 East Boulevard Avenue
Department 110
Bismarck, ND 58505
P: (701) 328-2680
F: (701) 328-3230
E: speterson@nd.gov

**NORTHERN MARIANA
ISLANDS**
Ms. Esther Fleming
Chief of Staff
Office of Management &
Budget
Caller Box 10007, Capitol Hill
Saipan, MP 96950
P: (670) 664-2280
F: (670) 664-2211

OKLAHOMA
Ms. Jill Geiger
Budget Director
Office of State Finance
2300 North Lincoln Boulevard,
Room 122
Oklahoma City, OK 73105
P: (405) 521-2141
F: (405) 521-3902

OREGON
Mr. George M. Naughton
Administrator
Budget & Management Division
Department of Administrative
Services
155 Cottage Street, Northeast,
U20
Salem, OR 97301
P: (503) 378-5460
F: (503) 373-7643
E: george.m.naughton
@das.state.or.us

PENNSYLVANIA
Mr. Charles Zogby
Secretary of the Budget
Office of the Budget
238 Capitol Building
Harrisburg, PA 17120
P: (717) 787-4472
F: (717) 787-4590

PUERTO RICO
Mr. Juan C. Pavia
Director
Office of Budget &
Management
P.O. Box 9023228
San Juan, PR 00902
P: (787) 725-9420
F: (787) 721-8329

RHODE ISLAND
Mr. Thomas A. Mullaney
State Budget Officer
Department of Administration
Budget Office
One Capitol Hill
Providence, RI 02908
P: (401) 222-6300
E: tomm@budget.ri.gov

SOUTH CAROLINA
Mr. Les Boles
Director
Office of State Budget
1201 Main Street, Suite 870
Columbia, SC 29201
P: (803) 734-2280
F: (803) 734-0645
E: Lboles@budget.sc.gov

SOUTH DAKOTA
Mr. Jason Dilges
Commissioner
Bureau of Finance &
Management
500 East Capitol Avenue
Pierre, SD 57501
P: (605) 773-3411
F: (605) 773-4711
E: jason.dilges@state.sd.us

TENNESSEE
Mr. Mark Emkes
Commissioner
Department of Finance &
Administration
312 Rosa Parks Avenue, 21st
Floor
Nashville, TN 37243
P: (615) 741-2401

TEXAS
Ms. Mary Katherine Stout
Director
Budget, Planning & Policy
Division
Office of the Governor
P.O. Box 12428
Austin, TX 78711
P: (512) 463-1778
F: (512) 463-1975

U.S. VIRGIN ISLANDS
Ms. Debra Gottlieb
Director
Office of Management &
Budget
#41 Norre Gade
Emancipation Garden Station,
2nd Floor
St. Thomas, VI 00802
P: (340) 776-0750
F: (340) 776-0069
E: debra.gottlieb
@omb.vi.gov

Budget

UTAH
Mr. Ron Bigelow
Executive Director
Governor's Office of Planning &
Budget
State Capitol, Suite 150
P.O. Box 132210
Salt Lake City, UT 84114
P: (801) 538-1555
F: (801) 538-1547
E: ronbigelow@utah.gov

VERMONT
Mr. James B. Reardon
Commissioner
Department of Finance &
Management
109 State Street
Montpelier, VT 05602
P: (802) 828-2376
F: (802) 828-2428
E: jim.reardon@state.vt.us

VIRGINIA
Mr. Daniel Timberlake
Director
Department of Planning &
Budget
1111 East Broad Street
Room 5040
Richmond, VA 23219
P: (804) 786-7455
F: (804) 225-3291
E: dan.timberlake
     @dpb.virginia.gov

WASHINGTON
Mr. Marty Brown
Director
Office of Financial Management
P.O. Box 43113
Olympia, WA 98504
P: (360) 902-0555

Mr. Marty Brown
Director
Office of Financial Management
P.O. Box 43113
Olympia, WA 98504
P: (360) 902-0555

WEST VIRGINIA
Mr. Mike McKown
Director
State Budget Office
Building 1, Room 310-W
Capitol Building
Charleston, WV 25305
P: (304) 558-0040
F: (304) 558-1588
E: Mike.P.McKown@wv.gov

WISCONSIN
Mr. David Schmiedicke
Administrator
Division of Executive Budget &
Finance
101 East Wilson Street
Madison, WI 53703
P: (608) 266-1035
E: david.schmiedicke
     @wisconsin.gov

WYOMING
Mr. Richard Cox
Administrator, Budget Division
Department of Administration &
Information
2001 Capitol Avenue
Emerson Building, Room 105
Cheyenne, WY 82002
P: (307) 777-6045

Building Codes

Establishes and enforces standards of construction, materials and occupancy for all buildings.

ALABAMA
Ms. Katherine Lynn
Director
Building Commission
P.O. Box 301150
Montgomery, AL 36130
P: (334) 242-4082
F: (334) 242-4182
E: katherine.lynn
@bc.alabama.gov

ALASKA
Mr. David Tyler
Director
Division of Fire & Life Safety
Department of Public Safety
5700 East Tudor Road
Anchorage, AK 99507
P: (907) 269-5491
F: (907) 338-4375
E: david.tyler@alaska.gov

ARIZONA
Mr. Gene Palma
Director
Department of Fire, Building & Life Safety
1110 West Washington, Suite 100
Phoenix, AZ 85007
P: (602) 364-1003
F: (602) 364-1052

ARKANSAS
Mr. Whit Waller
Director
Manufactured Home Commission
101 East Capitol Avenue, Suite 210
Little Rock, AR 72201
P: (501) 324-9032
F: (501) 683-3538
E: Whit.Waller@arkansas.gov

CALIFORNIA
Mr. Richard Conrad
Manager
Division of the State Architect
Architectural Code & Building Systems
1102 Q Street, Suite 5100
Sacramento, CA 95814
P: (916) 324-7180
F: (916) 445-3521
E: Richard.Conrad
@dgs.ca.gov

Mr. Howard Smith
Acting State Architect
Division of the State Architect
1102 Q Street, Suite 5100
Sacramento, CA 95814
P: (916) 445-8100
F: (916) 445-3521

COLORADO
Ms. Pat Coyle
Director
Division of Housing
Department of Local Affairs
1313 Sherman, Room 518
Denver, CO 80203
P: (303) 866-4977
F: (303) 866-4077
E: pat.coyle@state.co.us

CONNECTICUT
Ms. Lisa R. Humble
State Building Inspector
Division of Fire, Emergency & Building Services
Department of Public Safety
1111 Country Club Road
Middletown, CT 06457
P: (860) 685-8310
F: (860) 685-8365
E: lisa.humble
@po.state.ct.us

DELAWARE
Mr. Grover P. Ingle
State Fire Marshal
Office of the State Fire Marshal
1537 Chestnut Grove Road
Dover, DE 19904
P: (302) 739-5665
F: (302) 739-3696
E: grover.ingle@state.de.us

DISTRICT OF COLUMBIA
Mr. Nicholas A. Majett
Director
Department of Consumer & Regulatory Affairs
1100 4th Street, Southwest
Washington, DC 20024
P: (202) 442-4400
F: (202) 442-9445
E: dcra@dc.gov

FLORIDA
Mr. Ken Reecy
Director
Division of Housing & Community Development
Department of Community Affairs
2555 Shumard Oak Boulevard
Tallahassee, FL 32399
P: (850) 922-7956
F: (850) 922-5623
E: ken.reecy
@dca.state.fl.us

GEORGIA
Mr. Theodore N. Miltiades
Office Director, Construction Codes
Planning & Environmental Management Division
Department of Community Affairs
60 Executive Park South, Northeast
Atlanta, GA 30329
P: (404) 679-3106
E: ted.miltiades@dca.ga.gov

HAWAII
Mr. Kenneth Silva
Chair
State Fire Council
690 South Street
Honolulu, HI 96813
P: (808) 723-7151
F: (808) 723-7179

IDAHO
Mr. C. Kelly Pearce
Administrator
Division of Building Safety
1090 East Watertower Street
Meridian, ID 83642
P: (208) 334-3950
F: (877) 810-2840
E: kelly.pearce
@dbs.idaho.gov

ILLINOIS
Ms. Mary Hunt
Division Staff
Building Codes & Regulations
3rd Floor Stratton
401 South Spring Street
Springfield, IL 62706
P: (217) 782-8529
F: (217) 524-4208
E: Mary.Hunt@illinois.gov

INDIANA
Mr. James L. Greeson
State Fire Marshall
Division of Fire & Building Safety
Department of Homeland Security
302 West Washington Street, Room E-241
Indianapolis, IN 46204
P: (317) 232-2226
E: jgreeson@dhs.in.gov

IOWA
Mr. W. Stuart Crine
Building Code Commissioner
State Building Code Bureau
State Fire Marshal Division
215 East 7th Street
Des Moines, IA 50319
P: (515) 725-6145
F: (515) 242-6299
E: crine@dps.state.ia.us

KANSAS
Mr. Douglas Jorgensen
Acting State Fire Marshal
Office of the Fire Marshal
Suite 600, Jayhawk Tower
700 Southwest Jackson Street
Topeka, KS 66603
P: (785) 296-3401
F: (785) 296-0151

KENTUCKY
Mr. Jerry T. Lunsford
Commissioner
Department of Housing, Buildings & Construction
101 Sea Hero Road, Suite 100
Frankfort, KY 40601
P: (502) 573-0364
F: (502) 573-1057

LOUISIANA
Mr. John L. Davis
Director
Office of Facility Planning & Control
Division of Administration
P.O. Box 94095
Baton Rouge, LA 70804
P: (225) 342-0820
F: (225) 342-7624
E: john.davis@la.gov

MAINE
Mr. Robert V. LeClair
Executive Director
Manufactured Housing Board
Office of Licensing & Registration
35 State House Station
Augusta, ME 04333
P: (207) 624-8612
F: (207) 624-8637
E: manuhousing.board
@maine.gov

MARYLAND
Mr. Ed Landon
Director, Codes Administration
Department of Housing & Community Development
100 Community Place
Crownsville, MD 21032
P: (410) 514-7444
F: (410) 987-8902
E: landon@mdhousing.org

Building Codes

MASSACHUSETTS
Mr. Thomas G. Gatzunis
Commissioner
Department of Public Safety
One Ashburton Place, Suite
2133
Boston, MA 02108
P: (617) 727-7775
F: (617) 727-4764
E: thomas.gatzunis
@state.ma.us

MICHIGAN
Mr. Irvin Poke
Executive Director
Bureau of Construction Codes
P.O. Box 30254
Lansing, MI 48909
P: (517) 241-9302
F: (517) 241-9570

MINNESOTA
Mr. Steve Hernick
State Building Official
Building Codes & Standards
Department of Labor & Industry
443 Lafayette Road, North
St. Paul, MN 55155
P: (651) 284-5848
F: (651) 284-5749
E: steve.hernick
@state.mn.us

MISSISSIPPI
Mr. Ricky Davis
Chief Deputy Fire Marshal
State Fire Marshal's Office
Insurance Department
P.O. Box 79
Jackson, MS 39205
P: (601) 359-3569
F: (601) 359-1076
E: ricky.davis
@mid.state.ms.us

MISSOURI
Mr. Ron Pleus
Manager
Manufactured Housing
Department
Public Service Commission
P.O. Box 360
Jefferson City, MO 65102
P: (573) 751-7119
F: (573) 522-2509
E: ron.pleus@psc.mo.gov

MONTANA
Mr. Dave Cook
Bureau Chief
Business Standards Section
Department of Labor & Industry
301 South Park, Rm. 430, P.O.
Box 200517
Helena, MT 59620
P: (406) 841-2053
F: (406) 841-2050

NEBRASKA
Mr. Mark Luttich
Director
Housing & Recreational
Vehicles
Public Service Commission
1200 N Street, Suite 300
Lincoln, NE 68508
P: (402) 471-3101
F: (402) 471-0254
E: mark.luttich
@nebraska.gov

NEVADA
Mr. Terry Johnson
Director
Department of Business &
Industry
555 East Washington Avenue,
Suite 4900
Las Vegas, NV 89101
P: (775) 684-2570
F: (702) 486-2758
E: TerryJohnson
@business.nv.gov

NEW HAMPSHIRE
Mr. J. William Degnan
State Fire Marshal
Division of Fire Safety
Department of Safety
33 Hazen Drive
Concord, NH 03305
P: (603) 223-4289
F: (603) 223-4294
E: john.degnan@dos.nh.gov

NEW JERSEY
Mr. Edward Smith
Director
Division of Codes & Standards
Department of Community
Affairs
101 South Broad Street, P.O.
Box 802
Trenton, NJ 08625
P: (609) 292-7899
F: (609)-633-6729

NEW MEXICO
Ms. Lisa Martinez
Director
Construction Industries Division
Regulation & Licensing
Department
2550 Cerrillos Road
Santa Fe, NM 87505
P: (505) 476-4700
E: lisa.martinez
@state.nm.us

NEW YORK
Mr. Ronald E. Piester
Director
Division of Code Enforcement
& Administration
One Commerce Plaza
99 Washington Avenue
Albany, NY 12231
P: (518) 474-4073
F: (518) 486-4487
E: codes@dos.state.ny.us

NORTH CAROLINA
Mr. Chris Noles
Deputy Commissioner,
Engineering & Codes
Office of the State Fire Marshal
Department of Insurance
322 Chapanoke Road, Suite 200
Raleigh, NC 27603
P: (919) 661-5880
F: (919) 662-4414
E: chris.noles@ncdoi.gov

NORTH DAKOTA
Mr. Paul T. Govig
Director
Division of Community
Services
Department of Commerce
1600 East Century Avenue, Suite
2
Bismarck, ND 58503
P: (701) 328-4499
F: (701) 328-2308
E: pgovig@state.nd.us

**NORTHERN MARIANA
ISLANDS**
Mr. Donald Anderson
Building Safety Official
Building Safety Code Division
2nd Floor, Joeten Commercial
Center
Gualo Rai
Saipan, MP 96950
P: (670) 235-5827
F: (670) 235-6346

OHIO
Ms. Regina Hanshaw
Executive Secretary
Board of Building Standards
Division of Industrial
Compliance
6606 Tussing Road
Reynoldsburg, OH 43068
P: (614) 644-2613
F: (614) 644-3147
E: regina.hanshaw
@com.state.oh.us

OKLAHOMA
Mr. Robert Doke
State Fire Marshal
Office of the State Fire Marshal
2401 NW 23rd, Suite 4
Oklahoma City, OK 73107
P: (405) 522-5011
F: (405) 522-5028
E: robert.doke@fire.ok.gov

OREGON
Mr. Pat Allen
Acting Administrator
Building Codes Division
1535 Edgewater Street,
Northwest
P.O. Box 14470
Salem, OR 97309
P: (503) 378-4130
F: (503) 378-2322
E: Patrick.Allen
@state.or.us

PENNSYLVANIA
Mr. Mark Conte
Chief, Housing Standards
Division
Department of Community &
Economic Development
Center for Community
Development
Commonwealth Keystone
Building, 4th Fl.
Harrisburg, PA 17120
P: (717) 720-7416
F: (717) 783-4663
E: mconte@state.pa.us

RHODE ISLAND
Mr. John Leyden
Commissioner
Building Code Commission
Department of Administration
One Capitol Hill
Providence, RI 02908
P: (401) 222-3032
E: jleyden
@gw.doa.state.ri.us

Building Codes

SOUTH CAROLINA
Mr. Gary Wiggins
Administrator
Building Codes Council
110 Centerview Drive, Suite 102
P.O. Box 11329
Columbia, SC 29211
P: (803) 896-4688
F: (803) 896-4814
E: wigginsg@llr.sc.gov

SOUTH DAKOTA
Mr. Allen Christie
State Fire Marshal
Department of Public Safety
118 West Capitol Avenue
Pierre, SD 57501
P: (605) 773-3562
F: (605) 773-6631
E: fireinfo@state.sd.us

TENNESSEE
Mr. Gary L. West
Assistant Commissioner
Fire Prevention Division
Department of Commerce &
Insurance
500 James Robertson Parkway,
3rd Floor
Nashville, TN 37243
P: (615) 741-2981
F: (615) 741-1583
E: Fire.Prevention@TN.Gov

UTAH
Mr. Dan S. Jones
Bureau Manager, Uniform
Building Codes
Division of Occupational &
Professional Licensing
Department of Commerce
P.O. Box 146741
Salt Lake City, UT 84114
P: (801) 530-6720
F: (801) 530-6511
E: dansjones@utah.gov

VERMONT
Mr. John Wood
Director
Division of Fire Safety
Department of Public Safety
1311 U.S. Route 302-Berlin,
Suite 600
Barre, VT 05641
P: (802) 479-7561
F: (802) 479-7562
E: jwood@dps.state.vt.us

VIRGINIA
Mr. Emory Rodgers
Deputy Director of Building &
Fire Regulation
Department of Housing &
Community Development
501 North Second Street
Richmond, VA 23219
P: (804) 371-7000
F: (804) 371-7090
E: emory.rodgers
 @dhcd.virginia.gov

WASHINGTON
Mr. Tim Nogler
Managing Director
State Building Code Council
210 11th Avenue, Southwest
P.O. Box 41011
Olympia, WA 98504
P: (360) 902-7296
F: (360) 586-0493
E: tim.nogler@ga.wa.gov

WEST VIRGINIA
Mr. Sterling Lewis Jr.
State Fire Marshal
Office of the State Fire Marshal
1207 Quarrier Street, 2nd Floor
Charleston, WV 25301
P: (304) 558-2191
F: (304) 558-2537
E: sterling.lewis@wv.gov

WISCONSIN
Mr. Tom Nardelli
Division Administrator
Safety & Buildings Division
Department of Commerce
P.O. Box 2599
Madison, WI 53701
P: (608) 266-1816
F: (608) 266-9946
E: thomas.nardelli@wi.gov

WYOMING
Mr. Lanny Applegate
State Fire Marshal
Department of Fire Prevention
& Electrical Safety
Herschler 1 West
Cheyenne, WY 82002
P: (307) 777-7288
F: (307) 777-7119

Campaign Finance Administration

Administers and enforces campaign finance laws.

ALABAMA

Hon. Beth Chapman (R)
Secretary of State
Office of the Secretary of State
P.O. Box 5616
Montgomery, AL 36103
P: (334) 242-7200
F: (334) 242-4993
E: Beth.Chapman
@sos.alabama.gov

ALASKA

Mr. Paul Dauphinais
Director
Public Offices Commission
2221 East Northern Lights
Boulevard
Room 128
Anchorage, AK 99508
P: (907) 276-4176
F: (907) 276-7018
E: Paul.Dauphinais
@alaska.gov

AMERICAN SAMOA

Mr. Soliai T. Fuimaono
Chief Election Officer
Territorial Election Office
P.O. Box 3790
Pago Pago, AS 96799
P: (684) 633-2522
F: (684) 633-7116

ARKANSAS

Hon. Mark Martin (R)
Secretary of State
Office of the Secretary of State
256 State Capitol Building
Little Rock, AR 72201
P: (501) 682-1010
F: (501) 682-3510
E: sos@sos.arkansas.gov

CALIFORNIA

Ms. Cathy Mitchell
Chief
Elections Division
1500 11th Street, 5th Floor
Sacramento, CA 95814
P: (916) 657-2166
F: (916) 653-3214
E: cmitchel@sos.ca.gov

COLORADO

Mr. Judd Choate
Director of Elections
Elections Division
Department of State
1700 Broadway, Suite 200
Denver, CO 80290
P: (303) 894-2200 Ext. 6307
F: (303) 869-4861
E: judd.choate
@sos.state.co.us

CONNECTICUT

Hon. Denise W. Merrill (D)
Secretary of State
Office of the Secretary of State
State Capitol, Room 104
Hartford, CT 06105
P: (860) 509-6200
F: (860) 509-6209
E: denise.merrill@ct.gov

DELAWARE

Ms. M. Elaine Manlove
State Election Commissioner
Department of Elections
905 South Governors Ave, Suite 170
Dover, DE 19904
P: (302) 739-4277
F: (302) 739-6794

DISTRICT OF COLUMBIA

Ms. Cecily E.
Collier-Montgomery
Director
Office of Campaign Finance
Frank D. Reeves Municipal Building
2000 14th Street, Northwest, Suite 433
Washington, DC 20009
P: (202) 671-0547
F: (202) 671-0658
E: ocf@dc.gov

FLORIDA

Hon. Kurt S. Browning (R)
Secretary of State
Office of the Secretary of State
500 South Bronough, Suite 100
Tallahassee, FL 32399
P: (850) 245-6500
F: (850) 245-6125
E: secretaryofstate
@dos.state.fl.us

GEORGIA

Ms. Stacy Kalberman
Executive Secretary
State Ethics Commission
200 Piedmont Avenue, Southeast
Suite 1402, West Tower
Atlanta, GA 30334
P: (404) 463-1980
F: (404) 463-1988
E: gaethics@ethics.ga.gov

GUAM

Mr. John Blas
Executive Director
Elections Commission
P.O. Box BG
Hagatna, GU 96932
P: (671) 477-9791
F: (671) 477-1895
E: director@gec.guam.gov

HAWAII

Ms. Kristin E. Izumi-Nitao
Executive Director
Campaign Spending
Commission
235 South Beretania Street, Room 300
Honolulu, HI 96813
P: (808) 586-0285
F: (808) 586-0288

IDAHO

Hon. Ben T. Ysursa (R)
Secretary of State
Office of the Secretary of State
P.O. Box 83720
Boise, ID 83720
P: (208) 334-2300
F: (208) 334-2282
E: secstate@sos.idaho.gov

ILLINOIS

Mr. Rupert Borgsmiller
Executive Director
State Board of Elections
1020 South Spring Street
Springfield, IL 62704
P: (217) 782-4141
F: (217) 782-5959
E: rborgsmiller
@elections.il.gov

INDIANA

Mr. J. Bradley King
Co-Director
Election Division
302 West Washington, Room E204
Indianapolis, IN 46204
P: (317) 233-0929
F: (317) 233-6793
E: bking@iec.IN.gov

KANSAS

Ms. Carol E. Williams
Executive Director
Governmental Ethics
Commission
109 Southwest 9th Street, Suite 504
Topeka, KS 66612
P: (785) 296-4219
F: (785) 296-2548

KENTUCKY

Ms. Sarah M. Jackson
Executive Director
Registry of Election Finance
140 Walnut Street
Frankfort, KY 40601
P: (502) 573-2226
F: (502) 573-5622
E: sarahm.jackson@ky.gov

LOUISIANA

Ms. Kathleen Allen
Ethics Administrator
Ethics Administration
617 North Third Street, Suite 10-36
P.O. Box 4368
Baton Rouge, LA 70821
P: (225) 219-5600
F: (225) 381-7271

MAINE

Mr. Jonathan Wayne
Executive Director
Commission on Governmental
Ethics & Election Practices
135 State House Station
Augusta, ME 04333
P: (207) 287-4179
F: (207) 287-6775
E: Jonathan.Wayne@maine.gov

MARYLAND

Mr. Jared DeMarinis
Director
Division of Candidacy &
Campaign Finance
151 West Street, Suite 200
P.O. Box 6486
Annapolis, MD 21401
P: (410) 269-2853
F: (410) 974-5415
E: jdemarinis
@elections.state.md.us

MASSACHUSETTS

Mr. Michael J. Sullivan
Director
Office of Campaign & Political
Finance
One Ashburton Place, Room 411
Boston, MA 02108
P: (617) 727-8352
F: (617) 727-6549

Campaign Finance Administration

MICHIGAN
Mr. Christopher M. Thomas
Director
Bureau of Elections
Richard H. Austin Building,
First Floor
430 West Allegan Street
Lansing, MI 48918
P: (517) 373-2450
F: (517) 241-4785
E: ChristopherT
    @michigan.gov

MINNESOTA
Mr. Gary Goldsmith
Executive Director
Campaign Finance & Public
Disclosure Board
Centennial Office Building,
Suite 190
658 Cedar Street
St. Paul, MN 55155
P: (651) 296-1721
F: (651) 296-1722
E: gary.goldsmith
    @state.mn.us

MISSISSIPPI
Mr. W. Heath Hillman
Assistant Secretary of State for
Elections
Elections Division
401 Mississippi Street
P.O. Box 136
Jackson, MS 39205
P: (601) 359-6368
F: (601) 359-5019

MISSOURI
Ms. Julie A. Allen
Executive Director
Ethics Commission
3411A Knipp Drive
Jefferson City, MO 65109
P: (573) 751-2020
F: (573) 526-4506
E: helpdesk@mec.mo.gov

MONTANA
Ms. Jennifer L. Hensley
Commissioner
Commissioner of Political
Practices
1205 Eighth Avenue
P.O. Box 202401
Helena, MT 59620
P: (406) 444-2942
F: (406) 444-1643
E: JLHensley@mt.gov

NEBRASKA
Mr. Frank Daley
Executive Director
Accountability & Disclosure
Commission
P.O. Box 95086
Lincoln, NE 68509
P: (402) 471-2522
F: (402) 471-6599
E: frank.daley@nebraska.gov

NEVADA
Hon. Ross Miller (D)
Secretary of State
Office of the Secretary of State
101 North Carson Street, Suite 3
Carson City, NV 89701
P: (775) 684-5708
F: (775) 684-5724
E: sosmail@sos.nv.gov

NEW HAMPSHIRE
Hon. William M. Gardner (D)
Secretary of State
Office of the Secretary of State
State House, Room 204
Concord, NH 03301
P: (603) 271-3242
F: (603) 271-6316
E: kladd@sos.state.nh.us

NEW JERSEY
Mr. Jeffrey M. Brindle
Executive Director
Election Law Enforcement
Commission
P.O. Box 185
Trenton, NJ 08625
P: (609) 292-8700
F: (609) 777-1448

NEW MEXICO
Ms. Bobbi Shearer
Director
Bureau of Elections
State Capitol Annex North
325 Don Gaspar, Suite 300
Santa Fe, NM 87503
P: (505) 827-8403
F: (505) 827-8403
E: bobbi.shearer
    @state.nm.us

NEW YORK
Mr. Robert A. Brehm
Co-Executive Director
State Board of Elections
40 Steuben Street
Albany, NY 12207
P: (518) 474-8100
F: (518) 486-4068

Mr. Todd D. Valentine
Co-Executive Director
State Board of Elections
40 Steuben Street
Albany, NY 12207
P: (518) 474-8100
F: (518) 486-4068

NORTH CAROLINA
Ms. Kim Westbrook Strach
Deputy Director, Campaign
Reporting
State Board of Elections
Campaign Finance Division
P.O. Box 27255
Raleigh, NC 27611
P: (919) 733-7173
F: (919) 715-8047
E: campaign.reporting
    @ncmail.net

NORTH DAKOTA
Ms. LeeAnn Oliver
Elections Specialist
Office of the Secretary of State
600 East Boulevard Avenue, 1st
Floor
Department 108
Bismarck, ND 58505
P: (701) 328-4146
F: (701) 328-4214
E: loliver@nd.gov

**NORTHERN MARIANA
ISLANDS**
Mr. Michael S. Pai
Public Auditor
Office of the Public Auditor
P.O. Box 501399
Saipan, MP 96950
P: (670) 322-6481
F: (670) 322-7812
E: mpai@opacnmi.com

OHIO
Mr. J. Curtis Mayhew
Campaign Finance
Administrator
Office of the Secretary of State
Rhodes Tower
180 East Broad Street
Columbus, OH 43215
P: (614) 466-1231

OKLAHOMA
Ms. Marilyn Hughes
Executive Director
Ethics Commission
2300 North Lincoln Boulevard,
Room B-5
Oklahoma City, OK 73105
P: (405) 521-3451
F: (405) 521-4905

OREGON
Ms. Brenda J. Bayes
Acting Director
Secretary of State, Elections
Division
255 Capitol Street, Northeast,
Suite 501
Salem, OR 97310
P: (503) 986-1518
F: (503) 373-7414
E: brenda.j.bayes
    @state.or.us

PENNSYLVANIA
Mr. Shannon Royer
Deputy Secretary for External
Affairs & Elections
Department of State
210 North Office Building
Harrisburg, PA 17120
P: (717) 787-6458
F: (717) 787-1734

PUERTO RICO
Mr. Ramon Gomez
President
State Election Commission
P.O. Box 19555
Hato Rey, PR 00919
P: (787) 777-8682
F: (787) 296-0173

RHODE ISLAND
Mr. Richard E. Thornton
Director of Campaign Finance
Board of Elections
50 Branch Avenue
Providence, RI 02904
P: (401) 222-2345
F: (401) 222-3135
E: campaignfinance
    @elections.ri.gov

SOUTH CAROLINA
Mr. Herbert R. Hayden Jr.
Executive Director
State Ethics Commission
5000 Thurmond Mall, Suite 250
Columbia, SC 29201
P: (803) 253-4192
F: (803) 253-7539
E: herb@ethics.state.sc.us

SOUTH DAKOTA
Hon. Jason M. Gant (R)
Secretary of State
Office of the Secretary of State
500 East Capitol Avenue, Suite
204
Pierre, SD 57501
P: (605) 773-3537
F: (605) 773-6580
E: sdsos@state.sd.us

Campaign Finance Administration

TENNESSEE
Ms. Patricia Heim
Chair
Registry of Election Finance
404 James Robertson Parkway,
Suite 104
Nashville, TN 37243
P: (615) 741-7959
F: (615) 532-8905
E: registry.info
　　@state.tn.us

TEXAS
Mr. David A. Reisman
Executive Director
Ethics Commission
201 East 14th Street, 10th Floor
P.O. Box 12070
Austin, TX 78711
P: (512) 463-5800
F: (512) 463-5777

U.S. VIRGIN ISLANDS
Mr. John Abramson
Supervisor of Elections
Election System of the Virgin
Islands
P.O. Box 1499, Kingshill
St. Croix, VI 00851
P: (340) 773-1021
F: (340) 773-4523

VERMONT
Hon. Jim Condos (D)
Secretary of State
Office of the Secretary of State
26 Terrace Street
Montpelier, VT 05609
P: (802) 828-2148
F: (802) 828-2496
E: jim.condos
　　@sec.state.vt.us

VIRGINIA
Mr. Don Palmer
Secretary
Board of Elections
200 North 9th Street, Room 101
Richmond, VA 23219
P: (804) 864-8903
F: (804) 371-0194

WASHINGTON
Mr. Doug Ellis
Interim Executive Director
Public Disclosure Commission
711 Capitol Way, #206
P.O. Box 40908
Olympia, WA 98504
P: (360) 664-2735
F: (360) 753-1112
E: Dellis@pdc.wa.gov

WISCONSIN
Mr. Kevin J. Kennedy
Executive Director
Government Accountability
Board
17 West Main Street, Suite 310
Madison, WI 53703
P: (608) 266-8005
F: (608) 267-0500
E: kevin.kennedy
　　@seb.state.wi.us

WYOMING
Hon. Max Maxfield (R)
Secretary of State
Office of the Secretary of State
State Capitol Building
200 West 24th
Cheyenne, WY 82002
P: (307) 777-7378
F: (307) 777-6217
E: Secofstate@state.wy.us

Chief Information Officer

Oversees state information technology operations and develops, implements, and monitors state IT initiatives.

ALABAMA
Mr. Jack Doane
Director
Information Services Division
Folsom Administrative Building
64 North Union Street
Montgomery, AL 36130
P: (334) 242-3658
F: (334) 242-7002
E: jack.doane
  @isd.alabama.gov

ALASKA
Mr. Pat Shier
Director
Enterprise Technology Services
333 Willoughby Avenue
State Office Building, 5th Floor
Juneau, AK 99801
P: (907) 382-3512
F: (907) 465-3450
E: pat.shier@alaska.gov

ARIZONA
Mr. Aaron Sandeen
Chief Information Officer
Goverment Information
Technology Agency
100 North 15th Avenue, Suite 440
Phoenix, AZ 85007
P: (602) 364-4482
F: (602) 367-4799
E: asandeen@azgita.gov

ARKANSAS
Ms. Claire Bailey
Chief Technology Officer
Department of Information
Systems
#1 Capitol Mall, 3rd Floor
Little Rock, AR 72203
P: (501) 682-9990
F: (501) 682-9465
E: claire.bailey
  @arkansas.gov

CALIFORNIA
Ms. Christy Quinlan
Acting Secretary of Technology
Technology Agency
1325 J Street, Suite 1600
Sacramento, CA 95814
P: (916) 319-9223
E: christy.quinlan
  @state.ca.gov

COLORADO
Ms. Kristin Russell
Chief Information Officer
Governor's Office of
Information Technology
601 East 18th Avenue, Suite 250
Denver, CO 80203
P: (303) 764-7700
F: (303) 764-7725
E: kristin.russell
  @state.co.us

CONNECTICUT
Mr. Mark Raymond
Chief Information Officer
Department of Information
Technology
101 East River Drive
East Hartford, CT 06108
P: (860) 622-2200
F: (860) 291-8665
E: mark.raymond@ct.gov

DELAWARE
Mr. James Sills III
Secretary
Department of Technology &
Information
801 Silver Lake Boulevard
Dover, DE 19904
P: (302) 739-9629
F: (302) 739-1442

FLORIDA
Mr. David W. Taylor
Executive Director & Chief
Information Officer
Agency for Enterprise
Information Technology
4030 Esplanade Way, Suite 135
Tallahassee, FL 32399
P: (850) 922-7502
F: (850) 487-9937
E: David.Taylor
  @aeit.myflorida.com

GEORGIA
Mr. Calvin Rhodes
Executive Director
Technology Authority
47 Trinity Avenue, Southwest
Atlanta, GA 30334
P: (404) 463-2340
F: (404) 463-2380
E: calvn.rhodes@gta.ga.gov

GUAM
Mr. Ed Cruz
Chief Information Officer
Bureau of Information
Technology
P.O. Box 2950
Hagatna, GU 96932
P: (671) 475-1113
F: (671) 472-9508
E: jim.lacson@bit.guam.gov

HAWAII
Mr. Bruce Coppa
State Comptroller
Department of Accounting &
General Services
P.O. Box 119
Honolulu, HI 96810
P: (808) 586-0400
F: (808) 586-0775
E: bruce.a.coppa@hawaii.gov

IDAHO
Ms. Teresa Luna
Director
Department of Administration
650 West State Street, Room 100
P.O. Box 83720
Boise, ID 83720
P: (208) 332-1827
F: (208) 334-2307
E: teresa.luna
  @adm.idaho.gov

ILLINOIS
Mr. Sean Vinck
Chief Information Officer
Office of the Governor
207 State House
Springfield, IL 62706
P: (217) 782-0244
E: sean.vinck@illinois.gov

INDIANA
Mr. Brian Arrowood
Office of Technology
1000 North Senate Avenue,
Room N551
Indianapolis, IN 46204
P: (317) 234-3843
F: (317) 234-0917
E: barrowood@iot.in.gov

IOWA
Ms. Lorrie Tritch
Chief Operating Officer
Information Technology
Enterprise
Department of Administrative
Services
Hoover Building, Level B
Des Moines, IA 50319
P: (515) 232-5898
F: (515) 281-6137
E: lori.tritch@iowa.gov

KANSAS
Mr. Morey Sullivan
Director
Division of Information Systems
& Communications
900 Southwest Jackson, Room
751S
Topeka, KS 66612
P: (785) 296-3463
F: (785) 296-1168
E: morey.sullivan
  @da.state.ks.us

KENTUCKY
Ms. Lori Flanery
Cabinet Secretary
Finance & Administration
Cabinet
Room 383, Capitol Annex
Frankfort, KY 40601
P: (502) 564-4240
F: (502) 564-5856
E: Lori.Flanery@ky.gov

LOUISIANA
Mr. Edward J. Driesse
Chief Information Officer
Office of Information
Technology
Division of Administration
P.O. Box 94095
Baton Rouge, LA 70804
P: (225) 342-7105
F: (225) 219-4994
E: cio@la.gov

MAINE
Mr. Greg McNeal
Chief Information Officer
Office of Information
Technology
26 Edison Drive
145 State House Station
Augusta, ME 04333
P: (207) 624-8800

MARYLAND
Mr. Elliot H. Schlanger
Secretary
Department of Information
Technology
45 Calvert Street
Annapolis, MD 21401
P: (410) 260-2994
F: (410) 974-5615
E: Elliot.Schlanger
  @doit.state.md.us

Chief Information Officer

MASSACHUSETTS
Mr. John Letchford
Assistant Secretary for
Information Technology & CIO
Information Technology
Division
One Ashburton Place, Room 804
Boston, MA 02108
P: (617) 727-2040
F: (617) 727-2779

MICHIGAN
Mr. David Behen
Director & CIO
Department of Technology,
Management & Budget
320 South Walnut Street, 2nd
Floor
Lansing, MI 48933
P: (517) 373-1006
F: (517) 373-8213

MINNESOTA
Ms. Carolyn Parnell
Chief Information Officer
Office of Enterprise Technology
658 Cedar Street, Floor 4
St. Paul, MN 55155
P: (651) 556-8007
F: (651) 215-3877
E: carolyn.parnell
    @state.mn.us

MISSISSIPPI
Mr. David L. Litchliter
Executive Director
Department of Information
Technology Services
301 North Lamar Street, Suite
508
Jackson, MS 39201
P: (601) 359-1395
F: (601) 354-6016
E: david.litchliter
    @its.state.ms.us

MISSOURI
Mr. Doug Young
Chief Information Officer
Information Technology
Services Division
301 West High Street, Room
280
P.O. Box 809
Jefferson City, MO 65102
P: (573) 526-7746
F: (573) 751-3299
E: Doug.Young@oa.mo.gov

MONTANA
Mr. Richard Clark
Chief Information Officer
Information Technology
Services Division
Department of Administration
P.O. Box 200113
Helena, MT 59620
P: (406) 444-2700
F: (406) 444-2701
E: dclark@mt.gov

NEBRASKA
Ms. Brenda L. Decker
Chief Information Officer
Office of the Chief Information
Officer
501 South 14th Street
P.O. Box 95045
Lincoln, NE 68509
P: (402) 471-2761
F: (402) 471-4864
E: brenda.decker
    @nebraska.gov

NEVADA
Mr. David Gustafson
Acting Director
Department of Information
Technology
400 West King Street, Room
300
Carson City, NV 89703
P: (775) 684-5849
F: (775) 684-5846

NEW HAMPSHIRE
Mr. Bill Rogers
Chief Information Officer
Department of Information
Technology
27 Hazen Drive
Concord, NH 03301
P: (603) 223-5703
F: (603) 271-6531

NEW JERSEY
Mr. Adel W. Ebeid
Chief Technology Officer
Office of Information
Technology
200/300 Riverview Plaza
P.O. Box 212
Trenton, NJ 08625
P: (609) 984-4082
F: (609) 633-9100
E: abel.ebeid
    @oit.state.nj.us

NEW MEXICO
Mr. Darryl Ackley
Secretary
Department of Information
Technology
P.O. Box 22550
Santa Fe, NM 87502
P: (505) 827-0000

NEW YORK
Mr. Daniel Chan
Director & Chief Information
Officer
Office for Technology
State Capitol, Empire State
Plaza
P.O. Box 2062
Albany, NY 12220
P: (518) 408-2140
F: (518) 408-2223

NORTH CAROLINA
Mr. Gerald L. Fralick
Chief Information Officer
Information Technology
Services
P.O. Box 17209
Raleigh, NC 27619
P: (919) 754-6575
E: jerry.fralick@nc.gov

NORTH DAKOTA
Dr. Lisa Feldner
Chief Information Officer
Information Technology
Department
600 East Boulevard Avenue
Department 112
Bismarck, ND 58505
P: (701) 328-1000
F: (701) 328-3000
E: lfeldner@nd.gov

OHIO
Mr. Stuart R. Davis
Chief Information Officer
Office of Information Techology
30 East Broad Street, 40th Floor
Columbus, OH 43215
P: (614) 644-6446
F: (614) 644-9152
E: stu.davis@oit.ohio.gov

OKLAHOMA
Mr. Alex Pettit
Chief Information Officer
Office of State Finance
3115 North Lincoln Boulevard
Oklahoma City, OK 73105
P: (405) 522-4667
E: alex.pettit@osf.ok.gov

OREGON
Mr. Dugan Petty
Division Administrator & State
Chief Information Officer
Enterprise Information Strategy
& Policy Division
Department of Administrative
Services
955 Center Street, Northeast,
Room 470
Salem, OR 97301
P: (503) 378-2128
F: (503) 378-4351
E: dugan.a.petty
    @state.or.us

PENNSYLVANIA
Mr. George White
Chief Information Officer
Office for Information
Technology
209 Finance Building
Harrisburg, PA 17120
P: (717) 787-5440
F: (717) 787-4523

RHODE ISLAND
Mr. John E. Landers
Chief Information Officer
Division of Information
Technology
Department of Administration
One Capitol Hill
Providence, RI 02908
P: (401) 222-4444
F: (401) 422-4260
E: John.Landers@doit.ri.gov

SOUTH CAROLINA
Mr. Jimmy Earley
Division Director
Division of State Information
Technology
4430 Broad River Road
Columbia, SC 29210
P: (803) 896-0222
F: (803) 896-0789
E: jimmy.earley@cio.sc.gov

SOUTH DAKOTA
Mr. Dom Bianco
Commissioner & Chief
Information Officer
Bureau of Information &
Telecommications
Kneip Building
700 Governors Drive
Pierre, SD 57501
P: (605) 773-5110
F: (605) 773-6040
E: dom.bianco@state.sd.us

TENNESSEE
Mr. Mark Bengel
Chief Information Officer
Office for Information
Resources
312 Rosa L. Parks Avenue
16th Floor, Tennessee Tower
Nashville, TN 37343
P: (615) 741-7951
F: (615) 532-0471

TEXAS
Ms. Karen W. Robinson
Chief Technology Officer
Department of Information
Resources
300 West 15th Street, Suite 1300
P.O. Box 13564
Austin, TX 78711
P: (512) 475-4720
F: (512) 475-4759

UTAH
Mr. Stephen Fletcher
Chief Information Officer /
Executive Director
Department of Technology
Services
1 State Office Building, Floor 6
Salt Lake City, UT 84114
P: (801) 538-3298
F: (801) 538-3622
E: sfletcher@utah.gov

VERMONT
Ms. Ruthann Sullivan
Interim Commissioner & Chief
Information Officer
Department of INformation &
Innovation
Agency of Administration
133 State Street
Montpelier, VT 05633
P: (802) 828-4141
F: (802) 828-3398
E: ruthann.sullivan
   @state.vt.us

VIRGINIA
Mr. Samuel A. Nixon Jr.
Chief Information Officer
Information Technologies
Agency
11751 Meadowville Lane
P.O. Box 406
Chester, VA 23836
P: (804) 416-6004
E: sam.nixon
   @vita.virginia.gov

WASHINGTON
Mr. Mike Ricchio
Acting Director
Department of Information
Services
1110 Jefferson Street, Southeast
Olympia, WA 98504
P: (360) 902-3500
F: (360) 586-5885
E: mike.ricchio@dis.wa.gov

WEST VIRGINIA
Mr. Kyle Schafer
Chief Technology Officer
Governor's Office of
Technology
One Davis Square
321 Capitol Street
Charleston, WV 25301
P: (304) 558-3784
F: (304) 558-0136
E: kyle.d.schafer@wv.gov

WISCONSIN
Ms. Diane Kohn
Acting Chief Information
Officer
Division of Enterprise
Technology
Department of Administration
P.O. Box 7844
Madiso, WI 53707
P: (608) 264-9502
F: (608) 267-0626
E: dian.kohn@wisconsin.gov

WYOMING
Mr. Flint Waters
Chief Information Officer
Office of the Chief Information
Officer
Emerson Building, Suite 214
2001 Capitol Avenue
Cheyenne, WY 82002
P: (307) 777-5492
F: (307) 777-3696
E: cio@wyo.gov

Chief Justice

The chief justice or judge of the state court of last resort.

ALABAMA
Hon. Sue Bell Cobb
Chief Justice
Supreme Court
300 Dexter Avenue
Montgomery, AL 36104
P: (334) 242-4609

ALASKA
Hon. Walter L. Carpeneti
Chief Justice
Supreme Court
303 K Street
Anchorage, AK 99501
P: (907) 463-4771
F: (907) 264-0768

AMERICAN SAMOA
Hon. F. Michael Kruse
Chief Justice
High Court
Courthouse, P.O. Box 309
Pago Pago, AS 96799
P: (684) 633-1410
F: (684) 633-1318

ARIZONA
Hon. Rebecca White Berch
Chief Justice
Supreme Court
1501 West Washington Street
Phoenix, AZ 85007
P: (602) 542-9300

ARKANSAS
Hon. Jim Hannah
Chief Justice
Supreme Court
625 Marshall Street
Justice Building
Little Rock, AR 72201
P: (501) 682-6873
F: (501) 683-4006

CALIFORNIA
Hon. Tani Cantil-Sakauye
Chief Justice
Supreme Court
350 McAllister Court
San Francisco, CA 94102
P: (415) 865-7015

COLORADO
Hon. Michael L. Bender
Chief Justice
Supreme Court
2 East 14th Avenue, Fourth
Floor
Denver, CO 80203
P: (303) 861-1111 Ext. 241

CONNECTICUT
Hon. Chase T. Rogers
Chief Justice
Supreme Court
231 Capitol Avenue
Hartford, CT 06106
P: (860) 757-2200
F: (860) 757-2217

DELAWARE
Hon. Myron T. Steele
Chief Justice
Supreme Court
57 The Green
Dover, DE 19901
P: (302) 739-4214
F: (302) 739-2004

DISTRICT OF COLUMBIA
Hon. Eric T. Washington
Chief Judge
Supreme Court
Moultrie Courthouse
500 Indiana Avenue, Northwest,
6th Floor
Washington, DC 20001
P: (202) 879-2771

GEORGIA
Hon. Carol W. Hunstein
Chief Justice
Supreme Court
244 Washington Street,
Southwest
Room 572, State Office Annex
Atlanta, GA 30334
P: (404) 656-3470
F: (404) 656-2253

GUAM
Hon. F. Phillip Carbullido
Chief Justice
Supreme Court
Suite 300, Guam Judicial Center
120 West O'Brien Drive
Hagatna, GU 96910
P: (671) 475-3162
F: (671) 475-3140

HAWAII
Mr. Mark E. Recktenwald
Chief Justice
Supreme Court
Aliiolani Hale
417 South King Street
Honolulu, HI 96813
P: (808) 539-4919
F: (808) 539-4928

IDAHO
Hon. Daniel T. Eismann
Chief Justice
Supreme Court
P.O. Box 83720
451 West State Street
Boise, ID 83720
P: (208) 334-2149
F: (208) 947-7590

ILLINOIS
Hon. Thomas L. Kilbride
Chief Justice
Supreme Court
Supreme Court Building
200 East Capitol Avenue
Springfield, IL 62701
P: (217) 782-2035

INDIANA
Hon. Randall T. Shepard
Chief Justice
Supreme Court
315 Indiana State House
Indianapolis, IN 46204
P: 317.232.1930

KANSAS
Hon. Lawton R. Nuss
Chief Justice
Supreme Court
Judicial Center
301 West 10th Street
Topeka, KS 66612
P: (785) 296-3229
F: (785) 296-1028

KENTUCKY
Hon. John D. Minton Jr.
Chief Justice
Supreme Court
1001 Center Street, 2nd Floor
Room 204
Bowling Green, KY 42101
P: (270) 746-7867

LOUISIANA
Hon. Catherine D. Kimball
Chief Justice
Supreme Court
400 Royal Street
New Orleans, LA 70130
P: (504) 310-2300

MAINE
Hon. Leigh I. Saufley
Chief Justice
Supreme Judicial Court
142 Federal Street
P.O. Box 368
Portland, ME 04112
P: (207) 822-4286

MARYLAND
Hon. Robert M. Bell
Chief Judge
Court of Appeals
634 Courthouse East
111 North Calvert Street
Baltimore, MD 21202
P: (410) 333-6396

MASSACHUSETTS
Hon. Roderick L. Ireland
Chief Justice
Supreme Judicial Court
One Pemberton Square
Boston, MA 02108
P: (617) 557-1000

MICHIGAN
Hon. Robert P. Young Jr.
Chief Justice
Supreme Court
P.O. Box 30052
Lansing, MI 48909
P: (517) 373-0120

MINNESOTA
Hon. David R. Stras
Chief Justice
Supreme Court
305 Minnesota Judicial Center
25 Rev. Martin Luther King Jr.
Boulevard
St. Paul, MN 55155
P: (651) 296-2581

MISSISSIPPI
Hon. William L. Waller Jr.
Chief Justice
Supreme Court
Gartin Building, 3rd Floor
P.O. Box 249
Jackson, MS 39205
P: (601) 359-3694
F: (601) 359-2407

MISSOURI
Hon. William Ray Price Jr.
Chief Justice
Supreme Court
Supreme Court
P.O. Box 150
Jefferson City, MO 65102
P: (573) 751-4144
F: (573) 751-7514

MONTANA
Hon. Mike McGrath (D)
Chief Justice
Supreme Court
215 North Sanders
P.O. Box 203001
Helena, MT 59620
P: (406) 444-5490
F: (404) 444-3274

NEBRASKA
Hon. Michael G. Heavican
Chief Justice
Supreme Court
State Capitol, Room 2214
Lincoln, NE 68509
P: (402) 471-3738
F: (402) 471-2197

NEVADA
Hon. Michael L. Douglas
Chief Justice
Supreme Court
201 South Carson Street
Carson City, NV 89701
P: (775) 684-1600

NEW HAMPSHIRE
Hon. Linda S. Dalianis
Chief Justice
Supreme Court
Supreme Court Building
One Charles Doe Drive
Concord, NH 03301
P: (603) 271-2646

NEW JERSEY
Hon. Stuart Rabner (D)
Chief Justice
Supreme Court
Richard J. Hughes Justice
Complex
P.O. Box 970
Trenton, NJ 08625
P: (609) 292-4837

NEW MEXICO
Hon. Charles W. Daniels
Chief Justice
Supreme Court
P.O. Box 848
Santa Fe, NM 87504
P: (505) 827-4860

NEW YORK
Hon. Jonathan Lippman
Chief Judge
Supreme Court
20 Eagle Street
Albany, NY 12207
P: (212) 661-6787

NORTH CAROLINA
Hon. Sarah Parker
Chief Justice
Supreme Court
P.O. Box 2170
Raleigh, NC 27602
P: (919) 733-3723

NORTH DAKOTA
Hon. Gerald W. VandeWalle
Chief Justice
Supreme Court
State Capitol Building
600 East Boulevard Avenue,
Dept. 180
Bismark, ND 58505
P: (701) 328-2221
F: (701) 328-4480
E: GVandeWalle
   @ndcourts.gov

**NORTHERN MARIANA
ISLANDS**
Hon. Miguel S. Demapan
Chief Justice
Supreme Court
P.O. Box 502165
Saipan, MP 96950
P: (670) 236-9700
F: (670) 236-9702

OHIO
Hon. Maureen O'Connor (R)
Chief Justice
Supreme Court
65 South Front Street, 9th Floor
Columbus, OH 43215
P: (614) 466-5201
F: (614) 752-4418

OKLAHOMA
Hon. Steven W. Taylor
Chief Justice
Supreme Court
Room 200, State Capitol
Building
Oklahoma City, OK 73105
P: (405) 521-3844

OREGON
Hon. Paul J. De Muniz
Chief Justice
Supreme Court
1163 State Street
Salem, OR 97310
P: (503) 986-5709
F: (503) 986-5700
E: paul.j.demuniz
   @ojd.state.or.us

PENNSYLVANIA
Hon. Ronald D. Castille
Chief Justice
Supreme Court
1818 Market Street
Suite 3730
Philadelphia, PA 19103
P: (215) 560-5663
F: (215) 560-5807

PUERTO RICO
Hon. Federico
   Hernandez-Denton
Chief Justice
Supreme Court
P.O. Box 9022392
San Juan, PR 00902
P: (787) 724-3535
F: (787) 724-3551

RHODE ISLAND
Hon. Paul A. Suttell
Chief Justice
Supreme Court
250 Benefit Street, 7th Floor
Providence, RI 02903
P: (401) 222-3272
F: (401) 222-3599

SOUTH CAROLINA
Hon. Jean Hoefer Toal
Chief Justice
Supreme Court
P.O. Box 11330
Columbia, SC 29211
P: (803) 734-1080
F: (803) 734-1499

SOUTH DAKOTA
Hon. David Gilbertson
Chief Justice
Supreme Court
500 East Capitol Avenue
Pierre, SD 57501
P: (605) 773-3511
F: (605) 773-6128

TENNESSEE
Hon. Cornelia Clark
Chief Justice
Supreme Court
318 Supreme Court Building
401 7th Avenue, North
Nashville, TN 37219
P: (615) 741-2681

TEXAS
Hon. Wallace B. Jefferson
Chief Justice
Supreme Court
201 West Fourteenth Street
P.O. Box 12248, Capitol Station
Austin, TX 78711
P: (512) 463-7899
F: (512) 708-8191

U.S. VIRGIN ISLANDS
Hon. Rhys S. Hodge
Chief Justice
Supreme Court
P.O. Box 590
St. Thomas, VI 00804
P: (340) 774-2237
F: (340) 774-2258

UTAH
Hon. Christine M. Durham
Chief Justice
Supreme Court
450 South State Street
P.O. Box 140210
Salt Lake City, UT 84114
P: (801) 238-7945
F: (801) 238-7980

VERMONT
Hon. Paul L. Reiber
Chief Justice
Supreme Court
109 State Street
Montpelier, VT 05609
P: (802) 828-3278
F: (802) 828-4750

VIRGINIA
Hon. Cynthia D. Kinser
Chief Justice
Supreme Court
100 North 9th Street
P.O. Box 1315
Richmond, VA 23218
P: (804) 786-2251
F: (804) 786-6249

WASHINGTON
Hon. Barbara A. Madsen
Chief Justice
Supreme Court
415 12th Avenue, Southwest
P.O. Box 40929
Olympia, WA 98504
P: (360) 357-2037
F: (360) 357-2102

WEST VIRGINIA
Hon. Margaret L.
   Workman (D)
Chief Justice
Supreme Court
State Capitol, Room E-317
Charleston, WV 25305
P: (304) 558-2601
F: (304) 558-3815

WISCONSIN
Hon. Shirley S. Abrahamson
Chief Justice
Supreme Court
16 East State Capitol
P.O. Box 1688
Madison, WI 53701
P: (608) 266-1885
F: (608) 261-8299

Chief Justice

WYOMING
Hon. Marilyn S. Kite
Chief Justice
Supreme Court
Supreme Court Building
2301 Capitol Avenue
Cheyenne, WY 82001
P: (307) 777-7316
F: (307) 777-6129

Child Support Enforcement

Processes child support cases and implements required provisions of child support enforcement program.

ALABAMA
Ms. Faye Nelson
Director
Child Support Enforcement
Division
Department of Human
Resources
P.O. Box 304000
Montgomery, AL 36130
P: (334) 242-9300
F: (334) 242-0606
E: fnelson@dhr.alabama.gov

ALASKA
Mr. John Mallonee
Director
Child Support Services Division
Department of Revenue
550 West 7th Avenue, Suite 310
Anchorage, AK 99501
P: (907) 269-6900
F: (907) 269-6650

AMERICAN SAMOA
Ms. Leilua Stevenson
Director
Department of Human & Social
Services
American Samoa Government
P.O. Box 997534
Pago Pago, AS
P: (684) 633-7506
F: (684) 633-7449

ARIZONA
Ms. Veronica Hart Ragland
Assistant Director
Division of Child Support
Enforcement
Department of Economic
Security
1717 West Jefferson Street
Phoenix, AZ 85007
P: (602) 274-1482

ARKANSAS
Mr. Dan McDonald
Administrator
Office of Child Support
Enforcement
Department of Finance &
Administration
400 East Capitol Avenue, P.O.
Box 8133
Little Rock, AR 72203
P: (501) 682-6169
F: (501) 682-6002
E: dan.mcdonald
    @ocse.state.ar.us

COLORADO
Mr. John Bernhart
Director
Division of Child Support
Enforcement
Department of Human Services
1575 Sherman Street, 5th Floor
Denver, CO 80203
P: (303) 866-4300
F: (303) 866-4360
E: john.bernhart
    @state.co.us

CONNECTICUT
Mr. David Mulligan
Director
Bureau of Child Support
Enforcement
Department of Social Services
25 Sigourney Street
Hartford, CT 06106
P: (860) 424-5269
F: (860) 951-2996
E: david.mulligan@ct.gov

DELAWARE
Mr. Charles E. Hayward
Director
Division of Child Support
Enforcement
Churchmans Corporate Center
Suite 84A, Christiana Road
New Castle, DE 19720
P: (302) 395-6520
F: (302) 395-6735
E: chayward@state.de.us

DISTRICT OF COLUMBIA
Ms. Benidia A. Rice
Deputy
Child Support Services Division
Office of the Attorney General
441 4th Street, Northwest, Suite
550N
Washington, DC 20001
P: (202) 442-9900
E: cssd.oag@dc.gov

FLORIDA
Ms. Ann Coffin
Director
Child Support Enforcement
Program
Department of Revenue
P.O. Box 8030
Tallahassee, FL 32314
P: (850) 488-8726
E: CoffinA@dor.state.fl.us

GEORGIA
Mr. Keith Horton
Director
Office of Child Support
Services
Two Peachtree Street, Northwest
Room 20-460
Atlanta, GA 30303
P: (404) 657-3851
F: (404) 657-3226

GUAM
Ms. Barbara P. Cepeda
Deputy Attorney General
Child Support Enforcement
Division
Office of the Attorney General
287 West O'Brien Drive
Hagatna, GU 96910
P: (671) 475-3360
F: (671) 477-2159

HAWAII
Mr. Garry Kemp
Administrator
Child Support Enforcement
Agency
Department of the Attorney
General
601 Kamokila Boulevard, #207
Kapolei, HI 96707
P: (808) 692-7000
F: (808) 692-7134

IDAHO
Mr. M. Scott Keim
Deputy Attorney General
Child Support Services
Department of Health & Welfare
450 West State Street, 2nd Floor
Boise, ID 83720
P: (208) 334-5524
F: (208) 334-0666
E: keims@dhw.idaho.gov

ILLINOIS
Ms. Pam Compton Lowry
Administrator
Division of Child Support
Enforcement
509 South 6th Street, Floor 6
Springfield, IL 62701
P: (800) 447-4278
F: (217) 524-4608

INDIANA
Mr. James W. Payne
Director
Department of Child Services
302 West Washington Street,
Room E306
Indianapolis, IN 46204
P: (317) 234-1391
F: (317) 232-4490
E: James.Payne@dcs.IN.gov

KANSAS
Ms. Janis DeBoer
Director
Child Support Enforcement
915 Southwest Harrison Street,
6th Floor
Topeka, KS 66612
P: (785) 296-3237
F: (785) 296-5206

KENTUCKY
Mr. Steven P. Veno
Deputy Commissioner
Division of Child Support
Department for Income Support
P.O. Box 2150
Frankfort, KY 40602
P: (502) 564-2285
F: (502) 564-5988
E: steven.veno@ky.gov

LOUISIANA
Ms. Robbie Endris
Executive Director
Child Support Enforcement
Department of Children &
Family Services
627 North Fourth Street
Baton Rouge, LA 70802
P: (225) 342-4780
F: (225) 342-7397
E: rendris@dss.state.la.us

MAINE
Mr. Jerry Joy
Division Director, Child Support
Office of Integrated Access &
Support
11 State House Station
442 Civic Center Drive
Augusta, ME 04333
P: (207) 624-4100
F: (207) 287-3455
E: jerry.joy@maine.gov

MARYLAND
Mr. Theodore Dallas
Interim Secretary
Department of Human
Resources
311 West Saratoga Street
Baltimore, MD 21201
P: (410) 767-7109

Child Support Enforcement

MASSACHUSETTS
Ms. Laurie McGrath
Deputy Commissioner
Child Support Enforcement
Division
Department of Revenue
100 Cambridge Street
Boston, MA 02114
P: (617) 660-1234

MICHIGAN
Ms. Marilyn F. Stephen
Director
Office of Child Support
Department of Human Services
P.O. Box 30037
Lansing, MI 48909
P: (517) 241-7460
F: (517) 335-6236
E: StephenM3@michigan.gov

MINNESOTA
Mr. Wayland Campbell
Director
Child Support Enforcement
Division
Department of Human Services
P.O. Box 64946
St. Paul, MN 55164
P: (651) 431-4403
F: (651) 431-7517
E: wayland.campbell
@state.mn.us

MISSISSIPPI
Mr. Walley Naylor
Director
Division of Child Support
Enforcement
Department of Human Services
75 North State Street
Jackson, MS 39202
P: (601) 359-4500

MISSOURI
Ms. Janel Luck
Director
Family Support Division
Department of Social Services
P.O. Box 2320
Jefferson City, MO 65102
P: (573) 751-3221

MONTANA
Mr. Lonnie J. Olson
Administrator
Child Support Enforcement
Division
3075 North Montana, Suite 112
P.O. Box 202943
Helena, MT 59620
P: (406) 444-3338
F: (406) 444-1370

NEBRASKA
Mr. Todd Reckling
Director
Division of Children & Family
Services
Department of Health & Human
Services
P.O. Box 95026
Lincoln, NE 60509
P: (402) 471-1878

NEVADA
Ms. E. L. Bush
Social Services Chief 3
Division of Welfare &
Supportive Services
Child Support Enforcement
Program
1470 College Parkway
Carson City, NV 89706
P: (775) 684-0500
F: (775) 684-0587
E: lbush@dwss.nv.gov

NEW HAMPSHIRE
Ms. Mary S. Weatherill
System Specialist
Division of Child Support
Services
Department of Health & Human
Services
129 Pleasant Street
Concord, NH 03301
P: (603) 271-4221
F: (603) 271-4787
E: mweather
@dhhs.state.nh.us

NEW JERSEY
Ms. Jeanette Page-Hawkins
Director
Division of Family
Development
P.O. Box 716
Trenton, NJ 08625
P: (609) 588-2400
F: (609) 584-4404

NEW MEXICO
Mr. Stephen M. Klump
Acting Director
Child Support Enforcement
Division
Human Services Department
2009 South Pacheco
Santa Fe, NM 87504
P: (800) 585-7631

NEW YORK
Mr. Kevin Boyle
Acting Deputy Commissioner
Center for Child Well-Being
40 North Pearl Street
Albany, NY 12243
P: (888) 208-4485

NORTH CAROLINA
Ms. Sherry S. Bradsher
Director
Division of Social Services
325 North Salisbury Street
2401 Mail Service Center
Raleigh, NC 27699
P: (919) 733-3055
F: (919) 733-9386
E: sherry.bradsher
@dhhs.nc.gov

NORTH DAKOTA
Mr. James Fleming
Director
Child Support Enforcement
Division
Department of Human Services
P.O. Box 7190
Bismarck, ND 58507
P: (701) 328-3582
F: (701) 328-5425
E: jfleming@nd.gov

OKLAHOMA
Mr. Gary Dart
Director
Child Support Enforcement
Division
Department of Human Services
P.O. Box 53552
Oklahoma City, OK 73152
P: (405) 522-2273
E: OCSS.Director@OKDHS.org

OREGON
Ms. Jean Fogarty
Director
Division of Child Support
Department of Justice
494 State Street, Suite 300
Salem, OR 97301
P: (503) 986-6166
F: (503) 986-6158
E: jean.fogarty@state.or.us

PENNSYLVANIA
Mr. Daniel N. Richard
Director
Bureau of Child Support
Enforcement
P.O. Box 8018
Harrisburg, PA 17110
P: (717) 783-9659
F: (717) 772-4936

RHODE ISLAND
Ms. Sharon A. Santilli
Associate Director
Office of Child Support
Services
Department of Human Services
77 Dorrance Street
Providence, RI 02903
P: (401) 458-4404
E: richildsupport
@cse.state.ri.us

SOUTH CAROLINA
Ms. Lillian B. Koller
Director
Department of Social Services
1535 Confederate Avenue
Extension
P.O. Box 1520
Columbia, SC 29202
P: (803) 898-7360
F: (803) 898-7277

SOUTH DAKOTA
Mr. Terry Walter
Director
Office of Child Support
Enforcement
Department of Social Services
700 Governors Drive
Pierre, SD 57501
P: (605) 773-3641
F: (605) 773-7295
E: DCS@state.sd.us

TENNESSEE
Mr. Michael L. Adams
Assistant Commissioner
Child Support Services
Department of Human Services
400 Deaderick Street, 15th Floor
Nashville, TN 37243
P: (615) 253-4394
F: (615) 741-4165

TEXAS
Ms. Alicia Key
Deputy Attorney General for
Child Support
Office of the Attorney General
209 West 14th Street
P.O. Box 12548
Austin, TX 78711
P: (512) 460-6000
F: (512) 463-2063
E: child.support
@oag.state.tx.us

U.S. VIRGIN ISLANDS
Ms. Regina De Chabert
Director
Paternity & Child Support
Division
2 Nisky Center, Second Floor
Suite 500
St. Thomas, VI 00802
P: (340) 775-3070
F: (340) 775-3248

UTAH
Mr. Mark Brasher
Director
Office of Recovery Services
Department of Human Services
515 East 100 South
Salt Lake City, UT 84102
P: (801) 536-8500 Ext. 68901
F: (801) 536-8509
E: mbrasher@utah.gov

VERMONT
Mr. Jeffrey P. Cohen
Director
Office of Child Support
103 South Main Street
Waterbury, VT 05671
P: (802) 241-2319
F: (802) 244-1483
E: jeff.cohen
    @ahs.state.vt.us

VIRGINIA
Mr. Nathaniel L. Young
Deputy Commissioner &
Director
Division of Child Support
Enforcement
Department of Social Services
7 North 8th Street
Richmond, VA 23219
P: (804) 726-7000
E: nick.young
    @dss.virginia.gov

WASHINGTON
Mr. David Stillman
Director
Division of Child Support
Department of Social & Health
Services
P.O. Box 45130
Tacoma, WA 98504
P: (360) 725-4350
F: (360) 664-5303

WEST VIRGINIA
Mr. Garrett M. Jacobs
Commissioner
Bureau for Child Support
Enforcement
350 Capitol Street, Room 147
Charleston, WV 25301
P: (304) 558-0909
F: (304) 558-4092
E: garrett.m.jacobs@wv.gov

WISCONSIN
Ms. Eloise Anderson
Secretary
Department of Children &
Families
P.O. Box 8916
Madison, WI 53224
P: (608) 267-3905

WYOMING
Ms. Brenda J. Lyttle
Director
Child Support Enforcement
Department of Family Services
122 West 21st Street, Herschler
Building
Cheyenne, WY 82002
P: (307) 777-6948
F: (307) 777-5588

Children and Youth Services

Implements programs designed to protect children and youth against abuse, neglect and exploitation.

ALABAMA
Dr. Marquita Davis
Commissioner
Department of Children's Affairs
2 North Jackson Street, Suite 602
Montgomery, AL 36104
P: (334) 223-0502
F: (334) 240-3054
E: marquita.davis
  @dca.alabama.gov

ALASKA
Ms. Christy Lawton
Acting Director
Office of Children's Services
Department of Health & Social Services
323 East 4th Avenue
Anchorage, AK 99501
P: (907) 269-3440
F: (907) 465-3397
E: christy.lawton
  @alaska.gov

AMERICAN SAMOA
Ms. Leilua Stevenson
Director
Department of Human & Social Services
American Samoa Government
P.O. Box 997534
Pago Pago, AS
P: (684) 633-7506
F: (684) 633-7449

ARIZONA
Ms. Cassandra A. Larsen
Director
Governor's Office for Children, Youth & Families
1700 West Washington Street, Suite 101
Phoenix, AZ 85007
P: (602) 542-4043
F: (602) 542-3520

ARKANSAS
Ms. Cecile Blucker
Director
Division of Children & Family Services
P.O. Box 1437, Slot S560
Little Rock, AR 72203
P: (501) 682-8772
E: cecile.blucker
  @arkansas.gov

CALIFORNIA
Mr. Will Lightbourne
Director
Department of Social Services
744 P Street
Sacramento, CA 95814
P: (916) 657-2598
F: (916) 651-6569

COLORADO
Mr. Lloyd Malone
Director
Division of Child Welfare
Department of Human Services
1575 Sherman Street, 1st Floor
Denver, CO 80203
P: (303) 866-4365
F: (303) 866-5563
E: lloyd.malone@state.co.us

CONNECTICUT
Ms. Joette Katz
Commissioner
Department of Children & Families
505 Hudson Street
Hartford, CT 06106
P: (860) 550-6300
E: commissioner.dcf@ct.gov

DELAWARE
Ms. Vivian Rapposelli
Secretary
Department of Services for Children, Youth & Their Families
1825 Faulkland Road
Wilmington, DE 19805
P: (302) 633-2503
F: (302) 995-8290

DISTRICT OF COLUMBIA
Mr. Roque R. Gerald
Director
Child & Family Services Agency
400 6th Street, Southwest
Washington, DC 20024
P: (202) 442-6000
F: (202) 442-6498
E: cfsa@dc.gov

FLORIDA
Mr. David Wilkins
Secretary
Department of Children & Families
1317 Winewood Boulevard
Building 1, Room 202
Tallahassee, FL 32399
P: (850) 487-1111
F: (850) 922-2993
E: david_wilkins
  @dcf.state.fl.us

GEORGIA
Ms. Rachelle Carnesale
Director
Division of Family & Children Services
Two Peachtree Street, Northwest
Room 19-400
Atlanta, GA 30303
P: (404) 651-8409
F: (404) 657-5105

HAWAII
Mr. Bert Matsuoka
Executive Director
Office of Youth Services
820 Mililani Street, Suite 817
Honolulu, HI 96813
P: (808) 587-5706
F: (808) 587-5734

IDAHO
Mr. Ron Luce
Administrator
Division of Family & Community Services
450 West State Street
5th Floor, Pete T. Cenarrusa Building
Boise, ID 83720
P: (208) 334-5680
F: (208) 332-7331
E: lucer@dhw.idaho.gov

ILLINOIS
Mr. Erwin McEwen
Director
Department of Children & Family Services
406 East Monroe Street
Springfield, IL 62701
P: (217) 785-2509
F: (217) 785-1052

INDIANA
Mr. Mike Carr
Director, Division of Family Resources
Family & Social Services Administration
402 West Washington Street, Room W392
P.O. Box 7083
Indianapolis, IN 46207
P: (317) 233-4450
E: michael.carr@fssa.in.gov

IOWA
Ms. Wendy Rickman
Administrator
Division of Adult, Children & Family Services
Department of Human Services
1305 East Walnut
Des Moines, IA 50319
P: (515) 281-5521
F: (515) 242-6036
E: wrickma@dhs.state.ia.us

KANSAS
Ms. Tanya Keys
Director
Children & Family Services
Room 603N, Docking State Office Building
915 Southwest Harrison Street
Topeka, KS 66612
P: (785) 296-4653
F: (785) 368-8159
E: Tanya.Keys@srs.ks.gov

KENTUCKY
Ms. Patricia R. Wilson
Commissioner
Department for Community Based Services
275 East Main Street
Mail Stop 3W-A
Frankfort, KY 40621
P: (502) 564-3703
F: (502) 564-6907

MAINE
Mr. James Beougher
Director
Office of Child & Family Services
2 Anthony Avenue
Augusta, ME 04333
P: (207) 624-7900
F: (207) 287-5282

MARYLAND
Ms. Rosemary King Johnston
Executive Director
Governor's Office for Children
301 West Preston Street, Suite 1502
Baltimore, MD 21201
P: (410) 767-6211
F: (410) 333-5248
E: rjohnston
  @goc.state.md.us

MASSACHUSETTS
Ms. Jane E. Tewksbury
Commissioner
Department of Youth Services
27 Wormwood Street, Suite 400
Boston, MA 02110
P: (617) 727-7575
F: (617) 727-0696

MICHIGAN
Mr. Steve Yager
Acting Director
Children's Services Administration
P.O. Box 30037
Lansing, MI 48909
P: (517) 373-2101

MISSISSIPPI
Ms. Jill Dent
Director
Division of Early Childhood
Care & Development
750 North State Street
P.O. Box 352
Jackson, MS 39205
P: (601) 359-4544
F: (601) 359-4422

MISSOURI
Mr. Tim Decker
Director
Division of Youth Services
3418 Knipp, Suite A-1
P.O. Box 447
Jefferson City, MO 65102
P: (573) 751-3324
F: (573) 526-4494
E: tim.decker@dss.mo.gov

MONTANA
Ms. Anna Whiting Sorrell
Director
Department of Public Health &
Human Services
111 North Sanders, Room 301
P.O. Box 4210
Helena, MT 59604
P: (406) 444-5622
F: (406) 444-1970

NEBRASKA
Mr. Todd Reckling
Director
Division of Children & Family
Services
Department of Health & Human
Services
P.O. Box 95026
Lincoln, NE 60509
P: (402) 471-1878

NEVADA
Ms. Diane J. Comeaux
Administrator
Division of Child & Family
Services
Department of Health & Human
Services
4126 Technology Way, Room
100
Carson City, NV 89706
P: (775) 684-4000
F: (775) 684-4010
E: dcomeaux@dcfs.nv.gov

NEW HAMPSHIRE
Ms. Nancy Rollins
Director
Division for Children, Youth &
Families
Department of Health & Human
Services
105 Pleasant Street, Main
Building
Concord, NH 03301
P: (603) 271-8560
F: (603) 271-5058
E: nrollins
@dhhs.state.nh.us

NEW JERSEY
Dr. Allison Blake
Commissioner
Department of Children &
Families
222 South Warren Street
P.O. Box 729, 3rd Floor
Trenton, NJ 08625
P: (609) 984-4500
E: dcf_commissioner
@dcf.state.nj.us

NEW MEXICO
Ms. Yolanda Berumen-Deines
Secretary
Children, Youth & Families
Department
P.O. Drawer 5160
Santa Fe, NM 87502
P: (505) 827-7602

NEW YORK
Ms. Gladys Carrion
Commissioner
Office of Children & Family
Services
Capitol View Office Park
52 Washington Street
Rensselaer, NY 12144
P: (518) 473-7793
F: (518) 486-7550

NORTH CAROLINA
Ms. Sherry S. Bradsher
Director
Division of Social Services
325 North Salisbury Street
2401 Mail Service Center
Raleigh, NC 27699
P: (919) 733-3055
F: (919) 733-9386
E: sherry.bradsher
@dhhs.nc.gov

NORTH DAKOTA
Ms. Tara Muhlhauser
Director
Children & Family Services
600 East Boulevard Avenue
Department 325
Bismarck, ND 58505
P: (701) 328-2316
F: (701) 328-3538
E: tmuhlhauser@nd.gov

**NORTHERN MARIANA
ISLANDS**
Mr. Melvin Faisao
Secretary
Department of Community &
Cultural Affairs
Caller Box 10007, Capitol Hill
Saipan, MP 96950
P: (670) 664-2550
F: (670) 664-2560
E: dysdir@saipan.com

OHIO
Mr. Michael B. Colbert
Director
Department of Job & Family
Services
30 East Broad Street, 32nd Floor
Columbus, OH 43215
P: (614) 466-6283
F: (614) 466-2815

Ms. Sandra T. Holt
Deputy Director
Office for Children & Families
Department of Job & Family
Services
50 West Town Street, 6th Floor
Columbus, OH 43215
P: (614) 466-1213
F: (614) 466-4359

OKLAHOMA
Ms. Deborah G. Smith
Director
Children & Family Services
Division
P.O. Box 25352
Oklahoma City, OK 73125
P: (405) 522-1487
F: (405) 521-4373
E: Deborahg.smith@okdhs.org

OREGON
Ms. Erinn L. Kelley-Siel
Acting Director
Department of Human Services
500 Summer Street, Northeast,
E-62
Salem, OR 97301
P: (503) 945-5944
F: (503) 378-2897
E: erinn.kelley-siel
@state.or.us

Mr. Mickey Lansing
Executive Director
Commission on Children &
Families
The Equitable Building
530 Center Street, Northeast,
Suite 405
Salem, OR 97301
P: (503) 373-1283
F: (503) 378-8395
E: mickey.lansing
@state.or.us

PENNSYLVANIA
Ms. Cathy Utz
Deputy Secretary
Office of Children, Youth &
Families
131 Health & Welfare Building
P.O. Box 2675
Harrisburg, PA 17110
P: (717) 787-4756
F: (717) 787-0414

PUERTO RICO
Ms. Yanitsia Irizarry
Mendez
Secretary
Department of the Family
P.O. Box 11398
San Juan, PR 00910
P: (787) 294-4900
F: (787) 294-0732

RHODE ISLAND
Mr. Kevin J. Aucoin
Interim Director
Department of Children, Youth
& Families
101 Friendship Street
Providence, RI 02903
P: (401) 528-3540
F: (401) 528-3580
E: Kevin.Aucoin@dcyf.ri.gov

SOUTH CAROLINA
Ms. Lillian B. Koller
Director
Department of Social Services
1535 Confederate Avenue
Extension
P.O. Box 1520
Columbia, SC 29202
P: (803) 898-7360
F: (803) 898-7277

Children and Youth Services

SOUTH DAKOTA
Ms. Virgena Wieseler
Division Director
Department of Social Services
Division of Child Protection
Services
700 Governors Drive
Pierre, SD 57505
P: (605) 773-3227
F: (605) 773-6834
E: CPS@state.sd.us

TENNESSEE
Dr. Viola Miller
Commissioner
Department of Children's
Services
Cordell Hull Building, 7th Floor
436 Sixth Avenue, North
Nashville, TN 37243
P: (615) 741-9699
F: (615) 532-8079

Ms. Kate O'Day
Commissioner
Department of Children's
Services
Cordell Hull Building, 7th Floor
436 Sixth Avenue, North
Nashville, TN 37243
P: (615) 741-9699
F: (615) 532-8079

TEXAS
Ms. Anne Heiligenstein
Commissioner
Department of Family &
Protective Services
701 West 51st Street
P.O. Box 149030
Austin, TX 78714
P: (512) 438-4870

U.S. VIRGIN ISLANDS
Mr. Christopher Finch
Commissioner
Department of Human Services
Knud Hansen Complex,
Building A
1303 Hospital Grounds
St. Thomas, VI 00802
P: (340) 774-0930
F: (340) 774-3466

UTAH
Mr. Duane Betournay
Director
Division of Child & Family
Services
195 North 1950 West
Salt Lake City, UT 84116
P: (801) 538-4100
F: (801) 538-3993
E: dbetournay@utah.gov

VERMONT
Mr. Dave Yacovone
Commissioner
Department for Children &
Families
103 South Main Street
Montpelier, VT 05671
P: (802) 241-2100
E: dave.yacovone
@ahs.state.vt.us

VIRGINIA
Mr. Martin D. Brown
Commissioner
Department of Social Services
801 East Main Street
Richmond, VA 23219
P: (804) 726-7000
E: martin.brown
@dss.virginia.gov

WASHINGTON
Ms. Denise Revels-Robinson
Assistant Secretary
Children's Administration
Department of Social & Health
Services
P.O. Box 45710
Olympia, WA 98504
P: (360) 902-7820

WEST VIRGINIA
Ms. Anne Williams
Director
Office of Maternal, Child &
Family Health
350 Capitol Street, Room 427
Charleston, WV 25301
P: (304) 558-5388
F: (304) 558-1035
E: Anne.A.Williams@wv.gov

WISCONSIN
Ms. Eloise Anderson
Secretary
Department of Children &
Families
P.O. Box 8916
Madison, WI 53224
P: (608) 267-3905

WYOMING
Mr. Steve Corsi
Director of Family Services
Department of Family Services
Hathaway Building, 3rd Floor
2300 Capitol Avenue
Cheyenne, WY 82002
P: (307) 777-7564
F: (307) 777-7747

Civil Rights

Overall responsibility for preventing and redressing discrimination in employment, education, housing, public accommodations and credit (because of race, color, sex, age, national origin, religion or disability.)

ALABAMA
Ms. Desiree Jackson
Civil Rights/Equal Employment Opportunity
Department of Human Resources
50 North Ripley Street
Montgomery, AL 36130
P: (334) 242-1553
E: Desiree.Jackson
   @dhr.alabama.gov

ALASKA
Ms. Paula Haley
Executive Director
Human Rights Commission
Office of the Governor
800 A Street, Suite 204
Anchorage, AK 99501
P: (907) 274-4692
F: (907) 278-8588

AMERICAN SAMOA
Hon. Fepulea'i A.
   Ripley Jr.
Attorney General
Office of the Attorney General
American Samoa Government
Executive Office Building,
Utulei
Pago Pago, AS 96799
P: (684) 633-4163
F: (684) 633-1838

ARIZONA
Ms. Melanie Pate
Division Chief Counsel
Office of the Attorney General
Civil Rights Division
1275 West Washington Street
Phoenix, AZ 85007
P: (602) 542-5263
E: civilrightsinfo@azag.gov

ARKANSAS
Hon. Dustin McDaniel (D)
Attorney General
Office of the Attorney General
323 Center Street, Suite 200
Little Rock, AR 72201
P: 501) 682-2341
F: (501) 682-8084

CALIFORNIA
Mr. Jim Tashima
Acting Bureau Chief
Civil Rights Bureau
744 P Street
Sacramento, CA 95814
P: (916) 654-2107
E: jim.tashima@dss.ca.gov

COLORADO
Mr. Steve Chavez
Director
Civil Rights Division
1560 Broadway, Suite 1050
Denver, CO 80202
P: (303) 894-2997
F: (303) 894-7830

CONNECTICUT
Mr. Robert Brothers Jr.
Executive Director
Commission on Human Rights
& Opportunities
21 Grand Street
Hartford, CT 06106
P: (860) 541-3451
F: (860) 246-5419

DELAWARE
Mr. Vincent Petroff
Supervisor, Acting Director
Office of Human Relations
Carvel State Office Building
820 North French Street, 4th
Floor
Wilmington, DE 19801
P: (302) 577-5050
F: (302) 577-3486

DISTRICT OF COLUMBIA
Mr. Gustavo F. Velasquez
Director
Office of Human Rights
441 4th Street, Northwest
Suite 570 North
Washington, DC 20001
P: (202) 727-4559
F: (202) 727-9589
E: ohr@dc.gov

FLORIDA
Hon. Pam Bondi (R)
Attorney General
Office of the Attorney General
The Capitol, PL 01
Tallahassee, FL 32399
P: (850) 414-3300
F: (954) 712-4826

GEORGIA
Mr. Gordon L. Joyner
Executive Director &
Administrator
Commission on Equal
Opportunity
Suite 1002, West Tower
2 Martin Luther King Jr. Drive
Southeast
Atlanta, GA 30334
P: (404) 657-7477
F: (404) 656-4399
E: gjoyner@gceo.state.ga.us

GUAM
Mr. Tony Lamorena
Director
Civil Service Commission
P.O. Box 1356
Hagatna, GU 98932
P: (671) 647-1855
F: (671) 647-1867

Ms. Leah Beth Naholowaa
Director
Department of Labor
Government of Guam
P.O. Box 9970
Tamuning, GU 96931
P: (671) 647-6510
F: (671) 674-6517

HAWAII
Mr. William D. Hoshijo
Executive Director
Civil Rights Commission
830 Punchbowl Street, Room
411
Honolulu, HI 96813
P: (808) 586-8636
F: (808) 586-8655
E: dlir.hcrc.infor
   @hawaii.gov

IDAHO
Ms. Pamela Parks
Director
Human Rights Commission
1109 Main Street
Owyhee Plaza, Suite 450
Boise, ID 83720
P: (208) 334-2873
F: (208) 334-2664
E: pparks@ihrc.idaho.gov

ILLINOIS
Mr. Rocco J. Claps
Director
Department of Human Rights
James R. Thompson Center
100 West Randolph Street, Suite
10-100
Chicago, IL 60601
P: (312) 814-6200
F: (312) 814-1436

INDIANA
Mr. Jamal L. Smith
Executive Director
Civil Rights Commission
100 North Senate Avenue
IGCN, Room N103
Indianapolis, IN 46204
P: (317) 232-2600
F: (317) 232-6580

IOWA
Mr. Ralph Rosenberg
Executive Director
Civil Rights Commission
Grimes State Office Building
400 East 14th Street
Des Moines, IA 50319
P: (515) 242-6537
F: (515) 242-5840
E: ralph.rosenberg@iowa.gov

KANSAS
Mr. William V. Minner
Executive Director
Human Rights Commission
900 Southwest Jackson Street
Suite 568-S
Topeka, KS 66612
P: (785) 296-3206
F: (785) 296-0589

KENTUCKY
Mr. John J. Johnson
Executive Director
Commission on Human Rights
332 West Broadway, 7th Floor
Louisville, KY 40202
P: (502) 595-4024
F: (502) 595-4801
E: john.johnson@ky.gov

LOUISIANA
Hon. James D. Caldwell (D)
Attorney General
Office of the Attorney General
1885 North 3rd Street
P.O. Box 94005
Baton Rouge, LA 70804
P: (225) 326-6705
F: (225) 326-6797
E: executive@ag.state.la.us

MAINE
Ms. Patricia E. Ryan
Executive Director
Human Rights Commission
51 State House Station
Augusta, ME 04330
P: (207) 624-6062
F: (207) 624-6063
E: Patricia.Ryan@maine.gov

Civil Rights

MARYLAND
Mr. Henry B. Ford
Executive Director
Commission on Human
Relations
William Donald Schefer Tower
6 Saint Paul Street, 9th Floor
Baltimore, MD 21202
P: (410) 767-8563
F: (410) 333-1841
E: hford
@mail.mchr.state.md.us

MASSACHUSETTS
Ms. Sunila
   Thomas-George Jr.
Commissioner
Commission Against
Discrimination
One Ashburton Place, Room 601
Boston, MA 02108
P: (617) 994-6000
F: (617) 994-6024

Mr. Julian Tynes
Commission Against
Discrimination
One Ashburton Place, Room 601
Boston, MA 02108
P: (617) 994-6000
F: (617) 994-6024

Jamie Williamson
Chair
Commission Against
Discrimination
One Ashburton Place, Room 601
Boston, MA 02108
P: (617) 994-6000
F: (617) 994-6024

MICHIGAN
Mr. Daniel Krichbaum
Director
Department of Civil Rights
Capitol Tower Building
110 West Michigan Avenue,
Suite 900
Lansing, MI 48933
P: (517) 335-3164
F: (517) 335-6513
E: krichbaumd@michigan.gov

MINNESOTA
Mr. Kevin Lindsey
Commissioner
Department of Human Rights
190 East 5th Street, Suite 700
St. Paul, MN 55101
P: (651) 296-5675
F: (651) 296-9042
E: Kevin.Lindsey
   @state.mn.us

MISSISSIPPI
Hon. Jim Hood (D)
Attorney General
Office of the Attorney General
550 High Street, Suite 1200
P.O. Box 220
Jackson, MS 39205
P: (601) 359-3680
E: msag05@ago.state.ms.us

MISSOURI
Ms. Alisa Warren
Executive Director
Commission on Human Rights
3315 West Truman Boulevard,
Room 212
P.O. Box 1129
Jefferson City, MO 65102
P: (573) 751-3325
F: (573) 751-2905
E: mchr@labor.mo.gov

MONTANA
Ms. Katherine Kountz
Bureau Chief
Human Rights Bureau
1625 11th Avenue
P.O. Box 1728
Helena, MT 59624
P: (406) 444-2884
F: (406) 444-2798
E: kkountz@mt.gov

NEBRASKA
Ms. Barbara Albers
Executive Director
Equal Opportunity Commission
301 Centennial Mall Sourth, 5th
Floor
P.O. Box 94934
Lincoln, NE 68509
P: (402) 471-2024
F: (402) 471-4059

NEVADA
Mr. Dennis Perea
Commission Administrator
Department of Employment,
Training & Rehabilitation
Equal Rights Commission
555 East Washington Avenue,
Suite 4000
Las Vegas, NV 89101
P: (702) 486-7161
F: (702) 486-7054

NEW HAMPSHIRE
Ms. Joni N. Esperian
Executive Director
Commission for Human Rights
2 Chennell Drive, #2
Concord, NH 03301
P: (603) 271-6838
F: (603) 271-6339
E: joni.esperian@nh.gov

NEW JERSEY
Mr. Chinh Q. Le
Director
Division on Civil Rights
P.O. Box 090
Trenton, NJ 08625
P: (609) 292-4605
F: (609) 984-3812

NEW MEXICO
Ms. Francie Cordova
Labor Relations Division
Director
Human Rights Bureau
Department of Labor
1596 Pacheco Street
Santa Fe, NM 87505
P: (505) 827-6838
F: (505) 827-6878

NEW YORK
Mr. Galen D. Kirkland
Commissioner
Division of Human Rights
One Fordham Plaza, 4th Floor
Bronx, NY 10458
P: (718) 741-8400

NORTH DAKOTA
Mr. Tony Weiler
Commissioner of Labor
Department of Labor
600 East Boulevard Avenue
Department 406
Bismarck, ND 58505
P: (701) 328-2660
F: (701) 328-2031
E: tjweiler@nd.gov

OHIO
Mr. G. Michael Payton
Executive Director
Civil Rights Commission
Rhodes State Office Tower
30 East Broad Street, 5th Floor
Columbus, OH 43215
P: (614) 466-2785
F: (614) 466-7742
E: paytonm@ocrc.state.oh.us

OKLAHOMA
Mr. John Carrington
Executive Director
Human Rights Commission
Jim Thorpe Building
2101 North Lincoln Boulevard,
Room 480
Oklahoma City, OK 73105
P: (405) 522-1488
F: (405) 522-3635
E: John.Carrington
   @ohrc.state.ok.us

OREGON
Ms. Amy K. Klare
Administrator
Civil Rights Bureau
800 Northeast Oregon Street
Suite 1045
Portland, OR 97232
P: (971) 673-0792
F: (503) 731-4606
E: Amy.K.Klare@state.or.us

PENNSYLVANIA
Mr. Michael Hardiman
Acting Executive Director
Human Relations Commission
Pennsylvania Place, Suite 300
301 Chestnut Street
Harrisburg, PA 17101
P: (717) 787-4412

PUERTO RICO
Mr. Lorenzo Villalba Rolon
Executive Director
Civil Rights Commission
P.O. Box 192338
San Juan, PR 00919
P: (787) 764-8686
F: (787) 250-1756

RHODE ISLAND
Mr. Michael D. Evora
Executive Director
Commission for Human Rights
180 Westminster Street, 3rd
Floor
Providence, RI 02903
P: (401) 222-2661
F: (401) 222-2616

SOUTH CAROLINA
Mr. Jesse Washington Jr.
Commissioner
Human Affairs Commission
P.O. Box 4490
2611 Forest Drive, Suite 200
Columbia, SC 29204
P: (803) 737-7800
E: jesse@schac.state.sc.us

SOUTH DAKOTA
Mr. James E. Marsh
Director
Division of Human Rights
700 Governors Drive
Pierre, SD 57501
P: (605) 773-3681
F: (605) 773-4211
E: james.marsh@state.sd.us

Ms. Pamela S. Roberts
Secretary
Department of Labor
700 Governors Drive
Pierre, SD 57501
P: (605) 773-3101
F: (605) 773-4211
E: pamela.roberts
    @state.sd.us

TENNESSEE
Ms. Beverly L. Watts
Executive Director
Human Rights Commission
710 James Robertson Parkway,
Suite 100
Corner of Rosa Parks Boulevard
Nashville, TN 37243
P: (615) 741-5825
F: (615) 253-1886

TEXAS
Mr. Timothy Braaten
Executive Director
Commission on Law
Enforcement Officer Standards
& Education
6330 East Highway 290, Suite
200
Austin, TX 78723
P: (512) 936-7700
F: (512) 936-7714
E: timothyb
    @tcleose.state.tx.us

U.S. VIRGIN ISLANDS
Mr. Lunsford Williams
Executive Director
Department of Justice
P.O. Box 6645
St. Thomas, VI 00804
P: (340) 776-2485
F: (340) 774-9710

UTAH
Ms. Heather Gunnarson
Director
Antidiscrimination & Labor
Division
160 East 300 South, 3rd Floor
P.O. Box 146630
Salt Lake City, UT 84114
P: (801) 530-6921
F: (801) 530-7609
E: hgunnarson@utah.gov

VERMONT
Mr. Robert Appel
Executive Director
Human Rights Commission
14-16 Baldwin Street
Montpelier, VT 05633
P: (802) 828-1625
F: (802) 828-2481
E: robert.appel@state.vt.us

VIRGINIA
Ms. Sandra D. Norman
Director
Human Rights Council
900 East Main Street
Pocahontas Building, 4th Floor
Richmond, VA 23219
P: (804) 225-2292
F: (804) 225-3294
E: sandra.norman
    @chr.virginia.gov

WEST VIRGINIA
Ms. Ivin B. Lee
Executive Director
Human Rights Commission
1321 Plaza East
Room 108A
Charleston, WV 25301
P: (304) 558-2616
F: (304) 558-0085
E: ivinlee@wvdhhr.org

WISCONSIN
Ms. Claire Dehnert
Division of Affirmative Action
P.O. Box 7855
Madison, WI 53707
P: (608) 267-1005
E: claire.dehnert
    @wisconsin.gov

WYOMING
Hon. Greg Phillips (D)
Attorney General
Office of the Attorney General
State Capitol Building
Cheyenne, WY 82002
P: (307) 777-7841

Clerk of the State's Highest Court

Individual who keeps records of the state's highest court.

ALABAMA
Mr. Robert G. Esdale Sr.
Clerk
Supreme Court
300 Dexter Avenue
Montgomery, AL 36104
P: (334) 229-0700

ALASKA
Ms. Marilyn May
Clerk of the Appellate Courts
Appellate Courts
303 K Street
Anchorage, AK 99501
P: (907) 264-0612
F: (907) 264-0878
E: mmay
@appellate.courts.state.ak.us

AMERICAN SAMOA
Mr. Robert Gorniak
Chief Clerk
High Court of American Samoa
American Samoa Government
Pago Pago, AS 96799
P: (684) 633-4131
F: (684) 633-1318

ARIZONA
Ms. Rachelle M. Resnick
Clerk of the Court
Supreme Court
1501 West Washington, Suite 402
Phoenix, AZ 85007
P: (602) 452-3396
E: scclerk@courts.az.gov

ARKANSAS
Mr. Leslie W. Steen
Clerk of the Courts
Supreme Court
1320 Justice Building
625 Marshall Street
Little Rock, AR 72201
P: (501) 682-6849

CALIFORNIA
Mr. Frederick K. Ohlrich
Clerk of the Court
Supreme Court
350 McAllister Street
San Francisco, CA 94102
P: (415) 865-7015

COLORADO
Ms. Susan J. Festag
Clerk of the Supreme Court
Supreme Court
2 East 14th Avenue, 4th Floor
Denver, CO 80203
P: (303) 837-3790
E: susan.festag
@judicial.state.co.us

CONNECTICUT
Ms. Michele T. Angers
Chief Clerk
Supreme Court
231 Capitol Avenue
Hartford, CT 06106
P: (860) 757-2200
F: (860) 757-2217

DELAWARE
Ms. Cathy L. Howard
Clerk of the Court
Supreme Court
Carvel State Office Building
820 North French Street, 11th Floor
Wilmington, DE 19801
P: (302) 739-4187
F: (302) 577-3702

DISTRICT OF COLUMBIA
Mr. Julio A. Castillo
Clerk of the Court
Court of Appeals
Historic Courthouse
430 E Street, Northwest
Washington, DC 20001
P: (202) 879-2725

FLORIDA
Mr. Thomas D. Hall
Clerk
Supreme Court
500 South Duval Street
Tallahassee, FL 32399
P: (850) 488-0125
E: supremecourt
@flcourts.org

GEORGIA
Ms. Therese S. Barnes
Clerk
Supreme Court
244 Washington Street
Room 572, State Office Annex Building
Atlanta, GA 30334
P: (404) 656-3470
F: (404) 656-2253

GUAM
Ms. Hannah M.
    Gutierrez-Arroyo
Supreme Court
Guam Judicial Center
120 West O'Brien Drive
Hagatna, GU 96910
P: (671) 475-3162
E: hgutierrezarroyo
@guamsupremecourt.com

HAWAII
Ms. Naomi Komenaka
Chief Clerk
Supreme Court
Aliiolani Hale
417 South King Street
Honolulu, HI 96813
P: (808) 539-4919
F: (808) 539-4928

IDAHO
Mr. Stephen W. Kenyon
Clerk of the Supreme Court
Supreme Court
P.O. Box 83720
Boise, ID 83720
P: (208) 334-2210
F: (208) 947-7590

ILLINOIS
Ms. Carolyn Taft Grosboll
Clerk of the Supreme Court
Supreme Court
Supreme Court Building
200 East Capitol
Springfield, IL 62701
P: (217) 782-2035

INDIANA
Mr. Kevin Smith
Clerk of Supreme Court, Court of Appeals & Tax Court
State Courts
200 West Washington Street
216 State House
Indianapolis, IN 46204
P: (317) 232-1930
F: (317) 232-8365

IOWA
Ms. Donna Humpal
Clerk
Supreme Court
Iowa Judicial Branch Building
1111 East Court Avenue
Des Moines, IA 50319
P: (515) 281-5911
E: Donna.Humpal
@iowacourts.gov

KANSAS
Ms. Carol Gilliam Green
Clerk of the Appellate Courts
Office of the Clerk of the Appellate Courts
Judicial Center
301 Southwest 10th Avenue, Room 374
Topeka, KS 66612
P: (785) 296-3229
F: (785) 296-1028
E: appellateclerk
@kscourts.org

KENTUCKY
Ms. Susan Stokley Clary
Clerk of the Supreme Court
Supreme Court
State Capitol
700 Capitol Avenue, Room 235
Frankfort, KY 40601
P: (502) 564-5444
F: (502) 564-2665

LOUISIANA
Mr. John Tarlton Olivier
Clerk of Court
Supreme Court
400 Royal Street, Suite 4200
New Orleans, LA 70130
P: (504) 310-2300

MAINE
Mr. Matthew Pollack
Clerk of the Law Court
Supreme Court
205 Newbury Street, Room 139
Portland, ME 04101
P: (207) 822-4146

MARYLAND
Ms. Bessie M. Decker
Clerk of Court of Appeals
Judiciary of Maryland
Robert Murphy Courts of Appeal Building
361 Rowe Boulevard
Annapolis, MD 21401
P: (410) 260-1508

MASSACHUSETTS
Ms. Susan Mellen
Clerk
Supreme Judicial Court of Commonwealth
John Adams Courthouse, Suite 1-400
One Pemberton Square
Boston, MA 02108
P: (617) 557-1020
F: (617) 557-1145

MICHIGAN
Mr. Corbin R. Davis
Clerk
Supreme Court
P.O. Box 30052
Lansing, MI 48909
P: (517) 373-0120
E: MSC_Clerk@courts.mi.gov

MINNESOTA
Mr. Frederick K. Grittner
Clerk of Appellate Courts
Supreme Court
305 Minnesota Judicial Center
25 Rev. Martin Luther King Jr.
Boulevard
St. Paul, MN 55155
P: (651) 296-2581

MISSISSIPPI
Ms. Kathy Gillis
Clerk
Supreme Court
P.O. Box 117
Jackson, MS 39205
P: (601) 359-2175
F: (601) 359-2407
E: sctclerk
@mssc.state.ms.us

MISSOURI
Mr. Thomas F. Simon
Supreme Court Clerk
Supreme Court
P. O. Box 150
Jefferson City, MO 65102
P: (573) 751-4144
F: (573) 751-7514

MONTANA
Mr. Ed Smith
Clerk
Supreme Court
215 North Sanders, Room 323
P.O. Box 203003
Helena, MT 59620
P: (406) 444-3858
F: (406) 444-5705

NEBRASKA
Ms. Lanet S. Asmussen
Clerk
Supreme Court
2413 State Capitol
P.O. Box 98910
Lincoln, NE 68509
P: (402) 471-3731
F: (402) 471-3480

NEVADA
Ms. Tracie K. Lindeman
Chief Clerk
Supreme Court
201 South Carson Street
Carson City, NV 89701
P: (775) 684-1600
F: (775) 684-1601
E: tlindeman
@nvcourts.nv.gov

NEW HAMPSHIRE
Ms. Eileen Fox
Clerk of Court
Supreme Court
Supreme Court Building
One Charles Doe Drive
Concord, NH 03301
P: (603) 271-2646
F: (603) 271-6630

NEW JERSEY
Mr. Mark Neary
Clerk
Supreme Court
Richard J. Hughes Justice
Complex
P.O. Box 970
Trenton, NJ 08625
P: (609) 292-4837

NEW MEXICO
Ms. Kathleen Jo Gibson
Chief Clerk
Supreme Court
237 Don Gaspar Avenue
Santa Fe, NM 87501
P: (505) 827-4860
F: (505) 827-4837

NEW YORK
Mr. Andrew Klein
Clerk of the Court
Court of Appeals
20 Eagle Street
Albany, NY 12207
P: (518) 455-7700
F: (518) 463-6869

NORTH CAROLINA
Ms. Christie Speir Cameron
Clerk
Supreme Court
Clerk's Office
2 East Morgan Street, P.O. Box
2170
Raleigh, NC 27602
P: (919) 831-5700

NORTH DAKOTA
Ms. Penny Miller
Clerk of Supreme Court
Supreme Court
State Capitol
600 East Boulevard Avenue
Bismarck, ND 58505
P: (701) 328-2221
F: (701) 328-4480
E: PMiller@ndcourts.gov

**NORTHERN MARIANA
ISLANDS**
Mr. Chris Kaipat
Clerk
Supreme Court
P.O. Box 502165
Saipan, MP 96950
P: (670) 236-9700
F: (670) 236-9702
E: supreme.court@saipan.com

OHIO
Ms. Kristina D. Frost
Clerk of the Court
Supreme Court
65 South Front Street, 8th Floor
Columbus, OH 43215
P: (614) 387-9530
F: (614) 387-9539

OKLAHOMA
Mr. Michael S. Richie
Supreme Court Clerk
Supreme Court
P.O. Box 53126
Oklahoma City, OK 73152
P: (405) 521-2163

OREGON
Ms. Kingsley W. Click
State Court Administrator
Judicial Department
Supreme Court Building
1163 State Street
Salem, OR 97301
P: (503) 986-5500
F: (503) 986-5503
E: kingsley.w.click
@state.or.us

PENNSYLVANIA
Ms. Patricia Johnson
Chief Clerk
Supreme Court
468 City Hall
Philadelphia, PA 19107
P: (215) 560-6370

Ms. Patricia A. Niccola
Chief Clerk
Supreme Court
801 City-County Building
Pittsburgh, PA 15219
P: (412) 565-2816

Ms. Elizabeth Zisk
Chief Clerk
Supreme Court
601 Commonwealth Avenue,
Suite 4500
P.O. Box 62575
Harrisburg, PA 17106
P: (717) 787-6181

PUERTO RICO
Ms. Patricia Oton Oliveri
Secretary of Supreme Court
Supreme Court
P.O. Box 9022392
San Juan, PR 00902
P: (787) 723-6033
F: (787) 723-9199

RHODE ISLAND
Ms. Debra A. Saunders
Supreme Court Clerk
Supreme Court
Frank Licht Judicial Complex
250 Benefit Street
Providence, RI 02903
P: (401) 222-3599

SOUTH CAROLINA
Mr. Daniel E. Shearouse
Clerk of Court
Supreme Court
1231 Gervais Street
P.O. Box 11330
Columbia, SC 29211
P: (803) 734-1080
F: (803) 734-1499

SOUTH DAKOTA
Ms. Shirley A.
Jameson-Fergel
Clerk
Supreme Court
500 East Capitol Avenue
Pierre, SD 57501
P: (605) 773-3511
F: (605) 773-6128

TENNESSEE
Mr. Mike Catalano
Appellate Court Clerk
Appellate Courts
Supreme Court Building
401 7th Avenue, North
Nashville, TN 37219
P: (615) 741-2681
F: (615) 532-8757

Clerk of the State's Highest Court

TEXAS
Mr. Blake A. Hawthorne
Clerk of the Court
Supreme Court
Supreme Court Building-A
P.O. Box 12248
Austin, TX 78711
P: (512) 463-1312
F: (512) 463-1365

U.S. VIRGIN ISLANDS
Ms. Veronica J. Handy
Clerk of the Court
Supreme Court
P.O. Box 590
St. Thomas, VI 00804
P: (340) 774-2237
F: (340) 774-2258

UTAH
Ms. Pat H. Bartholomew
Clerk of Court
Supreme Court
450 South State Street, 5th Floor
P.O. Box 140210
Salt Lake City, UT 84114
P: (801) 238-7974
F: (801) 238-7980
E: pathb@email.utcourts.gov

VERMONT
Mr. Robert Greemore
Court Administrator and Clerk
Supreme Court
109 State Street
Montpelier, VT 05609
P: (802) 828-3278
F: (802) 828-4750
E: bob.greemore@state.vt.us

VIRGINIA
Ms. Patricia L. Harrington
Clerk
Supreme Court
100 North 9th Street, 5th Floor
Richmond, VA 23219
P: (804) 786-2251

WASHINGTON
Mr. Ronald R. Carpenter
Clerk
Supreme Court
415 12th Avenue, Southwest
P.O. Box 40929
Olympia, WA 98504
P: (360) 357-2077
F: (360) 357-2102
E: supreme@courts.wa.gov

WEST VIRGINIA
Mr. Rory L. Perry II
Clerk of Court
Supreme Court of Appeals
State Capitol, Room E-317
Charleston, WV 25305
P: (304) 558-2601
F: (304) 558-3815

WISCONSIN
Mr. A. John Voelker
Director of State Courts/Acting
Clerk
Supreme Court
16 East State Capitol
P.O. Box 1688
Madison, WI 53701
P: (608) 266-6828
F: (608) 267-0980
E: john.voelker
  @courts.state.wi.us

WYOMING
Ms. Judy Pacheco
Clerk of Court
Supreme Court
2301 Capitol Avenue
Cheyenne, WY 82001
P: (307) 777-7316
F: (307) 777-6129
E: jpacheco
  @courts.state.wy.us

Commerce

Umbrella agency of commerce responsible for the overall regulation and growth of the state's economy.

ALABAMA
Mr. Seth Hammett
Director
Development Office
401 Adams Avenue, 6th Floor
Montgomery, AL 36130
P: (334) 242-0400
F: (334) 242-5669
E: seth.hammett
    @ado.alabama.gov

ALASKA
Ms. Susan K. Bell
Commissioner
Department of Commerce,
Community & Economic
Development
P.O. Box 110800
Juneau, AK 99811
P: (907) 465-2500
F: (907) 465-5442
E: susan.bell@alaska.gov

AMERICAN SAMOA
Mr. Faleseu Eliu Paopao
Director
Department of Commerce
American Samoa Government
Executive Office Building,
Utulei
Pago Pago, AS 96799
P: (684) 633-5155
F: (684) 633-4195

ARIZONA
Mr. Donald E. Cardon
President & CEO
Commerce Authority
1110 West Washington Street,
Suite 600
Phoenix, AZ 85007
P: (602) 771-1160
F: (602) 771-1200
E: commerce@azcommerce.com

ARKANSAS
Ms. Maria Haley
Executive Director
Economic Development
Commission
#1 Capitol Mall, 4C-300
Little Rock, AR 72201
P: (501) 682-2052
F: (501) 682-7394
E: mhaley@1800Arkansas.gov

CALIFORNIA
Ms. Traci Stevens
Acting Undersecretary
Business, Transportation &
Housing Agency
980 9th Street, Suite 2450
Sacramento, CA 95814
F: (916) 323-5440

COLORADO
Mr. Dwayne Romero
Director
Office of Economic
Development & International
Trade
1625 Broadway, Suite 2700
Denver, CO 80202
P: (303) 892-3840
F: (303) 892-3848
E: dwayne.romero
    @state.co.us

CONNECTICUT
Ms. Marie C. O'Brien
President
Connecticut Development
Authority
999 West Street
Rocky Hill, CT 06067
P: (860) 258-7811
F: (860) 257-8331
E: cdainfo@po.state.ct.us

DISTRICT OF COLUMBIA
Mr. Victor L. Hoskins
Deputy Mayor for Planning and
Economic Development
Office of the Deputy Mayor for
Planning & Economic
Development
John A. Wilson Building, Suite
317
1350 Pennsylvania Avenue,
Northwest
Washington, DC 20004
P: (202) 727-6365
F: (202) 727-6703
E: dmped.eom@dc.gov

FLORIDA
Chris Hart
Director
Office of Tourism, Trade &
Economic Development
Office of the Governor
The Capitol, Suite 2001
Tallahassee, FL 32399
P: (850) 487-2568
F: (850) 487-3014
E: chris.hart
    @eog.myflorida.com

GEORGIA
Mr. Chris Cummiskey
Commissioner
Department of Economic
Development
75 Fifth Street, Northwest
Suite 1200
Atlanta, GA 30308
P: (404) 962-4003
F: (404) 962-4009
E: ccummiskey@geogia.org

HAWAII
Ms. Keali'i S. Lopez
Director
Department of Commerce &
Consumer Affairs
King Kalakaua Building
335 Merchant Street
Honolulu, HI 96813
P: (808) 586-2850
F: (808) 586-2856
E: dcca@dcca.hawaii.gov

IDAHO
Mr. Donald A. Dietrich
Director
Department of Commerce
700 West State Street
P.O. Box 83720
Boise, ID 83720
P: (208) 334-2470
F: (208) 334-2631
E: don.dietrich
    @commerce.idaho.gov

ILLINOIS
Mr. Warren Ribley
Director
Department of Commerce &
Economic Opportunity
James R. Thompson Center
100 West Randolph
Chicago, IL 60601
P: (312) 814-7179

INDIANA
Mr. E. Mitch Roob Jr.
Chief Executive Officer &
Secretary of Commerce
Economic Development
Corporation
One North Capitol Avenue,
Suite 700
Indianapolis, IN 46204
P: (317) 232-8992
F: (317) 233-5123
E: mroob@iedc.in.gov

IOWA
Mr. James M. Schipper
Superintendent
Division of Banking
200 East Grand Avenue, Suite
300
Des Moines, IA 50309
P: (515) 281-4014
F: (515) 281-4862
E: jschipper
    @idob.state.ia.us

KANSAS
Mr. Pat George
Secretary
Department of Commerce
1000 Southwest Jackson Street,
Suite 100
Topeka, KS 66612
P: (785) 296-3481
F: (785) 296-5055
E: pgeorge
    @kansascommerce.com

KENTUCKY
Ms. Marcheta Sparrow
Secretary
Tourism, Arts & Heritage
Cabinet
24th Floor, Capital Plaza Tower
500 Mero Street
Frankfort, KY 40601
P: (502) 564-4270
F: (502) 564-1512

LOUISIANA
Mr. Stephen Moret
Secretary
Economic Development
1051 North Third Street
Baton Rouge, LA 70802
P: (225) 342-5388
F: (225) 342-9095
E: Allison.Gilmore@la.gov

MAINE
Mr. George Gervais
Acting Commissioner
Department of Economic &
Community Development
59 State House Station
Augusta, ME 04330
P: (207) 624-9800

MARYLAND
Mr. Christian Johansson
Secretary
Department of Business &
Economic Development
401 East Pratt Street
Baltimore, MD 21202
P: (410) 767-6301
F: (410) 767-8628
E: CJohansson
    @choosemaryland.org

Commerce

MICHIGAN
Mr. Steven Hilfinger
Director
Department of Licensing &
Regulatory Affairs
P.O. Box 30004
Lansing, MI 48909
P: (517) 373-1820
F: (517) 373-2129
E: bcslic@michigan.gov

Mr. Andrew S. Levin
Acting Director
Department of Energy, Labor &
Economic Growth
P.O. Box 30004
Lansing, MI 48909
P: (517) 373-7230
F: (517) 373-2129
E: LevinA@michigan.gov

MINNESOTA
Mr. Mike Rothman
Commissioner of Commerce
Department of Commerce
85 7th Place East, Suite 500
St. Paul, MN 55101
P: (651) 296-6025
F: (651) 297-1959
E: commerce.commissioner
   @state.mn.us

MISSISSIPPI
Dr. Lester Spell Jr.
Commissioner
Department of Agriculture &
Commerce
P.O. Box 1609
Jackson, MS 39201
P: (601) 359-1100
F: (601) 354-6290

MISSOURI
Mr. David Kerr
Director
Department of Economic
Development
301 West High Street
P.O. Box 1157
Jefferson City, MO 65102
P: (573) 751-4962
F: (573) 526-7700
E: ecodev@ded.mo.gov

MONTANA
Mr. Dore Schwinden
Director
Department of Commerce
301 South Park
P.O. Box 200501
Helena, MT 59620
P: (406) 841-2704
F: (406) 841-2701
E: dschwinden@mt.gov

NEBRASKA
Mr. Richard Baier
Director
Department of Economic
Development
P.O. Box 94666
Lincoln, NE 68509
P: (402) 471-3111
F: (402) 471-3778
E: richard.baier
   @nebraska.gov

NEVADA
Mr. Terry Johnson
Director
Department of Business &
Industry
555 East Washington Avenue,
Suite 4900
Las Vegas, NV 89101
P: (775) 684-2570
F: (702) 486-2758
E: TerryJohnson
   @business.nv.gov

NEW HAMPSHIRE
Mr. George Bald
Commissioner
Department of Resources &
Economic Development
172 Pembroke Road
P.O. Box 1856
Concord, NH 03302
P: (603) 271-2411
F: (603) 271-2629
E: gbald@dred.state.nh.us

NEW JERSEY
Mr. Mike Chrobak
Chief Economic Development
Officer
Economic Development Bank
Choose New Jersey
134 East Munsell Avenue
Linden, NJ 07036
P: (512) 789-8131
E: Mike@Chrobak.com

Ms. Caren S. Franzini
Chief Executive Officer
Economic Development
Authority
36 West State Street
P.O. Box 990
Trenton, NJ 08625
P: (609) 292-1800
F: (609) 292-0885
E: njeda@njeda.com

NEW YORK
Mr. Kenneth Adams
President & CEO
Empire State Development
Corporation
633 Third Avenue
New York, NY 10017
P: (212) 803-3700
F: (212) 803-3715

NORTH CAROLINA
Mr. J. Keith Crisco
Secretary of Commerce
Department of Commerce
4301 Mail Service Center
Raleigh, NC 27699
P: (919) 733-4151
E: kcrisco@nccommerce.com

NORTH DAKOTA
Mr. Al Anderson
Commissioner
Department of Commerce
1600 East Century Avenue,
Suite 2
P.O. Box 2057
Bismarck, ND 58503
P: (701) 328-7284
F: (701) 328-5320
E: alrandeson@nd.gov

**NORTHERN MARIANA
ISLANDS**
Mr. Sixto Igisomar
Acting Secretary
Department of Commerce
Caller Box 10007
Saipan, MP 96950
P: (670) 664-3064
F: (670) 664-3067

OHIO
Mr. David Goodman
Director
Department of Commerce
77 South High Street, 23rd Floor
Columbus, OH 43266
P: (614) 466-3636
F: (614) 752-5078
E: Directorsoffice
   @com.state.oh.us

OKLAHOMA
Mr. Dave Lopez
Secretary of Commerce &
Tourism
Department of Commerce
900 North Stiles Avenue
Oklahoma City, OK 73104
P: (405) 815-6552

OREGON
Mr. Tim McCabe
Director
Business Oregon
775 Summer Street, Northeast,
Suite 200
Salem, OR 97301
P: (503) 986-0110
F: (503) 581-5115
E: tim.mccabe@state.or.us

PENNSYLVANIA
Mr. C. Alan Walker
Acting Secretary
Department of Community &
Economic Development
Commonwealth Keystone
Building
400 North Street, 4th Floor
Harrisburg, PA 17120
P: (866) 466-3972
F: (717) 787-6866

PUERTO RICO
Mr. Jose R. Perez Riera
Executive Director
Industrial Development
Company
#355 FD Roosevelt Avenue
Suite 404
Hato Rey, PR 00918
P: (787) 758-4747
F: (787) 764-1415

RHODE ISLAND
Mr. Paul McGreevy
Director
Department of Business
Regulation
1511 Pontiac Avenue
Cranston, RI 02920
P: (401) 462-9500
F: (401) 462-9532
E: pmcgreevy@dbr.ri.gov

SOUTH CAROLINA
Mr. Robert M. Hitt III
Secretary
Department of Commerce
1201 Main Street, Suite 1600
Columbia, SC 29201
P: (803) 737-0400
F: (803) 737-0418

SOUTH DAKOTA
Mr. Pat Costello
Commissioner
Governor's Office of Economic
Development
711 East Wells Avenue
Pierre, SD 57501
P: (605) 773-3301
F: (605) 773-3256
E: goedinfo@state.sd.us

TENNESSEE
Ms. Julie Mix McPeak
Commissioner
Department of Commerce
500 James Robertson Parkway
Davy Crockett Tower
Nashville, TN 37243
P: (615) 741-2176
F: (615) 532-6934
E: ask.tdci@tn.gov

U.S. VIRGIN ISLANDS
Ms. Beverly Nicholson Doty
Commissioner
Department of Tourism
Elainco Building
78 Contant 1-2-3
St. Thomas, VI 00802
P: (340) 774-8784
F: (340) 774-4390

UTAH
Ms. Francine A. Giani
Executive Director
Department of Commerce
160 East 300 South, 2nd Floor
P.O. Box 146701
Salt Lake City, UT 84114
P: (801) 530-6431
F: (801) 530-6446
E: fgiani@utah.gov

VERMONT
Mr. Lawrence Miller
Secretary
Agency of Commerce &
Community Development
National Life Building North
Drawer 20
Montpelier, VT 05620
P: (802) 828-3211
F: (802) 828-3383
E: lawrence.miller
    @state.vt.us

VIRGINIA
Mr. James Cheng
Secretary
Office of Commerce & Trade
1111 East Broad Street
Patrick Henry Building
Richmond, VA 23219
P: (804) 786-7831
F: (804) 371-0250
E: jim.cheng
    @governor.virginia.gov

WASHINGTON
Mr. Rogers Weed
Director
Department of Commerce
128 10th Avenue, Southwest
P.O. Box 42525
Olympia, WA 98504
P: (360) 725-4000
F: (360) 586-8440
E: rogersw@cted.wa.gov

WEST VIRGINIA
Mr. J. Keith Burdette
Secretary of Commerce
Department of Commerce
Capitol Complex Building 6,
Room 525
1900 Kanawha Boulevard East
Charleston, WV 25305
P: (304) 558-2234
F: (304) 558-1189
E: J.Keith.Burdette@wv.gov

WISCONSIN
Mr. Paul Jadin
Secretary
Department of Commerce
123 West Washington
P.O. Box 7970
Madison, WI 53707
P: (608) 266-7088
E: Paul.Jadin@wisconsin.gov

WYOMING
Mr. Bob Jensen
Chief Executive Officer
Business Council
214 West 15th Street
Cheyenne, WY 82002
P: (307) 777-2800
F: (307) 777-2837
E: bob.jensen
    @wybusiness.org

Comptroller

The principal accounting and dispersing officer of the state.

Information provided by:

National Association of State Auditors, Comptrollers & Treasurers
Kinney Poynter
Executive Director
449 Lewis Hargett Circle
Suite 290
Lexington, KY 40503
P: (859) 276-1147
F: (859) 278-0507
kpoynter@nasact.org
www.nasact.org

ALABAMA
Mr. Thomas White
State Comptroller
Office of the State Comptroller
100 North Union Street, Suite 220
Montgomery, AL 36104
P: (334) 242-7063
F: (334) 242-7466
E: tom.white
@comptroller.alabama.gov

ALASKA
Ms. Kim Garnero
Director
Division of Finance
Department of Administration
P.O. Box 110204
Juneau, AK 99811
P: (907) 465-3435
F: (907) 465-2169
E: kim.garnero@alaska.gov

ARIZONA
Mr. D. Clark Partridge
State Comptroller
General Accounting Office
100 North 15th Avenue, Suite 302
Phoenix, AZ 85007
P: (602) 542-8168
F: (602) 542-3093
E: clark.partridge
@azdoa.gov

ARKANSAS
Hon. Charlie Daniels (D)
Auditor of State
Office of the State Auditor
P.O. Box 251906
Little Rock, AR 72201
P: (501) 371-2124
F: (501) 682-6005
E: lisar@arauditor.com

Mr. Richard Weiss
Administrator
Department of Finance & Administration
P.O. Box 2485
Little Rock, AR 72203
P: (501) 682-2242
F: (501) 682-1029
E: richard.weiss
@dfa.state.ar.us

CALIFORNIA
Hon. John Chiang (D)
State Controller
Office of the State Controller
300 Capitol Mall, Suite 1850
Sacramento, CA 94250
P: (916) 445-2636
F: (916) 445-6379
E: john@sco.ca.gov

Mr. Fred Klass
Chief Operating Officer
Department of Finance
State Capitol, Room 1145
Sacramento, CA 95814
P: (916) 445-4923
F: (916) 445-7997
E: david.botelho@dof.ca.gov

COLORADO
Mr. David James McDermott
State Controller
Department of Personnel & Administration
633 17th Street, Suite 1500
Denver, CO 80202
P: (303) 866-2739
F: (303) 866-4233
E: david.mcdermott
@state.co.us

CONNECTICUT
Mr. Kevin Lembo
Comptroller
Office of the Comptroller
55 Elm Street, Suite 307
Hartford, CT 06106
P: (860) 702-3301
F: (860) 702-3319
E: Kevin.Lembo
@po.state.ct.us

DELAWARE
Mr. Thomas J. Cook
Secretary of Finance
Department of Finance
Carvel State Building, 8th Floor
820 North French Street
Wilmington, DE 19801
P: (302) 577-8984
F: (302) 577-8982
E: tom.cook@state.de.us

DISTRICT OF COLUMBIA
Mr. Anthony Pompa
(appointed)
Deputy Chief Financial Officer
Office of Financial Operations & Systems
Office of the Chief Financial Officer
1100 4th Street Southwest, 8th Floor
Washington, DC 20024
P: (202) 442-8200
F: (202) 442-8201
E: anthony.pompa@dc.gov

FLORIDA
Hon. Jeffrey H. Atwater (R)
Chief Financial Officer
Department of Financial Services
PL-11, The Capitol
Tallahassee, FL 32399
P: (850) 413-2907
F: (850) 413-2950
E: allison@jeffatwater.com

GEORGIA
Mr. Greg S. Griffin
State Accounting Officer
State Accounting Office
200 Piedmont Avenue, Suite 1604 West
Atlanta, GA 30334
P: (404) 651-7392
F: (404) 463-5089
E: ggriffin@sao.ga.gov

GUAM
Ms. Lourdes M. Perez
Director
Department of Administration
P.O. Box 884
Hagatna, GU 96932
P: (671) 475-1122
F: (671) 475-1243
E: lou.perez@doa.guam.gov

HAWAII
Mr. Bruce Coppa
State Comptroller
Department of Accounting & General Services
P.O. Box 119
Honolulu, HI 96810
P: (808) 586-0400
F: (808) 586-0775
E: bruce.a.coppa@hawaii.gov

IDAHO
Hon. Donna Jones (R)
State Controller
Office of the State Controller
700 West State Street
P.O. Box 83720
Boise, ID 83720
P: (208) 334-3100
F: (208) 334-2671
E: djones@sco.idaho.gov

ILLINOIS
Hon. Judy Baar Topinka (R)
State Comptroller
Office of the State Comptroller
201 State Capitol Building
Springfield, IL 62706
P: (217) 782-6000
F: (217) 782-7561
E: stevebe
@mail.ioc.state.il.us

INDIANA
Hon. Tim Berry (R)
Auditor of State
Office of the Auditor of State
State House, Room 240
200 West Washington Street
Indianapolis, IN 46204
P: (317) 232-3300
F: (317) 233-2794
E: tberry@auditor.in.gov

IOWA
Mr. Calvin McKelvogue
Chief Operating Officer
Department of Administrative Services
State Accounting Enterprise
Hoover State Office Building, 3rd Floor
Des Moines, IA 50319
P: (515) 281-4877
F: (515) 281-5255
E: calvin.mckelvogue
@iowa.gov

KANSAS
Mr. Kent Olson
Director
Division of Accounts & Reports
900 Southwest Jackson Street
Room 351-S
Topeka, KS 66612
P: (785) 296-2318
F: (785) 296-6841
E: kent.olson@da.ks.gov

KENTUCKY
Mr. Edgar C. Ross
Controller
Office of the Controller
Room 384, Capitol Annex
702 Capitol Avenue
Frankfort, KY 40601
P: (502) 564-2210
F: (502) 564-6597
E: edc.ross@ky.gov

LOUISIANA
Mr. Afranie Adomako
Director
Office of Statewide Reporting &
Accounting Policy
Division of Administration
P.O. Box 94095
Baton Rouge, LA 70804
P: (225) 342-6322
F: (225) 342-1053
E: afranie.adomako@la.gov

MAINE
Mr. Terry Brann
State Controller
Office of the State Controller
Station 14, 4th Floor, Cross
Building
Augusta, ME 04353
P: (207) 626-8420
F: (207) 626-8422
E: terry.brann@maine.gov

MARYLAND
Hon. Peter Franchot (D)
Comptroller
Office of the Comptroller
L.L. Goldstein Treasury
Building
P.O. Box 466
Annapolis, MD 21404
P: (410) 260-7801
F: (410) 974-3808
E: pfrachot
   @comp.state.md.us

MASSACHUSETTS
Mr. Martin J. Benison
Comptroller
Office of the Comptroller
Onc Ashburton Place, Suite 901
Boston, MA 02108
P: (617) 973-2315
F: (617) 727-2163
E: martin.benison
   @state.ma.us

MICHIGAN
Mr. Michael J. Moody
Director
Office of Financial Management
Department of Management and
Budget
111 South Capitol Avenue
Lansing, MI 48913
P: (517) 335-1942
F: (517) 373-6458
E: moodym1@michigan.gov

MINNESOTA
Mr. Jim Schowalter
Commissioner
Management & Budget
658 Cedar Street, Suite 400
St. Paul, MN 55155
P: (651) 201-8010
F: (651) 296-7714
E: James.Schowalter
   @state.mn.us

MISSISSIPPI
Ms. Leila Malatesta
Director of Fiscal Management
Department of Finance &
Administration
501 North West Street
1301 Woolfolk Building
Jackson, MS 39201
P: (601) 359-3402
F: (601) 359-2405
E: malatel@dfa.state.ms.us

MISSOURI
Mr. Mark A. Kaiser
Director, Division of Accounting
Office of Administration
Truman State Office Building,
Room 570
P.O. Box 809
Jefferson City, MO 65102
P: (573) 751-4013
F: (573) 526-9810
E: mark.a.kaiser@oa.mo.gov

MONTANA
Mr. Paul Christofferson
Administrator
State Accounting Division
Mitchell Building, Room 255
P.O. Box 200102
Helena, MT 59620
P: (406) 444-4609
F: (406) 444-2812
E: pachristofferson@mt.gov

NEBRASKA
Mr. Michael Keays
State Accounting Administrator
Department of Administrative
Services
Room 1309, State Capitol
P.O. Box 94664
Lincoln, NE 68509
P: (402) 471-0600
F: (402) 471-2583
E: michael.keays
   @nebraska.gov

NEVADA
Hon. Kim R. Wallin (D)
State Controller
Office of the State Controller
101 North Carson Street, Suite 5
State Capitol
Carson City, NV 89701
P: (775) 684-5632
F: (775) 684-5696
E: kwallin
   @controller.state.nv.us

NEW HAMPSHIRE
Mr. Edgar Carter
State Comptroller
Department of Administrative
Services
State House Annex, Room 310
25 Capitol Street
Concord, NH 03301
P: (603) 271-6566
F: (603) 271-6666
E: edgar.carter@nh.gov

NEW JERSEY
Ms. Charlene Holzbaur
State Comptroller
Office of Management &
Budget
33 West State Street
P.O. Box 221
Trenton, NJ 08625
P: (609) 292-6746
F: (609) 633-8179
E: charlene.holzbaur
   @treas.state.nj.us

NEW MEXICO
Mr. Anthony Armijo
State Controller & Director
Financial Control Division,
Department of Finance &
Administration
Bataan Memorial Building,
Suite 166
407 Galisteo Street
Santa Fe, NM 87501
P: (505) 827-3681
F: (505) 827-3692
E: aiacpa@state.nm.us

NEW YORK
Hon. Thomas P. DiNapoli (D)
Comptroller
Office of the State Comptroller
633 3rd Avenue, 21st Floor
New York, NY 10017
P: (518) 474-4040
F: (518) 474-3004
E: tdinapoli
   @osc.state.ny.us

Ms. Joan Sullivan
Executive Deputy Comptroller
for Operations
Office of the State Comptroller
633 3rd Avenue, 21st Floor
New York, NY 10017
P: (518) 474-4040
F: (518) 474-3004
E: jsullivan
   @osc.state.ny.us

NORTH CAROLINA
Mr. David McCoy
State Controller
Office of the State Controller
1410 Mail Service Center
3512 Bush Street
Raleigh, NC 27699
P: (919) 981-5406
F: (919) 981-5567
E: david.mccoy@osc.nc.gov

NORTH DAKOTA
Ms. Pam Sharp
Director
Office of Management &
Budget
600 East Boulevard Avenue
Department 110
Bismarck, ND 58505
P: (701) 328-2680
F: (701) 328-3230
E: psharp@nd.gov

**NORTHERN MARIANA
ISLANDS**
Ms. Connie Agulto
Acting Secretary of Finance
Department of Finance
P.O. Box 5234 CHRB
Saipan, MP 96950
P: (670) 664-1100
F: (670) 664-1115

OHIO
Mr. Timothy S. Keen
Director
Office of Budget &
Management
30 East Broad Street, 34th Floor
Columbus, OH 43215
P: (614) 466-4034
F: (614) 466-3813
E: tim.keen@obm.state.oh.us

Comptroller

OKLAHOMA
Ms. Brenda Bolander
State Controller
Division of Central Accounting
& Reporting
2300 North Lincoln Boulevard,
Room 122
State Capitol Building
Oklahoma City, OK 73105
P: (405) 521-2141
F: (405) 521-3902
E: brenda.bolander
 @osf.ok.gov

OREGON
Mr. John J. Radford
State Controller
State Controller's Division
155 Cottage Street, Northeast
Salem, OR 97301
P: (503) 378-3156
F: (503) 378-3514
E: john.j.radford
 @state.or.us

PENNSYLVANIA
Ms. Anna Maria Kiehl
Chief Accounting Officer
Office of Comptroller
Operations
Governor's Office of Budget
6th Floor, Verizon Tower
Harrisburg, PA 17101
P: (717) 787-6496
F: (717) 787-3376
E: akiehl@state.pa.us

PUERTO RICO
Ms. Migdalia Mendez
Audit Associate Director
Office of Budget &
Management
Office of the Governor
254 Cruz Street, Box 9023228
San Juan, PR 00936
P: (809) 977-9200
F: (809) 977-3790
E: mbonilla@ogp.gobierno.pr

Yesmin Valdivieso-Galib
Comptroller
Office of the Comptroller
P.O. Box 366069
San Juan, PR 00963
P: (787) 250-3300
F: (787) 751-6768
E: ocpr@ocpr.gov.pr

RHODE ISLAND
Mr. Marc Leonetti
State Controller
Office of Accounts & Control
Department of Administration
One Capitol Hill
Providence, RI 02908
P: (401) 222-6731
F: (401) 222-6437
E: mleonetti@doa.ri.gov

SOUTH CAROLINA
Hon. Richard Eckstrom (R)
Comptroller General
Office of the Comptroller
General
305 Wade Hampton Office
Building
1200 Senate Street
Columbia, SC 29201
P: (803) 734-2588
F: (803) 734-2064
E: reckstrom@cg.sc.gov

SOUTH DAKOTA
Hon. Steve Barnett (R)
State Auditor
Office of the State Auditor
State Capitol Building
500 East Capitol
Pierre, SD 57501
P: (605) 773-3341
F: (605) 773-5929
E: steve.barnett
 @state.sd.us

Mr. Jason Dilges
Commissioner
Bureau of Finance &
Management
500 East Capitol Avenue
Pierre, SD 57501
P: (605) 773-3411
F: (605) 773-4711
E: jason.dilges@state.sd.us

TENNESSEE
Ms. Jan I. Sylvis
Chief of Accounts
Department of Finance &
Administration
312 Rosa Parks Avenue, Suite
2100
Nashville, TN 37243
P: (615) 741-2382
F: (615) 532-8532
E: jan.sylvis@tn.gov

TEXAS
Ms. Susan Combs
Comptroller of Public Accounts
Office of the Comptroller of
Public Accounts
111 East 17th
P.O.Box 13528
Austin, TX 78711
P: (512) 463-4444
F: (512) 463-4965
E: susan.combs
 @cpa.state.tx.us

U.S. VIRGIN ISLANDS
Ms. Debra Gottlieb
 (appointed)
Director
Office of Management &
Budget
#41 Norre Gade
Emancipation Garden Station,
2nd Floor
St. Thomas, VI 00802
P: (340) 776-0750
F: (340) 776-0069
E: debra.gottlieb
 @omb.vi.gov

UTAH
Mr. John Reidhead
Director
Division of Finance
2110 State Office Building
450 North State Street
Salt Lake City, UT 84114
P: (801) 538-3020
F: (801) 538-3244
E: jreidhead@utah.gov

VERMONT
Mr. James B. Reardon
Commissioner
Department of Finance &
Management
109 State Street
Montpelier, VT 05602
P: (802) 828-2376
F: (802) 828-2428
E: jim.reardon@state.vt.us

VIRGINIA
Mr. David Von Moll
State Comptroller
Department of Accounts
101 North 14th Street
P. O. Box 1971
Richmond, VA 23219
P: (804) 225-3038
F: (804) 371-8587
E: david.vonmoll
 @doa.virginia.gov

WEST VIRGINIA
Hon. Glen B. Gainer III (D)
State Auditor
Office of the State Auditor
Building 1, Room W-100
State Capitol Complex
Charleston, WV 25305
P: (304) 558-2251
F: (304) 558-5200
E: glen.gainer@wvsao.gov

Mr. Ross Taylor
State Comptroller & Director
Finance Division
Department of Administration
2101 Washington Street East,
Building 17
Charleston, WV 25305
P: (304) 558-4250
F: (304) 558-1950
E: ross.a.taylor@wv.gov

WISCONSIN
Mr. Stephen J. Censky
State Controller
Department of Administration
101 East Wilson Street, 5th
Floor
P.O. Box 7932
Madison, WI 53707
P: (608) 266-8158
F: (608) 266-7734
E: steve.censky
 @wisconsin.gov

WYOMING
Hon. Cynthia Cloud (R)
State Auditor
Office of the State Auditor
200 West 24th Street
Cheyenne, WY 82002
P: (307) 777-7831
F: (307) 777-6983
E: cynthia.cloud
 @state.wy.us

Consumer Protection

Investigates consumer complaints, develops consumer education programs and alerts citizens to current consumer concerns within the state.

ALABAMA
Hon. Luther Strange (R)
Attorney General
Office of the Attorney General
500 Dexter Avenue
Montgomery, AL 36130
P: (334) 242-7300

ALASKA
Ms. Signe Andersen
Chief Assistant Attorney General
Fair Business Practices
Department of Law
1031 West 4th Avenue, Suite 200
Anchorage, AK 99501
P: (907) 269-5200
F: (907) 276-8554
E: signe.andersen
   @alaska.gov

AMERICAN SAMOA
Mr. Faleseu Eliu Paopao
Director
Department of Commerce
American Samoa Government
Executive Office Building,
Utulei
Pago Pago, AS 96799
P: (684) 633-5155
F: (684) 633-4195

Hon. Fepulea'i A.
   Ripley Jr.
Attorney General
Office of the Attorney General
American Samoa Government
Executive Office Building,
Utulei
Pago Pago, AS 96799
P: (684) 633-4163
F: (684) 633-1838

ARIZONA
Mr. Dena Epstein
Chief Counsel
Consumer Protection &
Advocacy
Office of the Attorney General
1275 West Washington Street
Phoenix, AZ 85007
P: (602) 542-3702
E: consumerinfo@azag.gov

ARKANSAS
Hon. Dustin McDaniel (D)
Attorney General
Office of the Attorney General
323 Center Street, Suite 200
Little Rock, AR 72201
P: 501) 682-2341
F: (501) 682-8084

CALIFORNIA
Ms. Melissa Wiekel
Manager
Public Inquiry Unit
Department of Justice
P.O. Box 944255
Sacramento, CA 94244
P: (916) 322-3360

COLORADO
Ms. Janet Zavislan
Director
Consumer Protection Division
Department of Law
1525 Sherman Street, 5th Floor
Denver, CO 80203
P: (303) 866-5076
F: (303) 866-5443
E: jan.zavislan@state.co.us

CONNECTICUT
Mr. William M. Rubenstein
Commissioner
Department of Consumer
Protection
165 Capitol Avenue
Hartford, CT 06106
P: (860) 713-6050
F: (860) 713-7243
E: william.rubenstein
   @ct.gov

DELAWARE
Mr. Timothy Mullaney
Director
Fraud & Consumer Protection
Division
Carvel State Office Building
820 North French Street
Wilmington, DE 19801
P: (302) 577-8600
F: (302) 577-6499

DISTRICT OF COLUMBIA
Mr. Nicholas A. Majett
Director
Department of Consumer &
Regulatory Affairs
1100 4th Street, Southwest
Washington, DC 20024
P: (202) 442-4400
F: (202) 442-9445
E: dcra@dc.gov

FLORIDA
Hon. Pam Bondi (R)
Attorney General
Office of the Attorney General
The Capitol, PL 01
Tallahassee, FL 32399
P: (850) 414-3300
F: (954) 712-4826

GEORGIA
Mr. John Sours
Administrator
Governor's Office of Consumer
Affairs
2 Martin Luther King Jr. Drive
Southeast
Suite 356, East Tower
Atlanta, GA 30334
P: (404) 463-8962
F: (404) 463-8683
E: john.sours@ocp.ga.gov

GUAM
Mr. J. Patrick Mason
Deputy Attorney General
Office of the Attorney General
Civil Litigation & Solicitor
Division
287 W. O'Brien Drive
Hagatna, GU 96910
P: (671) 475-3324
F: (671) 472-2493

HAWAII
Mr. Stephen H. Levins
Executive Director
Office of Consumer Protection
Leiopapa A. Kamehameha
Building
235 South Beretania Street, Suite
801
Honolulu, HI 96813
P: (808) 586-2630
F: (808) 586-2640

IDAHO
Hon. Lawrence Wasden (R)
Attorney General
Office of the Attorney General
700 West State Street
P.O. Box 83720
Boise, ID 83720
P: (208) 334-2400
F: (208) 854-8071

ILLINOIS
Ms. Deborah Hagan
Chief
Division of Consumer
Protection
Office of the Attorney General
500 South Second Street
Springfield, IL 62706
P: (207) 782-9021

IOWA
Mr. William Brauch
Director
Consumer Protection Division
Office of the Attorney General
1305 East Walnut Street
Des Moines, IA 50319
P: (515) 281-5926
F: (515) 281-6771
E: william.brauch@iowa.gov

KANSAS
Hon. Derek Schmidt (R)
Attorney General
Office of the Attorney General
120 Southwest 10th Avenue
2nd Floor
Topeka, KS 66612
P: (785) 296-2215
F: (785) 296-6296

KENTUCKY
Mr. Todd Leatherman
Executive Director
Office of Consumer Protection
Office of the Attorney General
1024 Capital Center Drive
Frankfort, KY 40601
P: (502) 696-5389
F: (502) 573-8317
E: consumer.protection
   @ag.ky.gov

LOUISIANA
Hon. James D. Caldwell (D)
Attorney General
Office of the Attorney General
1885 North 3rd Street
P.O. Box 94005
Baton Rouge, LA 70804
P: (225) 326-6705
F: (225) 326-6797
E: executive@ag.state.la.us

MAINE
Mr. William N. Lund
Superintendent
Department of Professional &
Financial Regulation
Bureau of Consumer Credit
Protection
35 State House Station
Augusta, ME 04333
P: (207) 624-8527
F: (207) 582-7699
E: william.n.lund@maine.gov

Consumer Protection

MARYLAND
Mr. William D. Gruhn
Chief
Consumer Protection Division
Office of the Attorney General
200 Saint Paul Place
Baltimore, MD 21202
P: (410) 576-6558
F: (410) 576-6566
E: wgruhn@oag.state.md.us

MASSACHUSETTS
Ms. Barbara Anthony
Undersecretary
Office of Consumer Affairs &
Business Regulation
Ten Park Plaza, Suite 5170
Boston, MA 02116
P: (617) 973-8700
F: (617) 973-8798

MICHIGAN
Mr. Steven Hilfinger
Director
Department of Licensing &
Regulatory Affairs
P.O. Box 30004
Lansing, MI 48909
P: (517) 373-1820
F: (517) 373-2129
E: bcslic@michigan.gov

Mr. Andrew S. Levin
Acting Director
Department of Energy, Labor &
Economic Growth
P.O. Box 30004
Lansing, MI 48909
P: (517) 373-7230
F: (517) 373-2129
E: LevinA@michigan.gov

Hon. Bill Schuette (R)
Attorney General
Office of the Attorney General
P.O. Box 30212
525 West Ottawa Street
Lansing, MI 48909
P: (517) 373-1110

MINNESOTA
Hon. Lori Swanson (DFL)
Attorney General
Office of the Attorney General
State Capitol, Suite 102
St. Paul, MN 55155
P: (651) 296-3353
F: (651) 297-4193
E: attorney.general
    @state.mn.us

MISSISSIPPI
Ms. Meredith Aldridge
Special Assistant Attorney
Consumer Protection Division
P.O. Box 220
Jackson, MS 39225
P: (601) 359-3860
F: (601) 359-3796

MONTANA
Mr. Matthew Dale
Director
Office of Consumer Protection
& Victim Services
2225 11th Avenue
P.O. Box 201410
Helena, MT 59620
P: (406) 444-1907
F: (406) 444-9680
E: contactocp@mt.gov

NEBRASKA
Hon. Jon C. Bruning (R)
Attorney General
Office of the Attorney General
State Capitol
P.O. Box 98920
Lincoln, NE 68509
P: (402) 471-2682
F: (402) 471-3297

NEVADA
Mr. Eric P. Witkoski
Chief Deputy Attorney General
Consumer Protection Bureau
Office of the Attorney General
100 North Carson Street
Carson City, NV 89701
P: (702) 486-3129
F: (775) 684-1108
E: ewitkoski@ag.nv.gov

NEW HAMPSHIRE
Ms. Lauren J. Noether
Attorney IV
Office of the Attorney General
Department of Justice
33 Capitol Street
Concord, NH 03301
P: (603) 271-3641
F: (603) 271-2110
E: lauren.noether
    @doj.nh.gov

NEW JERSEY
Mr. Thomas R. Calcagni
Acting Director
Division of Consumer Affairs
124 Halsey Street
Newark, NJ 07102
P: (973) 504-6200
F: (973) 273-8035
E: askconsumeraffairs
    @lps.state.nj.us

NEW MEXICO
Hon. Gary K. King (D)
Attorney General
Office of the Attorney General
P.O. Drawer 1508
Santa Fe, NM 87504
P: (505) 827-6000
F: (505) 827-5826

NEW YORK
Ms. Mindy A. Bockstein
Chairperson & Executive
Director
Division of Consumer
Protection
5 Empire State Plaza, Suite 2101
Albany, NY 12223
P: (518) 474-3514
F: (518) 474-2474

NORTH CAROLINA
Hon. Roy A. Cooper III (D)
Attorney General
Office of the Attorney General
Department of Justice
P.O. Box 629
Raleigh, NC 27602
P: (919) 716-6400
F: (919) 716-6750

NORTH DAKOTA
Mr. Parrell Grossman
Director
Consumer Protection &
Antitrust Division
Gateway Professional Center
1050 East Interstate Avenue,
Suite 200
Bismarck, ND 58503
P: (701) 328-3404
F: (701) 328-3535
E: pgrossman@nd.gov

OHIO
Hon. Mike DeWine (R)
Attorney General
Office of the Attorney General
State Office Tower
30 East Broad Street
Columbus, OH 43266
P: (614) 466-4320

OKLAHOMA
Mr. Scott Lesher
Administrator
Department of Consumer Credit
4545 North Lincoln Boulevard,
Suite 164
Oklahoma City, OK 73105
P: (405) 521-3653
F: (405) 521-6740

OREGON
Ms. Teresa Miller
Insurance Administrator
Insurance Division
P.O. Box 14480
350 Winter Street, Northeast
Salem, OR 97309
P: (503) 947-7980
F: (503) 378-4351
E: teresa.d.miller
    @state.or.us

PENNSYLVANIA
Ms. Linda J. Williams
Director & Chief Deputy
Attorney General
Bureau of Consumer Protection
Office of the Attorney General
16th Floor, Strawberry Square
Harrisburg, PA 17120
P: (717) 787-3391
F: (717) 787-8242

PUERTO RICO
Mr. Luis Rivera Marin
Secretary
Department of Consumer
Affairs
P.O. Box 41059
San Juan, PR 00940
P: (787) 722-7555
F: (787) 726-0077

RHODE ISLAND
Hon. Peter F. Kilmartin (D)
Attorney General
Office of the Attorney General
150 South Main Street
Providence, RI 02903
P: (401) 274-4400

SOUTH CAROLINA
Mr. Elliott F. Elam Jr.
Director
Department of Consumer
Affairs
2221 Devine Street
P.O. Box 5757
Columbia, SC 29250
P: (803) 734-4189
F: (803) 734-4299
E: eelam@scconsumer.gov

SOUTH DAKOTA
Ms. Delane Smith
Director
Division of Consumer
Protection
Office of the Attorney General
1302 East Highway 14, Suite 1
Pierre, SD 57501
P: (605) 773-4400
F: (605) 773-7163
E: consumerhelp@state.sd.us

TENNESSEE
Mr. Gary Cordell
Director
Division of Consumer Affairs
Department of Commerce and
Insurance
500 James Robertson Parkway
Nashville, TN 37243
P: (615) 741-4737
F: (615) 532-4994
E: consumer.affairs@tn.gov

TEXAS
Mr. Rudy Aguilar
Consumer Protection Director
Office of Consumer Credit
Commissioner
2601 North Lamar
Austin, TX 78705
P: (512) 936-7627
F: (512) 936-7610
E: rudy.aguilar
      @occc.state.tx.us

U.S. VIRGIN ISLANDS
Mr. Kenrick Robertson
Commissioner
Department of Licensing &
Consumer Affairs
Property & Procurement
Building
Sub Base Building 1, Room 205
St. Thomas, VI 00802
P: (340) 774-3130
F: (340) 776-0675
E: dlcacommissioner
      @dlca.gov.vi

UTAH
Mr. Kevin Olsen
Director
Division of Consumer
Protection
160 East 300 South
Salt Lake City, UT 84111
P: (801) 366-0270
F: (801) 530-6001
E: kvolsen@utah.gov

VIRGINIA
Hon. Ken T.
   Cuccinelli II (R)
Attorney General
Office of the Attorney General
900 East Main Street
Richmond, VA 23219
P: (804) 786-2071

WASHINGTON
Hon. Rob McKenna (R)
Attorney General
Office of the Attorney General
1125 Washington Street,
Southeast
P.O. Box 40100
Olympia, WA 98504
P: (360) 753-6200
F: (360) 664-0228

WEST VIRGINIA
Ms. Fran Hughes
Chief Deputy Attorney General
Consumer Protection &
Antitrust Division
Office of the Attorney General
P.O. Box 1789
Charleston, WV 25326
P: (304) 558-2021
F: (304) 558-0184

WISCONSIN
Ms. Sandy Chalmers
Administrator, Trade &
Consumer Protection
Department of Agriculture,
Trade & Consumer Protection
2811 Agriculture Drive
P.O. Box 8911
Madison, WI 53708
P: (608) 224-4920
F: (608) 224-4939
E: Sandy.Chalmers
      @wisconsin.gov

WYOMING
Hon. Greg Phillips (D)
Attorney General
Office of the Attorney General
State Capitol Building
Cheyenne, WY 82002
P: (307) 777-7841

Corporate Records

Maintains a variety of corporate filings, records and documents.

ALABAMA
Ms. Sharon Staton
Corporations Director
Corporations Division
RSA Union Building , Suite 770
100 North Union Street
Montgomery, AL 36103
P: (334) 242-5328
F: (334) 240-3138
E: Sharon.Staton
   @sos.alabama.gov

ALASKA
Mr. Don Habeger
Director
Division of Corporations,
Business & Professional
Licensing
P.O. Box 110806
Juneau, AK 99811
P: (907) 465-2534
F: (907) 465-2974
E: don.habeger@alaska.gov

AMERICAN SAMOA
Mr. Faleseu Eliu Paopao
Director
Department of Commerce
American Samoa Government
Executive Office Building,
Utulei
Pago Pago, AS 96799
P: (684) 633-5155
F: (684) 633-4195

ARIZONA
Mr. Jeff Grant
Director
Corporations Division
Corporation Commission
1300 West Washington Street,
1st Floor
Phoenix, AZ 85007
P: (602) 542-3026
F: (602) 542-0900
E: director.corp@azcc.gov

ARKANSAS
Hon. Mark Martin (R)
Secretary of State
Office of the Secretary of State
256 State Capitol Building
Little Rock, AR 72201
P: (501) 682-1010
F: (501) 682-3510
E: sos@sos.arkansas.gov

CALIFORNIA
Ms. Betsy Bogart
Chief
Business Programs Division
1500 11th Street
Sacramento, CA 95814
P: (916) 653-6973

COLORADO
Mr. Michael Hardin
Business Director
Department of State, Business
Division
1560 Broadway, Suite 200
Denver, CO 80202
P: (303) 894-2200
F: (303) 869-4864
E: michael.hardin
   @sos.state.co.us

CONNECTICUT
Hon. Denise W. Merrill (D)
Secretary of State
Office of the Secretary of State
State Capitol, Room 104
Hartford, CT 06105
P: (860) 509-6200
F: (860) 509-6209
E: denise.merrill@ct.gov

DELAWARE
Mr. Robert Mathers
Administrator
Division of Corporations
401 Federal Street, Suite 4
P.O. Box 898
Dover, DE 19903
P: (302) 857-3456
F: (302) 739-3812

DISTRICT OF COLUMBIA
Mr. Nicholas A. Majett
Director
Department of Consumer &
Regulatory Affairs
1100 4th Street, Southwest
Washington, DC 20024
P: (202) 442-4400
F: (202) 442-9445
E: dcra@dc.gov

FLORIDA
Mr. Jay Kassees
Director
Division of Corporations
Clifton Building
2661 Executive Center Circle
Tallahassee, FL 32301
P: (850) 245-6000
E: jkassees@dos.state.fl.us

GEORGIA
Mr. Chauncey Newsome
Director
Corporations Division
2 Martin Luther King Jr. Drive
Southeast
Suite 315, Floyd West Tower
Atlanta, GA 30334
P: (404) 656-2817
F: (404) 657-2248

GUAM
Mr. Juan Carlos
Administrator
Department of Revenue &
Taxation
Regulatory Division
P.O. Box 23607
GMF, GU 96921
P: (671) 635-1846
E: jqcarlos@revtax.gov.gu

HAWAII
Ms. Keali'i S. Lopez
Director
Department of Commerce &
Consumer Affairs
King Kalakaua Building
335 Merchant Street
Honolulu, HI 96813
P: (808) 586-2850
F: (808) 586-2856
E: dcca@dcca.hawaii.gov

IDAHO
Kim Hunter
Supervisor
Business Entity Division
450 North 4th Street
Boise, ID 83702
P: (208) 334-2301
F: (208) 334-2080
E: khunter@sos.idaho.gov

ILLINOIS
Mr. Robert Durchholz
Administrator
Corporation Division
Howlett Building, Room 350
501 South 2nd Street
Springfield, IL 62756
P: (217) 782-4909

INDIANA
Hon. Charlie White (R)
Secretary of State
Office of the Secretary of State
201 State House
Indianapolis, IN 46204
P: (317) 232-6532
F: (317) 233-3283
E: sos@sos.in.gov

IOWA
Hon. Matt Schultz (R)
Secretary of State
Office of the Secretary of State
State Capitol, Room 105
1007 East Grand Avenue
Des Moines, IA 50319
P: (515) 281-8993
F: (515) 242-5952
E: sos@sos.state.ia.us

KENTUCKY
Ms. Gail Hance
Assistant Director of
Corporations
Office of the Secretary of State
700 Capitol Avenue, Suite 152
Frankfort, KY 40601
P: (502) 564-3490
F: (502) 564-5687

LOUISIANA
Hon. Tom Schedler (R)
Secretary of State
Office of Secretary of State
P.O. Box 94125
Baton Rouge, LA 70804
P: (225) 342-4479
F: (225) 342-5577

MAINE
Ms. Julie L. Flynn
Deputy Secretary of State
Bureau of Corporation,
Elections & Commissions
101 State House Station
Augusta, ME 04333
P: (207) 624-7736
F: (207) 287-5874

MARYLAND
Mr. C. John Sullivan Jr.
Director
Department of Assessments &
Taxation
300 West Preston Street, Room
605
Baltimore, MD 21201
P: (410) 767-1184
F: (410) 333-5873

MASSACHUSETTS
Hon. William Francis
   Galvin (D)
Secretary of the Commonwealth
Office of the Secretary of the
Commonwealth
220 Morrissey Blvd.
Boston, MA 02125
P: (617) 727-2816
F: (617) 288-8429
E: cis@sec.state.ma.us

MICHIGAN
Mr. Steven Hilfinger
Director
Department of Licensing &
Regualtory Affairs
P.O. Box 30004
Lansing, MI 48909
P: (517) 373-1820
F: (517) 373-2129
E: bcslic@michigan.gov

MINNESOTA
Hon. Mark Ritchie (DFL)
Secretary of State
Office of the Secretary of State
180 State Office Building
100 Martin Luther King Jr.
Boulevard
St. Paul, MN 55155
P: (651) 201-1328
F: (651) 215-0682
E: secretary.state
@state.mn.us

MISSISSIPPI
Mr. Thomas Riley
Assistant Secretary of State
Business Services Division
P.O. Box 136
Jackson, MS 39205
P: (601) 359-1350
F: (601) 359-1499

MISSOURI
Ms. Carol Fischer
Deputy Secretary of State for
Business Services
Business Services
Kirkpatrick State Information
Center
P.O. Box 778
Jefferson City, MO 65102
P: (573) 751-4153
F: (573) 526-3124
E: cfisher
@mail.dor.state.mo.us

MONTANA
Hon. Linda McCulloch (D)
Secretary of State
Office of the Secretary of State
P.O. Box 202801
Helena, MT 59620
P: (406) 444-2034
F: (406) 444-4249
E: sos@mt.gov

NEBRASKA
Hon. John A. Gale (R)
Secretary of State
Office of the Secretary of State
P.O. Box 94608
Lincoln, NE 68509
P: (402) 471-2554
F: (402) 471-3237
E: secretaryofstate
@nebraska.gov

NEVADA
Hon. Ross Miller (D)
Secretary of State
Office of the Secretary of State
101 North Carson Street, Suite 3
Carson City, NV 89701
P: (775) 684-5708
F: (775) 684-5724
E: sosmail@sos.nv.gov

NEW HAMPSHIRE
Hon. William M. Gardner (D)
Secretary of State
Office of the Secretary of State
State House, Room 204
Concord, NH 03301
P: (603) 271-3242
F: (603) 271-6316
E: kladd@sos.state.nh.us

NEW JERSEY
Mr. James J. Fruscione
Director
Division of Revenue
P.O. Box 628
Trenton, NJ 08646
P: (609) 984-3997

NEW MEXICO
Hon. Dianna J. Duran (R)
Secretary of State
Office of the Secretary of State
325 Don Gaspar, Suite 300
Capitol Annex
Santa Fe, NM 87503
P: (505) 827-3600
F: (505) 827-3634
E: diannaj.duran
@state.nm.us

Ms. Ann Echols
Bureau Chief
Corporations Bureau
Public Regulation Commission
P.O. Box 1269
Santa Fe, NM 87504
P: (505) 827-4502
F: (505) 827-4387

NEW YORK
Ms. Sandra J. Tallman
Acting Director
Division of Corporations, State
Records & Uniform
Commercial Code
99 Washington Avenue, 6th
Floor
Albany, NY 12231
P: (518) 473-2281
F: (518) 474-1418

NORTH CAROLINA
Ms. Cheri Myers
Director
Department of the Secretary of
State
Corporations Division
2 South Salisbury Street
Raleigh, NC 27601
P: (919) 807-2225
F: (919) 807-2039
E: corpinfo@sosnc.com

NORTH DAKOTA
Ms. Clara Jenkins
Director, Central Indexing
Office of the Secretary of State
600 East Boulevard Avenue
Department 108, 1st Floor
Bismarck, ND 58505
P: (701) 328-3662
F: (701) 328-2992
E: cjenkins@nd.gov

OHIO
Hon. Jon Husted (R)
Secretary of State
Office of the Secretary of State
180 East Broad Street
Columbus, OH 43215
P: (614) 466-2655
F: (614) 644-0649
E: jhusted@sos.state.oh.us

OREGON
Mr. Peter Threlkel
Director
Secretary of State, Corporation
Division
Public Service Building
255 Capitol Street, Northeast,
Suite 151
Salem, OR 97310
P: (503) 986-2200
F: (503) 986-6355
E: peter.threlkel
@state.or.us

PENNSYLVANIA
Mr. Richard K. House
Director
Corporation Bureau
401 North Street, Room 206
Harrisburg, PA 17120
P: (717) 787-1057
F: (717) 783-2244
E: RA-CORPS@state.pa.us

RHODE ISLAND
Hon. A. Ralph Mollis (D)
Secretary of State
Office of the Secretary of State
82 Smith Street
217 State House
Providence, RI 02903
P: (401) 222-1035
F: (401) 222-1356
E: armollis@sos.ri.gov

SOUTH CAROLINA
Hon. Mark Hammond (R)
Secretary of State
Office of the Secretary of State
P.O. Box 11350
Columbia, SC 29211
P: (803) 734-2170
F: (803) 734-1661
E: rdaggerhart@sos.sc.gov

SOUTH DAKOTA
Hon. Jason M. Gant (R)
Secretary of State
Office of the Secretary of State
500 East Capitol Avenue, Suite
204
Pierre, SD 57501
P: (605) 773-3537
F: (605) 773-6580
E: sdsos@state.sd.us

TENNESSEE
Mr. Nathan Burton
Director
Division of Business Services
312 Rosa L. Parks Avenue
Snodgrass Tower, 6th Floor
Nashville, TN 37243
P: (615) 741-2286
F: (615) 741-7310
E: business.services
@state.tn.us

Corporate Records

TEXAS
Ms. Lorna Wassdorf
Division Director
Business & Public Fillings
Division
Capitol Building, Rm. 1E.8
1100 Congress Avenue, P.O. Box
12697
Austin, TX 78711
P: (512) 463-5591
F: (512) 463-5709
E: lwassdorf
@sos.state.tx.us

U.S. VIRGIN ISLANDS
Mr. John McDonald
Director
Division of Banking &
Insurance
#18 Kongens Gade
St. Thomas, VI 00802
P: (340) 774-7166
F: (340) 774-9458

UTAH
Ms. Kathy Berg
Director
Division of Corporations &
Commericial Code
160 East 300 South, 2nd Floor
Salt Lake City, UT 84111
P: (801) 530-6216
F: (801) 530-6438
E: kberg@utah.gov

VERMONT
Ms. Betty Poulin
Director
Corporations Division
Redstone Building
26 Terrace Street
Montpelier, VT 05609
P: (802) 828-2386
F: (802) 828-2853
E: bpoulin@sec.state.vt.us

VIRGINIA
Mr. Joel Peck
Clerk
State Corporation Commission
State Corporation Commission
Tyler Building, 1300 East Main
Street
Richmond, VA 23219
P: (804) 371-9733
F: (804) 371-9521
E: joel.peck
@scc.virginia.gov

WASHINGTON
Hon. Sam Reed (R)
Secretary of State
Office of the Secretary of State
P.O. Box 40220
Olympia, WA 98504
P: (360) 902-4151
F: (360) 586-5629
E: sam.reed@sos.wa.gov

WISCONSIN
Ms. Jennifer Acker
Director
Corporations Bureau
P.O. Box 7846
Madison, WI 53707
P: (608) 261-7577
F: (608) 267-6813
E: Jennifer.Acker
@dfi.wisconsin.gov

WYOMING
Hon. Max Maxfield (R)
Secretary of State
Office of the Secretary of State
State Capitol Building
200 West 24th
Cheyenne, WY 82002
P: (307) 777-7378
F: (307) 777-6217
E: Secofstate@state.wy.us

Corrections

Manages the state's corrections systems.

ALABAMA
Mr. Kim T. Thomas
Commissioner
Department of Corrections
301 South Ripley Street
P.O. Box 301501
Montgomery, AL 36130
P: (334) 353-3883
F: (334) 353-3967

ALASKA
Mr. Joe Schmidt
Commissioner
Department of Corrections
802 3rd Street
Douglas, AK 99824
P: (907) 465-4652
F: (907) 465-3390
E: jschmidt@asca.net

ARIZONA
Mr. Charles L. Ryan
Director
Department of Corrections
1601 West Jefferson, MC 445
Phoenix, AZ 85007
P: (602) 542-5225
F: (602) 364-0159

ARKANSAS
Mr. Ray Hobbs
Director
Department of Correction
P.O. Box 8707
Pine Bluff, AR 71611
P: (870) 267-6300
F: (870) 267-6244

CALIFORNIA
Mr. Matthew Cate
Secretary
Department of Corrections &
Rehabilitation
1515 S Street, Suite 502 South
Sacramento, CA 95811
P: (916) 323-6001
F: (916) 442-2637

COLORADO
Mr. Tom Clements
Executive Director
Department of Corrections
2862 South Circle Drive, Suite
455
Colorado Springs, CO 80906
P: (719) 226-4701
F: (719) 226-4728

CONNECTICUT
Mr. Leo Arnone
Director
Department of Correction
24 Wolcott Hill Road
Wethersfield, CT 06106
P: (860) 692-7480

DELAWARE
Mr. Carl C. Danberg
Commissioner
Department of Correction
245 McKee Road
Dover, DE 19904
P: (302) 739-5601
F: (302) 739-8221
E: Carl.Danberg@state.de.us

DISTRICT OF COLUMBIA
Mr. Thomas P. Hoey
Director
Department of Corrections
1923 Vermont Avenue,
Northwest
#N-203
Washington, DC 20001
F: (202) 332-1470

FLORIDA
Mr. Edwin G. Buss
Secretary
Department of Corrections
2601 Blair Stone Road
Tallahassee, FL 32399
P: (850) 488-7480
F: (850) 922-2848
E: secretary
    @mail.dc.state.fl.us

GEORGIA
Mr. Brian Owens
Commissioner
Department of Corrections
Twin Towers East
2 Martin Luther King Jr. Drive
Southeast
Atlanta, GA 30334
P: (478) 992-5253
F: (478) 992-5259
E: gdccommish
    @dcor.state.ga.us

GUAM
Mr. J. B. Palacios
Director
Department of Corrections
P.O. Box 3236
Agana, GU 96932
P: (671) 473-7021
F: (671) 473-7024

HAWAII
Ms. Jodie F. Maesaka-Hirata
Director
Department of Public Safety
919 Ala Moana Boulevard,
Room 400
Honolulu, HI 96814
P: (808) 587-1288
F: (808) 587-1282

IDAHO
Mr. Brent Reinke
Director
Department of Corrections
1299 North Orchard Street,
Suite 110
Boise, ID 83706
P: (208) 658-2000
F: (208) 327-7404
E: breinke@idoc.idaho.gov

ILLINOIS
Mr. Tony Godinez
Director
Deparment of Corrections
1301 Concordia Court
P.O. Box 19277
Springfield, IL 62794
P: (217) 558-2200
F: (217) 522-8719

INDIANA
Mr. Bruce Lemmon
Commissioner
Department of Correction
302 West Washington Street,
Room E-334
Indianapolis, IN 46204
P: (317) 232-5711
F: (317) 232-6798
E: blemmon@idoc.in.gov

IOWA
Mr. John Baldwin
Director
Department of Corrections
510 East 12th Street
Des Moines, IA 50319
P: (515) 725-5708
F: (515) 725-5799
E: John.Baldwin@iowa.gov

KANSAS
Mr. Ray Roberts
Secretary
Department of Corrections
900 Southwest Jackson, 4th
Floor
Landon State Office Building
Topeka, KS 66612
P: (785) 296-3317
F: (785) 296-0014

KENTUCKY
Ms. LaDonna H. Thompson
Commissioner
Department of Corrections
P.O. Box 2400
Frankfort, KY 40602
P: (502) 564-4726
F: (502) 564-5037
E: lthompson@asca.net

LOUISIANA
Mr. James M. LeBlanc
Secretary
Department of Public Safety &
Corrections
504 Mayflower Street
P.O. Box 94304
Baton Rouge, LA 70804
P: (225) 342-6740
F: (225) 342-3095
E: jleblanc@asca.net

MAINE
Mr. Joseph Ponte
Commissioner
Department of Corrections
Augusta, ME 04333
P: (207) 287-4360
F: (207) 287-4370
E: marty.magnusson
    @state.me.us

MARYLAND
Mr. Gary Maynard
Secretary
Department of Public Safety &
Correctional Services
300 East Joppa Road, Suite 1000
Towson, MD 21286
P: (410) 339-5005
F: (410) 339-4243
E: gmaynard@asca.net

MASSACHUSETTS
Mr. Luis S. Spencer
Department of Correction
50 Maple Street, Suite 3
Milford, MA 01757
P: (508) 422-3330
F: (508) 422-3385

MICHIGAN
Mr. Daniel Heyns
Director
Department of Corrections
P.O. Box 30003
Lansing, MI 48909
P: (517) 373-1944
F: (517) 373-6883

Corrections

MINNESOTA
Mr. Tom Roy
Commissioner
Department of Corrections
1450 Energy Park Drive, Suite 200
St. Paul, MN 55108
P: (651) 361-7226
F: (651) 642-0414
E: tom.roy@state.mn.us

MISSISSIPPI
Mr. Christopher Epps
Commissioner
Department of Corrections
723 North President Street
Jackson, MS 39202
P: (601) 359-5621
F: (601) 359-5680
E: cepps@asca.net

MISSOURI
Mr. George Lombardi
Director
Department of Corrections
2729 Plaza Drive
Jefferson City, MO 65109
P: (573) 751-2389
F: (573) 751-4099

MONTANA
Mr. Mike Ferriter
Director
Department of Corrections
1539 11th Avenue
P.O. Box 201301
Helena, MT 59620
P: (406) 444-3930
F: (406) 444-4920
E: mferriter@asca.net

NEBRASKA
Mr. Bob Houston
Director
Department of Correctional Services
P.O. Box 94661
Folsom & Prospector Place, Building 1
Lincoln, NE 68509
P: (402) 479-5710
F: (402) 479-5623

NEVADA
Mr. Greg Cox
Acting Director
Department of Corrections
5500 Snyder Avenue
P.O. Box 7011
Carson City, NV 89702
P: (775) 887-3285
F: (775) 687-6715

NEW HAMPSHIRE
Mr. William Wrenn
Commissioner
Department of Corrections
P.O. Box 1806
Concord, NH 03302
P: (603) 271-5600
F: (603) 271-5643
E: wwrenn@nhdoc.state.nh.us

NEW JERSEY
Mr. Gary M. Lanigan
Commissioner
Department of Corrections
Whitlesey Road
P.O. Box 863
Trenton, NJ 08625
P: (609) 633-2335
F: (609) 777-0445

NEW MEXICO
Ms. Lupe Martinez
Secretary
Corrections Department
P.O. Box 27116
Santa Fe, NM 87502
P: (505) 827-8884
F: (505) 827-8533

NEW YORK
Mr. Brian Fischer
Commissioner
Department of Correctional Services
1220 Washington Avenue, Building 2
Albany, NY 12226
P: (518) 457-8126
F: (518) 457-7252
E: bfischer@asca.net

NORTH CAROLINA
Mr. Alvin Keller
Secretary
Department of Correction
214 West Jones Street, MSC 4201
Raleigh, NC 27699
P: (919) 716-3703
F: (919) 716-3794
E: Alvin.Keller@doc.nc.gov

NORTH DAKOTA
Ms. Leann Bertsch
Commissioner
Department of Corrections & Rehabilitation
Field Services Division
P.O. Box 5521
Bismarck, ND 58506
P: (701) 328-6190
F: (701) 328-6186
E: lbertsch@asca.net

OHIO
Mr. Gary C. Mohr
Director
Department of Rehabilitations & Correction
70 West Broad Street
Columbus, OH 43222
P: (614) 752-1164
F: (614) 752-1171

OKLAHOMA
Mr. Justin Jones
Director
Department of Corrections
3400 North Martin Luther King Avenue
P.O. Box 11400
Oklahoma City, OK 73136
P: (405) 425-2505
F: (405) 425-2578
E: jjones@asca.net

OREGON
Mr. Max Williams
Director
Department of Corrections
2575 Center Street, Northeast
Salem, OR 97310
P: (503) 945-0927
F: (503) 373-1173
E: mwilliams@asca.net

PENNSYLVANIA
Mr. Louis Giorla
Commissioner
Philadelphia Prison System
7901 State Road
Philadelphia, PA 19136
P: (215) 685-8201
F: (215) 685-8577

Mr. John E. Wetzel
Secretary
Department of Corrections
P.O. Box 598
Camp Hill, PA 17011
P: (717) 975-4918
F: (717) 731-0486

PUERTO RICO
Mr. Carlos Molina
Secretary
Department of Correction
P.O. Box 71308
Hato Rey, PR
P: (787) 775-0020
F: (787) 792-7677

RHODE ISLAND
Mr. Ashbel T. Wall II
Director
Department of Corrections
40 Howard Avenue
Cranston, RI 02920
P: (401) 462-2611
F: (401) 462-2630
E: at.wall@doc.ri.gov

SOUTH CAROLINA
Mr. William R. Byars Jr.
Director
Department of Corrections
4444 Broad River Road, Room 300
P.O. Box 21787
Columbia, SC 29221
P: (803) 896-8555
F: (803) 896-3972

SOUTH DAKOTA
Mr. Denny Kaemingk
Secretary
Department of Corrections
3200 East Highway 34
C/o 500 East Capitol Avenue
Pierre, SD 57501
P: (605) 773-3478
F: (605) 773-3194

TENNESSEE
Mr. Derrick Schofield
Commissioner
Department of Corrections
Rachel Jackson State Office Building
320 6th Avenue North, 6th Floor
Nashville, TN 37243
P: (615) 253-8139

TEXAS
Mr. Brad Livingston
Executive Director
Department of Criminal Justice
209 West 14th Street, 5th Floor
P. O. Box 13084 - Capitol Station
Austin, TX 78711
P: (512) 463-9988
F: (512) 305-9398
E: blivingston@asca.net

UTAH
Mr. Tom Patterson
Executive Director
Department of Corrections
14717 South Minuteman Drive
Draper, UT 84020
P: (801) 545-5513
F: (801) 545-5670
E: tompatterson@utah.gov

VERMONT

Mr. Andrew Pallito
Commissioner
Department of Corrections
103 South Main Street
Waterbury, VT 05671
P: (802) 241-2442
F: (802) 241-2565
E: Andrew.Pallito
    @ahs.state.vt.us

VIRGINIA

Mr. Harold Clarke
Director
Department of Corrections
6900 Atmore Drive
Richmond, VA 23225
P: (804) 674-3000
F: (804) 674-3509
E: harold.clarke
    @vadoc.virginia.gov

WASHINGTON

Mr. Eldon Vail
Secretary
Department of Corrections
P.O. Box 41101
Olympia, WA 98504
P: (360) 725-8810
F: (360) 664-4056

WEST VIRGINIA

Mr. Jim Rubenstein
Commissioner
Division of Corrections
112 California Avenue, Room 302
Charleston, WV 25305
P: (304) 558-2036 Ext. 35
F: (304) 558-5367
E: jrubenstein@asca.net

WISCONSIN

Mr. Gary Hamblin
Secretary
Department of Corrections
P.O. Box 7925
East Washington Avenue
Madison, WI 53707
P: (608) 240-5055

WYOMING

Mr. Robert Lampert
Director
Department of Corrections
700 West 21st Street
Cheyenne, WY 82002
P: (307) 777-7405
F: (307) 777-7479
E: rlampert@asca.net

Crime Victims Compensation

Provides compensation to victims of crime.

ALABAMA
Dr. Cassie T. Jones
Executive Director
Crime Victims Compensation
Commission
5845 Carmichael Road
P.O. Box 231267
Montgomery, AL 36123
P: (334) 290-4420
F: (334) 290-4455
E: cassie.jones
@acvcc.alabama.gov

ALASKA
Ms. Susan Browne
Administrator
Violent Crimes Compensation
Board
Department of Administration
P.O. Box 110230
Juneau, AK 99811
P: (907) 465-3040
F: (907) 465-2379
E: susan.browne@alaska.gov

AMERICAN SAMOA
Hon. Fepulea'i A.
   Ripley Jr.
Attorney General
Office of the Attorney General
American Samoa Government
Executive Office Building,
Utulei
Pago Pago, AS 96799
P: (684) 633-4163
F: (684) 633-1838

ARIZONA
Hon. Tom Horne (R)
Attorney General
Office of the Attorney General
1275 West Washington Street
Phoenix, AZ 85007
P: (602) 542-5025
F: (602) 542-4085

ARKANSAS
Ms. Avis Lane
Director
Community Relations Division
Office of the Attorney General
323 Center Street, Suite 200
Little Rock, AR 72201
P: (501) 682-3659
F: (501) 682-5313
E: avis.lane@arkansasag.gov

CALIFORNIA
Ms. Deborah Bain
Deputy Attorney General
Office of Victims' Services
P.O. Box 944255
Sacramento, CA 94244
P: (877) 433-9069

COLORADO
Ms. Nancy Feldman
Programs Manager
Office for Victims Programs
Division of Criminal Justice
700 Kipling Street, Suite 1000
Lakewood, CO 80215
P: (303) 239-5719
F: (303) 239-5743
E: nancy.feldman
@cdps.state.co.us

CONNECTICUT
Ms. Michelle Cruz
State Victim Advocate
Office of the Victim Advocate
505 Hudson Street
Hartford, CT 06106
P: (860) 550-6632
F: (860) 560-7065

DELAWARE
Ms. Barbara Brown
Executive Director
Victims Compensation
Assistance Program
900 North King Street, Suite 4
Wilmington, DE 19804
P: (302) 255-1770
F: (302) 577-1326
E: barb.brown@state.de.us

DISTRICT OF COLUMBIA
Ms. Laura B. Reed
Program Director
Crime Victims Compensation
Program
Court Building A
515 5th Street, Northwest, Room
109
Washington, DC 20001
P: (202) 879-4216
F: (202) 879-4230

FLORIDA
Hon. Pam Bondi (R)
Attorney General
Office of the Attorney General
The Capitol, PL 01
Tallahassee, FL 32399
P: (850) 414-3300
F: (954) 712-4826

Ms. Gwen Roache
Bureau Chief, Victim
Compensation
Division of Victim Services
Office of the Attorney General
The Capitol
Tallahassee, FL 32399
P: (850) 414-3300
F: (850) 487-1595

GUAM
Hon. Leonardo Rapadas
Attorney General
Office of the Attorney General
287 West O'Brien Drive
Hagatna, GU 96910
P: (671) 475-3324
F: (671) 472-2493

HAWAII
Ms. Pamela Ferguson-Brey
Executive Director
Crime Victims Compensation
Commission
1136 Union Mall
Room 600
Honolulu, HI 96813
P: (808) 587-1143
F: (808) 587-1146
E: cvcc@hawaii.rr.com

IDAHO
Mr. William Von Tagen
Division Chief
Intergovernmental & Fiscal Law
Division
700 West State Street
Boise, ID 83720
P: (208) 334-4155
F: (208) 854-8081
E: bill.vontagen
@ag.idaho.gov

ILLINOIS
Ms. Delores J. Martin
Director & Deputy Clerk
Court of Claims
630 South College Street
Springfield, IL 62756
P: (217) 782-7102

INDIANA
Ms. Sarah Davis
Program Coordinator
Victim Services Division
101 West Washington Street
Room 1170, East Tower
Indianapolis, IN 46204
P: (317) 232-3482
F: (317) 232-4979
E: sdavis@cji.IN.gov

IOWA
Ms. Marti Anderson
Division Director
Crime Victim Assistance
Division
Lucas Building, Ground Floor
321 East 12th
Des Moines, IA 50319
P: (515) 281-5044
F: (515) 281-8199
E: Marti.Anderson
@ag.state.ia.us

KANSAS
Mr. Frank Henderson Jr.
Executive Director
Crime Victims Compensation
Board
120 Southwest 10th Avenue, 2nd
Floor
Topeka, KS 66612
P: (785) 296-2359
F: (785) 296-0652

KENTUCKY
Ms. Virginia L. Woodward
Executive Director
Crime Victims Compensation
Board
130 Brighton Park Boulevard
Frankfort, KY 40601
P: (502) 573-7986
F: (502) 573-4817
E: beth.hicks@ky.gov

LOUISIANA
Mr. Joey Watson
Executive Director
Commission on Law
Enforcement & Administration
of Criminal Justice
602 North Fifth Street
P.O. Box 3133
Baton Rouge, LA 70821
P: (225) 342-1500
F: (225) 925-1998

MAINE
Ms. Denise Giles
Victim Service Coordinator
Department of Corrections
25 Tyson Drive, 3rd Floor
State House Station 111
Augusta, ME 04333
P: (207) 287-2711
F: (207) 287-4370
E: denise.giles@maine.gov

MARYLAND
Mr. Robin Woolford
Executive Director
Criminal Injuries Compensation
Board
6776 Reisterstown Road, Suite
200
Baltimore, MD 21215
P: (410) 585-3010
F: (410) 764-3815
E: rwoolford
@dpscs.state.md.us

MASSACHUSETTS
Ms. Janet E. Fine
Executive Director
Office for Victim Assistance
One Ashburton Place, Room
1101
Boston, MA 02108
P: (617) 727-5200
F: (617) 727-6552

Ms. Deborah Fogarty
Director
Office of the Attorney General
One Ashburton Place
Boston, MA 02108
P: (617) 727-2200
F: (617) 367-3906

MINNESOTA
Ms. Jeri Boisvert
Executive Director
Crime Victims Services
Bremer Tower, Suite 2300
445 Minnesota Street
St. Paul, MN 55101
P: (651) 201-7305
F: (651) 284-3317
E: jeri.boisvert
@state.mn.us

MISSISSIPPI
Ms. Janet Kennedy
Director
Crime Victims Compensation
Program
P.O. Box 267
Jackson, MS 39205
P: (601) 359-6766
F: (601) 359-3262

MISSOURI
Ms. Susan Sudduth
Program Manager
Crime Victims Compensation
Unit
Department of Public Safety
P.O. Box 1589
Jefferson City, MO 65102
P: (573) 526-3510
F: (573) 526-4940
E: susan.sudduth
@dolir.mo.gov

MONTANA
Mr. Mike Ferriter
Director
Department of Corrections
1539 11th Avenue
P.O. Box 201301
Helena, MT 59620
P: (406) 444-3930
F: (406) 444-4920
E: mferriter@asca.net

NEBRASKA
Ms. Lisa Stamm
Chief, Grants Division
Commission on Law
Enforcement & Criminal Justice
301 Centennial Mall South
P.O. Box 94946
Lincoln, NE 68509
P: (402) 471-3786
E: lisa.stamm@nebraska.gov

NEVADA
Mr. Bryan A. Nix
Senior Appeals Officer
Hearings Division
Department of Administration
2200 South Rancho Drive, Suite
210
Las Vegas, NV 89102
P: (702) 486-2527
F: (702) 486-2879
E: bnix
@hearings.state.nv.us

NEW HAMPSHIRE
Ms. Sandra Matheson Cochran
Director
Office of Victim/Witness
Assistance
Department of Justice
33 Capitol Street
Concord, NH 03301
P: (603) 271-3671
F: (603) 271-2110
E: sandi.matheson
@doj.nh.gov

NEW JERSEY
Ms. Marsetta Lee
Director
Victims of Crime Compensation
Office
50 Park Place
Newark, NJ 07102
P: (976) 648-2107
F: (976) 648-3937

NEW MEXICO
Ms. Kristy Ring
Director
Crime Victims Reparation
Commission
8100 Mountain Road Northeast,
Suite 106
Albuquerque, NM 87110
P: (505) 841-9432
F: (505) 841-9437
E: Kristy.Ring@state.nm.us

NEW YORK
Ms. Tina M. Stanford
Director
Office of Victim Services
1 Columbia Circle, Suite 200
Albany, NY 12203
P: (518) 485-5719
F: (518) 457-8658

NORTH CAROLINA
Ms. Janice W. Carmichael
Director
Department of Crime Control &
Public Safety
Victims Compensation Services
Division
4703 Mail Service Center
Raleigh, NC 27699
P: (919) 733-7974
F: (919) 715-4209
E: jcarmichael
@nccrimecontrol.org

NORTH DAKOTA
Mr. Paul J. Coughlin
Administrator
Department of Corrections &
Rehabilitation, Division of
Adult Services
Crime Victims Compensation
P.O. Box 5521
Bismarck, ND 58506
P: (701) 328-6195
F: (701) 328-6186
E: pcoughli@nd.gov

**NORTHERN MARIANA
ISLANDS**
Mr. Ramon Mafnas
Commissioner
Department of Public Safety
Caller Box 10007, Capitol Hill
Caller Box 10007, Capitol Hill
Saipan, MP 96950
P: (670) 664-9022
F: (670) 664-9027

OHIO
Hon. Mike DeWine (R)
Attorney General
Office of the Attorney General
State Office Tower
30 East Broad Street
Columbus, OH 43266
P: (614) 466-4320

OKLAHOMA
Ms. Suzanne Breedlove
Heckmaster
Director of Victims Services
Crime Victims' Compensation
Board
District Attorneys Council
421 Northwest 13th, Suite 290
Oklahoma City, OK 73103
P: (405) 264-5006
E: victimsservices
@dac.state.ok.us

OREGON
Ms. Cynthia Stinson
Director
Crime Victims' Services
Division
Department of Justice
1162 Court Street, Northeast
Salem, OR 97301
P: (503) 378-5348
F: (503) 378-5738
E: cynthia.stinson
@state.or.us

PENNSYLVANIA
Ms. Linda Rosenberg
Executive Director
Commission on Crime &
Deliquency
P.O. Box 1167
Harrisburg, PA 17108
P: (717) 705-0888
F: (717) 705-0891

PUERTO RICO
Ms. Lidice A.
Cardelario Matos
Director
Office of Crime Victims
Compensation
Department of Justice
P.O. Box 9020192
San Juan, PR 00902
P: (787) 641-7480
F: (787) 641-7477

Crime Victims Compensation

RHODE ISLAND
Ms. Melba Depena
Program Administrator
Crime Victims Compensation
Program
40 Fountain Street, 1st Floor
Providence, RI 02903
P: (401) 222-8590
F: (401) 222-4577

SOUTH CAROLINA
Dr. Larry Barker
Director
State Office of Victim
Assistance
Edgar A. Brown Building, Room
401
1205 Pendleton Street
Columbia, SC 29201
P: (803) 734-1900
F: (803) 734-1708
E: sova@oepp.sc.gov

SOUTH DAKOTA
Ms. Emily Paulsen
Administrator
Department of Social Services
Crime Victims' Compensation
Program
700 Governors Drive
Pierre, SD 57501
P: (605) 773-3656
F: (605) 773-6834
E: Emily.Paulsen
    @state.sd.us

TENNESSEE
Hon. David H. Lillard Jr.
State Treasurer
Department of Treasury
State Capitol, First Floor
Nashville, TN 37243
P: (615) 741-2956
F: (615) 253-1591
E: david.lillard
    @state.tn.us

TEXAS
Ms. Angie McCown
Director
Victim Services Division
Department of Criminal Justice
P.O. Box 13084
Austin, TX 78711
P: (512) 406-5900
F: (512) 452-0825

U.S. VIRGIN ISLANDS
Mr. Christopher Finch
Commissioner
Department of Human Services
Knud Hansen Complex,
Building A
1303 Hospital Grounds
St. Thomas, VI 00802
P: (340) 774-0930
F: (340) 774-3466

UTAH
Mr. Melvin Wilson
Director
Office of Crime Victims
Reparations
350 East 500 South, Suite 200
Salt Lake City, UT 84111
P: (801) 238-2367
F: (801) 533-4127
E: melwilson@utah.gov

VERMONT
Ms. Judy Rex
Executive Director
Center for Crime Victim
Services
58 South Main Street, Suite 1
Waterbury, VT 05676
P: (802) 241-1250 Ext. 106
F: (802) 241-4337

VIRGINIA
Mr. Garth Wheeler
Director
Department of Criminal Justice
Services
1100 Bank Street
Richmond, VA 23219
P: (804) 786-8718
F: (804) 371-8981
E: garth.wheeler
    @dcjs.virginia.gov

WASHINGTON
Mr. Cletus Nnanabu
Program Manager
Crime Victims Compensation
Program
Department of Labor &
Industries
P.O. Box 44520
Olympia, WA 98504
P: (360) 902-5340
F: (360) 902-5333

WEST VIRGINIA
Hon. Darrell V.
    McGraw Jr. (D)
Attorney General
Office of the Attorney General
State Capitol Complex, Building
1
Room E-26
Charleston, WV 25305
P: (304) 558-2021
F: (304) 558-0140

WISCONSIN
Ms. Jill Karofsky
Director
Office of Crime Victims
Services
17 West Main Street, 8th Floor
P.O. Box 7851
Madison, WI 53707
P: (608) 264-9497
E: karofskyjj
    @doj.state.wi.us

WYOMING
Hon. Greg Phillips (D)
Attorney General
Office of the Attorney General
State Capitol Building
Cheyenne, WY 82002
P: (307) 777-7841

Criminal Justice

Oversees the administration of justice by providing public safety, assisting victims of crime, analyzing criminal data, administering funds, and providing training and guidance to law enforcement officials.

ALABAMA
Mr. Jim Quinn
Assistant Director
Law Enforcement & Traffic
Safety Division
401 Adams Avenue
P.O. Box 5690
Montgomery, AL 36103
P: (334) 242-5100
F: (334) 242-5099
E: jim.quinn
    @adeca.alabama.gov

ALASKA
Mr. Joseph A. Masters
Commissioner
Department of Public Safety
5700 East Tudor Road
P.O. Box 111200
Anchorage, AK 99811
P: (907) 269-5086
F: (907) 269-4543
E: joseph.masters
    @alaska.gov

AMERICAN SAMOA
Mr. Alaalamua L. Filoiali'i
Director
Criminal Justice Planning
Agency
Executive Office Building,
Utulei
Territory of American Samoa
Pago Pago, AS 96799
P: (684) 633-5221
F: (684) 633-7552
E: faaulena@hotmail.com

ARIZONA
Mr. John A. Blackburn Jr.
Executive Director
Criminal Justice Commission
1110 West Washington, Suite
230
Phoenix, AZ 85007
P: (602) 364-1171
F: (602) 364-1175
E: JRBlackburn@azcjc.gov

ARKANSAS
Col. Winford E. Phillips
Director
State Police
1 State Police Plaza Drive
Little Rock, AR 72209
P: (501) 618-8299
F: (501) 618-8222
E: winford.phillips
    @asp.arkansas.gov

CALIFORNIA
Mr. Matthew R. Bettenhausen
Director
Office of Homeland Security
State Capitol
Sacramento, CA 95814
P: (916) 324-8908
F: (916) 323-9633
E: matthew.bettenhausen
    @ohs.ca.gov

COLORADO
Ms. Jeanne Smith
Director
Division of Criminal Justice
Department of Public Safety
700 Kipling Street, Suite 3000
Denver, CO 80203
P: (303) 239-4446
F: (303) 239-4491
E: jeanne.smith
    @cdps.state.co.us

CONNECTICUT
Mr. Kevin T. Kane
Chief State's Attorney
Division of Criminal Justice
300 Corporate Place
Rocky Hill, CT 06067
P: (860) 258-5800
F: (860) 258-5858
E: conndcj@po.state.ct.us

DELAWARE
Ms. Drewry Fennell
Executive Director
Criminal Justice Council
Carvel State Office Building
820 North French Street, 10th
Floor
Wilmington, DE 19801
P: (302) 577-5030
F: (302) 577-7056
E: drewry.fennell
    @state.de.us

DISTRICT OF COLUMBIA
Ms. Cathy L. Lanier
Chief of Police
Metropolitan Police Department
300 Indiana Avenue, Northwest
Washington, DC 20001
P: (202) 727-4218
F: (202) 727-9524
E: cathy.lanier@dc.gov

FLORIDA
Mr. Gerald M. Bailey
Commissioner
Department of Law
Enforcement
2331 Phillips Road
P.O. Box 1489
Tallahassee, FL 32302
P: (850) 410-7001
E: GeraldBailey
    @fdle.state.fl.us

GEORGIA
Ms. Barbara Lynn Howell
Executive Director
Criminal Justice Coordinating
Council
104 Marietta Street, Suite 440
Atlanta, GA 30303
P: (404) 657-1977
F: (404) 657-1957
E: bl.howell@cjcc.ga.gov

GUAM
Mr. Paul Suba
Commander
Police Department
233 Central Avenue
Tiyan, GU 96913
P: (671) 475-8512
F: (671) 472-2825

HAWAII
Hon. David Louie
Attorney General
Office of the Attorney General
425 Queen Street
Honolulu, HI 96813
P: (808) 586-1500
F: (808) 586-1239

IDAHO
Col. Jerry Russell
Director
State Police
P.O. Box 700
Meridian, ID 83680
P: (208) 884-7003
F: (208) 884-7090
E: jerry.russell
    @isp.idaho.gov

ILLINOIS
Mr. Jack Cutrone
Executive Director
Criminal Justice Information
Authority
300 West Adams Street, Suite
200
Chicago, IL 60606
P: (312) 793-8550
F: (312) 793-8422

INDIANA
Mr. Mark Massa
Executive Director
Criminal Justice Institute
101 West Washington Street
1170 East Tower
Indianapolis, IN 46204
P: (317) 232-2560
F: (317) 232-4979
E: MMassa@cji.IN.gov

IOWA
Mr. Mark J. Schouten
Director
Governor's Office of Drug
Control Policy
401 Southwest 7th, Suite N
Des Moines, IA 50309
P: (515) 725-0305
F: (515) 242-6390
E: mark.schouten@iowa.gov

KANSAS
Hon. Derek Schmidt (R)
Attorney General
Office of the Attorney General
120 Southwest 10th Avenue
2nd Floor
Topeka, KS 66612
P: (785) 296-2215
F: (785) 296-6296

KENTUCKY
Mr. J. Michael Brown
Secretary
Justice & Public Safety Cabinet
125 Holmes Street
Frankfort, KY 40601
P: (502) 564-7554
F: (502) 564-4840

LOUISIANA
Mr. Joey Watson
Executive Director
Commission on Law
Enforcement & Administration
of Criminal Justice
602 North Fifth Street
P.O. Box 3133
Baton Rouge, LA 70821
P: (225) 342-1500
F: (225) 925-1998

MAINE
Mr. John E. Morris
Commissioner
Department of Public Safety
45 Commerce Drive, Suite 1
104 State House Station
Augusta, ME 04333
P: (207) 626-3800
F: (207) 287-3042
E: john.e.morris@maine.gov

Criminal Justice

MARYLAND
Ms. Kristen Mahoney
Executive Director
Governor's Office of Crime
Control & Prevention Office
300 East Joppa Road
Suite 1105
Baltimore, MD 21286
P: (410) 821-2828
F: (410) 321-3116
E: Kmahoney
@goccp-state-md.org

MASSACHUSETTS
Ms. Mary Elizabeth
Heffernan
Secretary
Executive Office of Public
Safety
One Ashburton Place, Suite
2133
Boston, MA 02108
P: (617) 727-7775
F: (617) 727-4764

MICHIGAN
Colonel Kriste Kibbey Etue
Director
State Police
714 South Harrison Road
East Lansing, MI 48823
P: (517) 336-6157
F: (517) 336-6551

MINNESOTA
Ms. Ramona Dohman
Commissioner
Department of Public Safety
Bremer Tower, Suite 1000
445 Minnesota Street
St. Paul, MN 55101
P: (651) 201-7160
F: (651) 297-5728
E: Mona.Dohman@state.mn.us

MISSISSIPPI
Dr. Billy V. White Jr.
Executive Director
Division of Public Safety
Planning
Department of Public Safety
3750 I-55 North Frontage Road
Jackson, MS 39211
P: (601) 987-4990
F: (601) 987-4154
E: bwhite@mdps.state.ms.us

MISSOURI
Mr. John M. Britt
Director
Department of Public Safety
P.O. Box 749
Jefferson City, MO 65102
P: (573) 751-4905
F: (573) 751-5399

MONTANA
Mr. Don Merritt
Acting Executive Director
Board of Crime Control
3075 North Montana Avenue
P.O. Box 201408
Helena, MT 59620
P: (406) 444-3615
F: (406) 444-4722
E: dmerritt@mt.gov

NEBRASKA
Mr. Mike Behm
Executive Director
Commission on Law
Enforcement & Criminal Justice
P.O. Box 94946
Lincoln, NE 68509
P: (402) 471-3847
F: (402) 471-2837
E: Michael.Behm
@Nebraska.gov

NEVADA
Col. Chris Perry
Acting Director
Department of Public Safety
555 Wright Way
Carson City, NV 89711
P: (775) 684-4808
F: (775) 684-4809
E: cperry@dps.state.nv.us

NEW HAMPSHIRE
Ms. Rosemary Faretra
Director of Administration
Office of the Attorney General
Department of Justice
33 Capitol Street
Concord, NH 03301
P: (603) 271-1234
F: (603) 271-2110
E: rosemary.faretra
@doj.nh.gov

NEW JERSEY
Mr. Stephen J. Taylor
Director
Division of Criminal Justice
Richard J. Hughes Justice
Complex
25 Market Street, P.O. Box 80
Trenton, NJ 08625
P: (609) 984-6500
F: (609) 292-3508

NEW MEXICO
Mr. Gorden E. Eden Jr.
Secretary
Department of Public Safety
4491 Cerrillos Road
P.O. Box 1628
Santa Fe, NM 87504
P: (505) 827-3370

NEW YORK
Mr. Sean M. Byrne
Acting Commissioner
Division of Criminal Justice
Services
4 Tower Place, 10th Floor
Albany, NY 12203
P: (518) 457-5837
F: (518) 473-1271

NORTH CAROLINA
Ms. Gwendolyn W. Burrell
Executive Director
Governor's Crime Commission
1201 Front Street
Suite 200
Raleigh, NC 27609
P: (919) 733-4564
F: (919) 733-4625

NORTH DAKOTA
Hon. Wayne Stenehjem (R)
Attorney General
Office of the Attorney General
State Capitol, Department 125
600 East Boulevard Avenue
Bismarck, ND 58505
P: (701) 328-2210
F: (701) 328-2226
E: wstenehjem@nd.gov

**NORTHERN MARIANA
ISLANDS**
Mr. Jerome Ierome
Executive Director
Criminal Justice Planning
Agency
P.O. Box 5602, CHRB
Saipan, MP 96950
P: (670) 664-4550
F: (670) 664-4560
E: administration
@cda.gov.mp

OHIO
Mr. Karhlton F. Moore
Director
Office of Criminal Justice
Services
Department of Public Safety
1970 West Broad Street
Columbus, OH 43223
P: (614) 466-7782
F: (614) 466-0308

OKLAHOMA
Ms. Suzanne McClain Atwood
Executive Coordinator
District Attorneys Council
421 Northwest 13th, Suite 290
Oklahoma City, OK 73103
P: (405) 264-5000
F: (405) 264-5099
E: Trent.Baggett
@dac.state.ok.us

OREGON
Mr. Craig Prins
Executive Director
Criminal Justice Commission
885 Summer Street, Northeast
Salem, OR 97301
P: (503) 378-4858
F: (503) 378-4861
E: craig.prins@state.or.us

PENNSYLVANIA
Ms. Linda Rosenberg
Executive Director
Commission on Crime &
Delinquency
P.O. Box 1167
Harrisburg, PA 17108
P: (717) 705-0888
F: (717) 705-0891

PUERTO RICO
Mr. Luis M. Gonzalez-Javier
Director
Federal Funds Division
Calle Lindberg #6, Miramar
P.O. Box 9020192
San Juan, PR 00902
P: (787) 725-0335
F: (787) 721-7280
E: lgonzalez
@justicia.prstar.net

RHODE ISLAND
Mr. Thomas H. Mongeau
Administrative Manager
Public Safety Grant
Administration Office
One Capitol Hill, 2nd Floor
Providence, RI 02908
P: (401) 222-4493
F: (401) 222-1294
E: TMongeau
@gw.doa.state.ri.us

SOUTH CAROLINA
Mr. Hubert F. Harrell
Director
Criminal Justice Academy
5400 Broad River Road
Columbia, SC 29212
P: (803) 896-7777
F: (803) 896-7776
E: HFHarrell@sccja.sc.gov

SOUTH DAKOTA
Mr. Trevor Jones
Secretary
Department of Public Safety
118 West Capitol Avenue
Pierre, SD 57501
P: (605) 773-3178
F: (605) 773-3018
E: DPSInfo@state.sd.us

TENNESSEE
Mr. Bill Scollon
Director
Office of Criminal Justice
Programs
William R. Snodgrass Tennessee
Tower
312 Rosa L. Parks Avenue, 12th
Floor
Nashville, TN 37243
P: (615) 253-1984
E: bill.scollon@tn.gov

TEXAS
Mr. Brad Livingston
Executive Director
Department of criminal Justice
209 West 14th Street, 5th Floor
P. O. Box 13084 - Capitol
Station
Austin, TX 78711
P: (512) 463-9988
F: (512) 305-9398
E: blivingston@asca.net

U.S. VIRGIN ISLANDS
Mr. Renaldo Rivera
Adjutant General
National Guard
4031 LaGrande Princess, Lot 1B
Christiansted, VI 00820
P: (340) 712-7710
F: (340) 712-7711
E: renaldo.rivera
    @vi.ngb.army.mil

UTAH
Mr. Ronald Gordon
Executive Director
Commission on Criminal &
Juvenile Justice
Senate Building, Suite 330
P.O. Box 142330
Salt Lake City, UT 84114
P: (801) 538-1432
F: (801) 538-1024
E: rbgordon@utah.gov

VIRGINIA
Mr. Garth Wheeler
Director
Department of Criminal Justice
Services
1100 Bank Street
Richmond, VA 23219
P: (804) 786-8718
F: (804) 371-8981
E: garth.wheeler
    @dcjs.virginia.gov

WEST VIRGINIA
Mr. J. Norbert Federspiel
Director
Division of Justice &
Community Services
1204 Kanawha Boulevard, East
Charleston, WV 25301
P: (304) 558-8814
F: (304) 558-0391
E: j.norbert.federspiel
    @wv.gov

WISCONSIN
Mr. David O. Steingraber
Executive Director
Office of Justice Assistance
1 South Pinckney Street, Suite
615
Madison, WI 53703
P: (608) 266-3323
F: (608) 266-6676
E: david.steingraber
    @oja.state.wi.us

WYOMING
Hon. Greg Phillips (D)
Attorney General
Office of the Attorney General
State Capitol Building
Cheyenne, WY 82002
P: (307) 777-7841

Debt Management

Responsible for structuring debt issues.

ALABAMA
Mr. David Perry
Director
Department of Finance
State Capitol
600 Dexter Avenue, Suite N-105
Montgomery, AL 36130
P: (334) 242-7160
F: (334) 353-3300
E: david.perry
@finance.alabama.gov

ALASKA
Mr. Deven Mitchell
Debt Manager
Treasury Division
Department of Revenue
P.O. Box 110405
Juneau, AK 99811
P: (907) 465-3409
F: (907) 465-2902
E: deven.mitchell
@alaska.gov

AMERICAN SAMOA
Hon. Magalei Logovi'i
Treasurer
Department of the Treasury
American Samoa Government
Pago Pago, AS 96799
P: (684) 633-4155
F: (684) 633-4100

ARKANSAS
Mr. Mac Dodson
Director
Development Finance Authority
423 Main Street, Suite 500
Little Rock, AR 72201
P: (501) 682-5900
F: (501) 682-5939
E: mdodson@adfa.state.ar.us

CALIFORNIA
Ms. Ana J. Matosantos
Director of Finance
Department of Finance
915 L Street
Sacramento, CA 95814
P: (916) 445-4141

CONNECTICUT
Hon. Denise L. Nappier (D)
State Treasurer
Office of State Treasurer
55 Elm Street
Hartford, CT 06106
P: (860) 702-3010
F: (860) 702-3043
E: denise.nappier@ct.gov

DISTRICT OF COLUMBIA
Dr. Natwar M. Gandhi
Chief Financial Officer
Office of the Chief Financial
Officer
1350 Pennsylvania Avenue,
Northwest
Room 203
Washington, DC 20004
P: (202) 727-2476
F: (202) 727-1643
E: ocfo@dc.gov

FLORIDA
Mr. J. Ben Watkins III
Director
Division of State Bond Finance
State Board of Administration
P.O. Box 13300
Tallahassee, FL 32317
P: (850) 488-4782
F: (850) 413-1315
E: watkins_ben
@fsba.state.fl.us

GEORGIA
Hon. Tommy D. Hills (R)
Treasurer and Director
Office of Treasury & Fiscal
Services
200 Piedmont Avenue
Suite 1202, West Tower
Atlanta, GA 30334
P: (404) 656-2168
F: (404) 656-9048
E: OTFSweb@otfs.ga.gov

IDAHO
Hon. Ron G. Crane (R)
State Treasurer
State Treasurer's Office
P.O. Box 83720
Boise, ID 83720
P: (208) 334-3200
F: (208) 332-2960
E: ron.crane@sto.idaho.gov

ILLINOIS
Mr. David Vaught
Director
Office of Management &
Budget
108 State House
Springfield, IL 62706
P: (217) 782-4520
F: (217) 524-1514
E: BureauBudget.OMB
@illinois.gov

INDIANA
Ms. Kendra York
Public Finance Director
Finance Authority
One North Capitol Avenue,
Suite 900
Indianapolis, IN 46204
P: (317) 233-4337
F: (317) 232-6786
E: KeYork@ifa.IN.gov

IOWA
Hon. Michael L.
Fitzgerald (D)
State Treasurer
State Treasurer's Office
Room 114, Capitol Building
Des Moines, IA 50319
P: (515) 281-5368
F: (515) 281-7562
E: mike.fitzgerald@iowa.gov

KENTUCKY
Mr. Tom Howard
Executive Director
Office of Financial Management
702 Capitol Avenue, Room 76
Frankfort, KY 40601
P: (502) 564-2924
F: (502) 564-7416

LOUISIANA
Mr. Whitman J. Kling Jr.
Director
State Bond Commission
900 North 3rd Street, 21st Floor
State Capitol
Baton Rouge, LA 70802
P: (225) 342-0040
F: (225) 342-0064
E: wkling
@treasury.state.la.us

MARYLAND
Hon. Nancy K. Kopp (D)
State Treasurer
State Treasurer's Office
Goldstein Treasury Building
80 Calvert Street
Annapolis, MD 21401
P: (410) 260-7533
F: (410) 974-3530
E: nkopp
@treasurer.state.md.us

MASSACHUSETTS
Mr. Colin McNaught
Deputy Treasurer for Debt
Management
Department of State Treasury
One Ashburton Place, 12th Floor
Boston, MA 02108
P: (617) 367-9333 Ext. 226

MINNESOTA
Mr. Jim Schowalter
Commissioner
Management & Budget
658 Cedar Street, Suite 400
St. Paul, MN 55155
P: (651) 201-8010
F: (651) 296-7714
E: James.Schowalter
@state.mn.us

MISSISSIPPI
Ms. Betsy McLean
Director
Investment & Cash
Management Division
P.O. Box 138
Jackson, MS 39205
P: (601) 359-3536
F: (601) 359-2001

MONTANA
Mr. Paul Christofferson
Administrator
State Accounting Division
Mitchell Building, Room 255
P.O. Box 200102
Helena, MT 59620
P: (406) 444-4609
F: (406) 444-2812
E: pachristofferson@mt.gov

NEBRASKA
Mr. Carlos Castillo
Director
Department of Administrative
Services
State Capitol, Room 1315
Lincoln, NE 68509
P: (402) 471-2331
E: carlos.castillo
@email.state.ne.us

NEVADA
Hon. Kate Marshall (D)
State Treasurer
Office of the State Treasurer
101 North Carson Street, #4
Carson City, NV 89701
P: (775) 684-5600
F: (775) 684-5623
E: katemarshall
@NevadaTreasurer.gov

NEW HAMPSHIRE
Hon. Catherine Provencher
State Treasurer
State Treasury
25 Capitol Street, Room 121
Concord, NH 03301
P: (603) 271-2621
F: (603) 271-3922
E: cprovencher
    @treasury.state.nh.us

NEW JERSEY
Mr. James M. Petrino
Office of Public Finance
P.O. Box 002
Trenton, NJ 08625
P: (609) 633-6447
E: james.petrino
    @treas.state.nj.us

NEW MEXICO
Ms. Stephanie Schardin
    Clarke
Interim Director
Board of Finance Division
181 Bataan Memorial Building
407 Galisteo Street
Santa Fe, NM 87501
P: (505) 827-3930

NORTH DAKOTA
Ms. Pam Sharp
Director
Office of Management &
Budget
600 East Boulevard Avenue
Department 110
Bismarck, ND 58505
P: (701) 328-2680
F: (701) 328-3230
E: psharp@nd.gov

OHIO
Mr. Kurt Kauffman
Debt Manager
Office of Budget &
Management
30 East Broad Street, 34th Floor
Columbus, OH 43215
P: (614) 466-0691
F: (614) 728-9295

OKLAHOMA
Mr. James C. Joseph
State Bond Advisor
State Bond Advisor's Office
5900 North Classen Court
Oklahoma City, OK 73118
P: (405) 602-3100
F: (405) 848-3314
E: jjoseph@oksba.org

OREGON
Ms. Laura Lockwood-McCall
Director
Debt Management Division
Office of the State Treasurer
350 Winter Street, Northeast,
Suite 100
Salem, OR 97301
P: (503) 378-4930
F: (503) 378-2870
E: laura.lockwood-mccall
    @state.or.us

PENNSYLVANIA
Mr. Dan Meuser
Secretary
Department of Revenue
11th Floor, Stawberry Square
Harrisburg, PA 17128
P: (717) 783-3680
F: (717) 787-3990

PUERTO RICO
Mr. Carlos M. Garcia
President
Government Development Bank
for Puerto Rico
P.O. Box 42001
San Juan, PR 00940
P: (787) 722-2525
F: (787) 721-1443

SOUTH CAROLINA
Mr. Rick Harmon
Senior Assistant State Treasurer,
Debt
Office of the State Treasurer
1200 Senate St., Wade Hampton
Bldg.
P.O. Box 11778
Columbia, SC 29211
P: (803) 734-2114
F: (803) 734-2690
E: rick.harmon@sto.sc.gov

TENNESSEE
Mr. Mark Emkes
Commissioner
Department of Finance &
Administration
312 Rosa Parks Avenue, 21st
Floor
Nashville, TN 37243
P: (615) 741-2401

U.S. VIRGIN ISLANDS
Ms. Debra Gottlieb
Director
Office of Management &
Budget
#41 Norre Gade
Emancipation Garden Station,
2nd Floor
St. Thomas, VI 00802
P: (340) 776-0750
F: (340) 776-0069
E: debra.gottlieb
    @omb.vi.gov

VERMONT
Hon. Elizabeth Pearce
State Treasurer
Office of the State Treasurer
109 State Street, 4th Floor
Montpelier, VT 05609
P: (802) 828-1452
F: (802) 828-2772
E: Beth.Pearce@state.vt.us

VIRGINIA
Ms. Evelyn R. Whitley
Director of Debt Management
Debt Management Division
Department of Treasury
101 North 14th Street
Richmond, VA 23219
P: (804) 371-6006
F: (804) 225-3187
E: evie.whitley
    @trs.virginia.gov

WASHINGTON
Hon. James L. McIntire (D)
State Treasurer
Office of the State Treasurer
Legislative Building
P.O. Box 40200
Olympia, WA 98504
P: (360) 902-9001
F: (360) 902-9044
E: watreas@tre.wa.gov

WEST VIRGINIA
Mr. H. Craig Slaughter
Executive Director
Investment Management Board
500 Virginia Street, East, Suite
200
Charleston, WV 25301
P: (304) 345-2672
F: (304) 345-5939
E: craigs@wvimb.org

WYOMING
Hon. Joe B. Meyer (R)
State Treasurer
Office of the State Treasurer
200 West 24th Street, Suite 122
Cheyenne, WY 82002
P: (307) 777-7408
F: (307) 777-5411
E: jmeyer3@state.wy.us

Developmentally Disabled

Oversees the care, treatment and future service needs of the developmentally disabled.

ALABAMA
Ms. Cathy Crabtree
Associate Commissioner
Division of Intellectual
Disability Services
Department of Mental Health
100 North Union Street, P.O.
Box 301410
Montgomery, AL 36130
P: (334) 353-3701
F: (334) 242-0725
E: catherine.crabtree
    @mh.alabama.gov

ALASKA
Mr. Duane Mayes
Director
Senior & Disabilities Services
Department of Health & Social
Services
550 West 8th Street
Anchorage, AK 99501
P: (907) 269-3666
F: (907) 269-3688
E: duane.mayes@alaska.gov

ARIZONA
Ms. Barbara Brent
Assistant Director
Division of Developmental
Disabilities
Department of Economic
Security
1717 West Jefferson Street
Phoenix, AZ 85005
P: (602) 542-6857
F: (602) 624-1322
E: bbrent@azdes.gov

ARKANSAS
Dr. James C. Green
Director
Division of Developmental
Disabilities Services
Department of Human Services
P.O. Box 1437, Slot N501
Little Rock, AR 72203
P: (501) 682-8665
F: (501) 682-8380
E: charlie.green
    @arkansas.gov

CALIFORNIA
Ms. Terri Delgadillo
Director
Department of Developmental
Services
1600 9th Street
P.O. Box 944202
Sacramento, CA 94244
P: (916) 654-1897
F: (916) 654-2167
E: terri.delgadillo
    @dds.ca.gov

CONNECTICUT
Dr. Terrence Macy
Commissioner
Department of Developmental
Services
460 Capitol Avenue
Hartford, CT 06106
P: (860) 418-6011
F: (860) 418-6009
E: terry.macy@ct.gov

DELAWARE
Mr. Roy Lafontaine
Director
Developmental Disabilities
Services/DHSS
Woodbrook Professional Center,
1056
1056 South Governor's Avenue,
Suite 101
Dover, DE 19904
P: (302) 744-9600
F: (302) 744-9632
E: roy.lafontaine
    @state.de.us

DISTRICT OF COLUMBIA
Ms. Laura Nuss
Director
Department on Disability
Services
1125 15th Street, Northwest, 9th
Floor
Washington, DC 20005
P: (202) 730-1607
F: (202) 730-1843
E: laura.nuss@dc.gov

FLORIDA
Mr. Bryan Vaughan
Acting Director
Agency for Persons with
Disabilities
4030 Esplanade Way, Suite 380
Tallahassee, FL 32399
P: (850) 488-4257
F: (850) 922-6456
E: bryan_vaughan
    @apd.state.fl.us

GEORGIA
Ms. Beverly Rollins
Director
Division of Developmental
Disabilities
2 Peachtree Street, Northwest
22nd Floor
Atlanta, GA 30303
P: (404) 463-8037
F: (404) 657-2310
E: bdrollins@dhr.ga.gov

HAWAII
Dr. David F. Fray
Chief
Developmental Disabilities
Division
Department of Health
1250 Punchbowl Street, Room
463
Honolulu, HI 96813
P: (808) 586-5840
F: (808) 586-5844
E: david.fray
    @doh.hawaii.gov

IDAHO
Mr. Chad Cardwell
Developmental Disabilities
Program Manager
Family & Community Services
Department of Health & Welfare
P.O. Box 83720
Boise, ID 83720
P: (208) 334-5536
F: (208) 334-6664
E: cardwelc@dhw.idaho.gov

ILLINOIS
Ms. Reta Hoskin
Acting Director
Division of Developmental
Disabilities
319 East Madison, Suite 4N
Springfield, IL 62701
P: (217) 524-7065
E: reta.hoskin@illinois.gov

INDIANA
Ms. Julia Holloway
Director
Disability & Rehabilitative
Services
402 West Washington Stret,
W451
P.O. Box 7083
Indianapolis, IN 46207
P: (317) 232-1147
F: (317) 233-4693
E: julia.holloway
    @fssa.in.gov

IOWA
Ms. Jeanne Nesbit
Division Administrator
Division of Mental Health &
Disability Services
1305 East Walnut Street
Des Moines, IA 50319
P: (515) 281-8580
F: (515) 242-6036
E: jnesbit@dhs.state.ia.us

KANSAS
Ms. Margaret Zillinger
Director
Community Supports &
Services
Docking State Office Building,
9th Floor
915 Southwest Harrison
Topeka, KS 66612
P: (785) 296-6140
F: (785) 296-0557
E: margaret.zillinger
    @srs.ks.gov

KENTUCKY
Mr. Stephen Hall
Commissioner
Department for Behavioral
Health, Developmental &
Intellectual Disabilities
100 Fair Oaks Lane, 4E-B
Frankfort, KY 40621
P: (502) 564-4527
E: Stephen.Hall@ky.gov

LOUISIANA
Ms. Julia Kenny
Assistant Secretary
Office for Citizens with
Developmental Disabilities
628 North 4th Street
P.O. Box 629
Baton Rouge, LA 70821
P: (225) 342-9500
E: julia.kenny@la.gov

MAINE
Ms. Jane J. Gallivan
Director
Office of Adults with Cognitive
& Physical Disability Services
2nd Floor Marquart, 32 Blossom
Lane
State House Station, #11
Augusta, ME 04333
P: (207) 287-4242
F: (207) 287-9915
E: jane.gallivan@maine.gov

MARYLAND
Ms. Stephanie Garrity
Executive Director
Developmental Disabilities
Administration
201 West Preston Street, 4th
Floor
Baltimore, MD 21201
P: (410) 767-5216
E: sgarrity
@dhmh.state.md.us

MASSACHUSETTS
Ms. Elin Howe
Commissioner
Department of Mental
Retardation
500 Harrison Avenue
Boston, MA 02118
P: (617) 727-5608
E: elin.howe
@dmr.state.ma.us

MICHIGAN
Ms. Judy Webb
Division Director
Behavioral Health &
Developmental Disabilities
Administration
Lewis Cass Building, 6th Floor
320 South Walnut Street
Lansing, MI 48913
P: (517) 335-4419
F: (517) 241-2969
E: webb@michigan.gov

MINNESOTA
Mr. Alex Bartolic
Director
Disability Services Division
Department of Human Services
P.O. Box 64967
St. Paul, MN 55164
P: (651) 431-2381
F: (651) 431-7412
E: alex.e.bartolic
@state.mn.us

MISSISSIPPI
Ms. Kris Jones
Bureau Director
Bureau of Intellectual &
Developmental Disabilities
1101 Robert E. Lee Building
239 North Lamar Street
Jackson, MS 39201
P: (601) 359-6243
F: (601) 359-5330
E: kris.jones
@dmh.state.ms.us

MISSOURI
Mr. Bernie Simons
Director
Division of Developmental
Disabilities
Department of Mental Health
P.O. Box 687
Jefferson City, MO 65102
P: (573) 751-8676
F: (573) 751-9207
E: bernard.simons
@dmh.mo.gov

MONTANA
Mr. Jeff Sturm
Director
Developmental Disabilities
Program
111 North Sanders, Suite 305
P.O. Box 4210
Helena, MT 59604
P: (406) 444-2695
F: (406) 444-0230
E: jesturm@mt.gov

NEBRASKA
Ms. Jodi Fenner
Director
Division of Developmental
Disabilities
P.O. Box 95026
Lincoln, NE 68509
P: (402) 471-6038
F: (402) 471-9449
E: jodi.fenner@nebraska.gov

NEVADA
Ms. Jane Gruner
Deputy Administrator
Division of Mental Health &
Developmental Services
Department of Health & Human
Services
4126 Technology Way, 2nd
Floor
Carson City, NV 89706
P: (775) 684-4118
F: (775) 684-5966

NEW HAMPSHIRE
Mr. Matthew Ertas
Director
Bureau of Developmental
Services
Department of Health & Human
Services
105 Pleasant Street
Concord, NH 03301
P: (603) 271-5026
F: (603) 271-5166
E: mertas@dhhs.state.nh.us

NEW JERSEY
Ms. Dawn Apgar
Deputy Commissioner
Division of Developmental
Disabilities
Department of Human Services
P.O. Box 726
Trenton, NJ 08625
P: (609) 292-8155
E: dawn.apgar
@dhs.state.nj.us

NEW MEXICO
Ms. Mikki Rogers
Director
Developmental Disabilities
Supports Division
Department of Health
P.O. Box 26110
Santa Fe, NM 87502
P: (505) 476-2400
E: mikki.rogers@state.nm.us

NEW YORK
Ms. Courtney Burke
Acting Commissioner
Office for People With
Developmental Disabilities
44 Holland Avenue
Albany, NY 12229
P: (518) 473-1997
F: (518) 473-1271
E: courtney.burke
@opwdd.state.ny.us

NORTH CAROLINA
Mr. Steve Jordan
Director
Division of Mental Health,
Developmental Disabilities &
Substance Abuse Services
Department of Health & Human
Services
3001 Mail Service Center
Raleigh, NC 27699
P: 9919) 733-7011
F: (919) 508-0951
E: steve.jordan@dhhs.nc.gov

NORTH DAKOTA
Ms. Tina Bay
Director
Developmental Disabilities
Division
Department of Human Services
1237 West Divide Avenue, Suite
1A
Bismarck, ND 58501
P: (701) 328-8966
E: tbay@nd.gov

OHIO
Mr. John L. Martin
Director
Department of Developmental
Disabilities
30 East Broad Street, 12th Floor
Columbus, OH 43215
P: (614) 466-0129
F: (614) 644-5013
E: john.martin
@dmr.state.oh.us

OKLAHOMA
Mr. James Nicholson
Division Director
Developmental Disabilities
Services Division
Department of Human Services
P.O. Box 25352
Oklahoma City, OK 73125
P: (405) 521-6267
F: (405) 522-3037
E: james.nicholson
@okdhs.org

OREGON
Ms. Mary Lee Fay
Administrator
Developmental Disability
Services
Department of Human Services
500 Summer Street, Northeast,
E-09
Salem, OR 97301
P: (503) 945-9787
F: (503) 373-7274
E: marylee.fay@state.or.us

PENNSYLVANIA
Mr. Casey Friel
Acting Secretary
Office of Developomental
Programs
Department of Public Welfare
P.O. Box 2675
Harrisburg, PA 17110
P: (717) 787-3700
F: (717) 787-6583

RHODE ISLAND
Dr. Craig S. Stenning
Director
Department of Behavioral
Healthcare, Developmental
Disabilities & Hospitals
Barry Hall
14 Harrington Road
Cranston, RI 02920
P: (401) 462-2339
F: (401) 462-6636
E: cstenning@mhrh.ri.gov

Developmentally Disabled

SOUTH CAROLINA
Dr. Beverly A. H. Buscemi
Director
Department of Disabilities &
Special Needs
3440 Harden Street Extension
P.O. Box 4706
Columbia, SC 29240
P: (803) 898-9769
F: (803) 898-9653
E: bbuscemi@ddsn.sc.gov

SOUTH DAKOTA
Ms. Carol Ruen
Interim Director
Division of Developmental
Disabilities
Hillsview Plaza, East Highway
34
500 East Capitol
Pierre, SD 57501
P: (605) 773-3438
F: (605) 773-7562
E: carol.ruen@state.sd.us

TENNESSEE
Mr. James M. Henry
Deputy Commissioner
Division of Intellectual
Disabilities Services
Andrew Jackson Office Building
500 Deadrick Street
Nashville, TN 37243
P: (615) 532-6538
F: (615) 253-4089
E: james.henry@tn.gov

TEXAS
Mr. Chris Traylor
Commissioner
Department of Aging &
Disability Services
701 West 51st Street
P.O. Box 149030
Austin, TX 78714
P: (512) 438-3011
F: (512) 438-4220

UTAH
Mr. Alan Ormsby
Director
Division of Services for People
with Disabilities
Department of Human Services
195 North 1950 West
Salt Lake City, UT 84116
P: (801) 538-4135
F: (801) 538-4279
E: akormsby@utah.gov

VERMONT
Ms. Marybeth McCaffrey
Division Director
Department of Disabilities,
Aging & Independent Living
Division of Disability & Aging
Services
103 South Main Street
Waterbury, VT 05671
P: (802) 241-4592
F: (802) 241-4224
E: Mary.McCaffrey
    @ahs.state.vt.us

VIRGINIA
Mr. C. Lee Price
Director
Office of Developmental
Services
P.O. Box 1797
Richmond, VA 23218
P: (804) 786-5850
F: (804) 692-0077
E: lee.price
    @dbhds.virginia.gov

WASHINGTON
Ms. Linda Rolfe
Director
Division of Developmental
Disabilities
Aging & Disabilities Services
Admin.
P.O. Box 45310
Olympia, WA 98504
P: (360) 725-3461
F: (360) 407-0955
E: rolfela@dshs.wa.gov

WEST VIRGINIA
Ms. Victoria L. Jones
Commissioner
Bureau for Behavioral Health &
Health Facilities
Department of Health & Human
Resources
350 Capitol Street, Room 350
Charleston, WV 25301
P: (304) 558-0736
F: (304) 558-2230
E: Victoria.L.Jones@wv.gov

WISCONSIN
Ms. Beth Wroblewski
Director
Division of Long Term Care
1 West Wilson Street, Room 418
P.O. Box 7851
Madison, WI 53707
P: (608) 267-5139
F: (608) 261-6752
E: beth.wroblewski
    @wisconsin.gov

WYOMING
Ms. Chris Newman
Interim Administrator
Mental Health & Substance
Abuse Division
Department of Health
6101 Yellowstone Road, Room
220
Cheyenne, WY 82002
P: (307) 777-8763
F: (307) 777-5580
E: chris.newman
    @health.wyo.gov

Economic Development

Responsible for efforts designed to encourage industry to locate, develop and expand in the state.

ALABAMA
Mr. Seth Hammett
Director
Development Office
401 Adams Avenue, 6th Floor
Montgomery, AL 36130
P: (334) 242-0400
F: (334) 242-5669
E: seth.hammett
@ado.alabama.gov

ALASKA
Ms. Susan K. Bell
Commissioner
Department of Commerce,
Community & Economic
Development
P.O. Box 110800
Juneau, AK 99811
P: (907) 465-2500
F: (907) 465-5442
E: susan.bell@alaska.gov

AMERICAN SAMOA
Mr. Faleseu Eliu Paopao
Director
Department of Commerce
American Samoa Government
Executive Office Building,
Utulei
Pago Pago, AS 96799
P: (684) 633-5155
F: (684) 633-4195

ARIZONA
Mr. Donald E. Cardon
President & CEO
Commerce Authority
1110 West Washington Street,
Suite 600
Phoenix, AZ 85007
P: (602) 771-1160
F: (602) 771-1200
E: commerce@azcommerce.com

ARKANSAS
Ms. Maria Haley
Executive Director
Economic Development
Commission
#1 Capitol Mall, 4C-300
Little Rock, AR 72201
P: (501) 682-2052
F: (501) 682-7394
E: mhaley@1800Arkansas.gov

CALIFORNIA
Mr. Joel A. Ayala
Director
Governor's Office of Economic
Development
1130 K Street
Sacramento, CA 95814
P: (916) 322-0694

COLORADO
Mr. Dwayne Romero
Director
Office of Economic
Development & International
Trade
1625 Broadway, Suite 2700
Denver, CO 80202
P: (303) 892-3840
F: (303) 892-3848
E: dwayne.romero
@state.co.us

CONNECTICUT
Ms. Catherine Smith
Commissioner
Department of Economic &
Community Development
505 Hudson Street
Hartford, CT 06106
P: (860) 270-8010
E: catherine.smith@ct.gov

DELAWARE
Mr. Alan B. Levin
Director
Economic Development Office
99 Kings Highway
Dover, DE 19901
P: (302) 672-6809
F: (302) 739-2523

DISTRICT OF COLUMBIA
Mr. Victor L. Hoskins
Deputy Mayor for Planning and
Economic Development
Office of the Deputy Mayor for
Planning & Economic
Development
John A. Wilson Building, Suite
317
1350 Pennsylvania Avenue,
Northwest
Washington, DC 20004
P: (202) 727-6365
F: (202) 727-6703
E: dmped.eom@dc.gov

FLORIDA
Chris Hart
Director
Office of Tourism, Trade &
Economic Development
Office of the Governor
The Capitol, Suite 2001
Tallahassee, FL 32399
P: (850) 487-2568
F: (850) 487-3014
E: chris.hart
@eog.myflorida.com

GEORGIA
Mr. Chris Cummiskey
Commissioner
Department of Economic
Development
75 Fifth Street, Northwest
Suite 1200
Atlanta, GA 30308
P: (404) 962-4003
F: (404) 962-4009
E: ccummiskey@geogia.org

HAWAII
Mr. Richard C. Lim
Director
Department of Business,
Economic Development &
Tourism
P.O. Box 2359
Honolulu, HI 96804
P: (808) 586-2355
F: (808) 586-2377
E: director
@dbedt.hawaii.gov

IDAHO
Mr. Donald A. Dietrich
Director
Department of Commerce
700 West State Street
P.O. Box 83720
Boise, ID 83720
P: (208) 334-2470
F: (208) 334-2631
E: don.dietrich
@commerce.idaho.gov

ILLINOIS
Mr. Warren Ribley
Director
Department of Commerce &
Economic Opportunity
James R. Thompson Center
100 West Randolph
Chicago, IL 60601
P: (312) 814-7179

INDIANA
Mr. E. Mitch Roob Jr.
Chief Executive Officer &
Secretary of Commerce
Economic Development
Corporation
One North Capitol Avenue,
Suite 700
Indianapolis, IN 46204
P: (317) 232-8992
F: (317) 233-5123
E: mroob@iedc.in.gov

IOWA
Ms. Debi Durham
Director
Department of Economic
Development
200 East Grand Avenue
Des Moines, IA 50309
P: (515) 725-3022
F: (515) 725-3010
E: debi.durham@iowa.gov

KANSAS
Mr. Pat George
Secretary
Department of Commerce
1000 Southwest Jackson Street,
Suite 100
Topeka, KS 66612
P: (785) 296-3481
F: (785) 296-5055
E: pgeorge
@kansascommerce.com

KENTUCKY
Mr. Larry Hayes
Secretary
Cabinet for Economic
Development
Old Capitol Annex
300 West Broadway
Frankfort, KY 40601
P: (502) 564-7140
F: (502) 564-3256
E: econdev@ky.gov

LOUISIANA
Mr. Stephen Moret
Secretary
Economic Development
1051 North Third Street
Baton Rouge, LA 70802
P: (225) 342-5388
F: (225) 342-9095
E: Allison.Gilmore@la.gov

MAINE
Mr. George Gervais
Acting Commissioner
Department of Economic &
Community Development
59 State House Station
Augusta, ME 04330
P: (207) 624-9800

Economic Development

MARYLAND
Mr. Christian Johansson
Secretary
Department of Business &
Economic Development
401 East Pratt Street
Baltimore, MD 21202
P: (410) 767-6301
F: (410) 767-8628
E: CJohansson
    @choosemaryland.org

MASSACHUSETTS
Mr. Gregory Bialecki
Secretary
Executive Office of Housing &
Economic Development
One Ashburton Place, Room
2101
Boston, MA 02108
P: (617) 788-3610
F: (617) 788-3605

MICHIGAN
Mr. Michael A. Finney
President & CEO
Economic Development
Corporation
300 North Washington Square
Lansing, MI 48913
P: (517) 241-1400
F: (517) 241-3683

MINNESOTA
Mr. Mark R. Phillips
Commissioner
Department of Employment &
Economic Development
1st National Bank Building
332 Minnesota Street, Suite
E200
St. Paul, MN 55101
P: (651) 259-7119
F: (651) 296-4772
E: Mark.Phillips
    @state.mn.us

MISSISSIPPI
Mr. Leland R. Speed
Executive Director
Development Authority
501 North West Street
P.O. Box 849
Jackson, MS 39205
P: (601) 359-3449
F: (601) 359-3613
E: lspeed@mississippi.org

MISSOURI
Mr. David Kerr
Director
Department of Economic
Development
301 West High Street
P.O. Box 1157
Jefferson City, MO 65102
P: (573) 751-4962
F: (573) 526-7700
E: ecodev@ded.mo.gov

MONTANA
Mr. Evan D. Barrett
Chief Business Development
Officer
Governor's Office of Economic
Development
P.O. Box 200801
Helena, MT 59620
P: (406) 444-5634
F: (406) 444-3674
E: ebarrett@mt.gov

NEBRASKA
Mr. Richard Baier
Director
Department of Economic
Development
P.O. Box 94666
Lincoln, NE 68509
P: (402) 471-3111
F: (402) 471-3778
E: richard.baier
    @nebraska.gov

NEVADA
Mr. Michael E. Skaggs
Executive Director
Commission on Economic
Development
808 West Nye Lane
Carson City, NV 89703
P: (775) 687-4325
F: (775) 687-9924
E: mskaggs
    @diversifynevada.com

NEW HAMPSHIRE
Mr. Roy Duddy
Director, Division of Economic
Development
Department of Resources &
Economic Development
172 Pembroke Road
P.O. Box 1856
Concord, NH 03302
P: (603) 271-2341
F: (603) 271-6784
E: roy.duddy
    @dred.state.nh.us

NEW JERSEY
Ms. Caren S. Franzini
Chief Executive Officer
Economic Development
Authority
36 West State Street
P.O. Box 990
Trenton, NJ 08625
P: (609) 292-1800
F: (609) 292-0885
E: njeda@njeda.com

NEW YORK
Mr. Kenneth Adams
President & CEO
Empire State Development
Corporation
633 Third Avenue
New York, NY 10017
P: (212) 803-3700
F: (212) 803-3715

NORTH CAROLINA
Mr. J. Keith Crisco
Secretary of Commerce
Department of Commerce
4301 Mail Service Center
Raleigh, NC 27699
P: (919) 733-4151
E: kcrisco@nccommerce.com

NORTH DAKOTA
Mr. Paul Lucy
Director
Economic Development &
Finance Division
Department of Commerce
1600 East Century Avenue, Suite
2
Bismark, ND 58503
P: (701) 328-5388
F: (701) 328-5320
E: plucy@nd.gov

**NORTHERN MARIANA
ISLANDS**
Mr. Manuel Sablan
Director
Commonwealth Development
Authority
P.O. Box 502149
Saipan, MP 96950
P: (670) 234-6245
F: (670) 234-7144

OHIO
Mr. James A. Leftwich
Director
Department of Development
77 South High Street
P.O. Box 1001
Columbus, OH 43216
P: (614) 466-3379
F: (614) 644-0745
E: jim.leftwich
    @development.oh.gov

OKLAHOMA
Mr. Dave Lopez
Secretary of Commerce &
Tourism
Department of Commerce
900 North Stiles Avenue
Oklahoma City, OK 73104
P: (405) 815-6552

OREGON
Mr. Tim McCabe
Director
Business Oregon
775 Summer Street, Northeast,
Suite 200
Salem, OR 97301
P: (503) 986-0110
F: (503) 581-5115
E: tim.mccabe@state.or.us

PENNSYLVANIA
Mr. C. Alan Walker
Acting Secretary
Department of Community &
Economic Development
Commonwealth Keystone
Building
400 North Street, 4th Floor
Harrisburg, PA 17120
P: (866) 466-3972
F: (717) 787-6866

PUERTO RICO
Mr. Jose R. Perez Riera
Executive Director
Industrial Development
Company
#355 FD Roosevelt Avenue
Suite 404
Hato Rey, PR 00918
P: (787) 758-4747
F: (787) 764-1415

RHODE ISLAND
Mr. Keith Stokes
Executive Director
Economic Development
Corporation
315 Iron Horse Way, Suite 101
Providence, RI 02908
P: (401) 278-9100 Ext. 171
F: (401) 273-8270
E: executivedirector
@riedc.com

SOUTH CAROLINA
Mr. Robert M. Hitt III
Secretary
Department of Commerce
1201 Main Street, Suite 1600
Columbia, SC 29201
P: (803) 737-0400
F: (803) 737-0418

SOUTH DAKOTA
Mr. Pat Costello
Commissioner
Governor's Office of Economic
Development
711 East Wells Avenue
Pierre, SD 57501
P: (605) 773-3301
F: (605) 773-3256
E: goedinfo@state.sd.us

TENNESSEE
Mr. Bill Hagerty
Commissioner
Department of Economic &
Community Development
312 Rosa L. Parks Avenue, 11th
Floor
Nashville, TN 37243
P: (615) 741-1888
F: (615) 741-7306
E: Bill.Hagerty@tn.gov

TEXAS
Mr. Aaron Demerson
Director
Economic Development &
Tourism Division
Office of the Governor
P.O. Box 12428
Austin, TX 78711
P: (512) 936-0101
F: (512) 936-0303

U.S. VIRGIN ISLANDS
Mr. Percival Clouden
Chief Executive Officer
Economic Development
Authority
1050 Norre Gade
P.O. Box 305038
St. Thomas, VI 00803
P: (340) 714-1700

UTAH
Mr. Spencer Peterson Eccles
Executive Director
Governor's Office of Economic
Development
324 South State Street, Suite
500
Salt Lake City, UT 84111
P: (801) 538-8700
F: (801) 538-8888
E: speccles@utah.gov

VERMONT
Ms. Noelle MacKay
Commissioner
Department of Economic
Development
1 National Life Drive
Montpelier, VT 05620
P: (802) 828-3080
F: (802) 828-3258
E: noelle.mackay
@state.vt.us

VIRGINIA
Mr. Jeffrey R. Anderson
Executive Director
Economic Development
Partnership
901 East Byrd Street
P.O. Box 798
Richmond, VA 23218
P: (804) 545-5612
F: (804) 371-6524
E: janderson
@yesvirginia.org

WASHINGTON
Mr. Rogers Weed
Director
Department of Commerce
128 10th Avenue, Southwest
P.O. Box 42525
Olympia, WA 98504
P: (360) 725-4000
F: (360) 586-8440
E: rogersw@cted.wa.gov

WEST VIRGINIA
Mr. J. Keith Burdette
Secretary of Commerce
Department of Commerce
Capitol Complex Building 6,
Room 525
1900 Kanawha Boulevard East
Charleston, WV 25305
P: (304) 558-2234
F: (304) 558-1189
E: J.Keith.Burdette@wv.gov

WISCONSIN
Mr. Jim O'Keefe
Administrator
Business Development Division
201 West Washington Avenue,
5th Floor
Madison, WI 53703
P: (608) 267-9384
E: jim.okeefe@wisconsin.gov

WYOMING
Mr. Bob Jensen
Chief Executive Officer
Business Council
214 West 15th Street
Cheyenne, WY 82002
P: (307) 777-2800
F: (307) 777-2837
E: bob.jensen
@wybusiness.org

Education (Chief State School Officer)

Overall responsibility for public elementary and secondary school systems.

ALABAMA
Dr. Joseph B. Morton
State Superintendent of Education
Department of Education
5114 Gordon Persons Office Building
50 North Ripley Street
Montgomery, AL 36104
P: (334) 242-9700
F: (334) 242-9708
E: jmorton@alsde.edu

AMERICAN SAMOA
Dr. Clarie Poumele
Director of Education
Department of Education
American Samoa Government
Pago Pago, AS 96799
P: (684) 633-5237
F: (684) 633-4240

ARKANSAS
Dr. Tom Kimbrell
Commissioner
Department of Education
Four Capitol Mall, Room 304A
Little Rock, AR 72201
P: (501) 682-4475
F: (501) 682-1079
E: tom.kimbrell
    @arkansas.gov

CALIFORNIA
Hon. Tom Torlakson (D)
State Superintendent of Public Instruction
Department of Education
1430 N Street, SUite 5111
Sacramento, CA 95814
P: (916) 319-0827
F: (916) 319-0175
E: superintendent
    @cde.ca.gov

COLORADO
Mr. Robert Hammond
Commissioner of Education
Department of Education
201 East Colfax Avenue, Room 500
Denver, CO 80203
P: (303) 866-6646
F: (303) 866-6938
E: commissioner
    @cde.state.co.us

CONNECTICUT
Mr. George A. Coleman
Acting Commissioner
Department of Education
165 Capitol Avenue
Hartford, CT 06106
P: (860) 713-6500
F: (860) 713-7001
E: george.coleman@ct.gov

DELAWARE
Dr. Lillian Lowery
Secretary of Education
Department of Education
Townsend Building, 401 Federal Street
Suite 2
Dover, DE 19901
P: (302) 739-4000
F: (302) 739-4654
E: llowery@doe.k12.de.us

FLORIDA
Mr. Eric J. Smith
Commissioner
Department of Education
Turlington Building, Suite 1514
325 West Gaines Street
Tallahassee, FL 32399
P: (850) 245-0505
F: (850) 245-9667
E: commissioner@fldoe.org

GEORGIA
Dr. John Barge
State Superintendent of Schools
Department of Education
Twin Towers East, Suite 2066
205 Butler Street, Southwest
Atlanta, GA 30334
P: (404) 656-2800
F: (404) 651-8737

GUAM
Dr. Nerissa Bretania-Shafer
Superintendent
Department of Education
P.O. Box DE
Hagatna, GU 96932
P: (671) 475-0462
F: (671) 472-5003
E: nbshafer@gdoe.net

HAWAII
Ms. Kathryn Matayoshi
Superintendent
Department of Education
P.O. Box 2360
Honolulu, HI 96804
F: (808) 586-3320

IDAHO
Hon. Tom Luna (R)
Superintendent of Public Instruction
State Department of Education
650 West State Street
P.O. Box 83720
Boise, ID 83720
P: (208) 332-6800
F: (208) 334-2228
E: trluna@sde.idaho.gov

ILLINOIS
Dr. Christopher Koch
Superintendent of Education
Board of Education
100 North First Street
Springfield, IL 62777
P: (217) 782-2221
F: (217) 785-3972

INDIANA
Dr. Tony Bennett
Superintendent of Public Instruction
Department of Education
151 West Ohio Street
Indianapolis, IN 46204
P: (317) 232-6665
F: (317) 232-8004
E: superintendent
    @doe.in.gov

IOWA
Dr. Jason Glass
Director
Department of Education
Grimes State Office Building
400 East 14th Street
Des Moines, IA 50319
P: (515) 281-3436
F: (515) 281-4122
E: jason.glass@iowa.gov

KANSAS
Dr. Diane DeBacker
Commissioner of Education
Department of Education
120 Southeast 10th Avenue
Topeka, KS 66612
P: (785) 296-3202
F: (785) 291-3791
E: ddebacker@ksde.org

KENTUCKY
Dr. Terry Holliday
Commissioner of Education
Department of Education
Capital Plaza Tower, 1st Floor
500 Mero Street
Frankfort, KY 40601
P: (502) 564-3141
F: (502) 564-5680

LOUISIANA
Mr. Paul G. Pastorek
Superintendent of Education
Department of Education
P.O. Box 94064
Baton Rouge, LA 70804
P: (225) 342-3602
F: (225) 342-7316

MAINE
Mr. Stephen Bowen
Commissioner
Department of Education
23 State House Station
Augusta, ME 04333
P: (207) 624-6600
F: (207) 624-6700

MARYLAND
Dr. Nancy S. Grasmick
State Superintendent
State Department of Education
State Education Building
200 West Baltimore Street
Baltimore, MD 21201
P: (410) 767-0462
F: (410) 333-6033
E: ngrasmick
    @msde.state.md.us

MASSACHUSETTS
Mr. Mitchell Chester
Commissioner
Department of Elementary & Secondary Education
75 Pleasant Street
Malden, MA 02148
P: (781) 338-3100
F: (781) 338-3770

MICHIGAN
Mr. Mike P. Flanagan
Superindendent of Public Instruction
Department of Education
608 West Allegan Street
P.O. Box 30008
Lansing, MI 48909
P: (517) 373-3324
F: (517) 375-4565

MINNESOTA
Ms. Brenda Cassellius
Commissioner
Department of Education
1500 Highway 36, West
Roseville, MN 55113
P: (651) 582-8200
F: (651) 582-8724
E: mde.commissioner
    @state.mn.us

MISSISSIPPI
Dr. Hank M. Bounds
Commissioner of Higher
Education
Institutions of Higher Learning
3825 Ridgewood Road
Jackson, MS 39211
P: (601) 432-6198
F: (601) 432-6972
E: hbounds@ihl.state.ms.us

MISSOURI
Dr. Chris Nicastro
Commissioner
Department of Elementary &
Secondary Education
P.O. Box 480
Jefferson City, MO 65102
P: (573) 751-4212
F: (573) 751-1179
E: pubinfo@dese.mo.gov

MONTANA
Hon. Denise Juneau (D)
Superintendent
Office of Public Instruction
P.O. Box 202501
Helena, MT 59620
P: (406) 444-5658
F: (406) 444-9299
E: OPISupt@mt.gov

NEBRASKA
Dr. Roger Breed
Commissioner
Department of Education
301 Centennial Mall South
P.O. Box 94987
Lincoln, NE 68509
P: (402) 471-5020
E: roger.breed@nebraska.gov

NEVADA
Mr. Keith W. Rheault
Superintendent
Department of Education
700 East Fifth Street
Carson City, NV 89701
P: (775) 687-9217
F: (775) 687-9101
E: krheault@doe.nv.gov

NEW HAMPSHIRE
Ms. Virginia M. Barry
Commissioner
Department of Education
101 Pleasant Street
Concord, NH 03301
P: (603) 271-3144
E: virginia.barry
@ed.state.nh.us

NEW JERSEY
Mr. Chris Cerf
Acting Commissioner
Department of Education
100 River View Plaza
P.O. Box 500
Trenton, NJ 08625
P: (609) 292-4450
F: (609) 777-4099

NEW MEXICO
Ms. Hanna Skandera
Secretary of Education
Public Education Department
Jerry Apodaca Education
Building
300 Don Gaspar
Santa Fe, NM 87501
P: (505) 827-5800
F: (505) 827-6520

NEW YORK
Mr. David M. Steiner
Commissioner
State Education Department
89 Washington Avenue
Albany, NY 12234
P: (518) 474-3852
E: commissioner
@mail.nysed.gov

NORTH CAROLINA
Dr. June Atkinson
Superintendent of Public
Instruction
Department of Public
Instruction
6301 Mail Service Center
Raleigh, NC 27699
P: (919) 807-3430
F: (919) 807-3445
E: jatkinson
@dpi.state.nc.us

NORTH DAKOTA
Dr. Wayne G. Sanstead
State Superintendent
Department of Public
Instruction
600 East Boulevard Avenue
Department 201
Bismarck, ND 58505
P: (701) 328-4570
F: (701) 328-2461
E: wsanstead@nd.gov

**NORTHERN MARIANA
ISLANDS**
Ms. Rita Sablan
Commissioner of Education
CNMI Public School System
P.O. Box 501370CK
Saipan, MP 96950
P: (670) 664-3700
F: (670) 664-3798

OHIO
Mr. Stan W. Heffner
Interim Superintendent of Public
Instruction
Department of Education
25 South Front Street
Columbus, OH 43215
P: (614) 466-7578
F: (614) 728-4781
E: stan.heffner
@ode.state.oh.us

OKLAHOMA
Hon. Janet Barresi
Superintendent of Public
Instruction
Department of Education
2500 North Lincoln Boulevard
Oklahoma City, OK 73105
P: (405) 521-3301
F: (405) 521-6205

OREGON
Hon. Susan Castillo (D)
Superintendent of Public
Instruction
Department of Education
255 Capitol Street, Northeast
Salem, OR 97310
P: (503) 947-5740
F: (503) 378-5156
E: superintendent.castillo
@state.or.us

PENNSYLVANIA
Mr. Ron Tomalis
Secretary of Education
Department of Education
333 Market Street
Harrisburg, PA 17126
P: (717) 787-5820

PUERTO RICO
Dr. Rafael Aragunde Torres
Secretary of Education
Department of Education
P.O. Box 190759
San Juan, PR 00919
P: (787) 759-2000
F: (787) 250-0275

RHODE ISLAND
Dr. Deborah A. Gist
Commissioner
Department of Elementary &
Secondary Education
255 Westminster Street
Providence, RI 02903
P: (401) 222-4600 Ext. 2001
F: (202) 727-2019
E: deborah.gist@ride.ri.gov

SOUTH CAROLINA
Hon. Mick Zais
Superintendent of Education
Department of Education
1429 Senate Street, Suite 1006
Columbia, SC 29201
P: (803) 734-8492
F: (803) 734-3389

SOUTH DAKOTA
Dr. Melody Schopp
Secretary
Department of Education
700 Governors Drive
Pierre, SD 57501
P: (605) 773-5669
F: (605) 773-6139
E: melody.schopp
@state.sd.us

TENNESSEE
Mr. Kevin Huffman
Commissioner
Department of Education
710 James Robertson Parkway
Andrew Johnson Tower, 6th
Floor
Nashville, TN 37243
P: (615) 741-5158
F: (615) 532-4791

TEXAS
Mr. Robert Scott
Commissioner
Education Agency
1701 Congress Avenue
Austin, TX 78701
P: (512) 463-8985
F: (512) 463-9008
E: commissioner
@tea.state.tx.us

U.S. VIRGIN ISLANDS
Dr. LaVerne Terry
Commissioner
Department of Education
1834 Kongens Gade
St. Thomas, VI 00802
P: (340) 774-0100

UTAH
Dr. Larry K. Shumway
Superintendent of Public
Instruction
Office of Education
250 East 500 South
P.O. Box 144200
Salt Lake City, UT 84114
P: (801) 538-7510
F: (801) 538-7768

Education (Chief State School Officer)

VERMONT
Mr. Armando Vilaseca
Commissioner
Department of Education
120 State Street
Montpelier, VT 05620
P: (802) 828-3135
F: (802) 828-3140
E: armando.vilaseca
    @state.vt.us

VIRGINIA
Dr. Patricia Wright
Superintendent of Public
Instruction
Department of Education
101 North 14th Street, 25th
Floor
James Monroe Building
Richmond, VA 23219
P: (804) 225-2023
F: (804) 371-2099
E: patricia.wright
    @doe.virginia.gov

WASHINGTON
Hon. Randy Dorn
Superintendent of Public
Instruction
Department of Public
Instruction
Old Capitol Building
P.O. Box 47200
Olympia, WA 98504
P: (360) 725-6004
F: (360) 753-6712
E: randy.dorn@k12.wa.us

WEST VIRGINIA
Mr. Jorea M. Marple
Superintendent of Schools
Department of Education
1900 Kanawha Boulevard, East
Building 6, Room 358-B
Charleston, WV 25305
P: (304) 558-2681
F: (304) 558-0048
E: dvermill
    @access.k12.wv.us

WISCONSIN
Hon. Tony Evers
Superintendent
Department of Public
Instruction
125 South Webster Street
P.O. Box 7841
Madison, WI 53707
P: (608) 266-1771
E: anthony.evers@dpi.wi.gov

WYOMING
Ms. Cindy Hill
Superintendent of Public
Instruction
Department of Education
2300 Capitol Avenue
Hathaway Building, 2nd Floor
Cheyenne, WY 82002
P: (307) 777-7690
F: (307) 777-6234
E: supt@educ.state.wy.us

Elections Administration

Administers state election laws and supervises the printing and distribution of ballots.

ALABAMA
Ms. Janice McDonald
Division Director
Elections Division
State Capitol Building, Suite E-208
600 Dexter Avenue
Montgomery, AL 36103
P: (334) 242-7559
F: (334) 242-2444
E: Janice.McDonald
    @sos.alabama.gov

ALASKA
Ms. Gail Fenumiai
Director
Division of Elections
Office of the Lieutenant Governor
P.O. Box 110017
Juneau, AK 99811
P: (907) 465-4611
F: (907) 465-3203
E: gail.fenumiai@alaska.gov

AMERICAN SAMOA
Mr. Soliai T. Fuimaono
Chief Election Officer
American Samoa Government
P.O. Box 3790
Pago Pago, AS 96799
P: (684) 633-2522
F: (684) 633-7116

ARIZONA
Ms. Amy Bjelland
Director
Election Services
Secretary of State's Office
1700 West Washington, 7th Floor
Phoenix, AZ 85007
P: (602) 542-8683
F: (602) 542-6172

ARKANSAS
Ms. Martha Adcock
Director of Elections
Secretary of State
State Capitol, Room 026
Little Rock, AR 72201
P: (501) 682-3733
F: (501) 682-3408

Ms. Susie Stormes
Director
State Board of Election Commissioners
501 Woodlane Drive, Suite 122
Little Rock, AR 72201
P: (501) 682-1834
F: (501) 682-1782
E: susie.stormes
    @sos.arkansas.gov

CALIFORNIA
Ms. Cathy Mitchell
Chief
Elections Division
1500 11th Street, 5th Floor
Sacramento, CA 95814
P: (916) 657-2166
F: (916) 653-3214
E: cmitchel@sos.ca.gov

COLORADO
Mr. Judd Choate
Director of Elections
Elections Division
Department of State
1700 Broadway, Suite 200
Denver, CO 80290
P: (303) 894-2200 Ext. 6307
F: (303) 869-4861
E: judd.choate
    @sos.state.co.us

CONNECTICUT
Ms. Peggy Reeves
Assistant To the Sec. for Elections, Legislative & Intergovernmental Affairs
Legislation & Elections Administration Division
30 Trinity Street
Hartford, CT 06106
P: (860) 509-6100
F: (860) 509-6127

DELAWARE
Ms. M. Elaine Manlove
State Election Commissioner
Department of Elections
905 South Governors Ave, Suite 170
Dover, DE 19904
P: (302) 739-4277
F: (302) 739-6794

DISTRICT OF COLUMBIA
Mr. Togo D. West Jr.
Chair
Board of Elections & Ethics
441 4th Street, Northwest
Suite 250 North
Washington, DC 20001
P: (202) 727-2525
F: (202) 347-2648
E: boee@dc.gov

FLORIDA
Hon. Kurt S. Browning (R)
Secretary of State
Office of the Secretary of State
500 South Bronough, Suite 100
Tallahassee, FL 32399
P: (850) 245-6500
F: (850) 245-6125
E: secretaryofstate
    @dos.state.fl.us

GEORGIA
Ms. Ann Hicks
Interim Director of Elections
Elections Division
Suite 802, Floyd West Tower
2 Martin Luther King Jr. Drive
Atlanta, GA 30334
P: (404) 656-2871
F: (404) 656-9531

GUAM
Mr. John Blas
Executive Director
Elections Commission
P.O. Box BG
Hagatna, GU 96932
P: (671) 477-9791
F: (671) 477-1895
E: director@gec.guam.gov

HAWAII
Mr. Scott Nago
Chief Election Officer
Office of Elections
802 Lehua Avenue
Pearl City, HI 96782
P: (808) 453-8683
F: (808) 453-6006
E: elections@hawaii.gov

IDAHO
Mr. Tim Hurst
Chief Deputy
Secretary of State
P.O. Box 83720
Boise, ID 83720
P: (208) 334-2300
F: (208) 334-2282
E: thurst@sos.idaho.gov

ILLINOIS
Mr. Rupert Borgsmiller
Executive Director
State Board of Elcctions
1020 South Spring Street
Springfield, IL 62704
P: (217) 782-4141
F: (217) 782-5959
E: rborgsmiller
    @elections.il.gov

INDIANA
Mr. Trent Deckard
Co-Director
Elections Division
302 West Washington, Room E204
Indianapolis, IN 46204
P: (317) 232-3940
F: (317) 233-6793
E: TDeckard@iec.IN.gov

Mr. J. Bradley King
Co-Director
Election Division
302 West Washington, Room E204
Indianapolis, IN 46204
P: (317) 233-0929
F: (317) 233-6793
E: bking@iec.IN.gov

IOWA
Ms. Sarah Reisetter
Director of Elections
Secretary of State Office
First Floor, Lucas Building
321 East 12th Street
Des Moines, IA 50319
P: (515) 281-0145
F: (515) 281-4682
E: sarah.reisetter
    @sos.state.ia.us

KANSAS
Mr. Brad Bryant
Deputy Assistant for Elections
Office of the Secretary of State - Elections & Legislative Matters
120 Southwest 10th Avenue
Memorial Hall, 1st Floor
Topeka, KS 66612
P: (785) 296-4561
F: (785) 368-8033

KENTUCKY
Ms. Sarah Ball Johnson
Executive Director
State Board of Elections
140 Walnut Street
Frankfort, KY 40601
P: (502) 573-7100
F: (502) 573-4369
E: sarahball.johnson@ky.gov

LOUISIANA
Ms. Angie Rogers
Commissioner of Elections
Elections Division
8585 Archives Avenue
P.O. Box 94125
Baton Rouge, LA 70804
P: (225) 922-0900
F: (225) 922-0945
E: angie.laplace
    @sos.louisiana.gov

Elections Administration

MAINE
Ms. Julie L. Flynn
Deputy Secretary of State
Bureau of Corporation,
Elections & Commissions
101 State House Station
Augusta, ME 04333
P: (207) 624-7736
F: (207) 287-5874

MARYLAND
Ms. Linda H. Lamone
State Administrator
State Board of Elections
151 West Street, Suite 200
P.O. Box 6486
Annapolis, MD 21401
P: (410) 269-2840
F: (410) 974-2019
E: llamone
   @elections.state.md.us

MASSACHUSETTS
Ms. Navjeet Bal
Commissioner
Department of Revenue
100 Cambridge Street, 8th Floor
Boston, MA 02114
P: (617) 626-2201
F: (617) 626-2299

Ms. Michelle Tassinari
Legal Counsel
Election Division
One Ashburton Place, Room
1705
Boston, MA 02108
P: (617) 727-2828
F: (617) 742-3238

MICHIGAN
Mr. Christopher M. Thomas
Director
Bureau of Elections
Richard H. Austin Building,
First Floor
430 West Allegan Street
Lansing, MI 48918
P: (517) 373-2450
F: (517) 241-4785
E: ChristopherT
   @michigan.gov

MINNESOTA
Mr. Gary Poser
Elections Director
Office of the Secretary of State
180 State Office Building
100 Dr. Martin Luther King Jr.
Blvd.
St. Paul, MN 55155
P: (651) 215-1440
E: Gary.Poser@state.mn.us

MISSISSIPPI
Mr. W. Heath Hillman
Assistant Secretary of State for
Elections
Elections Division
401 Mississippi Street
P.O. Box 136
Jackson, MS 39205
P: (601) 359-6368
F: (601) 359-5019

MISSOURI
Ms. Waylene Hiles
Acting Deputy Secretary of
State for Elections
Secretary of State's Office
Kirkpatrick State Information
Center
P.O. Box 1767
Jefferson City, MO 65102
P: (573) 751-2301
F: (573) 526-3242
E: elections@sos.mo.gov

MONTANA
Ms. Lisa Kimmet
Deputy
Elections & Government
Services
Capitol Building, Room 260
P.O. Box 202801
Helena, MT 59620
P: (406) 444-5376
F: (406) 444-2023
E: soselection@mt.gov

NEBRASKA
Mr. Neal Erickson
Assistant Secretary of State
Election Administration
State Capitol, Suite 2300
Lincoln, NE 68502
P: (402) 471-3229
F: (402) 471-3237
E: neal.erickson@sos.ne.gov

NEVADA
Mr. Scott Gilles
Deputy Secretary of State
Elections Division
Office of the Secretary of State
101 North Carson Street, Suite 3
Carson City, NV 89701
P: (775) 684-5793
F: (775) 684-5718
E: sgilles@sos.nv.gov

NEW HAMPSHIRE
Mr. Anthony B. Stevens
Assistant Secretary of State
Election Division
107 North Main Street
State House, Room 204
Concord, NH 03301
P: (603) 271-5335
F: (603) 271-6316
E: astevens@sos.state.nh.us

NEW MEXICO
Ms. Bobbi Shearer
Director
Bureau of Elections
State Capitol Annex North
325 Don Gaspar, Suite 300
Santa Fe, NM 87503
P: (505) 827-8403
F: (505) 827-8403
E: bobbi.shearer
   @state.nm.us

NEW YORK
Mr. Robert A. Brehm
Co-Executive Director
State Board of Elections
40 Steuben Street
Albany, NY 12207
P: (518) 474-8100
F: (518) 486-4068

Mr. Todd D. Valentine
Co-Executive Director
State Board of Elections
40 Steuben Street
Albany, NY 12207
P: (518) 474-8100
F: (518) 486-4068

NORTH CAROLINA
Mr. Johnnie McLean
Deputy Director, Administration
State Board of Elections
Elections Administration
Division
P.O. Box 27255
Raleigh, NC 27611
P: (919) 733-7173
F: (919) 715-0135

NORTH DAKOTA
Mr. Jim Silrum
Deputy Secretary of State
Office of the Secretary of State
600 East Boulevard Avenue
Department 108, 1st Floor
Bismarck, ND 58505
P: (701) 328-2900
F: (701) 328-2992
E: jsilrum@nd.gov

OHIO
Hon. Jon Husted (R)
Secretary of State
Office of the Secretary of State
180 East Broad Street
Columbus, OH 43215
P: (614) 466-2655
F: (614) 644-0649
E: jhusted@sos.state.oh.us

OREGON
Ms. Brenda J. Bayes
Acting Director
Secretary of State, Elections
Division
255 Capitol Street, Northeast,
Suite 501
Salem, OR 97310
P: (503) 986-1518
F: (503) 373-7414
E: brenda.j.bayes
   @state.or.us

PENNSYLVANIA
Mr. Shannon Royer
Deputy Secretary for External
Affairs & Elections
Department of State
210 North Office Building
Harrisburg, PA 17120
P: (717) 787-6458
F: (717) 787-1734

PUERTO RICO
Mr. Ramon Gomez
President
State Election Commission
P.O. Box 19555
Hato Rey, PR 00919
P: (787) 777-8682
F: (787) 296-0173

RHODE ISLAND
Mr. Robert Kando
Executive Director
Board of Elections
50 Branch Avenue
Providence, RI 02904
P: (401) 222-2345
F: (401) 222-3135
E: elections
   @elections.ri.gov

SOUTH CAROLINA
Ms. Marci Andino
Executive Director
State Election Commission
2221 Devine Street, Suite 105
P.O. Box 5987
Columbia, SC 29250
P: (803) 734-9060
F: (803) 734-9366
E: elections
   @elections.sc.gov

SOUTH DAKOTA
Hon. Jason M. Gant (R)
Secretary of State
Office of the Secretary of State
500 East Capitol Avenue, Suite 204
Pierre, SD 57501
P: (605) 773-3537
F: (605) 773-6580
E: sdsos@state.sd.us

TENNESSEE
Mr. Mark K. Goins
Coordinator of Elections
Secretary of State's Office
312 Rosa L. Parks Avenue
Snodgrass Tower, 9th Floor
Nashville, TN 37243
P: (615) 741-7956
F: (615) 741-1278
E: tennessee.elections
    @tn.gov

TEXAS
Ms. Ann McGeehan
Division Director
Elections Division
Office of the Secretary of State
P.O. Box 12697
Austin, TX 78711
P: (512) 463-9871
F: (512) 475-2811

U.S. VIRGIN ISLANDS
Mr. John Abramson
Supervisor of Elections
Election System of the Virgin Islands
P.O. Box 1499, Kingshill
St. Croix, VI 00851
P: (340) 773-1021
F: (340) 773-4523

UTAH
Hon. Gregory S. Bell (R)
Lieutenant Governor
Office of the Lieutenant Governor
P.O. Box 142325
Salt Lake City, UT 84114
P: (801) 538-1041
F: (801) 538-1133
E: gregbell@utah.gov

VERMONT
Ms. Kathy DeWolfe
Director
Elections & Campaign Finance Division
Office of the Secretary of State
26 Terrace Street
Montpelier, VT 05609
P: (802) 828-2304
F: (802) 828-5171
E: kdewolfe@sec.state.vt.us

VIRGINIA
Mr. Don Palmer
Secretary
Board of Elections
200 North 9th Street, Room 101
Richmond, VA 23219
P: (804) 864-8903
F: (804) 371-0194

WASHINGTON
Ms. Katie Blinn
Acting Co-Director of Elections
Office of the Secretary of State,
Elections Division
520 Union Avenue, Southeast
P.O. Box 40229
Olympia, WA 98504
P: (360) 902-4168
F: (360) 664-4619
E: katie.blinn@sos.wa.gov

Mr. Shane Hamlin
Acting Co-Director of Elections
Office of the Secretary of State,
Elections Division
520 Union Avenue, Southeast
P.O. Box 40229
Olympia, WA 98504
P: (360) 725-5781
F: (360) 664-4619
E: shane.hamlin@sos.wa.gov

WEST VIRGINIA
Mr. David Nichols
Manager, Elections
Office of the Secretary of State
1900 Kanawha Boulevard, East
Capitol Complex Building 1,
Suite 157-K
Charleston, WV 25305
P: (304) 558-6000
F: (304) 558-0900
E: dnichols@wvsos.com

WISCONSIN
Mr. Kevin J. Kennedy
Executive Director
Government Accountability Board
17 West Main Street, Suite 310
Madison, WI 53703
P: (608) 266-8005
F: (608) 267-0500
E: kevin.kennedy
    @seb.state.wi.us

WYOMING
Ms. Peggy Nighswonger
State Elections Director
Secretary of State's Office
Capitol Building, Room B-38
Cheyenne, WY 82002
P: (307) 777-3573
F: (307) 777-7640

Emergency Management

Prepares, maintains and/or implements state disasters plans and coordinates emergency activities.

Information provided by:

National Emergency Management Association
Trina Sheets
Executive Director
P.O. Box 11910
Lexington, KY 40578
P: (859) 244-8000
F: (859) 244-8239
tsheets@csg.org
www.nemaweb.org

ALABAMA
Mr. Art Faulkner
State Director
State Emergency Management Agency
5898 County Road 41
P.O. Drawer 2160
Clanton, AL 35046
P: (205) 280-2201
F: (205) 280-2410
E: art.faulkner
   @ema.alabama.gov

ALASKA
Mr. John Madden
State Director
Division of Homeland Security & Emergency Management
Building #49000, Suite B214
P.O. Box 5750
Fort Richardson, AK 99505
P: (907) 428-7062
F: (907) 428-7009
E: john.madden@alaska.gov

AMERICAN SAMOA
Mr. Mike Sala
State Director
State Department of Homeland Security
P.O. Box 4567
Pago Pago, AS 96799
P: (684) 633-2827
F: (684) 633-5111
E: mrsala@americansamoa.gov

ARIZONA
Mr. Lou Trammell
State Director
State Division of Emergency Management
5636 East McDowell Road
Phoenix, AZ 85008
P: (602) 464-6203
F: (602) 464-6356
E: Lou.Trammell@azdema.gov

ARKANSAS
Mr. David Maxwell
State Director
Department of Emergency Management
Building 9501
Camp Joseph T. Robinson
North Little Rock, AR 72199
P: (501) 683-7834
F: (501) 683-7890
E: david.maxwell
   @adem.arkansas.gov

CALIFORNIA
Mr. Mike Dayton
State Director
State Emergency Management Agency
3650 Schriever Avenue
Mather, CA 95655
P: (916) 845-8506
F: (916) 845-8511
E: mike.dayton
   @calema.ca.gov

COLORADO
Mr. Hans Kallam
State Director
Division of Emergency Management
9195 East Mineral Avenue, Suite 200
Centennial, CO 80112
P: (720) 852-6611
F: (720) 852-6750
E: hans.kallam@state.co.us

CONNECTICUT
Mr. William J. Hackett
State Director
State Emergency Management & Homeland Security
25 Sigourney Street, 6th Floor
Hartford, CT 06106
P: (860) 256-0818
F: (860) 256-0855
E: william.j.hackett@ct.gov

DISTRICT OF COLUMBIA
Ms. Millicent West
State Director
Homeland Security & Emergency Management Agency
2720 Martin Luther King Jr. Avenue, SE
2nd Floor
Washington, DC 20032
P: (202) 481-3010
F: (202) 715-7288
E: millicent.west@dc.gov

FLORIDA
Mr. Bryan Koon
State Director
Division of Emergency Management
2555 Shumard Oak Boulevard
Tallahassee, FL 32399
P: (850) 413-9969
F: (850) 488-1016
E: bryan.koon
   @em.myflorida.com

GEORGIA
Mr. Charley English
State Director
State Emergency Management & Homeland Security
935 East Confederate Avenue, Building 2
P.O. Box 18055
Atlanta, GA 30316
P: (404) 635-7001
F: (404) 635-7009
E: charley.english
   @gema.ga.gov

GUAM
Mr. Charles Ada II
State Director
Office of Homeland Security & Civil Defense
221 B. Chalan Palasyo
Agana Heights, GU 96910
P: (671) 475-9600
F: (671) 477-3727
E: chuck.ada@ghs.guam.gov

HAWAII
Mr. Edward T. Teixeira
State Director
State Civil Defense Division
3949 Diamond Head Road
Honolulu, HI 96816
P: (808) 733-4300 Ext. 501
F: (808) 733-4287
E: eteixeira@scd.hawaii.gov

IDAHO
Col. Bill Shawver
State Director
State Bureau of Homeland Security
4040 West Guard Street, Building 600
Boise, ID 83705
P: (208) 422-3001
F: (208) 422-3044
E: bshawver@bhs.idaho.gov

ILLINOIS
Mr. Jonathon E. Monken
State Director
State Emergency Management Agency
2200 South Dirksen Parkway
Springfield, IL 62703
P: (217) 557-6225
F: (217) 524-7967
E: jonathon.monken
   @illinois.gov

INDIANA
Mr. Joseph Wainscott
State Director
State Department of Homeland Security
302 West Washington Street, Room E208
Indianapolis, IN 46204
P: (317) 232-6139
F: (317) 232-3895
E: jwainscott@dhs.in.gov

IOWA
Brigadier Derek Hill
State Director
State Homeland Security & Emergency Management
7105 Northwest 70th Avenue
Camp Dodge, W4
Johnston, IA 50131
P: (515) 725-3230
F: (515) 725-3290
E: derek.hill@Iowa.gov

KANSAS
Ms. Angee Morgan
State Director
Division of Emergency Management
2800 Southwest Topeka Boulevard
Topeka, KS 66611
P: (785) 274-1403
F: (785) 274-1426
E: angelynn.t.morgan
   @us.army.mil

KENTUCKY
Brigadier John W. Heltzel
State Director
State Emergency Management
EOC Building
100 Minuteman Parkway, Room 106
Frankfort, KY 40601
P: (502) 607-1682
E: john.heltzel@us.army.mil

LOUISIANA
Mr. Mark Cooper
State Director
Governor's Office of Homeland Security & Emergency Preparedness
7667 Independence Boulevard
Baton Rouge, LA 70806
P: (225) 925-7345
F: (225) 925-7348
E: mark.a.cooper@la.gov

MAINE
Mr. Robert McAleer
State Director
State Emergency Management Agency
45 Commercial Drive, Suite #2, #72 SHS
Augusta, ME 04333
P: (207) 624-4402
F: (207) 287-3180
E: robert.mcaleer@maine.gov

MARYLAND
Mr. Richard Muth
State Director
State Emergency Management Agency
State EOC, Camp Fretterd Military Res.
5401 Rue St. Lo Avenue
Reisterstown, MD 21136
P: (410) 517-3625
F: (410) 517-5195
E: rmuth@mema.state.md.us

MASSACHUSETTS
Mr. Kurt Schwartz
State Director
State Emergency Management Agency
400 Worcester Road
Framingham, MA 01702
P: (508) 820-2014
F: (508) 820-2015
E: kurt.schwartz
    @state.ma.us

MICHIGAN
Captain W. Thomas Sands
State Director
State Police/EMHSD
4000 Collins Road
Lansing, MI 48910
P: (517) 333-5042
F: (517) 333-4987
E: SandsT@michigan.gov

MINNESOTA
Ms. Kris Eide
State Director
Division of Homeland Security & Emergency Management
444 Cedar Street, Suite 223
St. Paul, MN 55101
P: (651) 201-7404
F: (651) 296-0459
E: kris.eide@state.mn.us

MISSISSIPPI
Mr. Mike Womack
State Director
State Emergency Management Agency
#1 MEMA Drive
P.O. Box 5644
Pearl, MS 39288
P: (601) 933-6882
F: (601) 933-6810
E: mwomack@mema.ms.gov

MISSOURI
Mr. Paul Parmenter
State Director
State Emergency Management Agency
2302 Militia Drive
Jefferson City, MO 65102
P: (573) 526-9104
E: paul.parmenter
    @sema.dps.mo.gov

MONTANA
Mr. Ed Tinsley
State Director
State Disaster & Emergency Services
1956 Mt. Majo Street
P.O. Box 4789
Fort Harrison, MT 59636
P: (406) 324-4777
F: (406) 841-3965
E: edtinsley@mt.gov

NEBRASKA
Mr. Alan Berndt
State Director
State Emergency Management Agency
1300 Military Road
Lincoln, NE 68508
P: (402) 471-7410
F: (402) 471-7433
E: al.berndt@nebraska.gov

NEVADA
Mr. James Wright
State Director
Division of Emergency Management
2478 Fairview Drive
Carson City, NV 89701
P: (775) 687-0300
F: (775) 687-0322
E: jwright@dps.state.nv.us

NEW HAMPSHIRE
Mr. Christopher M. Pope
State Director
Homeland Security & Emergency Management
33 Hazen Drive
Concord, NH 03305
P: (603) 271-2231
F: (603) 271-6336
E: christopher.pope
    @hsem.nh.gov

NEW JERSEY
Lt. Col. Jerome Hatfield
State Director
State Police
P.O. Box 7068
1040 River Road
West Trenton, NJ 08648
P: (609) 882-2000 ext 6161
F: (609) 530-4593
E: lpphatfj@gw.njsp.org

NEW MEXICO
Mr. Michael Duvall
State Director
State Department of Homeland Security & Emergency Management
130 South Capitol
P.O. Box 27111
Santa Fe, NM 87502
P: (505) 476-9606
F: (505) 476-1057
E: michael.duvall
    @state.nm.us

NEW YORK
Mr. Andrew Feeney
State Director
State Office of Emergency Management
1220 Washington Avenue, Building 22
Suite 101
Albany, NY 12226
P: (518) 292-2301
F: (518) 322-4978
E: afeeney@dhses.ny.gov

NORTH CAROLINA
Mr. H. Douglas Hoell
State Director
State Division of Emergency Management
4713 Mail Service Center
Raleigh, NC 27699
P: (919) 733-3825
F: (919) 733-5406
E: dhoell@ncem.org

NORTH DAKOTA
Mr. Greg Wilz
State Director
State Department of Emergency Services
Building 35, Fraine Barracks Road
P.O. Box 5511
Bismarck, ND 58506
P: (701) 328-8100 x8101
F: (701) 328-8181
E: gwilz@state.nd.us

NORTHERN MARIANA ISLANDS
Mr. Joaquin P. Omar
State Director
Emergency Management Office
Caller Box 10007
Saipan, MP 96950
P: (670) 322-8001
F: (670) 322-7743
E: jpomar@cnmiemo.gov.mp

OHIO
Ms. Nancy Dragani
State Director
State Emergency Management Agency
2855 West Dublin-Granville Road
Columbus, OH 43235
P: (614) 889-7152
F: (614) 889-7183
E: ndragani@dps.state.oh.us

Emergency Management

OKLAHOMA
Mr. Albert Ashwood
State Director
Department of Emergency
Management
P.O. Box 53365
Oklahoma City, OK 73152
P: (405) 521-2481
F: (405) 521-4053
E: albert.ashwood
   @oem.ok.gov

OREGON
Brigadier Michael Caldwell
State Director
Office of Emergency
Management
3225 State Street
P.O. Box 14370
Salem, OR 97309
P: (503) 378-2911
F: (503) 373-7833
E: mike.caldwell
   @mil.state.or.us

PENNSYLVANIA
Mr. Glenn Cannon
State Director
State Emergency Management
Agency
2605 Interstate Drive
Harrisburg, PA 17110
P: (717) 651-2224
F: (717) 651-2040
E: glcannon@state.pa.us

PUERTO RICO
Mr. Heriberto Sauri
State Director
Emergency Management
Agency
P.O. Box 9066597
San Juan, PR 00906
P: (787) 724-0124
F: (787) 725-4244
E: hsauri
   @aemead.gobierno.pr

RHODE ISLAND
Mr. J. David Smith
State Director
State Emergency Management
Agency
645 New London Avenue
Cranston, RI 02920
P: (401) 946-9996
F: (401) 944-1891
E: james.d.smith18
   @us.army.mil

SOUTH CAROLINA
Kim Stenson
State Director
State Emergency Management
Division
2779 Fish Hatchery Road
West Columbia, SC 29172
P: (803) 737-8566
F: (803) 737-8570
E: bcboone@emd.sc.gov

SOUTH DAKOTA
Ms. Kristi Turman
State Director
Office of Emergency
Management
118 West Capitol Avenue
Pierre, SD 57501
P: (605) 773-3231
F: (605) 773-3580
E: kristi.turman
   @state.sd.us

TENNESSEE
Mr. James Bassham
State Director
State Emergency Management
Agency
3041 Sidco Drive
Nashville, TN 37204
P: (615) 741-4332
F: (615) 741-0006
E: jbassham@tnema.org

TEXAS
Nim Kidd
State Director
State Division of Emergency
Management
5805 North Lamar Boulevard
P.O. Box 4087
Austin, TX 78752
P: (512) 424-2443
F: (512) 424-2444
E: nim.kidd
   @txdps.state.tx.us

U.S. VIRGIN ISLANDS
Mr. Elton Lewis
State Director
Emergency Management
Agency
8221 Estate Nisky
St. Thomas, VI 00801
P: (340) 774-2244
F: (340) 715-5517
E: elton.lewis
   @vitema.vi.gov

UTAH
Col. Keith D. Squires
State Director
Department of Public Safety &
Homeland Security
4501 South 2700 West
P.O. Box 141775
Salt Lake City, UT 84114
P: (801) 965-4498
F: (801) 965-4608
E: ksquires@utah.gov

VERMONT
Mr. Mike O'Neil
State Director
State Emergency Management
Agency
103 South Main Street
Waterbury, VT 05671
P: (800) 347-0488
F: (802) 244-5556
E: meoneil@dps.state.vt.us

VIRGINIA
Mr. Michael Cline
State Director
State Department of Emergency
Management
10501 Trade Court
Richmond, VA 23236
P: (804) 897-6501
F: (804) 897-6506
E: michael.cline
   @vdem.virginia.gov

WASHINGTON
Mr. Jim Mullen
Director
State Emergency Management
Building 20, MS: TA-20
Camp Murray, WA 98430
P: (253) 512-7001
F: (253) 512-7207
E: j.mullen@emd.wa.gov

WEST VIRGINIA
Mr. Jimmy Gianato
State Director
Division of Homeland Security
& Emergency Management
1900 Kanawha Boulevard, East
Building 1, Room EB-80
Charleston, WV 25305
P: (304) 558-5380
F: (304) 344-4538
E: jimmy.j.gianato@wv.gov

WISCONSIN
Mr. Michael Hinman
State Director
Division of Emergency
Management
2400 Wright Street
P.O. Box 7865
Madison, WI 53707
P: (608) 242-3210
F: (608) 242-3247
E: mike.hinman
   @wisconsin.gov

Employment Services

Provides job counseling, testing and placement services in the state.

ALABAMA
Mr. Thomas Surtees
Director
Department of Industrial Relations
649 Monroe Street
Montgomery, AL 36131
P: (334) 242-8078
F: (334) 242-3960
E: tom.surtees
    @dir.alabama.gov

ALASKA
Mr. Thomas W. Nelson
Director
Department of Labor & Workforce Development
Division of Employment Security
P.O. Box 115509
Juneau, AK 99811
P: (907) 465-2712
F: (907) 465-4537
E: esd.director@alaska.gov

AMERICAN SAMOA
Lt. Col. Evelyn Vaiautolu Langford
Director
Department of Human Resources
American Samoa Government
Pago Pago, AS 96799
P: (684) 644-4485
F: (684) 633-1139

ARIZONA
Mr. James Apperson
Assistant Director
Division of Employment & Rehabilitation Services
Department of Economic Security
1717 West Jefferson Street
Phoenix, AZ 85007
P: (602) 542-4910
E: japperson@azdes.gov

ARKANSAS
Mr. Artee Williams
Director
Department of Workforce Services
#2 Capitol Mall
Little Rock, AR 72201
P: (501) 682-2121
E: artee.williams
    @arkansas.gov

COLORADO
Ms. Ellen Golombek
Executive Director
Department of Labor & Employment
633 17th Street, Suite 201
Denver, CO 80202
P: (303) 318-8000
F: (303) 318-8048
E: egolombek@state.co.us

CONNECTICUT
Mr. Glenn Marshall
Commissioner
Department of Labor
200 Folly Brook Boulevard
Wethersfield, CT 06109
P: (860) 263-6505
F: (860) 263-6529
E: glenn.marshall@ct.gov

DELAWARE
Ms. Lori Reeder
Director
Department of Labor
Division of Employment & Training
4425 North Market Street
Wilmington, DE 19802
P: (302) 761-8110
E: lori.reeder@state.de.us

DISTRICT OF COLUMBIA
Ms. Lisa Maria Mallory
Acting Director
Department of Employment Services
4058 Minnesota Avenue, Northeast
Washington, DC 20019
P: (202) 724-7000
F: (202) 673-6993
E: does@dc.gov

FLORIDA
Ms. Cynthia R. Lorenzo
Director
Agency for Workforce Innovation
107 East Madison Street
MSC 110, Caldwell Building
Tallahassee, FL 32399
P: (850) 245-7298
F: (850) 921-3223
E: cynthia.lorenzo
    @flaawi.com

GEORGIA
Hon. Mark Butler (R)
Commissioner
Department of Labor
148 International Boulevard Northeast
Atlanta, GA 30303
P: (404) 232-7300
F: (404) 656-2683
E: mark.butler
    @dol.state.ga.us

GUAM
Ms. Leah Beth Naholowaa
Director
Department of Labor
Government of Guam
P.O. Box 9970
Tamuning, GU 96931
P: (671) 647-6510
F: (671) 674-6517

HAWAII
Ms. Elaine Young
Administrator
Workforce Development Division
830 Punchbowl Street
Suite 329
Honolulu, HI 96813
P: (808) 586-8812
F: (808) 586-8822
E: dlir.workforce.develop
    @hawaii.gov

IDAHO
Mr. Roger B. Madsen
Director
Department of Labor
317 West Main Street
Boise, ID 83735
P: (208) 332-3579
F: (208) 334-6430
E: rmadsen@cl.idaho.gov

ILLINOIS
Ms. Maureen T. O'Donnell
Director
Department of Employment Security
33 South State Street
Chicago, IL 60603
P: (312) 793-9274
F: (312) 793-9834

INDIANA
Mr. Mark W. Everson
Commissioner
Department of Workforce Development
10 North Senate Avenue
Indianapolis, IN 46204
P: (317) 232-7676
E: MEverson@dwd.IN.gov

IOWA
Ms. Teresa Wahlert
Agency Director
Workforce Development
1000 East Grand Avenue
Des Moines, IA 50319
P: (515) 281-5364
E: teresa.wahlert
    @iwd.iowa.gov

KANSAS
Mr. Pat George
Secretary
Department of Commerce
1000 Southwest Jackson Street, Suite 100
Topeka, KS 66612
P: (785) 296-3481
F: (785) 296-5055
E: pgeorge
    @kansascommerce.com

LOUISIANA
Shannon Templet
Director
Department of State Civil Service
1201 North Third Street, Suite 3-280
P.O. Box 94111
Baton Rouge, LA 70804
P: (225) 342-8272
F: (225) 342-0966
E: shannon.templet@la.gov

MAINE
Ms. Laura Boyett
Acting Commissioner
Department of Labor
P.O. Box 259
Augusta, ME 04332
P: (207) 287-3787
F: (207) 623-7934
E: luara.l.boyett@maine.gov

MARYLAND
Ms. Cynthia Kollner
Executive Director
Office of Personnel Services & Benefits
Department of Budget & Management
301 West Preston Street, Room 609
Baltimore, MD 21201
P: (410) 767-4715
F: (410) 333-5262
E: ckollner@dbm.state.md.us

Employment Services

MASSACHUSETTS
Mr. Michael Taylor
Director
Department of Workforce
Development
Charles F. Hurley Building
19 Staniford Street
Boston, MA 02114
P: (617) 626-5680
F: (617) 727-8671

MINNESOTA
Mr. Mark R. Phillips
Commissioner
Department of Employment &
Economic Development
1st National Bank Building
332 Minnesota Street, Suite
E200
St. Paul, MN 55101
P: (651) 259-7119
F: (651) 296-4772
E: Mark.Phillips
    @state.mn.us

MISSISSIPPI
Mr. Les Range
Executive Director
Department of Employment
Security
1235 Echelon Parkway
P.O. Box 1699
Jackson, MS 39215
P: (601) 321-6100
F: (601) 321-6104
E: lrange@mdes.ms.gov

MISSOURI
Ms. Julie Gibson
Director
Department of Economic
Development
Division of Workforce
Development
P.O. Box 1157
Jefferson City, MO 65102
P: (573) 751-3349
F: (573) 751-8162
E: dwdsupport@ded.mo.gov

MONTANA
Mr. Keith Kelly
Commissioner
Department of Labor & Industry
P.O. Box 1728
Helena, MT 59624
P: (406) 444-9091
F: (406) 444-1394
E: dliquestions@mt.gov

NEBRASKA
Ms. Catherine D. Lang
Commissioner of Labor
Department of Labor
P.O. Box 94600
Lincoln, NE 68509
P: (402) 471-9000
F: (402) 471-2318
E: catherine.lang
    @nebraska.gov

NEVADA
Ms. Cindy A. Jones
Deputy Director/Administrator
for the Employment Security
Division
Department of Employment,
Training & Rehabilitation
Employment Security Division
500 East Third Street
Carson City, NV 89713
P: (775) 684-3909
F: (775) 684-3850
E: cajones@nvdetr.org

NEW JERSEY
Mr. Gary Altman
Director
One-Stop Coordination &
Support Division
P.O. Box 055
Trenton, NJ 08625
P: (609) 292-8852
F: (609) 633-2556

NEW MEXICO
Ms. Celina Bussey
Secretary
Department of Workforce
Solutions
401 Broadway Northeast
Albuquerque, NM 87103
P: (505) 841-8405
F: (505) 841-8491

NEW YORK
Ms. Colleen C. Gardner
Commissioner
Department of Labor
W. Averell Harriman State
Office Campus
Building 12
Albany, NY 12240
P: (518) 457-9000
F: (518) 485-6297
E: colleen.gardner
    @labor.state.ny.us

NORTH CAROLINA
Mr. Manfred Emmrich
Director of Employment Service
Employement Security
Commission
P.O. Box 25903
Raleigh, NC 27611
P: (919) 733-7522
E: manfred.emmrich
    @ncesc.gov

NORTH DAKOTA
Ms. Maren L. Daley
Executive Director
Job Service North Dakota
P.O. Box 5507
Bismarck, ND 58506
P: (701) 328-2825
F: (701) 328-4000
E: mdaley@nd.gov

**NORTHERN MARIANA
ISLANDS**
Mr. Alfred A. Pangelinan
Director of Employment
Services
Department of Labor
Afetnas Square
Caller Box 10007
Saipan, MP 96950
P: (670) 236-0926
F: (670) 236-0994

OHIO
Ms. Sara Hall Phillips
Deputy Director
Office of Unemployment
Compensation
Department of Job & Family
Services
30 East Broad Street, 32nd Floor
Columbus, OH 43215
P: (614) 995-7066
F: (614) 466-6873

OKLAHOMA
Mr. Oscar B. Jackson Jr.
Administrator & Cabinet
Secretary
Office of Personnel
Management
Human Resources &
Administration
2101 North Lincoln Boulevard,
Room G-80
Oklahoma City, OK 73105
P: (405) 521-6301
F: (405) 522-0694
E: oscar.jackson@opm.ok.gov

Mr. Richard McPherson
Executive Director
Employment Security
Commission
2401 North Lincoln Boulevard
Will Rogers Memorial Office
Building
Oklahoma City, OK 73105
P: (405) 557-7201

OREGON
Mr. Martin L. Burrows
Interim Assistant Director
Business & Employment
Services
Employment Department
875 Union Street, Northeast
Salem, OR 97311
P: (503) 947-1655
F: (503) 947-1658
E: martin.l.burrows
    @state.or.us

PENNSYLVANIA
Mr. James A. Honchar
Deputy Secretary for Human
Resources & Management
Governor's Office of
Administration
517 Finance Building
Harrisburg, PA 17110
P: (717) 787-5545
F: (717) 783-4429
E: jhonchar@state.pa.us

PUERTO RICO
Mr. Miguel Romero
Director
Department of Labor & Human
Resources
P.O. Box 191020
San Juan, PR 00919
P: (787) 754-5353
F: (787) 756-1149

RHODE ISLAND
Mr. Charles J. Fogarty
Director
Department of Labor & Training
1511 Pontiac Avenue
Cranston, RI 02920
P: (401) 462-8000
F: (401) 462-8872
E: director-dlt@dlt.ri.gov

SOUTH CAROLINA
Mr. John L. Finan
Executive Director
Employment Security
Commission
1550 Gadsden Street
P.O. Box 995
Columbia, SC 29202
P: (803) 737-2617

SOUTH DAKOTA
Ms. Marcia Hultman
Deputy Secretary of Labor
Division of Workforce Services
Division of Workforce Services
700 Governors Drive
Pierre, SD 57501
P: (605) 773-3101
F: (605) 773-6184

TENNESSEE
Ms. Karla Davis
Commissioner
Department of Labor &
Workforce Development
Andrew Johnson Tower
710 James Robertson Parkway
Nashville, TN 37243
P: (615) 741-6642
F: (615) 741-5078
E: karla.davis@state.tn.us

TEXAS
Mr. Larry E. Temple
Executive Director
Workforce Commission
101 East 15th Street
Austin, TX 78778
P: (512) 463-0735
F: (512) 475-2321
E: larry.temple
    @twc.state.tx.us

U.S. VIRGIN ISLANDS
Mr. Albert Bryan Jr.
Commissioner of Labor
Department of Labor
2203 Church Street,
Christiansted
St. Croix, VI 00820
P: (340) 773-1994
F: (340) 773-0094
E: abryan@vidol.gov

VERMONT
Ms. Annie Noonan
Commissioner
Department of Labor
P.O. Box 488
Montpelier, VT 05602
P: (802) 828-4301
F: (802) 828-4022
E: annie.noonan@state.vt.us

VIRGINIA
Mr. John R. Broadway
Commissioner
Employment Commission
703 East Main Street
Richmond, VA 23219
P: (804) 786-1485
E: john.broadway
    @vec.virginia.gov

WASHINGTON
Ms. Eva Santos
Director
Department of Personnel
P.O. Box 47500
Olympia, WA 98504
P: (360) 664-6350
F: (360) 753-1003
E: Eva.Santos@dop.wa.gov

Mr. Paul Trause
Commissioner
Employment Security
Department
212 Maple Park Avenue,
Southeast
P.O. Box 9046
Olympia, WA 98507
P: (360) 902-9301
E: ptrause@esd.wa.gov

WEST VIRGINIA
Mr. J. Keith Burdette
Secretary of Commerce
Department of Commerce
Capitol Complex Building 6,
Room 525
1900 Kanawha Boulevard East
Charleston, WV 25305
P: (304) 558-2234
F: (304) 558-1189
E: J.Keith.Burdette@wv.gov

WISCONSIN
Ms. Jane Pawasarat
Administrator
Division of Employment &
Training
201 East Washington Avenue
Madison, WI 53707
P: (608) 266-3485
E: Jane.Pawasarat
    @dwd.wisconsin.gov

Energy

Develops and administers programs relating to energy conservation, alternative energy research and development, and energy information.

Information provided by:

National Association of State Energy Officials
David Terry
Executive Director
1414 Prince Street, Suite 200
Alexandria, VA 22314
P: (703) 299-8800
F: (703) 299-6208
dterry@naseo.org
www.naseo.org

ALABAMA
Ms. Terri L. Adams
Division Director
Energy Division
Economic & Community Affairs
401 Adams Avenue, P.O. Box 5690
Montgomery, AL 36103
P: (334) 242-5292
F: (334) 242-5292
E: terri.adams
@adeca.alabama.gov

ALASKA
Ms. Rebecca Garrett
Program Manager
Industrial Development & Export Authority
Energy Authority
813 West Northern Lights Boulevard
Anchorage, AK 99503
P: (907) 771-3042
F: (907) 771-3044
E: rgarrett@aidea.org

AMERICAN SAMOA
Mr. Reupena Tagaloa
Director
Territorial Energy Office
American Samoa Government
Samoa Energy House, Tafuna
Pago Pago, AS 96799
P: (684) 699-1101
F: (684) 699-2835
E: rtagaloa@samoatelco.com

ARIZONA
Mr. Grady Bailey
Senior Director
Energy Office
Department of Commerce
1700 West Washington Street, Suite 220
Phoenix, AZ 85007
P: (602) 771-1244
F: (602) 771-1203
E: GradyB@azcommerce.com

ARKANSAS
Mr. Chris Benson
Director
Energy Office
One Capitol Mall
Little Rock, AR 72201
P: (501) 682-8065
F: (501) 682-2703
E: cbenson@arkansasedc.com

CALIFORNIA
Ms. Claudia Chandler
Chief Deputy Director
Energy Commission
1516 Ninth Street, MS #39
Sacramento, CA 95814
P: (916) 654-5403
F: (916) 654-4423
E: cchandle
@energy.state.ca.us

CONNECTICUT
Mr. Raymond L. Wilson
Energy Director
Energy Management & Policy Development Unit
Office of Policy & Management
450 Capitol Avenue
Hartford, CT 06106
P: (860) 418-6441
F: (860) 418-6495
E: raymond.wilson@ct.gov

DELAWARE
Mr. Charlie T. Smisson Jr.
State Energy Coordinator
Energy Office
149 Transportation Circle
Dover, DE 19901
P: (302) 739-5644
F: (302) 735-3480
E: charlie.smisson
@state.de.us

DISTRICT OF COLUMBIA
Mr. Keith Anderson
Department of the Environment
2000 14th Street Northwest
Suite 300 East
Washington, DC 20009
P: (202) 478-1417
F: (202) 478-1417
E: keith.anderson@dc.gov

FLORIDA
Mr. Robert Vickers
Executive Director
Energy & Climate Commission
Executive Office of the Governor
600 South Calhoun Street, Suite 251
Tallahassee, FL 32399
P: (850) 487-3800
F: (850) 922-9701
E: Robert.vickers
@eog.myflorida.com

GEORGIA
Mr. David Gipson
Director
Division of Energy Resources
233 Peachtree Street, Northeast
Harris Tower, Suite 900
Atlanta, GA 30303
P: (404) 584-1007
F: (404) 584-1008
E: dgipson@gefa.ga.gov

GUAM
Ms. Lorilee T. Crisostomo
Administrator
Energy Office
P.O. Box 22439
Tamuning, GU 96921
P: (671) 475-1658
F: (671) 649-1215
E: lorilee.crisostomo
@epa.guam.gov

HAWAII
Mr. Theodore Peck
Administrator
Strategic Industries Division
235 South Beretania Street, Room 502
P.O. Box 2359
Honolulu, HI 96804
P: (808) 587-3803
F: (808) 587-3815
E: tpeck@dbedt.hawaii.gov

IDAHO
Ms. Maria Barratt
Energy Services Manager (financial and Grants)
Office of Energy Resources
P.O. Box 83720
Boise, ID 83720
P: (208) 287-4807
F: (208) 287-6713
E: maria.barratt
@oer.idaho.gov

ILLINOIS
Mr. Jonathan Feipel
Energy Division Manager
Department of Commerce & Economic Opportunity
Bureau of Energy & Recycling
620 East Adams
Springfield, IL 62701
P: (217) 785-2009
F: (217) 785-2618
E: Jonathan.Feipel
@illinois.gov

INDIANA
Mr. Brandon Seitz
Director
Office of Energy Development
101 West Ohio Street, Suite 1250
Indianapolis, IN 46204
P: (317) 234-3158
F: (317) 232-8995
E: bseitz@oed.in.gov

IOWA
Ms. Roya L. Stanley
Director
Office of Energy Independence
Wallace State Office Building
502 East 9th Street
Des Moines, IA 50319
P: (515) 725-2063
F: (515) 281-8895
E: roya.stanley@iowa.gov

KANSAS
Mr. Ray Hammarlund
Director
Energy Office
Corporation Commission
1300 Southwest Arrowhead, Suite 100
Topeka, KS 66604
P: (785) 271-3779
F: (785) 271-3268
E: r.hammarlund@kcc.ks.gov

KENTUCKY
Mr. John H. Davies
Director
Department for Energy Development & Independence
663 Teton Trail
Frankfort, KY 40601
P: (502) 564-7192
F: (502) 564-7484
E: John.Davies@ky.gov

LOUISIANA
Ms. Lori LeBlanc
Deputy Secretary & Energy
Stimulus Director
Department of Natural
Resources
P.O. Box 94396
Baton Rouge, LA 70804
P: (225) 342-4505
F: (225) 242-3446
E: lori.leblanc@la.gov

MAINE
Mr. John Kerry
Director of Energy
Independence
Office of Energy Independence
Office of the Governor
C/o State House Station, #18
Augusta, ME 04333
P: (207) 287-3292
F: (207) 287-1039
E: John.Kerry@maine.gov

MARYLAND
Mr. Malcolm D. Woolf
Director
Energy Administration
60 West Street, Suite 300
Annapolis, MD 21401
P: (410) 260-7540
F: (410) 974-2250
E: mwoolf
    @energy.state.md.us

MASSACHUSETTS
Mr. Philip Giudice
Commissioner
Department of Energy
Resources
Department of Economic
Development
100 Cambridge Street, Suite
1020
Boston, MA 02114
P: (617) 626-7321
F: (617) 727-0030
E: Phil.Giudice@state.ma.us

MICHIGAN
Ms. Amy A. Butler
Chief
Bureau of Energy Systems
525 West Allegan Street
P.O. Box 30473
Lansing, MI 48909
P: (517) 241-0490
E: BUTLERA1@michigan.gov

MINNESOTA
Ms. Janet Streff
Manager
State Energy Office
Department of Commerce
85 7th Place, East, Suite 500
St. Paul, MN 55101
P: (651) 297-2545
F: (651) 297-7891
E: janet.streff@state.mn.us

MISSISSIPPI
Ms. Motice Bruce
Financial & Program Support
Manager
Energy Division
Development Authority
P.O. Box 849
Jackson, MS 39205
P: (601) 359-6601
F: (601) 359-6642
E: mbruce@mississippi.org

MISSOURI
Ms. Anita C. Randolph
Director
Energy Center
Department of Natural
Resources
P.O. Box 176
Jefferson City, MO 65102
P: (573) 751-2254
F: (573) 751-6860
E: Anita.Randolph
    @dnr.mo.gov

MONTANA
Ms. Louise Moore
Chief of Air, Energy & Pollution
Prevention Bureau
Department of Environmental
Quality
P.O. Box 200901
1100 North Last Chance Gulch,
Room 401-H
Helena, MT 59620
P: (406) 841-5280
F: (406) 841-5222
E: lmoore@mt.gov

NEBRASKA
Mr. Neil Moseman
Energy Office Director
State Energy Office
1111 O Street, Suite 223
P.O. Box 95085
Lincoln, NE 68509
P: (402) 471-2867
E: neil.moseman
    @nebraska.gov

NEVADA
Mr. Jim Groth
Director
State Office of Energy
755 North Roop Street, Suite
202
Carson City, NV 89701
P: (775) 687-1850 x7302
E: jgroth@energy.nv.gov

NEW HAMPSHIRE
Ms. Joanne O. Morin
Director
Office of Energy & Planning
4 Chennell Drive, 2nd Floor
Concord, NH 03301
P: (603) 271-2155
F: (603) 271-2615
E: joanne.morin@nh.gov

NEW JERSEY
Mr. Michael Winka
Director
Office of Clean Energy
Board of Public Utilities
44 South Clinton Avenue, P.O.
Box 350
Trenton, NJ 08625
P: (609) 777-3335
F: (609) 777-3330
E: michael.winka
    @bpu.state.nj.us

NEW MEXICO
Mr. Fernando Martinez
Director
Energy Conservation
Management Division
1220 South St. Francis Drive
P.O. Box 6429
Santa Fe, NM 87505
P: (505) 476-3312
F: (505) 476-3322
E: fernando.r.martinez
    @state.nm.us

NEW YORK
Mr. Frank Murray
President
NYSERDA
17 Columbia Circle
Albany, NY 12203
P: (518) 862-1090
F: (518) 862-1091
E: fjm@nyserda.org

NORTH CAROLINA
Mr. Ward Lenz
Director
State Energy Office
Department of Administration
1830A Tillery Place
Raleigh, NC 27699
P: (919) 733-1889
F: (919) 733-2953
E: wlenz@nccommerce.com

NORTH DAKOTA
Mr. Paul T. Govig
Director
Division of Community
Services
Department of Commerce
1600 East Century Avenue, Suite
2
Bismarck, ND 58503
P: (701) 328-4499
F: (701) 328-2308
E: pgovig@state.nd.us

**NORTHERN MARIANA
ISLANDS**
Ms. Thelma B. Inos
Acting Energy Director
Commonwealth of the Northern
Mariana Islands
Energy Division
P.O. Box 500340
Saipan, MP 96950
P: (670) 664-4480
F: (670) 664-4483
E: cnmienergy@gmail.com

OHIO
Ms. Nadeane Howard
Director
Energy Office, Department of
Development
77 South High Street, 26th Floor
P.O. Box 1001
Columbus, OH 43216
P: (614) 466-6797
F: (614) 466-1864
E: nadeane.howard
    @development.ohio.gov

OKLAHOMA
Mr. Vaughn Clark
Director
Division of Community Affairs
& Development
Department of Commerce
900 North Stiles Street
Oklahoma City, OK 73104
P: (405) 815-5370
F: (405) 605-2870
E: vaughn_clark
    @odoc.state.ok.us

Energy

OREGON
Mr. Mark S. Long
Acting Director
Department of Energy
625 Marion Street, Northeast
Salem, OR 97301
E: mark.long@state.or.us

PENNSYLVANIA
Mr. Dave Althoff
Director
Office of Energy & Technology
Deployment
Rachel Carson State Office
Building
400 Market Street, 15th Floor
Harrisburg, PA 17101
P: (717) 783-0542
F: (717) 783-2703
E: dalthoff@state.pa.us

PUERTO RICO
Mr. Luis Bernal-Jimenez
Executive Director
Energy Affairs Administration
P.O. Box 41314
San Juan, PR 00940
P: (787) 999-2200 x2886
F: (787) 999-2246
E: lbernal@aae.gobierno.pr

RHODE ISLAND
Mr. Andrew Kostrzewa
Project Manager
Office of Energy Resources
1 Capitol Hill
Providence, RI 02908
P: (401) 574-9108
F: (401) 574-9125
E: akostrzewa@energy.ri.gov

SOUTH CAROLINA
Mr. John Clark
Director
Energy Office
1200 Senate Street
Wade Hampton Building, Suite
408
Columbia, SC 29201
P: (803) 737-8039
F: (803) 737-9846
E: jclark@energy.sc.gov

SOUTH DAKOTA
Ms. Michele Farris
State Energy Manager
Energy Management Office
Office of the State Engineer
523 East Capitol Avenue
Pierre, SD 57501
P: (605) 773-3899
F: (605) 773-5980
E: Michele.Farris
   @state.sd.us

TENNESSEE
Mr. Ryan Gooch
Energy Policy Director
Department of Economic &
Community Development
Energy Policy Section
312 Eight Avenue, North, 10th
Floor
Nashville, TN 37243
P: (615) 741-2994
F: (615) 741-5070
E: ryan.gooch@state.tn.us

TEXAS
Mr. William E. Taylor
Director
State Energy Conservation
Office
Comptroller of Public Accounts
11th Floor, 111 East 17th Street
Austin, TX 78701
P: (512) 463-8352
F: (512) 475-2569
E: dub.taylor
   @cpa.state.tx.us

U.S. VIRGIN ISLANDS
Mr. Bevan R. Smith Jr.
Director
Energy Office
Dept. of Planning & Natural
Resources
#45 Mars Hill
Fredrickstead, St. Croix, VI
00840
P: (340) 773-1082 Ext. 2254
F: (340) 772-2133
E: bsmith@vienergy.org

UTAH
Mr. Jason Berry
State Energy Program Manager
Geological Survey
1594 West North Temple, Suite
3110
P.O. Box 146100
Salt Lake City, UT 84114
P: (801) 538-5413
E: jasonberry@utah.gov

VERMONT
Kelly Launder
Energy Program Specialist
Energy Efficiency Division
Department of Public Service
112 State Street, Drawer 20
Montpelier, VT 05620
P: (802) 828-4039
F: (802) 828-2342
E: kelly.launder
   @state.vt.us

VIRGINIA
Mr. Al Christopher
Director
Division of Energy
Department of Mines, Minerals
and Energy
1100 Bank Street, 8th Floor
Richmond, VA 23219
P: (804) 692-3216
E: al.chistopher
   @dmme.virginia.gov

WASHINGTON
Mr. Tony Usibelli
Assistant Director
Department of Commerce
P.O. Box 43173
925 Plum Street Southeast,
Building 4
Olympia, WA 98504
P: (360) 725-3110
F: (360) 956-2180
E: tonyu@cted.wa.gov

WEST VIRGINIA
Mr. Jeff F. Herholdt Jr.
Manager
Development Office
Building 6, Room 645
State Capitol Complex
Charleston, WV 25305
P: (304) 558-2234
F: (304) 558-0362
E: Jeff.F.Herholdt@wv.gov

WISCONSIN
Ms. Judy Ziewacz
Director
Office of Energy Independence
17 West Main Street, #429
Madison, WI 53702
P: (608) 261-0607
F: (608) 261-8427
E: judy.ziewacz
   @wisconsin.gov

WYOMING
Shannon Stanfill
State Energy Office Director
Business & Industry Division
Business Council
214 West 15th Street
Cheyenne, WY 82002
P: (307) 777-2841
F: (307) 777-8586
E: shannon.stanfill
   @wybusiness.org

Environmental Protection

Oversees the overall quality of the environment by coordinating and managing the state's pollution control programs and planning, permit granting and regulation of standards.

Information provided by:

Environmental Council of the States
R. Steven Brown
Executive Director
444 North Capitol Street, NW
Suite 445
Washington, DC 20001
P: (202) 624-3660
F: (202) 624-3666
sbrown@sso.org
www.ecos.org

ALABAMA
Mr. Lance LeFleur
Director
Department of Environmental Management
1400 Coliseum Boulevard
P.O. Box 301463
Montgomery, AL 36130
P: (334) 271-7710
F: (334) 271-7950

ALASKA
Mr. Larry Hartig
Commissioner
Department of Environmental Conservation
410 Willoughby, Suite 303
P.O. Box 111800
Juneau, AK 99811
P: (907) 465-5065
F: (907) 465-5070
E: larry.hartig@alaska.gov

ARIZONA
Mr. Henry Darwin
Director
Deaprtment of Environmental Quality
1110 West Washington Street
Phoenix, AZ 85007
P: (602) 771-2203
F: (602) 771-2218
E: hrd@azdeq.gov

ARKANSAS
Ms. Teresa Marks
Director
Department of Environmental Quality
5301 Northshore Drive
P.O. Box 8913
North Little Rock, AR 72118
P: (501) 682-0959
F: (501) 682-0798
E: marks@adeq.state.ar.us

CALIFORNIA
Ms. Linda Adams
Secretary
Environmental Protection Agency
1001 I Street, 25th Floor
Sacramento, CA 95814
P: (916) 445-3846
F: (916) 445-6401
E: ladams@calepa.ca.gov

Ms. Cindy Tuck
Under Secretary
Environmental Protection Agency
1001 I Street, 25th Floor
Sacramento, CA 95814
P: (916) 323-3708
F: (916) 445-6401
E: ctuck@calepa.ca.gov

COLORADO
Dr. Christopher E. Urbina
Executive Director
Department of Public Health & Environment
4300 Cherry Creek Drive, South
Denver, CO 80246
P: (303) 692-2000
F: (303) 691-7702
E: christopher.urbina
    @state.co.us

CONNECTICUT
Mr. Daniel C. Esty
Commissioner
Department of Environmental Protection
79 Elm Street
Hartford, CT 06106
P: (860) 424-3009
F: (860) 424-4054
E: daniel.esty@ct.gov

DELAWARE
Mr. Collin O'Mara
Secretary
Department of Natural Resources & Environmental Control
89 Kings Highway
P.O. Box 1401
Dover, DE 19903
P: (302) 739-9000
F: (302) 739-6242

DISTRICT OF COLUMBIA
Mr. Christophe A. G. Tulou
Acting Director
Department of the Environment
1200 First Street, Northeast, 5th Floor
Washington, DC 20002
P: (202) 535-2600
F: (202) 535-2881
E: ddoe@dc.gov

FLORIDA
Mr. Herschel T. Vinyard
Secretary
Department of Environmental Protection
3900 Commonwealth Boulevard
Mail Station 49
Tallahassee, FL 32399
P: (850) 245-2011
F: (850) 245-2128
E: herschel.vinyard
    @dep.state.fl.us

GEORGIA
Mr. F. Allen Barnes
Director, Environmental Protection Division
Department of Natural Resources
2 Martin Luther King Jr. Drive, SE
Suite 1252, East Tower
Atlanta, GA 30334
P: (404) 656-4713
F: (404) 651-5778

HAWAII
Mr. Gary Gill
Deputy Director for Environmental Health
Department of Health
1250 Punchbowl Street, 3rd Floor
Honolulu, HI 96801
P: (808) 586-4424
F: (808) 586-4368
E: gary.gill@doh.hawaii.gov

IDAHO
Ms. Toni Hardesty
Director
Department of Environmental Quality
1410 North Hilton
Boise, ID 83706
P: (208) 373-0240
F: (208) 373-0417
E: toni.hardesty
    @deq.idaho.gov

ILLINOIS
Ms. Lisa Bonnett
Acting Director
Environmental Protection Agency
1021 North Grand Avenue, East
P.O. Box 19276
Springfield, IL 62794
P: (217) 782-3397
F: (217) 782-9039

INDIANA
Mr. Thomas Easterly
Commissioner
Department of Environmental Management
100 North Senate Avenue, MC 50-01
P.O. Box 6015
Indianapolis, IN 46206
P: (317) 232-8611
F: (317) 233-6647
E: teasterl@idem.in.gov

IOWA
Mr. Wayne Gieselman
Division Administrator
Environmental Services Division
4th Floor Wallace Building
502 East 9th Street
Des Moines, IA 50319
P: (515) 281-5817
F: (515) 281-8895
E: wayne.gieselman
    @dnr.iowa.gov

KANSAS
Mr. John Mitchell
Director
Division of Environment
Department of Health & Environment
1000 Southwest Jackson, Suite 400
Topeka, KS 66612
P: (785) 296-1535
F: (785) 296-8464
E: jmitchell@kdheks.gov

KENTUCKY
Ms. Valerie Hudson
Deputy Commissioner
Department for Environmental Protection
14 Reilly Road
Frankfort, KY 40601
P: (502) 564-2150
F: (502) 564-2145
E: valerie.hudson@ky.gov

Environmental Protection

Mr. Bruce Scott
Commissioner
Department for Environmental
Protection
300 Fair Oaks Lane
Frankfort, KY 40601
P: (502) 564-2150 Ext. 152
F: (502) 564-3354
E: bruce.scott@ky.gov

LOUISIANA
Ms. Peggy Hatch
Secretary
Department of Environmental
Quality
602 North Fifth Street, #1022
P.O. Box 4301
Baton Rouge, LA 70821
P: (225) 219-3950
F: (225) 219-3970
E: peggy.hatch@la.gov

MAINE
Mr. James Brooks
Acting Commissioner
Department of Environmental
Protection
17 State House Station
Augusta, ME 04333
P: (207) 287-2812
F: (207) 287-2814
E: james.p.brooks@maine.gov

MARYLAND
Mr. Robert Summers
Acting Secretary
Department of the Environment
1800 Washington Boulevard
Baltimore, MD 21230
P: (410) 537-3084
F: (410) 537-3888
E: bsummers@mde.state.md.us

MASSACHUSETTS
Mr. Kenneth Kimmell
Commissioner
Department of Environmental
Protection
One Winter Street, #1022
Boston, MA 02108
P: (617) 292-5856
F: (617) 574-6880
E: ken.kimmell@state.ma.us

MICHIGAN
Mr. Jim Sygo
Deputy Director for
Environmental Protection
Department of Environmental
Quality
P.O. Box 30473
525 West Allegan Street
Lansing, MI 48909
P: (517) 373-7917
F: (517) 241-7401

MINNESOTA
Mr. Paul Aasen
Commissioner
Pollution Control Agency
520 Lafayette Road North, 6th
Floor
St. Paul, MN 55155
P: (651) 757-2016
F: (651) 296-6334
E: paul.aasen@state.mn.us

MISSISSIPPI
Ms. Trudy H. Fisher
Executive Director
Department of Environmental
Quality
2380 Highway 80 West
P.O. Box 2369
Jackson, MS 39289
P: (601) 961-5001
F: (601) 961-5093
E: trudy_fisher
 @deq.state.ms.us

MISSOURI
Ms. Sara Parker Pauley
Director
Department of Natural
Resources
P.O. Box 176
Jefferson City, MO 65102
P: (573) 751-4732
F: (573) 751-7627
E: sara.pauley@dnr.mo.gov

MONTANA
Mr. Richard H. Opper
Director
Department of Environmental
Quality
1520 East 6th Avenue
P.O. Box 200901
Helena, MT 59620
P: (406) 444-6815
F: (406) 444-4386
E: ropper@mt.gov

NEBRASKA
Mr. Michael J. Linder
Director
Department of Environmental
Quality
1200 N Street, Suite 400
P.O. Box 98922
Lincoln, NE 68509
P: (402) 471-3585
F: (402) 471-2909
E: mike.linder@nebraska.gov

NEVADA
Ms. Colleen Cripps
Administrator
Division of Environmental
Protection
901 South Stewart Street, Suite
4001
Carson City, NV 89701
P: (775) 687-9302
F: (775) 687-5856
E: cripps@ndep.nv.gov

NEW HAMPSHIRE
Mr. Thomas S. Burack
Commissioner
Department of Environmental
Services
29 Hazen Drive
P.O. Box 95
Concord, NH 03302
P: (603) 271-2958
F: (603) 271-2867
E: thomas.burack@des.nh.gov

NEW JERSEY
Mr. Bob Martin
Commissioner
Department of Environmental
Protection
401 East State Street
P.O. Box 402
Trenton, NJ 08625
P: (609) 292-2885
F: (609) 292-7695

NEW MEXICO
Mr. F. David Martin
Secretary
Environment Department
1190 Saint Francis Drive
Harold Runnels Building
Santa Fe, NM 87503
P: (505) 827-2855
F: (505) 827-2836

NEW YORK
Mr. Joe Martens
Commissioner
Department of Environmental
Conservation
625 Broadway, 14th Floor
Albany, NY 12233
P: (518) 402-8540
F: (518) 402-8541
E: joemartens
 @gw.dec.state.ny.us

NORTH CAROLINA
Ms. Dee A. Freeman
Secretary
Department of Environment &
Natural Resources
512 North Salisbury Street
1601 Mail Service Center
Raleigh, NC 27699
P: (919) 733-4984
F: (919) 715-3060
E: dee.freeman@ncdenr.gov

NORTH DAKOTA
Mr. L. David Glatt
Chief
Environmental Health Section
Department of Health
1200 Missouri Avenue, P.O. Box
5520
Bismarck, ND 58506
P: (701) 328-5152
F: (701) 328-5200
E: dglatt@nd.gov

OHIO
Mr. Scott Nally
Director
Environmental Protection
Agency
122 South Front Street, 6th
Floor
Columbus, OH 43215
P: (614) 644-2782
F: (614) 644-3184
E: scott.nally
 @epa.state.oh.us

OKLAHOMA
Mr. Steven A. Thompson
Executive Director
Department of Environmental
Quality
707 North Robinson, Suite 7100
P.O.Box 1677
Oklahoma City, OK 73101
P: (405) 702-7163
F: (405) 702-7101

OREGON
Mr. Dick Pedersen
Director
Department of Environmental
Quality
811 Southwest 6th Avenue
Portland, OR 97204
P: (503) 229-5300
F: (503) 229-5850
E: pedersen.dick
 @deq.state.or.us

PENNSYLVANIA
Mr. Michael Krancer
Secretary
Department of Environmental
Protection
Carson State Office Building,
16th Floor
400 Market Street
Harrisburg, PA 17101
P: (717) 787-2814
F: (717) 705-4980

RHODE ISLAND
Ms. Janet Coit
Director
Department of Environmental
Management
235 Promenade Street, 4th Floor
Providence, RI 02908
P: (401) 222-2771
F: (401) 222-6802
E: janet.coit@dem.ri.gov

SOUTH CAROLINA
Mr. Robert W. King Jr.
Deputy Commissioner
Department of Health &
Environmental Control
2600 Bull Street
Columbia, SC 29201
P: (803) 896-8940
F: (803) 896-8941

SOUTH DAKOTA
Mr. Steve M. Pirner
Secretary
Department of Environment &
Natural Resources
Joe Foss Building
523 East Capital Avenue
Pierre, SD 57501
P: (605) 773-3151
F: (605) 773-6035
E: steve.pirner@state.sd.us

TENNESSEE
Mr. Robert J. Martineau Jr.
Commissioner
Department of Environment and
Conservation
401 Church Street
1st Floor, L&C Annex
Nashville, TN 37243

Mr. Paul Sloan
Deputy Commissioner
Department of Environment &
Conservation
401 Church Street, Annex
Nashville, TN 37243
P: (615) 532-0102
F: (615) 532-0120
E: paul.sloan@state.tn.us

TEXAS
Dr. Bryan W. Shaw
Chairman
Commission on Environmental
Quality
12100 Park 35 Circle
P.O. Box 13087
Austin, TX 78711
P: (512) 239-5510
F: (512) 239-6377

UTAH
Ms. Amanda Smith
Executive Director
Department of Environmental
Quality
168 North 1950 West
P.O. Box 144810
Salt Lake City, UT 84114
P: (801) 538-1000
F: (801) 538-1557
E: amandasmith@utah.gov

VERMONT
Mr. David K. Mears
Commissioner
Department of Environmental
Conservation
103 South Main Street, Center
Building
Waterbury, VT 05671
P: (802) 241-3808
F: (802) 244-5141
E: david.mears@state.vt.us

VIRGINIA
Mr. David K. Paylor
Director
Department of Environmental
Quality
629 East Main Street
P.O. Box 1105
Richmond, VA 23218
P: (804) 698-4390
F: (804) 698-4019
E: dkpaylor
@deq.virginia.gov

WASHINGTON
Mr. Ted L. Sturdevant
Director
Department of Ecology
P.O. Box 47600
Olympia, WA 98504
P: (360) 407-7001
F: (360) 407-6989
E: tstu461@ecy.wa.gov

WEST VIRGINIA
Mr. Randy Huffman
Cabinet Secretary
Department of Environmental
Protection
601 57th Street, Southeast
Charleston, WV 25304
P: (304) 926-0440
F: (304) 926-0447
E: randy.c.huffman@wv.gov

WISCONSIN
Ms. Cathy Stepp
Secretary
Department of Natural
Resources
101 South Webster Street
P.O. Box 7921
Madison, WI 53707
P: (608) 267-7556
F: (608) 266-6983
E: cathy.stepp
@wisconsin.gov

WYOMING
Mr. John V. Corra
Director
Department of Environmental
Quality
Herschler Building
122 West 25th Street, 4th Floor,
West
Cheyenne, WY 82002
P: (307) 777-7937
F: (307) 777-7682
E: jcorra@wyo.gov

Equal Employment Opportunity

Enforces laws promoting equal employment opportunity in the state.

ALABAMA
Mr. Thomas Surtees
Director
Department of Industrial Relations
649 Monroe Street
Montgomery, AL 36131
P: (334) 242-8078
F: (334) 242-3960
E: tom.surtees
  @dir.alabama.gov

ALASKA
Ms. Camille Brill
EEO Program Manager
Department of Administration
619 East Ship Creek Avenue, Suite 309
Anchorage, AK 99501
P: (907) 375-7705
F: (907) 375-7719
E: camille.brill@alaska.gov

AMERICAN SAMOA
Lt. Col. Evelyn Vaiautolu Langford
Director
Department of Human Resources
American Samoa Government
Pago Pago, AS 96799
P: (684) 644-4485
F: (684) 633-1139

ARIZONA
Ms. Carolyn Pitre Wright
Director
Governor's Office of Equal Opportunity
State Capitol Building, Executive Tower
1700 West Washington, Suite 156
Phoenix, AZ 85007
P: (602) 542-3711
F: (602) 542-3712
E: EqualOpportunity@az.gov

ARKANSAS
Ms. Gloria Johnson
Equal Opportunity Manager
Department of Workforce Services
P.O. Box 2981
Little Rock, AR 72201
P: (501) 682-3106
F: (501) 682-3748
E: gloria.johnson
  @arkansas.gov

CALIFORNIA
Ms. Julie Escat
Chief
Equal Employment Opportunity Office
744 P Street
Sacramento, CA 95814
P: (916) 657-2326
F: (916) 657-2285
E: julie.escat@dss.ca.gov

COLORADO
Mr. Steve Chavez
Director
Civil Rights Division
1560 Broadway, Suite 1050
Denver, CO 80202
P: (303) 894-2997
F: (303) 894-7830

CONNECTICUT
Mr. Robert Brothers Jr.
Executive Director
Commission on Human Rights & Opportunities
21 Grand Street
Hartford, CT 06106
P: (860) 541-3451
F: (860) 246-5419

DELAWARE
Ms. Sandy Reyes
Manager, EEO & Diversity
Human Resource Management
122 William Penn Street
Dover, DE 19901
P: (302) 739-4195
F: (302) 739-7984
E: sandy.reyes@state.de.us

DISTRICT OF COLUMBIA
Mr. Gustavo F. Velasquez
Director
Office of Human Rights
441 4th Street, Northwest
Suite 570 North
Washington, DC 20001
P: (202) 727-4559
F: (202) 727-9589
E: ohr@dc.gov

FLORIDA
Mr. Peter De Haan
EO Officer
Office for Civil Rights
107 E. Madison Street
Caldwell Building, MSC 150
Tallahassee, FL 32399
P: (850) 921-3201
F: (850) 921-3122
E: peter.dehaan
  @awi.state.fl.us

GEORGIA
Mr. Gordon L. Joyner
Executive Director & Administrator
Commission on Equal Opportunity
Suite 1002, West Tower
2 Martin Luther King Jr. Drive Southeast
Atlanta, GA 30334
P: (404) 657-7477
F: (404) 656-4399
E: gjoyner@gceo.state.ga.us

GUAM
Ms. Leah Beth Naholowaa
Director
Department of Labor
Government of Guam
P.O. Box 9970
Tamuning, GU 96931
P: (671) 647-6510
F: (671) 674-6517

HAWAII
Mr. William D. Hoshijo
Executive Director
Civil Rights Commission
830 Punchbowl Street, Room 411
Honolulu, HI 96813
P: (808) 586-8636
F: (808) 586-8655
E: dlir.hcrc.infor
  @hawaii.gov

IDAHO
Ms. Pamela Parks
Director
Human Rights Commission
1109 Main Street
Owyhee Plaza, Suite 450
Boise, ID 83720
P: (208) 334-2873
F: (208) 334-2664
E: pparks@ihrc.idaho.gov

ILLINOIS
Mr. Rocco J. Claps
Director
Department of Human Rights
James R. Thompson Center
100 West Randolph Street, Suite 10-100
Chicago, IL 60601
P: (312) 814-6200
F: (312) 814-1436

INDIANA
Ms. Lavenia Haskett
Program Director
Employee Relations
Personnel Department
402 West Washington, Room W161
Indianapolis, IN 46204
P: (317) 232-4555
F: (317) 232-3089
E: lhaskett@spd.in.gov

IOWA
Mr. Ralph Rosenberg
Executive Director
Civil Rights Commission
Grimes State Office Building
400 East 14th Street
Des Moines, IA 50319
P: (515) 242-6537
F: (515) 242-5840
E: ralph.rosenberg@iowa.gov

KANSAS
Ms. Karin Brownlee
Secretary
Department of Labor
401 Southwest Topeka Boulevard
Topeka, KS 66603
P: (785) 296-5058
F: (785) 368-5286
E: karin.brownlee
  @dol.ks.gov

Ms. Karin Brownlee
Secretary
Department of Labor
401 Southwest Topeka Boulevard
Topeka, KS 66603
P: (785) 296-5058
F: (785) 368-5286
E: karin.brownlee
  @dol.ks.gov

Mr. William V. Minner
Executive Director
Human Rights Commission
900 Southwest Jackson Street
Suite 568-S
Topeka, KS 66612
P: (785) 296-3206
F: (785) 296-0589

KENTUCKY
Mr. Arthur B. Lucas Jr.
Executive Director
Office of Diversity & Equality
Personnel Cabinet
501 High Street, 1st Floor
Frankfort, KY 40601
P: (502) 564-8000
F: (502) 564-0182
E: arthurb.lucas@ky.gov

LOUISIANA
Mr. Curt Eysink
Executive Director
Workforce Commission
1001 North 23rd Street
Baton Rouge, LA 70802
P: (225) 342-3111
F: (225) 342-3778
E: ceysink@lwc.la.gov

MAINE
Ms. Laurel J. Shippee
State Equal Employment
Opportunity Coordinator
Department of Administrative &
Financial Services
Bureau of Human Resources
4 State House Station
Augusta, ME 04333
P: (207) 624-7761
F: (207) 287-4414
E: Laurel.J.Shippee
    @maine.gov

MARYLAND
Mr. Henry B. Ford
Executive Director
Commission on Human
Relations
William Donald Schefer Tower
6 Saint Paul Street, 9th Floor
Baltimore, MD 21202
P: (410) 767-8563
F: (410) 333-1841
E: hford
    @mail.mchr.state.md.us

MASSACHUSETTS
Ms. Sandra E. Borders
Director
Office of Diversity & Equal
Opportunity
One Ashburton Place, Room 213
Boston, MA 02108
P: (617) 727-7441
F: (617) 727-0568

Mr. Angelo McClain
Commissioner
Department of Children &
Families
24 Farnsworth Street
Boston, MA 02210
P: (617) 748-2000

MICHIGAN
Mr. Daniel Krichbaum
Director
Department of Civil Rights
Capitol Tower Building
110 West Michigan Avenue,
Suite 900
Lansing, MI 48933
P: (517) 335-3164
F: (517) 335-6513
E: krichbaumd@michigan.gov

MINNESOTA
Mr. Kevin Lindsey
Commissioner
Department of Human Rights
190 East 5th Street, Suite 700
St. Paul, MN 55101
P: (651) 296-5675
F: (651) 296-9042
E: Kevin.Lindsey
    @state.mn.us

MISSISSIPPI
Mr. Jim Nelson Jr.
Director
Equal Opportunity Department
1520 West Capitol
P.O. Box 1699
Jackson, MS 39215
P: (601) 969-7420
F: (601) 961-7405
E: jnelson@sos.state.ms.us

MISSOURI
Ms. Alisa Warren
Executive Director
Commission on Human Rights
3315 West Truman Boulevard,
Room 212
P.O. Box 1129
Jefferson City, MO 65102
P: (573) 751-3325
F: (573) 751-2905
E: mchr@labor.mo.gov

MONTANA
Ms. Paula Stoll
Administrator
Human Resources Division
Mitchell Building, Room 130
P.O. Box 200127
Helena, MT 59620
P: (406) 444-3819
F: (406) 444-0544
E: pstoll@mt.gov

NEBRASKA
Ms. Barbara Albers
Executive Director
Equal Opportunity Commission
301 Centennial Mall Sourth, 5th
Floor
P.O. Box 94934
Lincoln, NE 68509
P: (402) 471-2024
F: (402) 471-4059

NEVADA
Mr. Dennis Perea
Commission Administrator
Department of Employment,
Training & Rehabilitation
Equal Rights Commission
555 East Washington Avenue,
Suite 4000
Las Vegas, NV 89101
P: (702) 486-7161
F: (702) 486-7054

NEW HAMPSHIRE
Ms. Joni N. Esperian
Executive Director
Commission for Human Rights
2 Chennell Drive, #2
Concord, NH 03301
P: (603) 271-6838
F: (603) 271-6339
E: joni.esperian@nh.gov

NEW JERSEY
Ms. Parthenopy A. Bardis
EEO/AA Officer
Office of Equal Employment
Opportunity & Affirmative
Action
P.O. Box 317
Trenton, NJ 08625
P: (609) 292-6547
F: (609) 984-3800

NEW MEXICO
Ms. Francie Cordova
Labor Relations Division
Director
Human Rights Bureau
Department of Labor
1596 Pacheco Street
Santa Fe, NM 87505
P: (505) 827-6838
F: (505) 827-6878

NEW YORK
Ms. Nancy G. Groenwegen
Commissioner
Department of Civil Service
Alfred E. Smith State Office
Building
Albany, NY 12239
P: (518) 457-2487
F: (518) 473-5696
E: robin.farrell
    @cs.state.ny.us

NORTH CAROLINA
Ms. Nellie Riley
Director
Office of State Personnel
Equal Employment Opportunity
Services
1331 Mail Service Center
Raleigh, NC 27699
P: (919) 807-4800
F: (919) 733-0653
E: nellie.riley@osp.nc.gov

NORTH DAKOTA
Mr. Tony Weiler
Commissioner of Labor
Department of Labor
600 East Boulevard Avenue
Department 406
Bismarck, ND 58505
P: (701) 328-2660
F: (701) 328-2031
E: tjweiler@nd.gov

**NORTHERN MARIANA
ISLANDS**
Ms. Matilde A. Rosario
Chief
Office of Personnel
Management
P.O. Box 5153 CHRB
Saipan, MP 96950
P: (670) 233-1272
F: (670) 234-1013

OHIO
Mr. Bob Blair
Director
Department of Administrative
Services
30 East Broad Street, Suite 4040
Columbus, OH 43215
P: (614) 466-6511
F: (614) 644-8151
E: robert.blair
    @das.state.oh.us

Equal Employment Opportunity

OKLAHOMA
Ms. Brenda C. Thornton
Director
Equal Opportunity & Workforce
Diversity
Office of Personnel
Management
2101 North Lincoln Boulevard,
Room G-80
Oklahoma City, OK 73105
P: (405) 521-3082
F: (405) 524-6942
E: brenda.thornton
 @opm.ok.gov

OREGON
Hon. Brad Avakian (D)
Commissioner
Bureau of Labor & Industries
800 Northeast Oregon Street
Suite 1045
Portland, OR 97232
P: (503) 731-4070
F: (503) 731-4103
E: brad.avakian@state.or.us

PENNSYLVANIA
Ms. Julia Hearthway
Acting Secretary
Department of Labor & Industry
651 Boas Street, Room 1700
Harrisburg, PA 17121
P: (717) 787-5279
F: (717) 787-8826

PUERTO RICO
Mr. Miguel Romero
Director
Department of Labor & Human
Resources
P.O. Box 191020
San Juan, PR 00919
P: (787) 754-5353
F: (787) 756-1149

RHODE ISLAND
Mr. Raymond Lambert
Administrator
Equal Opportunity Office
1 Capitol Hill
Providence, RI 02908
P: (401) 222-3090
F: (401) 222-2490
E: Raymond.Lambert
 @hr.ri.gov

SOUTH CAROLINA
Mr. Jesse Washington Jr.
Commissioner
Human Affairs Commission
P.O. Box 4490
2611 Forest Drive, Suite 200
Columbia, SC 29204
P: (803) 737-7800
E: jesse@schac.state.sc.us

SOUTH DAKOTA
Ms. Sandy Zinter
Commissioner
Bureau of Personnel
500 East Capitol Avenue
Pierre, SD 57501
P: (605) 773-4918
F: (605) 773-4344
E: sandy.zinter@state.sd.us

TENNESSEE
Ms. Rebecca Hunter
Commissioner
Department of Human Services
James K. Polk Building, 1st
Floor
505 Deaderick Street
Nashville, TN 37243
P: (615) 741-2958
F: (615) 741-7880
E: rebecca.hunter@tn.gov

TEXAS
Mr. Jonathan Babiak
Director of Civil Rights
Civil Rights Division
Texas Workforce Commission
101 East 15th Street
Austin, TX 78778
P: (512) 463-4432

U.S. VIRGIN ISLANDS
Mr. Albert Bryan Jr.
Commissioner of Labor
Department of Labor
2203 Church Street,
Christiansted
St. Croix, VI 00820
P: (340) 773-1994
F: (340) 773-0094
E: abryan@vidol.gov

UTAH
Ms. Heather Gunnarson
Director
Antidiscrimination & Labor
Division
160 East 300 South, 3rd Floor
P.O. Box 146630
Salt Lake City, UT 84114
P: (801) 530-6921
F: (801) 530-7609
E: hgunnarson@utah.gov

VIRGINIA
Mrs. Sara Redding Wilson
Director
Department of Human Resource
Management
101 North 14th Street, 12th
Floor
Richmond, VA 23219
P: (804) 225-2237
F: (804) 371-7401
E: sara.wilson
 @dhrm.virginia.gov

WASHINGTON
Ms. Eva Santos
Director
Department of Personnel
P.O. Box 47500
Olympia, WA 98504
P: (360) 664-6350
F: (360) 753-1003
E: Eva.Santos@dop.wa.gov

WEST VIRGINIA
Ms. Jann Hoke
Director
Equal Employment Opportunity
Office
50 Dee Drive
Charleston, WV 25311
P: (304) 558-0400
F: (304) 558-3861
E: Jann.D.Hoke@wv.gov

WISCONSIN
Ms. Claire Dehnert
Division of Affirmative Action
P.O. Box 7855
Madison, WI 53707
P: (608) 267-1005
E: claire.dehnert
 @wisconsin.gov

WYOMING
Hon. Greg Phillips (D)
Attorney General
Office of the Attorney General
State Capitol Building
Cheyenne, WY 82002
P: (307) 777-7841

Ethics

Administers and enforces the state ethics laws applying to public officials.

ALABAMA
Mr. James L. Sumner Jr.
Director
Ethics Commission
100 North Union Street, Suite 104
P.O. Box 4840
Montgomery, AL 36103
P: (334) 242-2806
F: (334) 242-0248

ALASKA
Ms. Joyce Anderson
Administrator
Committee on Legislative Ethics
P.O. Box 101468
Anchorage, AK 99510
P: (907) 269-0150
F: (907) 269-0152
E: ethics_committee
@legis.state.ak.us

ARKANSAS
Mr. Graham Sloan
Director
State Ethics Commission
910 West 2nd Street, Suite 100
Little Rock, AR 72201
P: (501) 682-9600
F: (501) 682-9606
E: graham.sloan
@mail.state.ar.us

CALIFORNIA
Mr. Roman Porter
Executive Director
Fair Political Practices Commission
428 J Street, Suite 800
Sacramento, CA 95814
P: (916) 322-5660
F: (916) 322-0886

COLORADO
Ms. Jane T. Feldman
Executive Director
Independent Ethics Commission
633 17th Street, 13th Floor
Denver, CO 80202
P: (303) 866-5727
F: (303) 866-3777
E: jane.feldman@state.co.us

CONNECTICUT
Ms. Carol Carson
Executive Director
Office of State Ethics
18-20 Trinity Street, Suite 205
Hartford, CT 06106
P: (860) 263-2384
F: (860) 263-2402
E: carol.carson@ct.gov

DELAWARE
Ms. Janet Wright
Attorney
Public Integrity Commission
Margaret O'Neill Building
410 Federal Street, Suite 3
Dover, DE 19901
P: (302) 739-2399
F: (302) 739-2398

DISTRICT OF COLUMBIA
Mr. Togo D. West Jr.
Chair
Board of Elections & Ethics
441 4th Street, Northwest
Suite 250 North
Washington, DC 20001
P: (202) 727-2525
F: (202) 347-2648
E: boee@dc.gov

FLORIDA
Mr. Phillip Claypool
Executive Director & General Counsel
Commission on Ethics
P.O. Drawer 15709
Tallahassee, FL 32317
P: (904) 488-7864
F: (904) 488-3077
E: Claypool.Phil
@leg.state.fl.us

GEORGIA
Ms. Stacy Kalberman
Executive Secretary
State Ethics Commission
200 Piedmont Avenue, Southeast
Suite 1402, West Tower
Atlanta, GA 30334
P: (404) 463-1980
F: (404) 463-1988
E: gaethics@ethics.ga.gov

GUAM
Mr. John Blas
Executive Director
Elections Commission
P.O. Box BG
Hagatna, GU 96932
P: (671) 477-9791
F: (671) 477-1895
E: director@gec.guam.gov

HAWAII
Mr. Les Kondo
Executive Director & General Counsel
State Ethics Commission
P.O. Box 616
Honolulu, HI 96809
P: (808) 587-0460
F: (808) 587-0470
E: ethics@hawaiiethics.org

IDAHO
Hon. Lawrence Wasden (R)
Attorney General
Office of the Attorney General
700 West State Street
P.O. Box 83720
Boise, ID 83720
P: (208) 334-2400
F: (208) 854-8071

ILLINOIS
Mr. Chad Fornoff
Executive Director
Executive Ethics Commission
401 South Spring Street
513 William Stratton Building
Springfield, IL 62706
P: (217) 558-1393
F: (217) 558-1399
E: Chad.Fornoff
@illinois.gov

INDIANA
Ms. Cynthia Carrasco
Ethics Director
Office of the Inspector General
315 West Ohio Street, Room 104
Indianapolis, IN 46202
P: (317) 232-3850
F: (317) 232-0707
E: ccarrasco@ig.IN.gov

KANSAS
Ms. Carol E. Williams
Executive Director
Governmental Ethics Commission
109 Southwest 9th Street, Suite 504
Topeka, KS 66612
P: (785) 296-4219
F: (785) 296-2548

KENTUCKY
Mr. John R. Steffen
Executive Director
Executive Branch Ethics Commission
#3 Fountain Place
Frankfort, KY 40601
P: (502) 564-7954
E: john.steffen@ky.gov

Mr. Anthony M. Wilhoit
Executive Director
Legislative Ethics Commission
22 Mill Creek Park
Frankfort, KY 40601
P: (502) 573-2863
F: (502) 573-2929
E: tony.wilhoit@lrc.ky.gov

LOUISIANA
Ms. Kathleen Allen
Ethics Administrator
Ethics Administration
617 North Third Street, Suite 10-36
P.O. Box 4368
Baton Rouge, LA 70821
P: (225) 219-5600
F: (225) 381-7271

MAINE
Mr. Jonathan Wayne
Executive Director
Commission on Governmental Ethics & Election Practices
135 State House Station
Augusta, ME 04333
P: (207) 287-4179
F: (207) 287-6775
E: Jonathan.Wayne@maine.gov

MARYLAND
Mr. Robert A. Hahn
Executive Director
State Ethics Commission
Executive Department
45 Calvert Street, 3rd Floor
Annapolis, MD 21401
P: (410) 260-7770
F: (410) 260-7746
E: rhahn@gov.state.md.us

MASSACHUSETTS
Ms. Karen L. Nober
Executive Director
Ethics Commission
One Ashburton Place
Boston, MA 02108
P: (617) 727-0600

MICHIGAN
Ms. Janet McClelland
Chief Deputy Director
State Board of Ethics
400 South Pine Street
P.O. Box 30002
Lansing, MI 48909
P: (517) 373-3020
F: (517) 373-3103
E: mcclellandj@michigan.gov

Ethics

MINNESOTA
Mr. Gary Goldsmith
Executive Director
Campaign Finance & Public
Disclosure Board
Centennial Office Building,
Suite 190
658 Cedar Street
St. Paul, MN 55155
P: (651) 296-1721
F: (651) 296-1722
E: gary.goldsmith
   @state.mn.us

MISSISSIPPI
Mr. Tom Hood
Executive Director
Ethics Commission
P.O. Box 22746
Jackson, MS 39225
P: (601) 359-1285
F: (601) 354-6253
E: info@ethics.state.ms.us

MISSOURI
Ms. Julie A. Allen
Executive Director
Ethics Commission
3411A Knipp Drive
Jefferson City, MO 65109
P: (573) 751-2020
F: (573) 526-4506
E: helpdesk@mec.mo.gov

MONTANA
Ms. Jennifer L. Hensley
Commissioner
Commissioner of Political
Practices
1205 Eighth Avenue
P.O. Box 202401
Helena, MT 59620
P: (406) 444-2942
F: (406) 444-1643
E: JLHensley@mt.gov

NEBRASKA
Mr. Frank Daley
Executive Director
Accountability & Disclosure
Commission
P.O. Box 95086
Lincoln, NE 68509
P: (402) 471-2522
F: (402) 471-6599
E: frank.daley@nebraska.gov

NEVADA
Ms. Caren Jenkins
Executive Director
Commission on Ethics
3476 Executive Pointe Way,
Suite 10
Carson City, NV 89706
P: (775) 687-5469
F: (775) 687-1279
E: cjenkins@ethics.nv.gov

NEW HAMPSHIRE
Hon. Michael A. Delaney
Attorney General
Office of the Attorney General
Department of Justice
33 Capitol Street
Concord, NH 03301
P: (603) 271-1202
F: (603) 271-2110
E: michael.a.delaney
   @doj.nh.gov

NEW JERSEY
Mr. Peter J. Tober
Executive Director
State Ethics Commission
28 West State Street, Room
1407
P.O. Box 082
Trenton, NJ 08625
P: (609) 292-1892
F: (609) 633-9252
E: ethics
   @ethics.state.nj.us

NEW MEXICO
Ms. Bobbi Shearer
Director
Bureau of Elections
State Capitol Annex North
325 Don Gaspar, Suite 300
Santa Fe, NM 87503
P: (505) 827-8403
F: (505) 827-8403
E: bobbi.shearer
   @state.nm.us

NEW YORK
Mr. Barry Ginsberg
Executive Director
Commission on Public Integrity
540 Broadway
Albany, NY 12207
P: (518) 408-3976

NORTH CAROLINA
Mr. Perry Newson
Executive Director
State Ethics Commission
1324 Mail Service Center
Raleigh, NC 27699
P: (919) 715-2071
F: (919) 715-1644

NORTH DAKOTA
Mr. Jerod Tufte
Counsel
Governor's Office
600 East Boulevard Avenue
Bismark, ND 58505
P: (701) 328-1048
F: (701) 328-2205
E: jetufte@nd.gov

OHIO
Mr. Paul M. Nick
Executive Director
Ethics Commission
30 West Spring Street, L3
Columbus, OH 43215
P: (614) 466-7090
F: (614) 466-8368
E: ethics@ethics.ohio.gov

OKLAHOMA
Ms. Marilyn Hughes
Executive Director
Ethics Commission
2300 North Lincoln Boulevard,
Room B-5
Oklahoma City, OK 73105
P: (405) 521-3451
F: (405) 521-4905

OREGON
Mr. Ronald A. Bersin
Executive Director
Government Ethics Commission
3218 Pringle Road, Southeast,
Suite 220
Salem, OR 97302
P: (503) 378-5108
F: (503) 373-1456
E: ron.a.bersin@state.or.us

PENNSYLVANIA
Mr. John J. Contino
Exeuctive Director
State Ethics Commission
Room 309, Finance Building
P.O. Box 11470
Harrisburg, PA 17108
P: (717) 783-1610
F: (717) 787-0806

PUERTO RICO
Ms. Zulma L. Rosario Vega
Acting Executive Director
Office of Governmental Ethics
P.O. Box 194200
San Juan, PR 00919
P: (787) 722-0305
F: (787) 754-0977

RHODE ISLAND
Mr. Kent A. Willever
Executive Director/Chief
Prosecutor
Ethics Commission
40 Fountain Street, 8th Floor
Providence, RI 02903
P: (401) 222-3790
F: (401) 272-3382

SOUTH CAROLINA
Mr. Herbert R. Hayden Jr.
Executive Director
State Ethics Commission
5000 Thurmond Mall, Suite 250
Columbia, SC 29201
P: (803) 253-4192
F: (803) 253-7539
E: herb@ethics.state.sc.us

SOUTH DAKOTA
Hon. Jason M. Gant (R)
Secretary of State
Office of the Secretary of State
500 East Capitol Avenue, Suite
204
Pierre, SD 57501
P: (605) 773-3537
F: (605) 773-6580
E: sdsos@state.sd.us

TENNESSEE
Mr. Stephen Rawlins
Executive Director
Registry of Election Finance
404 James Robertson Parkway,
Suite 104
Nashville, TN 37243
P: (615) 741-7959
F: (615) 532-8905
E: registry.info
   @state.tn.us

TEXAS
Mr. David A. Reisman
Executive Director
Ethics Commission
201 East 14th Street, 10th Floor
P.O. Box 12070
Austin, TX 78711
P: (512) 463-5800
F: (512) 463-5777

U.S. VIRGIN ISLANDS
Mr. Elliott M. Davis
Solicitor General
Solicitor General's Office
34-38 Kron Prindsens Gade
GERS Building, 2nd Floor
St. Thomas, VI 00802
P: (340) 774-5666
F: (340) 776-3494
E: edavis@doj.vi.gov

UTAH
Hon. Mark L. Shurtleff (R)
Attorney General
Office of the Attorney General
350 North State Street, Suite
230
P.O. Box 142320
Salt Lake City, UT 84114
P: (801) 538-1191
F: (801) 538-1121
E: MSHURTLEFF@utah.gov

VERMONT
Hon. Jim Condos (D)
Secretary of State
Office of the Secretary of State
26 Terrace Street
Montpelier, VT 05609
P: (802) 828-2148
F: (802) 828-2496
E: jim.condos
     @sec.state.vt.us

VIRGINIA
Hon. Ken T.
     Cuccinelli II (R)
Attorney General
Office of the Attorney General
900 East Main Street
Richmond, VA 23219
P: (804) 786-2071

WASHINGTON
Mr. Doug Ellis
Interim Executive Director
Public Disclosure Commission
711 Capitol Way, #206
P.O. Box 40908
Olympia, WA 98504
P: (360) 664-2735
F: (360) 753-1112
E: Dellis@pdc.wa.gov

WISCONSIN
Mr. Jonathan Becker
Division Administrator
Ethics Division
P.O. Box 7984
Madison, WI 53707
P: (608) 267-0647
E: jonathan.becker@wi.gov

WYOMING
Hon. Max Maxfield (R)
Secretary of State
Office of the Secretary of State
State Capitol Building
200 West 24th
Cheyenne, WY 82002
P: (307) 777-7378
F: (307) 777-6217
E: Secofstate@state.wy.us

Facilities Management

Maintains, constructs, designs, renovates and delivers basic services to state-owned facilities.

Information provided by:

National Association of State Facilities Administrators
Marcia Stone
Association Manager
2760 Research Park Drive
P.O. Box 11910
Lexington, KY 40578
P: (859) 244-8181
F: (859) 244-8001
nasfa@nasfa.net
www.nasfa.net

ALABAMA
Ms. Katherine Lynn
Director
Building Commission
P.O. Box 301150
Montgomery, AL 36130
P: (334) 242-4082
F: (334) 242-4182
E: katherine.lynn
    @bc.alabama.gov

Searcy Rushing
Director
Service Division
Department of Finance
Suite N-105, 600 Dexter Avenue
Montgomery, AL 36130
P: (334) 353-0371

ALASKA
Mr. Joel St. Aubin
Engineer / Architect IV
Public Facilities
Department of Transportation
P.O. Box 196900, MS-2525
Anchorage, AK 99519
P: (907) 269-0823
F: (907) 269-0805
E: joel.staubin@alaska.gov

ARIZONA
Mr. Don Fitzpatrick
General Manager
Facilities Operation &
Maintenance
100 North 15th Avenue, Suite 202
Phoenix, AZ 85007
P: (602) 542-1579
E: don.fitzpatrick
    @azdoa.gov

ARKANSAS
Mr. Floyd Farmer
Director
Design Review Section
Building Authority
501 Woodlane, Suite 600
Little Rock, AR 72201
P: (501) 682-5563
E: ffarmer@aba.state.ar.us

CALIFORNIA
Mr. Michael Bocchicchio
Assistant Vice President,
Facilities Administration
University of California
1111 Franklin Street, 16th Floor
Suite 6201
Oakland, CA 94607
P: (510) 987-0777
F: (510) 987-0752
E: mike.bocchicchio
    @ucop.edu

Mr. Dan Burgoyne
Sustainability Manager,
Executive Office - Green Team
Department of General Services
707 3rd Street, 4th Floor
P.O. Box 989052
West Sacramento, CA 95605
P: (916) 376-5010
E: Daniel.Burgoyne
    @dgs.ca.gov

COLORADO
Mr. Bradford T. Membel
Director
Division of Facilities
Management
Department of Human Services
4112 South Knox Court
Denver, CO 80236
P: (303) 866-7290
F: (303) 866-7299
E: bradford.membel
    @state.co.us

CONNECTICUT
Mr. Bruce Bockstael
Chief Architect
Design & Construction
Department of Public Works
165 Capitol Avenue, Room 475
Hartford, CT 06106
P: (860) 713-5631
E: bruce.bockstael@ct.gov

DELAWARE
Mr. Mark Devore
Chief of Engineering &
Operations, Division of
Facilities Management
Office of Management &
Budget
Thomas Collins Building, Suite 1
540 South Dupont Highway
Dover, DE 19901
P: (302) 739-5644
E: mark.devore@state.de.us

DISTRICT OF COLUMBIA
Mr. Spencer Davis
Deputy Director, Facilities
Department of Real Estate
Services
2000 14th Street, Northwest
8th Floor
Washington, DC 20009
P: (202) 724-4400
E: spencer.davis@dc.gov

FLORIDA
Mr. Tom Berger
Deputy Director
Real Estate Development &
Management
Department of Management
Services
4050 Esplanade Way, Suite 315
Tallahassee, FL 32399
P: (850) 488-2074

GEORGIA
Mr. Steve Stancil
State Property Officer
Building Authority
47 Trinity Avenue, Suite G02
Atlanta, GA 30334
P: (404) 656-3253
F: (404) 656-6006
E: sstancil@gsfic.ga.gov

HAWAII
Mr. Bruce Coppa
State Comptroller
Accounting & General Services
P.O. Box 119
Honolulu, HI 96810
P: (808) 586-0400
F: (808) 586-0775
E: bruce.a.coppa@hawaii.gov

IDAHO
Mr. Tim Mason
Administrator
Division of Public Works
Department of Administration
502 North 4th Street
Boise, ID 83702
P: (208) 332-1911
F: (208) 334-4031
E: tim.mason@adm.idaho.gov

ILLINOIS
Mr. Bruce Washington
Deputy Director
Department of Central
Management Services
Property Management
WMG Stratton Building, 7th Floor
Springfield, IL 62706
P: (217) 785-0562

Mr. Ron Wright
Senior Executive Assistant
Construction
Capital Development Board
Stratton Building, 3rd Floor,
Suite 350S
Springfield, IL 62706
P: (217) 782-8532
F: (217) 524-4208
E: ron.wright@Illinois.gov

INDIANA
Mr. Brian Renner
Deputy Commissioner of
Operations
Office of the Commissioner
Department of Administration
302 West Washington Street,
Room E-024
Indianapolis, IN 46204
P: (317) 232-3125

IOWA
Mr. Lee Hammer
Public Service Executive 4
Facilities Support
Department of Transportation
800 Lincoln Way
Ames, IA 50010
P: (515) 239-1327
F: (515) 239-1964
E: lee.hammer@dot.iowa.gov

KANSAS
Mr. Gary Grimes
Department of Social &
Rehabilitation Services, SRS
Capital Improvements
915 Southwest Harrison Avenue
Docking State Office Building,
9th Floor
Topeka, KS 66612
P: (785) 296-3772
F: (785) 532-6363
E: gwg@ksu.edu

KENTUCKY
Mr. Jerry Graves
Deputy Commissioner
Department of Facilities
403 Wapping Street
Frankfort, KY 40601
P: (502) 564-3155
E: jerry.graves@ky.gov

LOUISIANA

Mr. William Morrison
Assistant Director (Detailed)
Division of Administration
Facility Planning & Control
Suite 7-160, 1201 North 3rd
Street
Baton Rouge, LA 70804
P: (225) 342-0855
F: (225) 342-7624
E: bill.morrison@la.gov

MAINE

Ms. Betty Lamoreau
Acting Director
Bureau of General Services
77 State House Station
Augusta, ME 04333
P: (207) 624-7314
F: (207) 624-5086
E: Betty.M.Lamoreau
@maine.gov

MARYLAND

Mr. Alvin Collins
Secretary
Department of General Services
301 West Preston Street, Suite
1401
Baltimore, MD 21201
P: (410) 767-4960
E: alvin.collins
@dgs.state.md.us

MASSACHUSETTS

Ms. Hope Davis
Acting Deputy Commissioner
Office of Facilities Maintenance
& Management
Division of Capital Asset
Management
One Ashburton Place, 15th Floor
Boston, MA 02108
P: (617) 727-4030 Ext. 447
F: (617) 727-4043
E: hope.davis@state.ma.us

Mr. William Tivnan
Director
Capital Asset Management
Office of Finance &
Administration
One Ashburton Place, 15th Floor
Boston, MA 02108
P: 617-727-4030
F: (617) 727-5363
E: bill.tivnan
@dcp.state.ma.us

MICHIGAN

Ms. Tina Richardson
Director, Facilities & Business
Services Administration
Technology, Management &
Budget
320 South Walnut Street
Lewis Cass Building, 2nd Floor
Lansing, MI 48933
P: (517) 241-9277

MINNESOTA

Mr. Wayne Waslaski
Senior Director, Real Estate &
Construction Services
Department of Administration
309 Administration Building
50 Sherburne Avenue
St. Paul, MN 55155
P: (612) 201-2548
E: Wayne.Waslaski
@state.mn.us

MISSISSIPPI

Mr. David Anderson
Director
Bureau of Building, Grounds &
Real Property Management
1401 Suite B, 501 Northwest
Street
Jackson, MS 39201
P: (601) 359-3898
F: (601) 359-2470
E: andersd@dfa.state.ms.us

Mr. Glenn Kornbrek
Assistant Director, Bureau of
Building
Department of Finance &
Administration
501 North West Street, Suite
1401 B
Jackson, MS 39201
P: (601) 359-3894
E: kornbrg@dfa.state.ms.us

MISSOURI

Mr. Gary Claspill
Design Development Survey
Manager
Facilities Management, Design
& Construction
Office of Administration
301 West High Street, Room 730
Jefferson City, MO 65109
P: (573) 751-3740
F: (573) 751-7277
E: gary.claspill@oa.mo.gov

MONTANA

Mr. Russ Katherman
Engineering Manager
Architecture & Engineering
Division
Department of Administration
P.O. Box 200103
Helena, MT 59620
P: (406) 444-3332
F: (406) 444-3399
E: rkatherman@mt.gov

NEBRASKA

Mr. Rodney Anderson
Administrator
State Building Division
Department of Administrative
Services
521 South 14th Street, Suite 500
Lincoln, NE 68508
P: (402) 471-3191

NEVADA

Mr. Patrick McMenomy
Facilities Supervisor
Administrative Division
Legislative Counsel Bureau
401 South Carson Street
Carson City, NV 89701
P: (775) 684-6771

NEW HAMPSHIRE

Ms. Michelle Juliano
Assistant Administrator
Bureau of Public Works, Design
& Construction
Public Works
7 Hazen Drive
Concord, NH 03302
P: (603) 271-1645
E: mjuliano@dot.state.nh.us

NEW JERSEY

Mr. Guy Bocage
Deputy Director
Purchase & Property
Department of the Treasury
33 West State Street, P.O. Box
230
Trenton, NJ 08625
P: (609) 292-5111
F: (609) 984-2575
E: guy.bocage
@treas.state.nj.us

NEW MEXICO

Mr. Manuel Sanchez
Office Manager
Building Services Division
General Services Department
P.O. Box 6850
Santa Fe, NM 87502
P: (505) 476-2438
E: manuel.sanchez
@state.nm.us

NEW YORK

Mr. Martin Gilroy
Group Director
Real Property Management
Corning Tower, 39th Floor
Empire State Plaza
Albany, NY 12242
P: (518) 474-6057
F: (518) 474-1523
E: martin.gilroy
@ogs.state.ny.us

NORTH CAROLINA

Mr. Gregory Driver
Director
State Construction Office
Department of Administration
1307 Mail Service Center
Raleigh, NC 27699
P: (919) 807-4100
F: (919) 807-4110
E: gregory.driver
@ncmail.net

NORTH DAKOTA

Mr. John Boyle
Director
Facilities Management
Office of Management &
Budget
600 East Boulevard Avenue, 4th
Floor
Bismarck, ND 58505
P: (701) 328-4002
E: jaboyle@nd.gov

Mr. Joel Leapaldt
State Facility Planner, Division
of Facility Management
Office of Management &
Budget
4th Floor, State Capitol Building
600 East Boulevard Avenue
Bismarck, ND 58505
P: (701) 328-1968
F: (701) 328-3230
E: jleapaldt@state.nd.us

OHIO

Lane Beougher
Architect Administrator
General Services Division/State
Architect's Office
Department of Administrative
Services
4200 Surface Road
Columbus, OH 43288
P: (614) 752-0013

Facilities Management

Mr. Peter Gunnell
Chief Administrator
General Services/Office of
Properties & Facilities
Department of Administrative
Services
4200 Surface Road
Columbus, OH 43228
P: (614) 752-0455

OKLAHOMA
Mr. Mark Sauchuk
Division Administrator
Facilities Services
Department of Central Services
P.O. Box 53187
Oklahoma City, OK 73152
P: (405) 522-0084
E: mark_sauchuk
    @dcs.state.ok.us

OREGON
Robin Harpster
Administrator
Facilities Division
Department of Administrative
Services
1225 Ferry Street, Southeast,
U100
Salem, OR 97301
P: (503) 373-7152
F: (503) 373-7210
E: robin.harpster
    @state.or.us

PENNSYLVANIA
Mr. Daniel Schiavoni
Deputy Director
Property & Asset Management
515 North Office Building
Harrisburg, PA 17125
P: (717) 787-5996

RHODE ISLAND
Mr. Marco Schiappa
Associate Director
Facilities Management
Department of Administration
One Capitol Hill, 2nd Floor
Providence, RI 02908
P: (401) 222-5717
E: MSchiappa
    @gw.doa.state.ri.us

SOUTH CAROLINA
Mr. Allen R. Carter
Architect
Procurement Services Division
Office of State Engineer
1201 Main Street, Suite 600
Columbia, SC 29201
P: (803) 737-0776
F: (803) 737-0639
E: acarter@mmo.state.sc.us

Mr. John St. C. White
State Engineer
Materials Management Office
Budget & Control Board
Suite 600, 1201 Main Street
Columbia, SC 29201
P: (803) 737-0768

TENNESSEE
Mr. J. Alan Robertson
State Architect, Real Property
Administration
Finance & Administration
312 Rosa L. Parks Avenue
Snodgrass Tennessee Tower, 21st
Floor
Nashville, TN 37243
P: (615) 741-3259

TEXAS
Mr. Terry Keel
Executive Director
Facilities Commission
1711 San Jacinto
Austin, TX 78701
P: (512) 463-3446
E: terry.keel
    @tfc.state.tx.us

UTAH
Mr. Bruce Whittington
Assistant Director
Facilities, Construction &
Management
Administrative Services
4130 State Office Bulding
Salt Lake City, UT 84114
P: (801) 538-3547
F: (801) 538-3378
E: bwhittington@utah.gov

VERMONT
Mr. William Laferriere
Director of Property
Management
Department of Buildings &
Property Management
Suite 300, 5 Perry Street
Barre, VT 05641
P: (802) 479-4462
F: (802) 828-6501
E: bill.laferriere
    @state.vt.us

VIRGINIA
Mr. Robert "Bert" Jones
Director, Engineering &
Buildings
Department of General Services
Washington Building
1100 Bank Street, Suite 506
Richmond, VA 23225
P: (804) 786-3263
F: (804) 371-7934
E: bert.jones
    @dgs.virginia.gov

WASHINGTON
Mr. John Lynch
Assistant Director
Engineering & Architectural
Services
General Administration
P.O. Box 41012
Olympia, WA 98504
P: (360) 902-7272
E: jlynch@ga.wa.gov

WEST VIRGINIA
Mr. David Oliverio
Director, General Services
Department of Administration
1900 Kanawha Boulevard, East
Building 1, Room MB60
Charleston, WV 25305
P: (304) 558-1301
F: (304) 558-2334
E: davido@wvadmin.gov

WISCONSIN
Mr. David W. Helbach
Administrator, Division of State
Facilities
State Building Commission
131 West Wilson Street
P.O. Box 7866
Madison, WI 53707
P: (608) 266-1031

WYOMING
Mr. Raymond Vigil Jr.
Facilities Program Manager,
Facility Maintenance
Department of Transportation
5300 Bishop Boulevard
Building 6101, Room B-25
Cheyenne, WY 82009
P: (307) 777-4474
F: (307) 777-3801
E: raymond.vigil
    @dot.state.wy.us

Federal Liaison

The individual, typically based in Washington D.C., who serves as the chief representative of state government in the nation's capital, and works to promote state-federal relations.

For more information contact:

National Governors Association
Ray Scheppach
Executive Director
Hall of States
444 North Capitol Street
Washington, DC 20001
P: (202) 624-5300
F: (202) 624-5313
www.nga.org

ALASKA
Mr. John Katz
Director
Governor's Washington Office
444 North Capitol Street, Suite 336
Washington, DC 20001
P: (202) 624-5858
F: (202) 624-5857

AMERICAN SAMOA
Ms. Janice Lipsen
Washington Representative for the Governor
Governor's Washington Office
1101 Vermont Avenue, Northwest
Suite 403
Washington, DC 20005
P: (202) 408-4998
F: (202) 408-4997

ARIZONA
Mr. Ryan Serote
Director of Federal Relations
Governor's Washington Office
444 North Capitol Street, Suite 428
Washington, DC 20001
P: (202) 220-1396
F: (202) 624-1475

CALIFORNIA
Ms. Katie Mathews
Deputy Director
Washington Office
444 North Capitol Street, Suite 134
Washington, DC 20001
P: (202) 624-5270
F: (202) 624-5280

DELAWARE
Ms. Missy Wier
Director
Washington Office
444 North Capitol Street, Suite 230
Washington, DC 20001
P: (202) 624-7724
F: (202) 624-5495

FLORIDA
Mr. Spencer Geissinger
Director
Washington Office
444 North Capitol Street, Suite 349
Washington, DC 20001
P: (202) 624-5885
F: (202) 624-5886

GEORGIA
Mr. Todd Smith
Washington Representative
Governor's Washington Office
1455 Pennsylvania Avenue, Northwest
Suite 400
Washington, DC 20004
P: (202) 652-2299
F: (202) 347-1142

GUAM
Ms. Sirena Ramirez
Washington Office
444 North Capitol Street, Suite 619
Washington, DC 20001
P: (202) 434-4855
F: (202) 434-4856

ILLINOIS
Ms. Jen Hoelzle
Director
Washington Office
444 North Capitol Street, Suite 400
Washington, DC 20001
P: (202) 624-7762
F: (202) 724-0689

INDIANA
Ms. Debbie Hohlt
Federal Representative
Washington Office
1455 Pennsylvania Avenue, Northwest
Suite 1140
Washington, DC 20004
P: (202) 624-1474
F: (202) 833-1587

IOWA
Mr. Doug Hoelscher
Director
Office for State-Federal Relation
400 North Capitol Street, Suite 359
Washington, DC 20001
P: (202) 624-5479
F: (202) 624-8189

KANSAS
Mr. Adam Nordstrom
Washington Representative for the Governor
Governor's Washington Office
500 New Jersey Avenue, Northwest
Suite 400
Washington, DC 20001
P: (202) 715-2923
F: (202) 638-1045

KENTUCKY
Ms. Rebecca Byers
Director
Governor's Washington Office
444 North Capitol Street, Suite 224
Washington, DC 20001
P: (202) 220-1350
F: (202) 220-1359

MARYLAND
Ms. Dana Thompson
Director
Governor's Washington Office
444 North Capitol Street, Suite 311
Washington, DC 20001
P: (202) 624-1430
F: (202) 783-3061

MASSACHUSETTS
Ms. Jewel James
Director
Office of Federal-State Relations
444 North Capitol Street, Suite 208
Washington, DC 20001
P: (202) 624-7713
F: (202) 624-7714

MICHIGAN
Mr. Bill McBride
Director
Governor's Washington Office
444 North Capitol Street, Suite 411
Washington, DC 20001
P: (202) 624-5840
F: (202) 624-5841

MINNESOTA
Mr. Bill Richard
Director
Governor's Washington Office
1017 8th Street, Northeast
Washington, DC 20002
P: (202) 236-3717

NEVADA
Mr. Ryan McGinness
Director
Washington Office
444 North Capitol Street, Suite 209
Washington, DC 20001
P: (202) 624-5405
F: (202) 624-8181

NEW JERSEY
Ms. Dona De Leon
Director
Washington Office
444 North Capitol Street, Suite 201
Washington, DC 20001
P: (202) 638-0631
F: (202) 638-2296

NEW YORK
Ms. Hilary Jochmans
Director
Governor's Washington Office
444 North Capitol Street, Northwest
Suite 301
Washington, DC 20001
P: (202) 434-7100
F: (202) 434-7110

NORTH CAROLINA
Mr. Jim McCleskey
Director
Governor's Washington Office
444 North Capitol Street, Suite 332
Washington, DC 20001
P: (202) 624-5830
F: (202) 624-5836

Federal Liaison

NORTH DAKOTA
Ms. Krista Carman
Washington Representative
Washington Office
444 North Capitol Street, Suite 837
Washington, DC 20001
P: (202) 256-9518
F: (202) 478-0811

PUERTO RICO
Ms. Nicole Guillemard
Executive Director
Federal Affairs Administration
1100 17th Street, Northwest, Suite 800
Washington, DC 20036
P: (202) 778-0710
F: (202) 822-0916

TEXAS
Mr. Charles Roy
Director
Office of State-Federal Relations
10 G Street, Northeast
Suite 650
Washington, DC 20002
P: (202) 638-3927
F: (202) 628-1943

U.S. VIRGIN ISLANDS
Mr. Steven Steele
Director
Governor's Washington Office
444 North Capitol Street, Suite 305
Washington, DC 20001
P: (202) 624-3560
F: (202) 624-3594

VIRGINIA
Ms. Jeannemarie Davis
Director
Liaison Office
444 North Capitol Street, Suite 214
Washington, DC 20001
P: (202) 783-1769
F: (202) 783-7687

WASHINGTON
Mr. Mark Rupp
Director
Washington, DC Office
444 North Capitol Street, Suite 411
Washington, DC 20001
P: (202) 624-3691
F: (202) 624-5841

WISCONSIN
Mr. Bill Kloiber
Deputy Director
Washington Office
444 North Capitol Street, Suite 613
Washington, DC 20001
P: (202) 624-5870
F: (202) 624-5871

Finance

Responsible for multiple financial functions (budget, payroll, accounting, revenue estimation.)

ALABAMA
Mr. David Perry
Director
Department of Finance
State Capitol
600 Dexter Avenue, Suite N-105
Montgomery, AL 36130
P: (334) 242-7160
F: (334) 353-3300
E: david.perry
@finance.alabama.gov

ALASKA
Ms. Kim Garnero
Director
Division of Finance
Department of Administration
P.O. Box 110204
Juneau, AK 99811
P: (907) 465-3435
F: (907) 465-2169
E: kim.garnero@alaska.gov

AMERICAN SAMOA
Hon. Magalei Logovi'i
Treasurer
Department of the Treasury
American Samoa Government
Pago Pago, AS 96799
P: (684) 633-4155
F: (684) 633-4100

ARIZONA
Mr. D. Clark Partridge
State Comptroller
General Accounting Office
100 North 15th Avenue, Suite 302
Phoenix, AZ 85007
P: (602) 542-8168
F: (602) 542-3093
E: clark.partridge
@azdoa.gov

ARKANSAS
Mr. Richard Weiss
Administrator
Department of Finance & Administration
P.O. Box 2485
Little Rock, AR 72203
P: (501) 682-2242
F: (501) 682-1029
E: richard.weiss
@dfa.state.ar.us

CALIFORNIA
Ms. Ana J. Matosantos
Director of Finance
Department of Finance
915 L Street
Sacramento, CA 95814
P: (916) 445-4141

CONNECTICUT
Mr. Benjamin Barnes
Secretary
Office of Policy & Management
450 Capitol Avenue
Hartford, CT 06106
P: (860) 418-6500
F: (860) 418-6487
E: benjamin.barnes@ct.gov

Ms. Brenda L. Sisco
Acting Secretary
Office of Policy & Management
450 Capitol Avenue
Hartford, CT 06106
P: (860) 418-6500
E: brenda.sisco@ct.gov

DELAWARE
Mr. Thomas J. Cook
Secretary of Finance
Department of Finance
Carvel State Building, 8th Floor
820 North French Street
Wilmington, DE 19801
P: (302) 577-8984
F: (302) 577-8982
E: tom.cook@state.de.us

DISTRICT OF COLUMBIA
Dr. Natwar M. Gandhi
Chief Financial Officer
Office of the Chief Financial Officer
1350 Pennsylvania Avenue, Northwest
Room 203
Washington, DC 20004
P: (202) 727-2476
F: (202) 727-1643
E: ocfo@dc.gov

GEORGIA
Hon. Tommy D. Hills (R)
Treasurer and Director
Office of Treasury & Fiscal Services
200 Piedmont Avenue
Suite 1202, West Tower
Atlanta, GA 30334
P: (404) 656-2168
F: (404) 656-9048
E: OTFSweb@otfs.ga.gov

GUAM
Ms. Lourdes M. Perez
Director
Department of Administration
P.O. Box 884
Hagatna, GU 96932
P: (671) 475-1122
F: (671) 475-1243
E: lou.perez@doa.guam.gov

HAWAII
Hon. Kalbert K. Young
Director of Finance
Department of Budget & Finance
P.O. Box 150
Honolulu, HI 96810
P: (808) 586-1518
F: (808) 586-1976
E: HI.BudgetandFinance
@hawaii.gov

IDAHO
Mr. Gavin M. Gee
Director
Department of Finance
800 Park Boulevard, Suite 200
Boise, ID 83712
P: (208) 332-8010
F: (208) 332-8097
E: ggee@finance.idaho.gov

ILLINOIS
Mr. David Vaught
Director
Office of Management & Budget
108 State House
Springfield, IL 62706
P: (217) 782-4520
F: (217) 524-1514
E: BureauBudget.OMB
@illinois.gov

INDIANA
Mr. Adam Horst
Director
State Budget Agency
200 West Washington Street, Room 212
Indianapolis, IN 46204
P: (317) 233-5707
F: (317) 233-3323
E: ahorst@sba.in.gov

IOWA
Ms. Courtney M. Kay-Decker
Director
Department of Revenue
Hoover State Office Building
1305 East Walnut Street
Des Moines, IA 50319
P: (515) 281-3204
E: courtney.decker@iowa.gov

KANSAS
Mr. Kent Olson
Director
Division of Accounts & Reports
900 Southwest Jackson Street
Room 351-S
Topeka, KS 66612
P: (785) 296-2318
F: (785) 296-6841
E: kent.olson@da.ks.gov

KENTUCKY
Ms. Lori Flanery
Cabinet Secretary
Finance & Administration Cabinet
Room 383, Capitol Annex
Frankfort, KY 40601
P: (502) 564-4240
F: (502) 564-5856
E: Lori.Flanery@ky.gov

LOUISIANA
Ms. Marianne Patin
Director
Office of Finance & Support Services
Division of Administration
P.O. Box 94095
Baton Rouge, LA 70804
P: (225) 342-0700
F: (225) 342-2606
E: Marianne.patin@la.gov

MAINE
Mr. H. Sawin Millett Jr.
Commissioner
Department of Administrative & Financial Services
78 State House Station
Augusta, ME 04333
P: (207) 624-7800
F: (207) 624-7804

MARYLAND
Ms. T. Eloise Foster
Secretary
Department of Budget & Management
45 Calvert Street, 1st Floor
Annapolis, MD 21401
P: (410) 260-7041
E: efoster@dbm.state.md.us

MASSACHUSETTS
Mr. Jay A. Gonzalez
Secretary of Administration and Finance
Executive Office for Administration & Finance
State House, Room 373
Boston, MA 02133
P: (617) 727-2040
F: (617) 727-2779

Finance

MICHIGAN
Mr. John Nixon
Director
Department of Technology,
Management & Budget
320 South Walnut Street
P.O Box 30026
Lansing, MI 48909
P: (517) 241-5150

MINNESOTA
Mr. Jim Schowalter
Commissioner
Management & Budget
658 Cedar Street, Suite 400
St. Paul, MN 55155
P: (651) 201-8010
F: (651) 296-7714
E: James.Schowalter
    @state.mn.us

MISSISSIPPI
Ms. Leila Malatesta
Director of Fiscal Management
Office of Fiscal Management
501 North West Street
1301 Woolfolk Building
Jackson, MS 39201
P: (601) 359-3402
F: (601) 359-2405
E: malatel@dfa.state.ms.us

Mr. Kevin J. Upchurch
Executive Director
Department of Finance &
Administration
P.O. Box 267
Jackson, MS 39201
P: (601) 359-3402
F: (601) 359-2405
E: kupchurch
    @dfa.state.ms.us

MISSOURI
Mr. Richard J. Weaver
Commissioner
Division of Finance
Truman State Office Building,
Room 630
P.O. Box 716
Jefferson City, MO 65102
P: (573) 751-3242
F: (573) 751-9192
E: finance@dof.mo.gov

MONTANA
Mr. Paul Christofferson
Administrator
State Accounting Division
Mitchell Building, Room 255
P.O. Box 200102
Helena, MT 59620
P: (406) 444-4609
F: (406) 444-2812
E: pachristofferson@mt.gov

Mr. David Ewer
Budget Director
Office of Budget & Program
Planning
State Capitol, Room 277
P.O. Box 200802
Helena, MT 59620
P: (406) 444-3616
F: (406) 444-4670
E: dewer@mt.gov

NEBRASKA
Mr. Carlos Castillo
Director
Department of Administrative
Services
State Capitol, Room 1315
Lincoln, NE 68509
P: (402) 471-2331
E: carlos.castillo
    @email.state.ne.us

NEVADA
Mr. Andrew K. Clinger
Director
Division of Budget & Planning
Balsdel Building
209 East Musser Street, Room
200
Carson City, NV 89701
P: (775) 684-0222
F: (775) 684-0260
E: aclinger
    @budget.state.nv.us

NEW HAMPSHIRE
Ms. Linda M. Hodgdon
Commissioner
Department of Administrative
Services
25 Capitol Street, Room 120
State House Annex
Concord, NH 03301
P: (603) 271-3201
F: (603) 271-6600
E: linda.hodgdon@nh.gov

NEW JERSEY
Ms. Charlene Holzbaur
State Comptroller
Office of Management &
Budget
33 West State Street
P.O. Box 221
Trenton, NJ 08625
P: (609) 292-6746
F: (609) 633-8179
E: charlene.holzbaur
    @treas.state.nj.us

NEW MEXICO
Mr. Richard May
Secretary
Department of Finance &
Administration
180 Bataan Memorial Building
407 Galisteo Street
Santa Fe, NM 87501
P: (505) 827-4985
F: (505) 827-4984

NEW YORK
Mr. Thomas H. Mattox
Commissioner
Department of Taxation &
Finance
W.A. Harriman Campus,
Building 9
Albany, NY 12227

NORTH CAROLINA
Mr. Andy Willis
State Budget Director
Office of State Budget &
Management
116 West Jones Street
Raleigh, NC 27603
P: (919) 807-4700
E: andy.willis@osbm.nc.gov

NORTH DAKOTA
Ms. Sheila Peterson
Director
Fiscal Management Division
600 East Boulevard Avenue
Department 110
Bismarck, ND 58505
P: (701) 328-2680
F: (701) 328-3230
E: speterson@nd.gov

Ms. Pam Sharp
Director
Office of Management &
Budget
600 East Boulevard Avenue
Department 110
Bismarck, ND 58505
P: (701) 328-2680
F: (701) 328-3230
E: psharp@nd.gov

OKLAHOMA
Mr. Preston Doerflinger
Director
Office of State Finance
2300 North Lincoln Boulevard,
Room 122
Oklahoma City, OK 73105
P: (405) 521-2444
F: (405) 521-2871

OREGON
Mr. George M. Naughton
Administrator
Budget & Management Division
Department of Administrative
Services
155 Cottage Street, Northeast,
U20
Salem, OR 97301
P: (503) 378-5460
F: (503) 373-7643
E: george.m.naughton
    @das.state.or.us

PENNSYLVANIA
Mr. Charles Zogby
Secretary of the Budget
Office of the Budget
238 Capitol Building
Harrisburg, PA 17120
P: (717) 787-4472
F: (717) 787-4590

PUERTO RICO
Mr. Juan C. Pavia
Director
Office of Budget &
Management
P.O. Box 9023228
San Juan, PR 00902
P: (787) 725-9420
F: (787) 721-8329

RHODE ISLAND
Mr. Thomas A. Mullaney
State Budget Officer
Department of Administration
Budget Office
One Capitol Hill
Providence, RI 02908
P: (401) 222-6300
E: tomm@budget.ri.gov

SOUTH DAKOTA
Mr. Jason Dilges
Commissioner
Bureau of Finance &
Management
500 East Capitol Avenue
Pierre, SD 57501
P: (605) 773-3411
F: (605) 773-4711
E: jason.dilges@state.sd.us

TENNESSEE
Mr. Mark Emkes
Commissioner
Department of Finance &
Administration
312 Rosa Parks Avenue, 21st
Floor
Nashville, TN 37243
P: (615) 741-2401

TEXAS
Ms. Susan Combs
Comptroller of Public Accounts
Office of the Comptroller of
Public Accounts
111 East 17th
P.O.Box 13528
Austin, TX 78711
P: (512) 463-4444
F: (512) 463-4965
E: susan.combs
    @cpa.state.tx.us

UTAH
Mr. John Reidhead
Director
Division of Finance
2110 State Office Building
450 North State Street
Salt Lake City, UT 84114
P: (801) 538-3020
F: (801) 538-3244
E: jreidhead@utah.gov

VERMONT
Mr. James B. Reardon
Commissioner
Department of Finance &
Management
109 State Street
Montpelier, VT 05602
P: (802) 828-2376
F: (802) 828-2428
E: jim.reardon@state.vt.us

VIRGINIA
Hon. Richard D. Brown
Secretary of Finance
Office of the Secretary of
Finance
1111 East Broad Street
Richmond, VA 23219
P: (804) 692-2551
F: (804) 692-0676
E: Ric.Brown
    @governor.virginia.gov

WASHINGTON
Mr. Marty Brown
Director
Office of Financial Management
P.O. Box 43113
Olympia, WA 98504
P: (360) 902-0555

WEST VIRGINIA
Mr. Charles O. Lorensen
Cabinet Secretary
Department of Revenue
Building 1, W-300
P.O. Box 963
Charleston, WV 25324
P: (304) 558-0211
F: (304) 558-2324
E: Charles.O.Lorensen
    @wv.gov

WISCONSIN
Mr. David Schmiedicke
Administrator
Division of Executive Budget &
Finance
101 East Wilson Street
Madison, WI 53703
P: (608) 266-1035
E: david.schmiedicke
    @wisconsin.gov

Firearms

Conducts background checks for firearm purchases, issues weapon permits, regulates firearm sales, and oversees all other matters relating to the buying and selling of firearms within the state.

ALABAMA
Hon. Luther Strange (R)
Attorney General
Office of the Attorney General
500 Dexter Avenue
Montgomery, AL 36130
P: (334) 242-7300

ALASKA
Mr. Joseph A. Masters
Commissioner
Department of Public Safety
5700 East Tudor Road
P.O. Box 111200
Anchorage, AK 99811
P: (907) 269-5086
F: (907) 269-4543
E: joseph.masters
    @alaska.gov

AMERICAN SAMOA
Mr. Tuaolo M. Fruean
Commissioner
Department of Public Safety
American Samoa Government
P.O. Box 3699
Pago Pago, AS 96799
P: (684) 633-1111
F: (684) 633-7296

ARIZONA
Ms. Donna J. Street
Supervisor
Concealed Weapons Permit Unit
Department of Public Safety
P.O. Box 6488
Phoenix, AZ 85005
P: (602) 256-6280
F: (602) 223-2928

ARKANSAS
Col. Winford E. Phillips
Director
State Police
1 State Police Plaza Drive
Little Rock, AR 72209
P: (501) 618-8299
F: (501) 618-8222
E: winford.phillips
    @asp.arkansas.gov

CALIFORNIA
Mr. Stephen Lindley
Acting Chief
Bureau of Firearms
P.O. Box 160487
Sacramento, CA 95816
P: (916) 263-6275
F: (916) 263-0676

COLORADO
Mr. Ron Sloan
Director
Bureau of Investigation
Department of Public Safety
690 Kipling Street
Lakewood, CO 80215
P: (303) 239-4201
F: (303) 235-0568

CONNECTICUT
Mr. Joseph T. Corradino
Chair
Board of Firearms Permit
Examiners
Department of Public Safety
1111 Country Club Road, Room 348
Hartford, CT 06106
P: (860) 566-7078
F: (860) 566-7079
E: joseph.corradino
    @po.state.ct.us

DELAWARE
Hon. Joseph R.
    Biden III (D)
Attorney General
Office of the Attorney General
Carvel State Office Building
820 North French Street
Wilmington, DE 19801
P: (302) 577-8400
E: Attorney.General
    @state.de.us

DISTRICT OF COLUMBIA
Ms. Cathy L. Lanier
Chief of Police
Metropolitan Police Department
300 Indiana Avenue, Northwest
Washington, DC 20001
P: (202) 727-4218
F: (202) 727-9524
E: cathy.lanier@dc.gov

FLORIDA
Mr. Gerald M. Bailey
Commissioner
Department of Law
Enforcement
2331 Phillips Road
P.O. Box 1489
Tallahassee, FL 32302
P: (850) 410-7001
E: GeraldBailey
    @fdle.state.fl.us

GEORGIA
Mr. Vernon M. Keenan
Director
Bureau of Investigation
3121 Panthersville Road
P.O. Box 370808
Decatur, GA 30037
P: (404) 244-2501
F: (404) 270-8352
E: vernon.keenan@gbi.ga.gov

IDAHO
Hon. Lawrence Wasden (R)
Attorney General
Office of the Attorney General
700 West State Street
P.O. Box 83720
Boise, ID 83720
P: (208) 334-2400
F: (208) 854-8071

ILLINOIS
Mr. Hiram Grau
State Director
State Police
2200 South Dirksen Parkway
Springfield, IL 62703
P: (217) 782-7263
E: hiram.grau@illinois.gov

INDIANA
Dr. Paul Whitesell
Superintendent
State Police
100 North Senate Avenue, Room
IGCN N340
Indianapolis, IN 46204
P: (317) 232-8241
E: pwhitesell@isp.in.gov

KANSAS
Mr. Robert E. Blecha
Director
Bureau of Investigation
1620 Southwest Tyler Street
Topeka, KS 66612
P: (785) 296-8200

Hon. Derek Schmidt (R)
Attorney General
Office of the Attorney General
120 Southwest 10th Avenue
2nd Floor
Topeka, KS 66612
P: (785) 296-2215
F: (785) 296-6296

KENTUCKY
Mr. Rodney Brewer
Commissioner
State Police
919 Versailles Road
Frankfort, KY 40601
P: (502) 695-6300
F: (502) 573-1479

LOUISIANA
Col. Michael D. Edmonson
Superintendent of State Police
Public Safety Services
7919 Independence Boulevard
Baton Rouge, LA 70806
P: (225) 925-6118
F: (225) 925-6006

MAINE
Col. Patrick J. Fleming
Chief
State Police
42 State House Station
45 Commerce Drive
Augusta, ME 04333
P: (207) 624-7200
E: patrick.j.fleming
    @maine.gov

MARYLAND
Colonel Terrence Sheridan
Superintendent
Department of State Police
1201 Reisterstown Road
Pikesville, MD 21208
P: (410) 653-4219
F: (410) 653-4269
E: superintendent@mdsp.org

MASSACHUSETTS
Colonel Marian McGovern
Superintendent
State Police
470 Worcester Road
Framingham, MA 01702
P: (508) 820-2300
F: (617) 727-6874

MICHIGAN
Colonel Kriste Kibbey Etue
Director
State Police
714 South Harrison Road
East Lansing, MI 48823
P: (517) 336-6157
F: (517) 336-6551

MINNESOTA
Ms. Ramona Dohman
Commissioner
Department of Public Safety
Bremer Tower, Suite 1000
445 Minnesota Street
St. Paul, MN 55101
P: (651) 201-7160
F: (651) 297-5728
E: Mona.Dohman@state.mn.us

MISSISSIPPI
Sgt. Eugene Williams Jr.
Director
Firearm Permits Unit
Highway Safety Patrol
P.O. Box 958
Jackson, MS 39205
P: (601) 987-1586
E: ewilliams
@mdps.state.ms.us

MISSOURI
Hon. Chris Koster (D)
Attorney General
Office of the Attorney General
207 West High Street
P.O. Box 899
Jefferson City, MO 65102
P: (573) 751-3321
F: (573) 751-0774

MONTANA
Hon. Steve Bullock (D)
Attorney General
Department of Justice
215 North Sanders, Third Floor
Helena, MT 59620
P: (406) 444-2026
F: (404) 444-3549
E: contactdoj@mt.gov

NEBRASKA
Colonel David Sankey
Superintendent of Law
Enforcement & Public Safety
State Police
P.O. Box 94907
Lincoln, NE 68509
P: (402) 471-4545
F: (402) 479-4002

NEW HAMPSHIRE
Mr. John J. Barthelmes
Commissioner
Department of Safety
James H. Hayes Safety Building
33 Hazen Drive
Concord, NH 03305
P: (603) 271-2791
F: (603) 271-3903
E: john.barthelmes
@dos.nh.gov

NEW JERSEY
Col. Rick Fuentes
Superintendent
State Police
P.O. Box 7068
West Trenton, NJ 08628
P: (609) 882-2000
F: (609) 530-4383

NEW MEXICO
Mr. Gorden E. Eden Jr.
Secretary
Department of Public Safety
4491 Cerrillos Road
P.O. Box 1628
Santa Fe, NM 87504
P: (505) 827-3370

NEW YORK
Mr. Joseph D'Amico
Superintendent
State Police
1220 Washington Avenue,
Building 22
Albany, NY 12226
P: 518) 457-6721

**NORTHERN MARIANA
ISLANDS**
Mr. Ramon Mafnas
Commissioner
Department of Public Safety
Caller Box 10007, Capitol Hill
Caller Box 10007, Capitol Hill
Saipan, MP 96950
P: (670) 664-9022
F: (670) 664-9027

OHIO
Mr. Thomas P. Charles
Director
Department of Public Safety
1970 West Broad Street
P.O. Box 182081
Columbus, OH 43223
P: (614) 466-3383
F: (614) 466-0433

OKLAHOMA
Mr. Stan Florence
Director
State Bureau of Investigation
6600 North Harvey
Oklahoma City, OK 73116
P: (405) 848-6724

OREGON
Mr. Randy Wampler
Director
Forensics
State Department of Police
255 Capitol Street, Northeast,
4th Floor
Salem, OR 97310
P: (503) 934-0237
F: (503) 363-5475
E: randy.wampler
@state.or.us

SOUTH CAROLINA
Mr. Reginald I. Lloyd
Director
State Law Enforcement Division
4400 Broad River Road
P.O. Box 21398
Columbia, SC 29221
P: (803) 737-9000
F: (803) 896-7041

SOUTH DAKOTA
Hon. Jason M. Gant (R)
Secretary of State
Office of the Secretary of State
500 East Capitol Avenue, Suite
204
Pierre, SD 57501
P: (605) 773-3537
F: (605) 773-6580
E: sdsos@state.sd.us

TENNESSEE
Ms. Lisa Knight
Manager
Handgun Carry Permits
Department of Safety &
Homeland Security
1150 Foster Avenue
Nashville, TN 37243
P: (866) 849-3548

TEXAS
Mr. Steve McCraw
Director
Department of Public Safety
5805 North Lamar Boulevard
P.O. Box 4087
Austin, TX 78773
P: (512) 424-2000
F: (512) 475-0876

U.S. VIRGIN ISLANDS
Mr. Novelle E. Francis Jr.
Commissioner
Police Department
Alexander Farrelly Criminal
Justice Ctr.
Charlotte Amalie
St. Thomas, VI 00802
P: (340) 774-2211
F: (340) 715-5517

UTAH
Ms. Alice Erickson
Bureau Chief
Department of Public Safety
Bureau of Criminal
Identification
3888 West 5400 South
Salt Lake City, UT 84118
P: (801) 965-4445
F: (801) 965-4749
E: AERICKSO@utah.gov

VIRGINIA
Col. W. Steven Flaherty
Superintendent
Department of State Police
7700 Midlothian Turnpike
P.O. Box 27472
Richmond, VA 23235
P: (804) 674-2087
F: (804) 674-2132
E: steve.flaherty
@vsp.virginia.gov

WEST VIRGINIA
Colonel Timothy S. Pack
Superintendent
State Police
725 Jefferson Road
South Charleston, WV 25309
P: (304) 746-2111
F: (304) 746-2230
E: tspack@wvsp.state.wv.us

WYOMING
Mr. Forrest Bright
Director
Division of Criminal
Investigation
316 West 22nd Street
Cheyenne, WY 82002
P: (307) 777-7181
F: (307) 777-7252

Fish and Wildlife

Protects and manages fish and wildlife resources and enforces the state's fish and game laws.

ALABAMA
Mr. Corky Pugh
Director
Division of Wildlife & Freshwater Fisheries
Conservation & Natural Resources
64 North Union Street
Montgomery, AL 36130
P: (334) 242-3465
F: (334) 242-3032
E: wanda.mccullers
@dcnr.alabama.gov

ALASKA
Ms. Cora Campbell
Commissioner
Department of Fish & Game
P.O. Box 25526
Juneau, AK 99802
P: (907) 465-6141
F: (907) 465-2332
E: dfg.commissioner
@alaska.gov

ARIZONA
Mr. Larry Voyles
Director
Game & Fish Department
5000 West Carefree Highway
Phoenix, AZ 85086
P: (623) 942-3000

ARKANSAS
Mr. Scott Henderson
Director
Game & Fish Commission
#2 Natural Resources Drive
Little Rock, AR 72205
P: (501) 223-6305
F: (501) 223-6448
E: shenderson
@agfc.state.ar.us

CALIFORNIA
Mr. John McCamman
Director
Department of Fish & Game
1416 Ninth Street, 12th Floor
P.O. Box 944209
Sacramento, CA 94244
P: (916) 653-7667
F: (916) 653-7387
E: director@dfg.ca.gov

COLORADO
Dr. Thomas Remington
Director
Division of Wildlife
6060 Broadway
Denver, CO 80216
P: (303) 297-1192
F: (303) 291-7105
E: tom.remington
@state.co.us

CONNECTICUT
Mr. William Hyatt
Chief
Bureau of Natural Resources
79 Elm Street
Hartford, CT 06106
P: (860) 424-3010
F: (860) 424-4070
E: william.hyatt@ct.gov

DELAWARE
Mr. Dave Saveikis
Director
Division of Fish & Wildlife
89 Kings Highway
Dover, DE 19901
P: (302) 739-9910
F: (302) 739-6157
E: David.Saveikis
@state.de.us

DISTRICT OF COLUMBIA
Mr. Bryan King
Associate Director
Fisheries & Wildlife Division
Department of the Environment
51 N Street, Northeast, 5th Floor
Washington, DC 20002
P: (202) 535-2273
F: (202) 535-1373

FLORIDA
Mr. Nick Wiley
Executive Director
Fish & Wildlife Conservation Commission
620 South Meridian Street
Tallahassee, FL 32399
P: (850) 487-3796
F: (850) 921-5786

GEORGIA
Mr. Dan Forster
Director
Wildlife Resources Division
2070 U.S. Highway 278, Southeast
Social Circle, GA 30025
P: (770) 918-6401
F: (706) 557-3030

GUAM
Mr. Celestino Aguan
Division of Aquatic & Wildlife Resources
Department of Agriculture
192 Dairy Road
Mangilao, GU 96923
P: (671) 735-3984
F: (671) 734-6570

HAWAII
Mr. William J. Aila Jr.
Chairperson
Department of Land & Natural Resources
1151 Punchbowl Street
P.O. Box 621
Kapolei, HI 96809
P: (808) 587-0400
F: (808) 587-0390
E: dlnr@hawaii.gov

IDAHO
Mr. Cal Groen
Director
Fish & Game Department
Box 25, 600 South Walnut
Boise, ID 83707
P: (208) 334-3772
F: (208) 334-2148
E: cal.groen@idfg.idaho.gov

ILLINOIS
Mr. Marc Miller
Director
Department of Natural Resources
One Natural Resources Way
Springfield, IL 62702
P: (217) 785-0075
F: (217) 785-9236

INDIANA
Mr. Mark Reiter
Fish & Wildlife - Central Office
Department of Natural Resources
402 West Washington Street, Room W-273
Indianapolis, IN 46204
P: (317) 232-8129
F: (317) 232-8150
E: MREITER@dnr.IN.gov

IOWA
Mr. Roger L. Lande
Director
Department of Natural Resources
East Ninth & Grand Avenue
Des Moines, IA 50319
P: (515) 281-5385
F: (515) 281-6794
E: roger.lande@dnr.iowa.gov

KANSAS
Mr. Keith Sexson
Assistant Secretary, Wildlife Operations
Department of Wildlife & Parks
512 Southeast 25th Avenue
Pratt, KS 67124
P: (316) 672-5911
F: (316) 672-6020

KENTUCKY
Dr. Jonathan Gassett
Commissioner
Department of Fish & Wildlife Resources
One Sportsman's Lane
Frankfort, KY 40601
P: (502) 564-7109 Ext. 4555
F: (502) 564-6508

LOUISIANA
Mr. Robert J. Barham
Secretary
Department of Wildlife & Fisheries
P.O. Box 98000
Baton Rouge, LA 70898
P: (225) 765-2623
F: (225) 765-0948

MAINE
Mr. R. Dan Martin
Commissioner
Department of Inland Fisheries & Wildlife
284 State Street, Station #41
Augusta, ME 04333
P: (207) 287-5202
F: (207) 287-6395

Mr. Chandler E. Woodcock
Commissioner
Department of Inland Fisheries & Wildlife
41 State House Station
Augusta, ME 04333
P: (207) 287-8000
F: (207) 287-6395

MARYLAND
Mr. Paul Peditto
Director
Wildlife & Heritage Service
Department of Natural Resources
580 Taylor Avenue, E-1
Annapolis, MD 21401
P: (410) 260-8549
F: (410) 260-8595
E: ppeditto@dnr.state.md.us

Fish and Wildlife

MASSACHUSETTS
Mr. Wayne MacCallum
Director
Division of Fisheries & Wildlife
One Rabbit Hill Road
Westborough, MA 01581
P: (508) 389-6300
F: (508) 389-7890

MINNESOTA
Mr. Dave Schad
Director
Division of Fish & Wildlife
Department of Natural
Resources
500 Lafayette Road
St. Paul, MN 55155
P: (651) 259-5180
F: (651) 297-7272
E: Dave.Schad@state.mn.us

MISSISSIPPI
Dr. Sam Polles
Executive Director
Department of Wildlife,
Fisheries & Parks
2906 Building
P.O. Box 451
Jackson, MS 39205
P: (601) 432-2001
F: (601) 432-2024

MISSOURI
Mr. Robert Ziehmer
Director
Department of Conservation
P.O. Box 180
Jefferson City, MO 65102
P: (573) 522-4115
F: (573) 751-4667

MONTANA
Mr. Joe Maurier
Director
Department of Fish, Wildlife &
Parks
1420 East Sixth Avenue
P.O. Box 200701
Helena, MT 59620
P: (406) 444-3186
F: (406) 444-4952

NEBRASKA
Mr. Rex Amack
Director
Game & Parks Commission
2200 North 33rd, Box 30370
Lincoln, NE 68510
P: (402) 471-5539
F: (402) 471-5528
E: rex.amack@nebraska.gov

NEVADA
Mr. Kenneth Mayer
Director
Department of Wildlife
1100 Valley Road
Reno, NV 89512
P: (775) 688-1500
F: (775) 688-1207
E: kemayer@ndow.org

NEW HAMPSHIRE
Mr. Glenn Normandeau
Executive Director
Fish & Game Department
11 Hazen Drive
Concord, NH 03301
P: (603) 271-3511
F: (603) 271-1438
E: glenn.normandeau
    @wildlife.nh.gov

NEW JERSEY
Mr. Dave Chanda
Director
Division of Fish & Wildlife
P.O. Box 400
Trenton, NJ 08625
P: (609) 292-9410
F: (609) 292-8207

NEW MEXICO
Mr. Tod Stevenson
Director
Game & Fish Department
One Wildlife Way
Santa Fe, NM 87507
P: (505) 476-8008
F: (505) 476-8124
E: tod.stevenson
    @state.mn.us

NEW YORK
Ms. Patricia Riexinger
Director
Division of Fish, Wildlife &
Marine Resources
625 Broadway
Albany, NY 12233
P: (518) 402-8924
F: (518) 402-9027
E: fwinfo
    @gw.dec.state.ny.us

NORTH CAROLINA
Mr. Gordon Myers
Executive Director
Wildlife Resources Commission
1722 Mail Service Center
1751 Varsity Drive, Room 451
Raleigh, NC 27695
P: (919) 707-0151
F: (919) 707-0020
E: gordon.myers
    @ncwildlife.org

NORTH DAKOTA
Mr. Terry Steinwand
Director
Game & Fish Department
100 North Bismarck
Expressway
Bismarck, ND 58501
P: (701) 328-6305
F: (701) 328-6352
E: tsteinwa@nd.gov

OHIO
Mr. David B. Lane
Chief
Division of Wildlife
2045 Morse Road, Building G
Columbus, OH 43229
P: (614) 265-6304
F: (614) 262-1143

OKLAHOMA
Mr. Richard Hatcher
Director
Department of Wildlife
Conservation
P.O. Box 53465
Oklahoma City, OK 73152
P: (405) 522-6279
F: (405) 521-6505

OREGON
Mr. Roy Elicker
Director
Department of Fish & Wildlife
3406 Cherry Avenue, Northeast
Salem, OR 97303
P: (503) 947-6044
F: (503) 947-6042
E: roy.elicker@state.or.us

PENNSYLVANIA
Mr. John Arway
Executive Director
Fish & Boat Commission
P.O. Box 67000
Harrisburg, PA 17106
P: (717) 705-7801
F: (717) 705-7802

Mr. Carl Roe
Executive Director
Game Commission
2001 Elmerton Avenue
Harrisburg, PA 17110
P: (717) 787-3633
F: (717) 772-0502

PUERTO RICO
Mr. Miguel A. Garcia
Director, Terrestrial Resources
Division
Department of Natural &
Environmental Resources
Bureau of Fish & Wildlife
P.O. Box 366147
San Juan, PR 00936
P: (787) 723-3090
F: (787) 724-0365

Mr. Craig G. Lilyestrom
Director, Marine Resources
Division
Department of Natural &
Environmental Resources
P.O. Box 366147
San Juan, PR 00936
P: (787) 723-3090
F: (787) 724-0365

RHODE ISLAND
Mr. Robert Ballou
Acting Chief
Division of Fish & Wildlife
3 Fort Wetherill Road
Jamestown, RI 02835
P: (401) 423-1920
F: (401) 423-1925
E: robert.ballou@dem.ri.gov

SOUTH CAROLINA
Mr. John E. Frampton
Director
Department of Natural
Resources
P.O. Box 167
Columbia, SC 29202
P: (803) 734-4007
F: (803) 734-6310
E: framptonj@dnr.sc.gov

SOUTH DAKOTA
Mr. Jeff Vonk
Secretary
Game, Fish & Parks Department
523 East Capitol Avenue
Pierre, SD 57501
P: (605) 773-3718
F: (605) 773-6245

TENNESSEE
Mr. Ed Carter
Executive Director
Wildlife Resources Agency
P.O. Box 40747
Nashville, TN 37204
P: (615) 781-6552
F: (615) 781-6551

Fish and Wildlife

TEXAS
Mr. Carter P. Smith
Executive Director
Parks & Wildlife Department
4200 Smith School Road
Austin, TX 78744
P: (512) 389-4802
F: (512) 389-4814

U.S. VIRGIN ISLANDS
Ms. Beulah Dalmida-Smith
Director
Division of Fish & Wildlife
6291 Estate Nazareth 101
St. Thomas, VI 00802
P: (340) 775-6762
F: (340) 775-3972
E: beulahdalmida@gmail.com

UTAH
Mr. Jim Karpowitz
Director
Division of Wildlife Resources
1594 West North Temple, Suite
2110
P.O. Box 146301
Salt Lake City, UT 84114
P: (801) 538-4745
F: (801) 538-4709
E: jimkarpowitz@utah.gov

VERMONT
Mr. Patrick Berry
Commissioner
Department of Fish & Wildlife
103 South Main Street, 10 South
Waterbury, VT 05671
P: (802) 241-3700
F: (802) 241-3295
E: patrick.berry
   @state.vt.us

VIRGINIA
Mr. Bob Duncan
Director
Department of Game & Inland
Fisheries
4010 West Broad Street, Box
11104
Richmond, VA 23230
P: (804) 367-9231
F: (804) 367-0405
E: bob.duncan
   @dgif.virginia.gov

WASHINGTON
Mr. Phil Anderson
Director
Department of Fish & Wildlife
600 Capitol Way North
Olympia, WA 98501
P: (360) 902-2225
F: (360) 902-2947
E: director@drw.wa.gov

WEST VIRGINIA
Mr. Curtis Taylor
Chief
Wildlife Resources Section
Division of Natural Resources
324 4th Avenue
South Charleston, WV 25303
P: (304) 558-2771
F: (304) 558-3147
E: curtis.i.taylor@wv.gov

WISCONSIN
Ms. Cathy Stepp
Secretary
Department of Natural
Resources
101 South Webster Street
P.O. Box 7921
Madison, WI 53707
P: (608) 267-7556
F: (608) 266-6983
E: cathy.stepp
   @wisconsin.gov

WYOMING
Mr. Scott Talbott
Director
Game & Fish Department
5400 Bishop Boulevard
Cheyenne, WY 82006
P: (307) 777-4600
F: (307) 777-4699

Gaming Officials

Head of the entity that administers and regulates state gaming laws.

ALASKA
Ms. Johanna Baier
Director
Tax Division
Department of Revenue
P.O. Box 110420
Juneau, AK 99811
P: (907) 465-2320
F: (907) 465-2375
E: johanna.baier@alaska.gov

ARIZONA
Mr. Mark Brnovich
Director
Department of Gaming
202 East Earll Drive, Suite 200
Phoenix, AZ 85012
P: (602) 604-1801
F: (602) 255-3883

ARKANSAS
Mr. Cecil Alexander
Chair
Racing Commission
1515 West 7th Street, Suite 505
P.O. Box 3076
Little Rock, AR 72203
P: (501) 682-1467
F: (501) 682-5273

CALIFORNIA
Hon. Kamala Harris (D)
Attorney General
Office of the Attorney General
1300 I Street, Suite 1740
Sacramento, CA 95814
P: (916) 445-9555

COLORADO
Mr. Ron Kammerzell
Director
Division of Gaming
Department of Revenue
1881 Pierce Street
Lakewood, CO 80214
P: (303) 205-1314
F: (303) 205-1342
E: ron.kammerzell
   @spike.dor.state.co.us

CONNECTICUT
Mr. Paul A. Young
Executive Director
Division of Special Revenue
555 Russell Road
P.O. Box 310424
Newington, CT 06131
P: (860) 594-0500
F: (860) 594-0509
E: paul.a.young
   @po.state.ct.us

DELAWARE
Mr. Wayne Lemons
Director
State Lottery
McKee Business Park
1575 McKee Road, Suite 102
Dover, DE 19904
P: (302) 739-5291
F: (302) 739-6706
E: brian.peters@state.de.us

FLORIDA
Mr. Ken Lawson
Secretary
Department of Business &
Professional Reguation
 1940 North Monroe Street
Tallahassee, FL 32399
P: (850) 413-0755
F: (850) 921-4094
E: ken_lawson
   @dbpr.state.fl.us

GEORGIA
Mr. Vernon M. Keenan
Director
Bureau of Investigation
3121 Panthersville Road
P.O. Box 370808
Decatur, GA 30037
P: (404) 244-2501
F: (404) 270-8352
E: vernon.keenan@gbi.ga.gov

GUAM
Mr. Artemio B. Ilagan
Director
Department of Revenue &
Taxation
P.O. Box 23607
GMF, GU 96921
P: (671) 635-1835
F: (671) 633-2643
E: ilagan@revtax.gov.gu

IDAHO
Mr. Jeffrey R. Anderson
Executive Director
State Lottery
1199 Shoreline Lane, Suite 100
P.O. Box 6537
Boise, ID 83707
P: (208) 334-2600
E: janderson
   @lottery.idaho.gov

ILLINOIS
Mr. Mark Ostrowski
Administrator
Gaming Board
160 North LaSalle, Suite 300
Chicago, IL 60601
P: (312) 814-4700
F: (312) 814-4602

INDIANA
Mr. Ernest Yelton
Executive Director
Gaming Commission
East Tower, Suite 1600
101 West Washington Street
Indianapolis, IN 46204
P: (317) 233-0046
F: (317) 233-0047
E: eyelton@igc.in.gov

IOWA
Mr. Jack P. Ketterer
Administrator
Racing & Gaming Commission
717 East Court
Suite B
Des Moines, IA 50309
P: (515) 281-7352
F: (515) 242-6560
E: irgc@iowa.gov

KANSAS
Mr. Richard Baldwin
Acting Executive Director
State Gaming Agency
420 Southwest 6th Street, Suite 3000
Topeka, KS 66607
P: (785) 368-6202
F: (785) 291-3798

Mr. Ed Van Petten
Executive Director
State Lottery
128 North Kansas Avenue
Topeka, KS 66603
P: (785) 296-5700
F: (785) 296-5712
E: lotteryinfo
   @kslottery.net

KENTUCKY
Mr. Arch Gleason
President & CEO
State Lottery
1011 West Main Street
Louisville, KY 40202
P: (502) 560-1500
F: (502) 560-1532
E: custsrvs@kylottery.com

Ms. Lisa E. Underwood
Executive Director
Horse Racing Commission
4063 Iron Works Parkway,
Building B
Lexington, KY 40511
P: (859) 246-2040
F: (859) 246-2039
E: lisa.underwood@ky.gov

LOUISIANA
Lt. Col. Val Penouilh
Deputy Superintendent
Bureau of Investigations
7919 Independence Boulevard
Baton Rouge, LA 70806
P: (225) 922-1467

MAINE
Mr. John E. Morris
Commissioner
Department of Public Safety
45 Commerce Drive, Suite 1
104 State House Station
Augusta, ME 04333
P: (207) 626-3800
F: (207) 287-3042
E: john.e.morris@maine.gov

MARYLAND
Mr. Michael J. Frenz
Executive Director
Stadium Authority
333 West Camden Street, Suite 500
Baltimore, MD 21201
P: (410) 333-1560
F: (410) 333-1888

MASSACHUSETTS
Ms. Barbara Anthony
Undersecretary
Office of Consumer Affairs &
Business Regulation
Ten Park Plaza, Suite 5170
Boston, MA 02116
P: (617) 973-8700
F: (617) 973-8798

Gaming Officials

MICHIGAN
Richard S. Kalm
Executive Director
Gaming Control Board
Cadillac Place
3062 West Grand Boulevard,
L-700
Detroit, MI 48202
P: (313) 456-4100
F: (313) 456-4200
E: Kalmrics@michigan.gov

MINNESOTA
Mr. Clint Harris
Executive Director
State Lottery
2645 Long Lake Road
Roseville, MN 55113
P: (651) 635-8100
F: (651) 297-7496
E: lottery@mnlottery.com

MISSISSIPPI
Mr. Larry Gregory
Executive Director
Gaming Commission
202 East Pearl
P.O. Box 23577
Jackson, MS 39225
P: (601) 351-2800
F: (601) 351-2843
E: lgregory@mgc.state.ms.us

MISSOURI
Mr. Roger D. Stottlemyre
Executive Director
Gaming Commission
3417 Knipp Dirve
P.O. Box 1847
Jefferson City, MO 65102
P: (573) 526-4080
F: (573) 526-1999
E: roger.stottlemyre
     @mgc.dps.mo.gov

MONTANA
Hon. Steve Bullock (D)
Attorney General
Department of Justice
215 North Sanders, Third Floor
Helena, MT 59620
P: (406) 444-2026
F: (404) 444-3549
E: contactdoj@mt.gov

NEBRASKA
Mr. Doug Ewald
Tax Commissioner
Department of Revenue
P.O. Box 94818
Lincoln, NE 68509
P: (402) 471-5605
F: (402) 471-5608
E: doug.ewald@nebraska.gov

NEVADA
Mr. Mark A. Lipparelli
Chair
Gaming Control Board
1919 College Parkway
P.O. Box 8003
Carson City, NV 89702
P: (775) 684-7700
F: (775) 687-5817

NEW JERSEY
Mr. Josh Lichtblau
Director
Division of Gaming
Enforcement
140 East Front Street
P.O. Box 047
Trenton, NJ 08625
P: (609) 292-9394
F: (609) 633-7355

NEW MEXICO
Mr. Frank A. Baca
Interim Executive Director
Gaming Control Board
4900 Alameda Boulevard,
Northeast
Albuquerque, NM 87113
P: (505) 841-9700
F: (505) 841-9725

NEW YORK
Mr. John D. Sabini
Chair
Racing & Wagering Board
One Broadway Center, Suite
600
Schenectady, NY 12305
P: (518) 395-5400
F: (518) 347-1250

NORTH CAROLINA
Ms. Alice Garland
Executive Director
Education Lottery
2100 Yonkers Road
Raleigh, NC 27604
P: (919) 301-3601
F: (919) 715-8825
E: playerinfo@lotterync.net

NORTH DAKOTA
Mr. Keith Lauer
Director
Gaming Division
Office of Attorney General
600 East Boulevard Avenue,
17th Floor
Bismarck, ND 58505
P: (701) 328-4848
F: (701) 328-3535
E: klauer@nd.gov

**NORTHERN MARIANA
ISLANDS**
Dr. Ignacio T. Dela Cruz
Secretary
Department of Lands & Natural
Resources
Caller Box 10007, Capitol Hill
Saipan, MP 96950
P: (670) 322-9830
F: (670) 322-2633
E: dlnrgov@vzpacifica.net

OHIO
Mr. William Crawford
Executive Director
Racing Commission
77 South High Street, 18th Floor
Columbus, OH 43215
P: (614) 466-2757
F: (614) 466-1900
E: bill.crawford
     @rc.state.oh.us

OKLAHOMA
Mr. A. Keith Burt
Director
Alcoholic Beverage Laws
Enforcement Commission
4545 North Lincoln Boulevard,
Suite 270
Oklahoma City, OK 73105
P: (405) 521-3484
F: (405) 521-6578
E: akburt
     @mhs.oklaosf.state.ok.us

Mr. Constantin A. Rieger
Executive Director
State Horse Racing Commission
Shepherd Mall
2401 Northwest 23rd Street,
Suite 78
Oklahoma City, OK 73107
P: (405) 943-6472
F: (405) 943-6474
E: ohrc@socket.net

OREGON
Maj. Craig Durbin
Gaming
State Department of Police
3400 State Street, G750
Salem, OR 97301
P: (503) 540-1406
F: (503) 378-8282
E: craig.durbin@state.or.us

PENNSYLVANIA
Mr. Gregory C. Fajt
Chair
Gaming Control Board
5th Floor, Strawberry Square
Harrisburg, PA 17101
P: (717) 346-8300
F: (717) 265-8323

PUERTO RICO
Mr. Guillermo J. Cabret
Director
Gaming Division
P.O. Box 9023960
San Juan, PR 00902
P: (787) 721-2400
F: (787) 724-3009
E: logarcia@prtourism.com

RHODE ISLAND
Colonel Steven G. O'Donnell
Superintendent
State Police
311 Danielson Pike
North Scituate, RI 02857
P: (401) 444-1000
F: (401) 444-1105
E: sodonnell
     @risp.state.ri.us

Lt. Col. Raymond S. White
Acting Superintendent & Interim
Commissioner
Department of Public Safety
Headquarters
311 Danielson Pike
Scituate, RI 02857
P: (401) 444-1010
F: (401) 444-1105
E: rwhite@risp.dps.ri.gov

SOUTH CAROLINA
Mr. John E. Frampton
Director
Department of Natural
Resources
P.O. Box 167
Columbia, SC 29202
P: (803) 734-4007
F: (803) 734-6310
E: framptonj@dnr.sc.gov

SOUTH DAKOTA
Mr. Larry Eliason
Executive Secretary
Gaming Commission
Department of Revenue &
Regulation
221 W. Capitol Avenue, Suite
101
Pierre, SD 57501
P: (605) 773-6050
F: (605) 773-6053

TENNESSEE
Ms. Rebecca Paul Hargrove
President & CEO
Education Lottery Corporation
Plaza Tower, MetroCenter
200 Athens Way, Suite 200
Nashville, TN 37228
P: (615) 324-6500
F: (615) 324-6512

TEXAS
Mr. Gary Grief
Executive Director
Lottery Commission
611 East 6th Street
P.O.Box 16630
Austin, TX 78761
P: (512) 344-5160
F: (512) 478-3682
E: gary.grief
    @lottery.state.tx.us

Mr. Chuck Trout
Interim Executive Director
State Racing Commission
8505 Cross Park Drive, Suite
110
P.O. Box 12080
Austin, TX 78711
P: (512) 833-6699
F: (512) 833-6907

U.S. VIRGIN ISLANDS
Ms. Eileen Peterson
Chair
Casino Control Commission
#5 Orange Grove
Christiansted
St. Croix, VI 00820
P: (340) 773-3616
F: (340) 773-3136

VERMONT
Mr. Alan R. Yandow
Executive Director
Lottery Commission
1311 U.S. Route 302 - Suite 100
Barre, VT 05641
P: (802) 479-5686
F: (802) 479-4294
E: ayandow@vtlottery.com

WASHINGTON
Mr. Rick Day
Director
Gambling Commission
P.O. Box 42400
Olympia, WA 98504
P: (360) 486-3440
F: (360) 486-3629

WEST VIRGINIA
Mr. Charles O. Lorensen
Cabinet Secretary
Department of Revenue
Building 1, W-300
P.O. Box 963
Charleston, WV 25324
P: (304) 558-0211
F: (304) 558-2324
E: Charles.O.Lorensen
    @wv.gov

WISCONSIN
Mr. Bob Sloey
Administrator
Division of Gaming
2005 West Beltline Highway,
Suite 201
P.O. Box 8979
Madison, WI 53708
P: (608) 270-2555
F: (608) 270-2564
E: RacingWeb
    @doa.state.wi.us

WYOMING
Mr. Charles Moore
Executive Director/Simulcast
Steward
State Pari-Mutuel Commission
Energy II Building, Suite 335
951 Werner Court
Casper, WY 82601
P: (307) 265-4015
F: (307) 265-4279
E: cmoore@state.wy.us

Geographic Information Systems

Coordinates geographic information systems within state government.

ALABAMA
Mr. Berry H. Tew Jr.
State Geologist & Oil and Gas Supervisor
Geological Survey of Alabama
P.O. Box 869999
420 Hackberry Lane
Tuscaloosa, AL 35486
P: (205) 349-2852
F: (205) 349-2861
E: ntew@gsa.state.al.us

ALASKA
Mr. Richard McMahon
IT Manager
Land Records Information Section
Department of Natural Resources
550 West 7th Avenue, Suite 706
Anchorage, AK 99501
P: (907) 269-8836
F: (907) 269-8920
E: richard.mcmahon
    @alaska.gov

ARIZONA
Mr. Gene Trobia
State Cartographer
Geographic Information Council
State Land Department
1616 West Adams Street
Phoenix, AZ 85007
P: (602) 542-3190
F: (602) 542-2600
E: gtrobia@land.az.gov

ARKANSAS
Mr. Shelby Johnson
Geographic Information Coordinator
Geographic Information Office
#1 Capitol Mall
3rd Floor, 3B 201
Little Rock, AR 72201
P: (501) 682-2767

CALIFORNIA
Mr. Scott Gregory
Geospatial Information Officer
Technology Agency
1325 J Street, Suite 1600
Sacramento, CA 95814
P: (916) 403-9625

COLORADO
Mr. Jon Gottsegen
State GIS Coordinator
Department of Local Affairs
1313 Sherman Street, Room 521
Denver, CO 80203
P: (303) 866-3190
F: (303) 866-4819
E: jon.gottsegen
    @state.co.us

CONNECTICUT
Mr. Steve O. Fish
Director
Office of Information Management
Department of Environmental Protection
79 Elm Street
Hartford, CT 06106
P: (860) 424-3540
F: (860) 424-4058
E: steve.fish@ct.gov

DELAWARE
Mr. Michael B. Mahaffie
GIS/Spatial Data Coordinator/Webmaster
Office of State Planning Coordination
122 William Penn Street, Suite 302
Haslet Building, Third Floor
Dover, DE 19901
P: (302) 739-3090
F: (302) 739-6958
E: mike.mahaffie
    @state.de.us

DISTRICT OF COLUMBIA
Mr. Barney Krucoff
GIS Director
Office of the Chief Technology Officer
441 4th Street, Northwest
Washington, DC 20001
P: (202) 727-2277
F: (202) 727-6857
E: dcgis@dc.gov

FLORIDA
Mr. John Willmott
Chief Information Officer
Office of Technology & Information Services
Department of Environmental Protection
3900 Commonwealth Boulevard, M.S. 200
Tallahassee, FL 32399
P: (850) 245-8238
F: (850) 421-0401
E: John.Willmott
    @dep.state.fl.us

GEORGIA
Mr. Eric McRae
Associate Director
Information Technology Outreach Services
Chicopee Complex, Suite 2058
1180 East Broad Street
Athens, GA 30602
P: (706) 542-3442
F: (706) 542-6535
E: mcrae@cviog.itos.uga.edu

IDAHO
Mr. Chris Clay
GIS Manager
Department of Lands
300 North 6th Street, Suite 103
P.O. Box 83720
Boise, ID 83720
P: (208) 334-0273
F: (208) 334-3698
E: cclay@idl.idaho.gov

ILLINOIS
Mr. Dan S. Thurston
Head
State Geological Survey
Geospatial Analysis & Modeling Section
615 East Peabody Drive
Champaign, IL 61820
P: (217) 333-4085
E: thurston
    @isgs.illinois.edu

INDIANA
Mr. Jim Sparks
Geographic Information Officer
Office of Technology
100 North Senate Avenue, Room N551
Indianapolis, IN 46204
P: (317) 234-5889
F: (317) 234-0917
E: jsparks@iot.in.gov

IOWA
Mr. Chris Ensminger
Section Supervisor
Geographic Information
Geological Survey
502 East 9th Street
Des Moines, IA 50319
P: (515) 281-4216
E: chris.ensminger
    @dnr.iowa.gov

KANSAS
Mr. Ivan Weichert
GIS Director
Kansas Information Technology Office
Landon State Office Building
Room 751-S
Topeka, KS 66612
P: (785) 296-0257

KENTUCKY
Mr. Tom Rossman
Acting Director
Division of Geographic Information
Office of Technology
101 Cold Harbor Drive
Frankfort, KY 40601
P: (502) 564-6412
F: (502) 564-0427
E: thomas.rossman@ky.gov

LOUISIANA
Mr. Craig Johnson
Administrative & Programmatic Support Manager
Geographic Information Center
E313a Howe-Russell Geoscience Complex
Louisiana State University
Baton Rouge, LA 70803
P: (225) 578-3479
F: (225) 578-2796
E: cjohnson@lsu.edu

Mr. Stacy Richardson
Administrator, Information Services
Office of Management & Finance
Department of Environmental Quality
P.O. Box 4303
Baton Rouge, LA 70821
P: (225) 219-3840
F: (225) 219-3846
E: deqomf@la.gov

MAINE
Mr. Michael Smith
Chair
Office of Information Technology
Office of Geographic Information Systems
145 State House Station
Augusta, ME 04333
P: (207) 215-5530
E: michael.smith@maine.gov

MARYLAND
Mr. Kenneth Miller
GIS/Information Management
Office for a Sustainable Future
Tawes State Office Building
580 Taylor Avenue
Annapolis, MD 21401
P: (410) 260-8987
E: kenmiller
    @dnr.state.md.us

Geographic Information Systems

MASSACHUSETTS
Mr. Rick Sullivan
Commissioner
Executive Office of Energy &
Environmental Affairs
100 Cambridge Street, Suite 900
Boston, MA 02114
P: (614) 626-1000
F: (614) 626-1181

MICHIGAN
Mr. Eric Swanson
Director
Center for Geographic
Information
111 South Capitol Avenue
Romney Building, 10th Floor
Lansing, MI 48913
P: (517) 373-7910
F: (517) 373-2939
E: swansone@michigan.gov

MINNESOTA
Mr. David Arbeit
Director
Geospatial Information Office
Department of Administration
658 Cedar Street, Room 300
St. Paul, MN 55155
P: (651) 201-2460
F: (651) 296-3698
E: david.arbeit@state.mn.us

MISSISSIPPI
Mr. Craig P. Orgeron
Director
Department of Information
Technology Services
Strategic Services Division
3771 Eastwood Drive
Jackson, MS 39211
P: (601) 432-8089
F: (601) 713-6380
E: craig.orgeron@its.ms.gov

MISSOURI
Mr. Timothy Haithcoat
Geographic Information Officer
Information Technology
Services Division
Truman Building, Room 280
301 W. High Street
Jefferson City, MO 65101
P: (573) 522-1650
E: tim.haithcoat@oa.mo.gov

MONTANA
Mr. Stewart Kirkpatrick
Chief
Base Map Service Center
Bureau
Geographic Information
Services Office
P.O. Box 200116
Helena, MT 59620
P: (406) 444-9013
F: (406) 444-1255
E: skirkpatrick@mt.gov

NEBRASKA
Mr. Larry K. Zink
GIS Administrative Manager
Information Technology
Commission
Executive Office Building
521 South 14th Street, Suite 101
Lincoln, NE 65808
P: (402) 471-3206
F: (402) 471-0421
E: larry.zink@nebraska.gov

NEVADA
Ms. Jennifer Mauldin
Executive Secretary
State Mapping Advisory
Committee
Bureau of Mines & Geology
University of Nevada-Reno, MS
178
Reno, NV 89557
P: (775) 682-8759
F: (775) 784-1709
E: mauldin@unr.edu

NEW HAMPSHIRE
Mr. Ken Gallager
Principal Planner
Geographic Information System
Office of Energy & Planning
4 Chenell Drive
Concord, NH 03301
P: (603) 271-1773
F: (603) 271-2615
E: ken.gallager@nh.gov

NEW JERSEY
Mr. Andrew Rowan
Geographic Information Officer
Office of Geographic
Information Systems
Office of Information
Technology
200 Riverview Plaza, P.O. Box
212
Trenton, NJ 08625
P: (609) 633-9103
F: (609) 633-0400
E: andrew.rowan
     @oit.state.nj.us

NEW MEXICO
Ms. Shirley Baros
GIS Program Manager
Earth Data Analysis Center
1 University of New Mexico
MSC01 1110
Albuquerque, NM 87131
P: (505) 277-3622
F: (505) 277-3614
E: sbaros@edac.unm.edu

NEW YORK
Mr. Thomas D. Smith
Director
Office of Cyber Security
1220 Washington Avenue, 4th
Floor
State Office Campus, Building
7A
Albany, NY 12242
P: (518) 242-5032
F: (518) 402-3799
E: OCS.info@dhses.ny.gov

NORTH CAROLINA
Mr. Tim Johnson
Director
Center for Geographic
Information & Analysis
20322 Mail Service Center
Raleigh, NC 27699
P: (919) 733-2090
F: (919) 715-0725
E: tim.johnson@nc.gov

NORTH DAKOTA
Mr. Bob Nutsch
GIS Coordinator
Information Technology
Department
600 East Boulevard Avenue
Department 112
Bismarck, ND 58505
P: (701) 328-3212
F: (701) 328-3000
E: bnutsch@nd.gov

OHIO
Mr. Dan Orr
Interim Chief Operating
Officer/Deputy Director
Infrastructure Services Division
Office of Information
Technology
1320 Arthur E. Adams Drive
Columbus, OH 43221
P: (614) 752-7320
F: (614) 466-7345
E: dan.orr@oit.ohio.gov

OKLAHOMA
Mr. Mike Sharp
Director of IT
Conservation Commission
2800 North Lincoln Boulevard
Suite 160
Oklahoma City, OK 73105
P: (405) 521-4813
F: (405) 521-6686
E: mike.sharp
     @conservation.ok.gov

Ms. May Yuan
Director
Center for Spatial Analysis
3100 Monitor Avenue, Suite 180
Norman, OK 73072
P: (405) 325-4871
F: (405) 325-1595
E: myuan@ou.edu

OREGON
Mr. Cy Smith
Manager / GIS Coordinator
Geospatial Enterprise Office
Department of Administrative
Services
955 Center Street, NE, Room
470
Salem, OR 97301
P: (503) 378-6066
E: cy.smith@state.or.us

PENNSYLVANIA
Ms. Stacey L. White
Geospatial Information Officer
Geospatial Technologies Office
Office for Information
Technology
5 Technology Park
Harrisburg, PA 17110
P: (717) 783-4883
F: (717) 783-6995

RHODE ISLAND
Mr. Shane White
GIS Coordinator
Statewide Planning Program
Division of Planning
One Capitol Hill, 3rd Floor
Providence, RI 02908
P: (401) 222-6483
F: (401) 222-2083
E: swhite@doa.ri.gov

SOUTH CAROLINA
Dr. Tim De Troye
State GIS Coordinator
State Geographic Information
Systems
1000 Assembly Street
Columbia, SC 29201
P: (803) 734-3894

Geographic Information Systems

SOUTH DAKOTA
Mr. Erik Nelson
GIS Coordinator
Bureau of Information &
Telecommunications
Foss Building
523 East Capitol Avenue
Pierre, SD 57501
P: (605) 773-6701
F: (605) 773-4068
E: erik.nelson@state.sd.us

TENNESSEE
Mr. Dennis Pedersen
Director, GIS Services
Office for Information
Resources
312 Rosa L. Parks Avenue
16th Floor, Tennessee Tower
Nashville, TN 37243
P: (615) 741-9356
F: (615) 532-0471
E: dennis.pedersen@tn.gov

TEXAS
Mr. Michael Ouimet
State GIS Coordinator
Department of Information
Resources
300 West 15th Street, Suite 1300
P.O. Box 13564
Austin, TX 78711
P: (512) 305-9076
E: michael.ouimet
    @dir.state.tx.us

UTAH
Mr. Spencer Jenkins
Director
Automated Geographic
Reference Center
1 State Office Building, Room
5130
Salt Lake City, UT 84114
P: (801) 538-3163
F: (801) 538-3317
E: spencerjenkins@utah.gov

VERMONT
Mr. David F. Brotzman
Executive Director
Center for Geographic
Information
58 South Main Street, Suite 2
Waterbury, VT 05676
P: (802) 882-3003
F: (802) 882-3001
E: davidb@vcgi.org

VIRGINIA
Mr. Dan Widner
Coordinator
Integrated Services Program
Geographic Information
Network
11751 Meadowville Lane
Chester, VA 23836
P: (804) 416-6198
F: (804) 416-6353
E: dan.widner
    @vita.virginia.gov

WASHINGTON
Ms. Joy Paulus
Coordinator
Department of Information
Services
Geographic Information Council
1110 Jefferson St., SE, P.O. Box
42445
Olympia, WA 98504
P: (360) 902-3447
E: joyp@dis.wa.gov

WEST VIRGINIA
Mr. J. Antonio Simental
State GIS Coordinator
Office of GIS Coordination
Suite LM-10
1124 Smith Street
Charleston, WV 25301
P: (304) 558-4218
F: (304) 558-4963
E: Tony.A.Simental@wv.gov

WISCONSIN
Mr. Curtis Pulford
State Geographic Information
Officer
Geographic Information Office
101 East Wilson Street
P.O. Box 7844
Madison, WI 53707
P: (608) 261-5042
E: curtis.pulford
    @wisconsin.gov

WYOMING
Mr. Jacob Mundt
Enterprise GIS Program
Coordinator
Office of the Chief Information
Officer
2001 Capitol Avenue, Room 237
Cheyenne, WY 82002
P: (307) 777-8252
F: (307) 777-3696

Geological Survey

Conducts research on the state's terrain, mineral resources, and possible geological hazards such as earthquakes, faults, etc.

ALABAMA
Mr. Berry H. Tew Jr.
State Geologist & Oil and Gas Supervisor
Geological Survey of Alabama
P.O. Box 869999
420 Hackberry Lane
Tuscaloosa, AL 35486
P: (205) 349-2852
F: (205) 349-2861
E: ntew@gsa.state.al.us

ALASKA
Mr. Robert F. Swenson
Director & State Geologist
Division of Geological & Geophysical Surveys
Department of Natural Resources
3354 College Road
Fairbanks, AK 99709
P: (907) 451-5000
F: (907) 451-5050
E: Robert_Swenson
    @dnr.state.ak.us

ARIZONA
Dr. M. Lee Allison
Director & State Geologist
Geological Survey
416 West Congress Street, Suite 100
Tucson, AZ 85701
P: (520) 770-3500
F: (520) 770-3505
E: Lee.Allison@azgs.az.gov

ARKANSAS
Ms. Bekki White
State Geologist & Director
Geological Commission
Vardelle Parham Geology Center
3815 West Roosevelt Road
Little Rock, AR 72204
P: (501) 296-1877
F: (501) 663-7360
E: bekki.white@arkansas.gov

CALIFORNIA
Dr. John Parrish
State Geologist
Geological Survey
801 K Street, MS 12-01
Sacramento, CA 95814
P: (916) 445-1825
F: (916) 445-5718
E: John.Parrish
    @conservation.ca.gov

COLORADO
Mr. Vincent Matthews
State Geologist
Geological Survey
1313 Sherman Street, Room 715
Denver, CO 80203
P: (303) 866-2611
F: (303) 866-2461
E: vince.matthews
    @state.co.us

CONNECTICUT
Ms. Margaret A. Thomas
State Geologist
Environmental & Geographic Information Center
Geological & Natural History Survey
79 Elm Street
Hartford, CT 06106
P: (860) 424-3583
F: (860) 424-4058
E: margaret.thomas@ct.gov

FLORIDA
Mr. Jonathan Arthur
State Geologist
Geological Survey
Gunter Building, MS#720
903 West Tennessee Street
Tallahassee, FL 32304
P: (850) 488-4191
F: (850) 488-8086
E: jonathan.arthur
    @dep.state.fl.us

GEORGIA
Mr. Jim Kennedy
State Geologist
Environmental Protection Division
2 Martin Luther King Jr. Dr., Southeast
Suite 1152 East Floyd Tower
Atlanta, GA 30334
P: (404) 463-0679
F: (404) 651-5778
E: jim.kennedy
    @dnr.state.ga.us

IDAHO
Mr. Roy M. Breckenridge
State Geologist
Geological Survey
University of Idaho, Morrill Hall
Room 332
Moscow, ID 83844
P: (208) 885-7991
F: (208) 885-5826
E: roybreck@uidaho.edu

ILLINOIS
Mr. E. Donald McKay III
Interim Director
State Geological Survey
121 Natural Resources Building
615 East Peabody Drive
Champaign, IL 61820
P: (217) 333-5111
F: (217) 244-7004
E: mckay@isgs.illinois.edu

INDIANA
Dr. John C. Steinmetz
Director & State Geologist
Geological Survey
Indiana University
611 North Walnut Grove
Bloomington, IN 47405
P: (812) 855-5067
F: (812) 855-2862
E: jsteinm@indiana.edu

IOWA
Mr. Robert L. Libra
State Geologist & Bureau Chief
Geological Survey Bureau
Department of Natural Resources
109 Trowbridge Hall
Iowa City, IA 52242
P: (319) 335-1585
F: (319) 335-2754
E: robert.libra
    @dnr.iowa.gov

KANSAS
Mr. Rex Buchanan
Interim Director
Geological Survey
1930 Constant Avenue, Campus West
The University of Kansas
Lawrence, KS 66047
P: (785) 864-2106
F: (785) 864-5317
E: rex@kgs.ku.edu

KENTUCKY
Mr. James C. Cobb
State Geologist & Director
Geological Survey
228 Mining & Mineral Resources Building
University of Kentucky
Lexington, KY 40506
P: (859) 257-5500
F: (859) 257-1147
E: cobb@kgs.mm.uky.edu

LOUISIANA
Mr. Chacko J. John
Director & State Geologist
Geological Survey
Louisiana State University
3085 Energy, Coast & Environment Bldg.
Baton Rouge, LA 70803
P: (225) 578-8681
F: (225) 578-3662
E: cjohn@lsu.edu

MAINE
Mr. Robert G. Marvinney
Director & State Geologist
Geological Survey
22 State House Station
Augusta, ME 04333
P: (207) 287-2804
F: (207) 287-2353
E: robert.g.marvinney
    @maine.gov

MARYLAND
Mr. Jeffrey P. Halka
Director & State Geologist
Geological Survey
2300 St. Paul Street
Baltimore, MD 21218
P: (410) 554-5503
F: (410) 554-5502
E: jhalka@dnr.state.md.us

MASSACHUSETTS
Mr. Stephen B. Mabee
State Geologist
Department of Geosciences
611 North Pleasant Street
University of Massachusetts
Amherst, MA 01003
P: (413) 545-4814
F: (413) 545-1200
E: sbmabee@geo.umass.edu

Geological Survey

MICHIGAN
Mr. Harold R. Fitch
State Geologist
Office of Geological Survey
Constitution Hall
525 West Allegan Street, Box 30256
Lansing, MI 48909
P: (517) 241-1548
F: (517) 241-1601
E: fitchh@michigan.gov

MINNESOTA
Mr. Harvey Thorleifson
Professor & Director
Geological Survey
University of Minnesota
2642 University Avenue West, Room 104
St. Paul, MN 55114
P: (612) 627-4780
F: (612) 627-4778
E: thorleif@umn.edu

MISSISSIPPI
Mr. Michael Bograd
State Geologist
Office of Geology
P.O. Box 20307
Jackson, MS 39289
P: (601) 961-5500
F: (601) 961-5521
E: Michael_Bograd
    @deq.state.ms.us

MISSOURI
Mr. Joe Gillman
Director & State Geologist
Division of Geology & Land Survey
Department of Natural Resources
111 Fairgrounds Road, P.O. Box 250
Rolla, MO 65402
P: (573) 368-2101
F: (573) 368-2111
E: joe.gillman@dnr.mo.gov

MONTANA
Mr. Edmond G. Deal
Director & State Geologist
Bureau of Mines & Geology
Montana Tech of the Univ. of Montana
1300 West Park Street
Butte, MT 59701
P: (406) 496-4180
F: (406) 496-4451
E: edeal@mtech.edu

NEBRASKA
Mr. Mark S. Kuzila
Director
Conservation & Survey Division
113 Nebraska Hall
University of Nebraska
Lincoln, NE 68588
P: (402) 472-3471
F: (402) 472-4608
E: mkuzila1@unl.edu

NEVADA
Dr. Jonathan G. Price
Director & State Geologist
Bureau of Mines & Geology
University of Nevada Reno, MS 178
Reno, NV 89557
P: (775) 784-6691
F: (775) 784-1709
E: jprice@unr.edu

NEW JERSEY
Dr. Karl Muessig
State Geologist
Geological Survey
Department of Environmental Protection
P.O. Box 427
Trenton, NJ 08625
P: (609) 292-1185
F: (609) 633-1004
E: karl.muessig
    @dep.state.nj.us

NEW MEXICO
Dr. Peter A. Scholle
Director & State Geologist
Bureau of Geology & Mineral Resources
New Mexico Tech
801 Leroy Place
Socorro, NM 87801
P: (575) 835-5402
F: (575) 835-6333
E: scholle1@nmt.edu

NEW YORK
Dr. William Kelly
State Geologist & Chief
State Geological Survey
New York State Museum
3000 Cultural Education Center
Albany, NY 12230
P: (518) 473-6262
F: (518) 486-2034
E: wkelly@mail.nysed.gov

NORTH CAROLINA
Mr. James D. Simons
Director & State Geologist
Geological Survey
Division of Land Resources
1612 Mail Service Center
Raleigh, NC 27699
P: (919) 733-3833
F: (919) 715-8801
E: Jim.Simons@ncdenr.gov

NORTH DAKOTA
Mr. Edward C. Murphy
Director & State Geologist
Geological Survey
600 East Boulevard Avenue
Bismarck, ND 58505
P: (701) 328-8000
F: (701) 328-8010
E: emurphy@nd.gov

OHIO
Mr. Lawrence H. Wickstrom
State Geologist & Division Chief
Division of Geological Survey
Department of Natural Resources
2045 Morse Road, Building C
Columbus, OH 43229
P: (614) 265-6988
F: (614) 447-1918
E: larry.wickstrom
    @dnr.state.oh.us

OKLAHOMA
Dr. G. Randy Keller
Director
Geological Survey
100 East Boyd, Suite N-131
Norman, OK 73019
P: (405) 325-3031
F: (405) 325-7069
E: grkeller@ou.edu

OREGON
Ms. Vicki S. McConnell
Director & State Geologist
Department of Geology & Mineral Industries
800 Northeast Oregon Street, #28
Suite 965
Portland, OR 97232
P: (971) 673-1550
F: (971) 673-1562
E: vicki.mcconnell
    @dogami.state.or.us

PENNSYLVANIA
Mr. George E.W. Love
Director & State Geologist
Department of Conservation & Natural Resources
Bureau of Topographic & Geologic Survey
3240 Schoolhouse Road
Harrisburg, PA 17057
P: (717) 702-2047
F: (717) 702-2065

PUERTO RICO
Ms. Ruth H. Velez
State Geologist
Area Recursos de Agua y Minerales
Apartado 9066600
Puerta De Tierra Station
San Juan, PR 00906
P: (787) 725-3852
F: (787) 722-5586
E: rhvelez@dnra.gobierno.pr

RHODE ISLAND
Dr. Jon C. Boothroyd
State Geologist
Geological Survey
9 East Alumni Ave., 314
Woodward Hall
University of Rhode Island
Kingston, RI 02881
P: (401) 874-2191
F: (401) 874-2190
E: rigsurv@etal.uri.edu

SOUTH CAROLINA
Mr. C. W. Clendenin Jr.
State Geologist & Chief
Geological Survey
5 Geology Road
Columbia, SC 29210
P: (803) 896-7708
F: (803) 896-7695
E: clendeninb@dnr.sc.gov

SOUTH DAKOTA
Mr. Derric L. Iles
State Geologist
Geological Survey
Akeley-Lawrence Science Center, USD
414 East Clark Street
Vermillion, SD 57069
P: (605) 677-5227
F: (605) 677-5895
E: diles@usd.edu

TENNESSEE
Mr. Ronald P. Zurawski
State Geologist
Division of Geology
401 Church Street
 L & C Tower, 13th Floor
Nashville, TN 37243
P: (615) 532-1500
F: (615) 532-1517
E: ronald.zurawski
   @state.tn.us

TEXAS
Dr. Scott W. Tinker
Director
Bureau of Economic Geology
University of Texas At Austin
University Station, Box X
Austin, TX 78713
P: (512) 471-7113
F: (512) 471-0140
E: scott.tinker
   @beg.utexas.edu

UTAH
Mr. Rick Allis
Director & State Geologist
Geological Survey
1594 West North Temple
P.O. Box 146100
Salt Lake City, UT 84114
P: (801) 537-3305
F: (801) 537-3400
E: rickallis@utah.gov

VERMONT
Mr. Laurence R. Becker
State Geologist
Geological Survey
Agency of Natural Resources
103 South Main Street
Waterbury, VT 05671
P: (802) 241-3496
F: (802) 241-4585
E: laurence.becker
   @state.vt.us

VIRGINIA
Mr. Conrad T. Spangler III
Director
Department of Mines, Minerals
& Energy
Washington Building, 8th Floor
1100 Bank Street
Richmond, VA 23219
P: (804) 692-3202
F: (804) 692-3237
E: conrad.spangler
   @dmme.virginia.gov

WASHINGTON
Mr. Dave Norman
State Geologist & Division
Manager
Division of Geology & Earth
Resources
1111 Washington Street,
Southeast
Room 148, P.O. Box 47007
Olympia, WA 98504
P: (360) 902-1439
F: (360) 902-1785
E: dave.norman@dnr.wa.gov

WEST VIRGINIA
Mr. Michael Ed Hohn
Director & State Geologist
Geological & Economic Survey
1 Mont Chateau Road
Morgantown, WV 26508
P: (304) 594-2331
F: (304) 594-2575
E: info@geosrv.wvnet.edu

WISCONSIN
Mr. James M. Robertson
Director & State Geologist
Geological & Natural History
Survey
3817 Mineral Point Road
Madison, WI 53705
P: (608) 262-1705
F: (608) 262-8086
E: jmrober1@wisc.edu

WYOMING
Mr. Wallace Ulrich
Director & State Geologist
State Geological Survey
P.O. Box 1347
University Station
Laramie, WY 82073
P: (307) 766-2286
F: (307) 766-2605
E: wulrich@uwyo.edu

Governor

Information provided by:

National Governors Association
Dan Crippen
Executive Director
Hall of the States
444 North Capitol Street
Suite 267
Washington, DC 20001
P: (202) 624-5300
F: (202) 624-5313
www.nga.org

The Council of State Governments
David Adkins
Executive Director/CEO
2760 Research Park Drive
Lexington, KY 40511
P: (859) 244-8000
F: (859) 244-8001
www.csg.org

ALABAMA
Hon. Robert J. Bentley (R)
Governor
Office of the Governor
State Capitol
600 Dexter Avenue
Montgomery, AL 36130
P: (334) 242-7100
F: (334) 242-0937

ALASKA
Hon. Sean R. Parnell (R)
Governor
Office of the Governor
State Capitol
P.O. Box 110001
Juneau, AK 99811
P: (907) 465-3500
F: (907) 465-3532

AMERICAN SAMOA
Hon. Togiola T.A.
  Tulafono (D)
Governor
Office of the Governor
Executive Office Building
Pago Pago, AS 96799
P: (684) 633-4116
F: (684) 633-2269

ARIZONA
Hon. Jan Brewer (R)
Governor
Office of the Governor
1700 West Washington
Phoenix, AZ 85007
P: (602) 542-4331
F: (602) 542-7601

ARKANSAS
Hon. Mike Beebe (D)
Governor
Office of the Governor
State Capitol, Suite 250
Little Rock, AR 72201
P: (501) 682-2345
F: (501) 682-1382

CALIFORNIA
Hon. Edmund G.
  Brown Jr. (D)
Governor
Office of the Governor
State Capitol
Sacramento, CA 95814
P: (916) 445-2841
F: (916) 445-4633

COLORADO
Hon. John Hickenlooper (D)
Governor
Office of the Governor
136 State Capitol
Denver, CO 80203
P: (303) 866-2471
F: (303) 866-2003

CONNECTICUT
Hon. Dan Malloy (D)
Governor
Office of the Governor
210 Capitol Avenue
Hartford, CT 06106
P: (800) 406-1527
F: (860) 524-7395

DELAWARE
Hon. Jack Markell (D)
Governor
Office of the Governor
Tatnall Building
William Penn Street
Dover, DE 19901
P: (302) 744-4101
F: (302) 739-2775

DISTRICT OF COLUMBIA
Hon. Vincent C. Gray (D)
Mayor
Office of the Mayor
1350 Pennsylvania Avenue,
Northwest
Suite 316
Washington, DC 20004
P: (202) 727-6300
F: (202) 727-8527

FLORIDA
Hon. Rick Scott (R)
Governor
Office of the Governor
The Capitol
Tallahassee, FL 32399
P: (850) 488-2272
F: (850) 922-4292

GEORGIA
Hon. Nathan Deal (R)
Governor
Office of the Governor
142 State Capitol
Atlanta, GA 30334
P: (404) 656-1776
F: (404) 656-5947

GUAM
Hon. Edward J.B. Calvo (R)
Governor
Office of the Governor
Executive Chamber
P.O. Box 2950
Hagatna, GU 96932
P: (671) 472-8931
F: (671) 477-4826

HAWAII
Hon. Neil Abercrombie (D)
Governor
Office of the Governor
State Capitol
Exeutive Chambers
Honolulu, HI 96813
P: (808) 586-0034
F: (808) 586-0006

IDAHO
Hon. C.L. "Butch" Otter (R)
Governor
Office of the Governor
P.O. Box 83720
Boise, ID 83720
P: (208) 334-2100
F: (208) 334-2175

ILLINOIS
Hon. Patrick Quinn (D)
Governor
Office of the Governor
State Capitol
207 State House
Springfield, IL 62706
P: (217) 782-6830
F: (217) 524-4049

INDIANA
Hon. Mitch Daniels (R)
Governor
Office of the Governor
State House
Indianapolis, IN 46204
P: (317) 232-4567
F: (317) 232-3443

IOWA
Hon. Terry Branstad (R)
Governor
Office of the Governor
State Capitol
Des Moines, IA 50319
P: (515) 281-5211
F: (515) 281-6611

KANSAS
Hon. Sam Brownback (R)
Governor
Office of the Governor
State Capitol, 2nd Floor
Topeka, KS 66612
P: (785) 296-3232
F: (785) 296-7973

KENTUCKY
Hon. Steve Beshear (D)
Governor
Office of the Governor
The Capitol Building
700 Capital Avenue, Suite 100
Frankfort, KY 40601
P: (502) 564-2611
F: (502) 564-0437

LOUISIANA
Hon. Bobby Jindal (R)
Governor
Office of the Governor
P.O. Box 94004
Baton Rouge, LA 70804
P: (225) 342-7015
F: (225) 342-7099

MAINE
Hon. Paul LePage (R)
Governor
Office of the Governor
1 State House Station
Augusta, ME 04333
P: (207) 287-3531
F: (207) 287-1034

MARYLAND
Hon. Martin O'Malley (D)
Governor
Office of the Governor
State House
100 State Circle
Annapolis, MD 21401
P: (410) 974-3901
F: (410) 974-3275

MASSACHUSETTS
Hon. Deval Patrick (D)
Governor
Office of the Governor
State House, Room 360
Boston, MA 02133
P: (617) 725-4000
F: (617) 727-9725

MICHIGAN
Hon. Rick Snyder (R)
Governor
Office of the Governor
P.O. Box 30013
Lansing, MI 48909
P: (517) 373-3400
F: (517) 335-6863

MINNESOTA
Hon. Mark Dayton (D)
Governor
Office of the Governor
130 State Capitol
75 Rev. Martin Luther King Jr.
Boulevard
St. Paul, MN 55155
P: (651) 296-3391
F: (651) 296-2089

MISSISSIPPI
Hon. Haley Barbour (R)
Governor
Office of the Governor
P.O. Box 139
Jackson, MS 39205
P: (601) 359-3150
F: (601) 359-3741
E: governor
@governor.state.ms.us

MISSOURI
Hon. Jay Nixon (D)
Governor
Office of the Governor
Capitol Building, Room 216
Jefferson City, MO 65101
P: (573) 751-3222
F: (573) 526-3291

MONTANA
Hon. Brian D.
Schweitzer (D)
Governor
Office of the Governor
P.O. Box 200801
Helena, MT 59620
P: (406) 444-3111
F: (406) 444-5529

NEBRASKA
Hon. Dave Heineman (R)
Governor
Office of the Governor
State Capitol
P.O. Box 94848
Lincoln, NE 68509
P: (402) 471-2244
F: (402) 471-6031

NEVADA
Hon. Brian Sandoval (R)
Governor
Office of Governor
State Capitol
101 North Carson Street
Carson City, NV 89701
P: (775) 684-5670
F: (775) 684-5683

NEW HAMPSHIRE
Hon. John Lynch (D)
Governor
Office of the Governor
107 North Main Street, Room 208
Concord, NH 03301
P: (603) 271-2121
F: (603) 271-7680

NEW JERSEY
Hon. Chris Christie (R)
Governor
Office of the Governor
125 West State Street
P.O. Box 001
Trenton, NJ 08625
P: (609) 292-6000
F: (609) 777-2922

NEW MEXICO
Hon. Susana Martinez (R)
Governor
Office of the Governor
State Capitol, Fourth Floor
Santa Fe, NM 87501
P: (505) 476-2200
F: (505) 476-2226

NEW YORK
Hon. Andrew M. Cuomo (D)
Governor
Office of the Governor
State Capitol
Albany, NY 12224
P: (518) 474-7516

NORTH CAROLINA
Hon. Beverly Perdue (D)
Governor
Office of the Governor
20301 Mail Service Center
Raleigh, NC 27699
P: (919) 733-5811
F: (919) 733-2120

NORTH DAKOTA
Hon. Jack Dalrymple (R)
Governor
Office of the Governor
State Capitol, Department 101
600 East Boulevard Avenue
Bismarck, ND 58505
P: (701) 328-2200
F: (701) 328-2205

NORTHERN MARIANA ISLANDS
Hon. Benigno R. Fitial (C)
Governor
Office of the Governor
Caller Box 10007
Capitol Hill
Saipan, MP 96950
P: (670) 664-2280
F: (670) 664-2211

OHIO
Hon. John Kasich (R)
Governor
Office of the Governor
77 South High Street, 30th Floor
Columbus, OH 43215
P: (614) 466-3555
F: (614) 466-9354

OKLAHOMA
Hon. Mary Fallin (R)
Governor
Office of the Governor
State Capitol Building
2300 Lincoln Boulevard, Suite 212
Oklahoma City, OK 73105
P: (405) 521-2342
F: (405) 521-3353

OREGON
Hon. John A. Kitzhaber (D)
Governor
Office of the Governor
900 Court Street, Northeast
Room 254
Salem, OR 97301
P: (503) 378-3111
F: (503) 378-8970

PENNSYLVANIA
Hon. Tom Corbett (R)
Governor
Office of the Governor
Room 225
Main Capitol Building
Harrisburg, PA 17120
P: (717) 787-2500
F: (717) 772-8284

PUERTO RICO
Hon. Luis Fortuño (NPP)
Governor
Office of the Governor
La Fortaleza
P.O. Box 9020082
San Juan, PR 00902
P: (787) 721-7000
F: (787) 721-5072

RHODE ISLAND
Hon. Lincoln D. Chafee (I)
Governor
Office of the Governor
State House
Providence, RI 02903
P: (401) 222-2080
F: (401) 273-5729

SOUTH CAROLINA
Hon. Nikki Haley (R)
Governor
Office of the Governor
1205 Pendleton Street
Columbia, SC 29201
P: (803) 734-2100
F: (803) 734-5167

SOUTH DAKOTA
Hon. Dennis Daugaard (R)
Governor
Office of the Governor
500 East Capitol Avenue
Pierre, SD 57501
P: (605) 773-3212
F: (605) 773-5844

TENNESSEE
Hon. Bill Haslam (R)
Governor
Office of the Governor
State Capitol
Nashville, TN 37243
P: (615) 741-2001
F: (615) 532-9711

TEXAS
Hon. Rick Perry (R)
Governor
Office of the Governor
P.O. Box 12428
Austin, TX 78711
P: (512) 463-2000
F: (512) 463-5571

U.S. VIRGIN ISLANDS
Hon. John DeJongh Jr. (D)
Governor
Office of the Governor
Government House, 21-22
Kongens Gade, Charlotte Amalie
St. Thomas, VI 00802
P: (340) 774-0001
F: (340) 693-4374

Governor

UTAH
Hon. Gary R. Herbert (R)
Governor
Office of the Governor
State Capitol, Suite 200
Salt Lake City, UT 84114
P: (801) 538-1000
F: (801) 538-1557
E: GHERBERT@utah.gov

VERMONT
Hon. Peter E. Shumlin (D)
Governor
Office of the Governor
109 State Street
Montpelier, VT 05609
P: (802) 828-3333
F: (802) 828-3339

VIRGINIA
Hon. Bob F. McDonnell (R)
Governor
Office of the Governor
Patrick Henry Building
1111 East Broad Street, 3rd Floor
Richmond, VA 23219
P: (804) 786-2211
F: (804) 371-6351

WASHINGTON
Hon. Christine Gregoire (D)
Governor
Office of the Governor
P.O. Box 40002
Olympia, WA 98504
P: (360) 902-4111
F: (360) 753-4110

WEST VIRGINIA
Hon. Earl Ray Tomblin (D)
Governor
Office of the Governor
State Capitol Complex
Charleston, WV 25305
P: (304) 558-2000
F: (304) 342-7025
E: senate.president
   @wvsenate.gov

WISCONSIN
Hon. Scott K. Walker (R)
Governor
Office of the Governor
115 East State Capitol
P.O. Box 7863
Madison, WI 53707
P: (608) 266-1212
F: (608) 267-8983

WYOMING
Hon. Matthew Mead (R)
Governor
Office of Governor
State Capitol Building, Room 124
Cheyenne, WY 82002
P: (307) 777-7434
F: (307) 632-3909

Governor's Chief of Staff

Manages the office of the governor and assists in all duties performed by the governor.

Information provided by:

National Governors Association
Dan Crippen
Executive Director
Hall of the States
444 North Capitol Street
Suite 267
Washington, DC 20001
P: (202) 624-5300
F: (202) 624-5313
www.nga.org

ALABAMA
Mr. Charles Malone
Chief of Staff
Office of the Governor
State Capitol
600 Dexter Avenue
Montgomery, AL 36130
P: (334) 242-0937
F: (334) 242-0937

ALASKA
Mr. Mike Nizich
Chief of Staff
Office of the Governor
State Capitol
P.O. Box 110001
Juneau, AK 99811
P: (907) 465-3500
F: (907) 465-3532
E: mike.nizich@alaska.gov

AMERICAN SAMOA
Mr. Pati Faiai
Chief of Staff
Office of the Governor
Executive Office Building
Pago Pago, AS 96799
P: (684) 633-4116
F: (684) 633-2269
E: chiefofstaff
    @americansamoa.gov

ARIZONA
Ms. Eileen Klein
Chief of Staff
Office of the Governor
1700 West Washington
Phoenix, AZ 85007
P: (602) 542-4331
F: (602) 542-7601
E: eklein@az.gov

ARKANSAS
Mr. Morril Harriman
Chief of Staff
Office of the Governor
State Capitol, Suite 250
Little Rock, AR 72201
P: (501) 682-2345
F: (501) 682-1382
E: morril.harriman
    @arkansas.gov

COLORADO
Ms. Roxane White
Chief of Staff
Office of the Governor
136 State Capitol
Denver, CO 80203
P: (303) 866-2471
F: (303) 866-2003

CONNECTICUT
Mr. Timothy F. Bannon
Chief of Staff
Office of the Governor
210 Capitol Avenue
Hartford, CT 06106
P: (800) 406-1527
F: (860) 524-7395

DELAWARE
Mr. Thomas McGonigle
Chief of Staff
Office of the Governor
Tatnall Building
William Penn Street
Dover, DE 19901
P: (302) 744-4101
F: (302) 739-2775
E: thomas.mcgonigle
    @state.de.us

FLORIDA
Mr. Mike Prendergast
Chief of Staff
Office of the Governor
The Capitol
Tallahassee, FL 32399
P: (850) 488-2272
F: (850) 922-4292

GEORGIA
Mr. Chris Riley
Chief of Staff
Office of the Governor
142 State Capitol
Atlanta, GA 30334
P: (404) 656-1776
F: (404) 656-5947

GUAM
Mr. Frank Arriola
Chief of Staff
Office of the Governor
Executive Chamber
P.O. Box 2950
Hagatna, GU 96932
P: (671) 472-8931
F: (671) 477-4826

HAWAII
Ms. Amy Asselbaye
Chief of Staff
Office of the Governor
State Capitol
Executive Chambers
Honolulu, HI 96813
P: (808) 586-0034

IDAHO
Mr. Jason Kreizenbeck
Chief of Staff
Office of the Governor
P.O. Box 83720
Boise, ID 83720
P: (208) 334-2100
F: (208) 334-2175
E: jkreizenbeck
    @gov.idaho.gov

ILLINOIS
Mr. Jack Lavin
Chief of Staff
Office of the Governor
State Capitol
207 Statehouse
Springfield, IL 62706
P: (217) 782-6830
F: (217) 524-4049

INDIANA
Mr. Earl Goode
Chief of Staff
Office of the Governor
State House
Indianapolis, IN 46204
P: (317) 232-4567
F: (317) 232-3443
E: egoode@gov.in.gov

IOWA
Mr. Jeff Boeyink
Chief of Staff
Office of the Governor
State Capitol
Des Moines, IA 50319
P: (515) 281-5211
F: (515) 281-6611

KANSAS
Mr. David Kensinger
Chief of Staff
Office of the Governor
State Capitol, 2nd Floor
Topeka, KS 66612
P: (785) 296-3232
F: (785) 296-7973

KENTUCKY
Mr. Mike Haydon
Chief of Staff
Office of the Governor
The Capitol Building
700 Capitol Avenue, Suite 100
Frankfort, KY 40601
P: (502) 564-2611
F: (502) 564-0437

LOUISIANA
Mr. Timmy Teepell
Chief of Staff
Office of the Governor
P.O. Box 94004
Baton Rouge, LA 70804
P: (225) 342-7015
F: (225) 342-7099
E: timmy.teepell@la.gov

MAINE
Mr. John McGough
Chief of Staff
Office of the Governor
1 State House Station
Augusta, ME 04333
P: (207) 287-3531
F: (207) 287-1034

MARYLAND
Mr. Matthew Gallagher
Chief of Staff
Office of the Governor
State House
100 State Circle
Annapolis, MD 21401
P: (410) 974-3901
F: (410) 974-3275

MASSACHUSETTS
Mr. William Cowan
Chief of Staff
Office of the Governor
State House, Room 360
Boston, MA 02133
P: (617) 725-4000
F: (617) 727-9725

MICHIGAN
Mr. Dennis Muchmore
Chief of Staff
Office of the Governor
P.O. Box 30013
Lansing, MI 48909
P: (517) 373-3400
F: (517) 335-6863

Governor's Chief of Staff

MINNESOTA
Ms. Tina Smith
Chief of Staff
Office of the Governor
130 State Capitol
75 Rev. Martin Luther King Jr.
Boulevard
St. Paul, MN 55155
P: (651) 201-3400
F: (651) 296-2089

MISSISSIPPI
Mr. Paul Hurst
Chief of Staff
Office of the Governor
P.O. Box 139
Jackson, MS 39205
P: (601) 359-3150
F: (601) 359-3741
E: phurst
@governor.state.ms.us

MISSOURI
Mr. John Watson
Chief of Staff
Office of the Governor
Capitol Building, Room 216
Jefferson City, MO 65101
P: (573) 751-3222
F: (573) 526-3291
E: judy.murray@mo.gov

MONTANA
Ms. Vivian Hammill
Chief of Staff
Office of the Governor
P.O. Box 200801
State Capitol
Helena, MT 59620
P: (406) 444-3111
F: (406) 444-5529
E: vhammill@mt.gov

NEBRASKA
Mr. Larry Bare
Chief of Staff
Office of the Governor
State Capitol
P.O. Box 94848
Lincoln, NE 68509
P: (402) 471-2244
F: (402) 471-6031
E: larry.bare@nebraska.gov

NEVADA
Ms. Heidi S. Gansert
Chief of Staff
Office of the Governor
State Capitol
101 North Carson Street
Carson City, NV 89701
P: (775) 684-5670
F: (775) 684-5683

NEW HAMPSHIRE
Mr. Rich Sigel
Chief of Staff
Office of the Governor
107 North Main Street, Room
208
Concord, NH 03301
P: (603) 271-2121
F: (603) 271-7680
E: rich.sigel@nh.gov

NEW JERSEY
Mr. Richard H. Bagger
Chief of Staff
Office of the Governor
125 West State Street
P.O. Box 001
Trenton, NJ 08625
P: (609) 292-6000
F: (609) 777-2922

NEW MEXICO
Mr. Keith J. Gardner
Chief of Staff
Office of the Governor
State Capitol, Fourth Floor
Santa Fe, NM 87501
P: (505) 476-2200
F: (505) 476-2226

NEW YORK
Mr. Steven Cohen
Chief of Staff
Office of the Governor
State Capitol
Albany, NY 12224
P: (518) 474-7516

NORTH CAROLINA
Mr. Britt Cobb
Chief of Staff
Office of the Governor
20301 Mail Service Center
Raleigh, NC 27699
P: (919) 733-5811
F: (919) 733-2120
E: britt.cobb@ncmail.net

NORTH DAKOTA
Mr. Ron Rauschenberger
Chief of Staff
Office of the Governor
State Capitol, Department 101
600 East Boulevard Avenue
Bismarck, ND 58505
P: (701) 328-2200
F: (701) 328-2205
E: rrausche@nd.gov

**NORTHERN MARIANA
ISLANDS**
Ms. Esther Fleming
Chief of Staff
Office of the Governor
Caller Box 10007, Capitol Hill
Saipan, MP 96950
P: (670) 664-2280
F: (670) 664-2211

OHIO
Ms. Beth Hansen
Chief of Staff
Office of the Governor
77 South High Street, 30th Floor
Columbus, OH 43215
P: (614) 466-3555
F: (614) 466-9354

OKLAHOMA
Ms. Denise Northrup
Chief of Staff
Office of the Governor
State Capitol Building
2300 Lincoln Boulevard, Suite
212
Oklahoma City, OK 73105
P: (405) 521-2342
F: (405) 521-3353

OREGON
Mr. Curtis Robinhold
Chief of Staff
Office of the Governor
900 Court Street, Northeast
Room 254
Salem, OR 97301
P: (503) 378-3111
F: (503) 378-8970

PENNSYLVANIA
Mr. William F. Ward
Chief of Staff
Office of the Governor
Main Capitol Building, Room
225
Harrisburg, PA 17120
P: (717) 787-2500
F: (717) 772-8284

PUERTO RICO
Mr. Marcos Rodriguez-Ema
Chief of Staff
Office of the Governor
La Fortaleza
P.O. Box 9020082
San Juan, PR 00902
P: (787) 721-7000
F: (787) 721-5072

RHODE ISLAND
Mr. Patrick Rogers
Chief of Staff
Office of the Governor
State House
Providence, RI 02903
P: (401) 222-2080
F: (401) 273-5729

SOUTH CAROLINA
Mr. Tim Pearson
Chief of Staff
Office of the Governor
1205 Pendleton Street
Columbia, SC 29201
P: (803) 734-2100
F: (803) 734-5167

SOUTH DAKOTA
Mr. Dustin Johnson
Chief of Staff
Office of the Governor
500 East Capitol Avenue
Pierre, SD 57501
P: (605) 773-3212
F: (605) 773-5844
E: dustin.johnson
@state.sd.us

TENNESSEE
Mr. Claude Ramsey
Chief of Staff
Office of the Governor
State Capitol
Nashville, TN 37243
P: (615) 741-2001
F: (615) 532-9711

TEXAS
Mr. Ray Sullivan
Chief of Staff
Office of the Governor
P.O. Box 12428
Austin, TX 78711
P: (512) 463-2000
F: (512) 463-5571

U.S. VIRGIN ISLANDS
Mr. Louis Penn
Chief of Staff
Office of the Governor
Government House, 21-22
Kongens Gade
Charlotte Amalie
St. Thomas, VI 00802
P: (340) 774-0001
F: (340) 693-4374
E: louis.penn@go.vi.gov

UTAH
Mr. Derek Miller
Chief of Staff
Office of the Governor
State Capitol, Suite 200
Salt Lake City, UT 84114
P: (801) 538-1000
F: (801) 538-1557

VERMONT
Mr. Bill Lofy
Chief of Staff
Office of the Governor
109 State Street
Montpelier, VT 05609
P: (802) 828-3333
F: (802) 828-3339

VIRGINIA
Mr. Martin Kent
Chief of Staff
Office of the Governor
Patrick Henry Building
1111 East Broad Street, 3rd Floor
Richmond, VA 23219
P: (804) 786-2211
F: (804) 371-6351
E: martin.kent
    @governor.virginia.gov

WASHINGTON
Mr. Jay Manning
Chief of Staff
Office of the Governor
P.O. Box 40002
Olympia, WA 98504
P: (360) 902-4111
F: (360) 753-4110
E: jay.manning@gov.wa.gov

WEST VIRGINIA
Mr. Rob Alsop
Chief of Staff
Office of the Governor
State Capitol Complex
Charleston, WV 25305
P: (304) 558-2000
F: (304) 342-7025

WISCONSIN
Mr. Keith Gilkes
Chief of Staff
Office of the Governor
115 East State Capitol
P.O. Box 7863
Madison, WI 53707
P: (608) 266-1212
F: (608) 267-8983

WYOMING
Ms. Kari Gray
Chief of Staff
Office of the Governor
State Capitol Building, Room 124
Cheyenne, WY 82002
P: (307) 777-7434
F: (307) 632-3909

Governor's Legislative Director

Oversees the governor's legislative priorities, aids in legislative administration, and assists the governor in all other legislative matters.

Information provided by:

National Governors Association
Ray Scheppach
Executive Director
Hall of the States
444 North Capitol Street
Suite 267
Washington, DC 20001
P: (202) 624-5300
F: (202) 624-5313
www.nga.org

ALABAMA
Mr. Jeff Raben
State-Legislative Relations
Office of the Governor
State Capitol
600 Dexter Avenue
Montgomery, AL 36130
P: (334) 242-7100
F: (334) 242-0937

ALASKA
Mr. Kelly Goode
Legislative Director
Office of the Governor
State Capitol
P.O. Box 110001
Juneau, AK 99811
P: (907) 465-3500
F: (907) 465-3532

AMERICAN SAMOA
Talauega Letumu
Legislative Liaison
Office of the Governor
Executive Office Building
Pago Pago, AS 96799
P: (684) 633-4116
F: (684) 633-2269

Tuiefano M. Vaela'a
Legislative Liaison
Office of the Governor
Executive Office Building
Pago Pago, AS 96799
P: (684) 633-4116
F: (684) 633-2269

ARKANSAS
Mr. Chris Masingill
Director of Agency & Constituency Affairs
Office of the Governor
State Capitol, Suite 120
Little Rock, AR 72201
P: (501) 682-2345
F: (501) 682-3596
E: chris.masingill
@governor.arkansas.gov

CALIFORNIA
Mr. Michael Prosio
Legislative Affairs Secretary
Office of the Governor
State Capitol
Sacramento, CA 95814
P: (916) 445-2841
F: (816) 445-4633

COLORADO
Ms. Mary Kay Hogan
Legislative Director
Office of the Governor
136 State Capitol
Denver, CO 80203
P: (303) 866-2471
F: (303) 866-2003

CONNECTICUT
Ms. Chelsea Turner
Director of Policy & Legislative Affairs
Office of the Governor
210 Capitol Avenue
Hartford, CT 06106
P: (800) 406-1527
F: (860) 524-7395

DELAWARE
Mr. Gregory Patterson
State-Legislative Relations
Office of the Governor
Tatnall Building
William Penn Street
Dover, DE 19901
P: (302) 744-4101
F: (302) 739-2775

FLORIDA
Ms. Kathy Mears
Deputy Chief of Staff
Office of the Governor
The Capitol
Tallahasseee, FL 32399
P: (850) 488-2272
F: (850) 922-4292

GEORGIA
Mr. Pat Wilson
State-Legislative Relations
Office of the Governor
142 State Capitol
Atlanta, GA 30334
P: (404) 656-1776
F: (404) 656-5947

GUAM
Mr. J. George Bamba
Chief of Staff
State-Legislative Relations
Executive Chamber
P.O. Box 2950
Hagatna, GU 96932
P: (671) 472-8931
F: (671) 477-4826
E: jgbamba@mail.gov.gu

HAWAII
Ms. Linda Smith
Senior Advisor - Policy
Office of the Governor
State Capitol
Executive Chambers
Honolulu, HI 96813
P: (808) 586-0034
F: (808) 586-0006

IDAHO
Mr. Jason Kreizenbeck
Chief of Staff
Office of the Governor
P.O. Box 83720
Boise, ID 83720
P: (208) 334-2100
F: (208) 334-2175
E: jkreizenbeck
@gov.idaho.gov

ILLINOIS
Ms. Lindsay Hansen Anderson
Legislative Director
Office of the Governor
State Capitol
207 Statehouse
Springfield, IL 62706
P: (217) 782-6830
F: (217) 524-4049

INDIANA
Mr. Joe Heerens
State-Legislative Relations
Office of the Governor
State House
Indianapolis, IN 46204
P: (317) 232-4567
F: (317) 232-3443

KENTUCKY
Mr. Mike Haydon
Chief of Staff
Office of the Governor
The Capitol Building
700 Capitol Avenue, Suite 100
Frankfort, KY 40601
P: (502) 564-2611
F: (502) 564-0437

LOUISIANA
Mr. Nick Cahanin
Deputy Legislative Director
Office of the Governor
P.O. Box 94004
Baton Rouge, LA 70804
P: (225) 342-7015
F: (225) 342-7099

MAINE
Ms. Jane Lincoln
Chief of Staff
Office of the Governor
1 State House Station
Augusta, ME 04333
P: (207) 287-3531
F: (207) 287-1034
E: jane.lincoln@maine.gov

MARYLAND
Mr. Joe Bryce
Chief Legislative Officer
Office of the Governor
State House
100 State Circle
Annapolis, MD 21401
P: (410) 974-3901
F: (410) 974-3275

MASSACHUSETTS
Ms. Lora Pellegrini
State-Legislative Relations
Office of the Governor
State House, Room 360
Boston, MA 02133
P: (617) 725-4000
F: (617) 727-9725

MICHIGAN
Mr. Tim Hughes
Director of Legislative Affairs
Office of the Governor
P.O. Box 30013
Lansing, MI 48909
P: (517) 373-3400
F: (517) 335-6863

MINNESOTA
Mr. Chris DeLaForest
Director of Legislative &
Cabinet Affairs
Office of the Governor
130 State Capitol
75 Martin Luther King Jr.
Boulevard
St. Paul, MN 55155
P: (651) 296-3391
F: (651) 296-2089

MISSISSIPPI
Mr. Neely Carlton
Legislative Affairs & Counselor
Office of the Governor
P.O. Box 139
Jackson, MS 39205
P: (601) 359-3150
F: (601) 359-3741

Mr. Andrew Ketchings
State-Legislative Relations
Office of the Governor
P.O. Box 139
Jackson, MS 39205
P: (601) 359-3150
F: (601) 359-3741

MISSOURI
Mr. Daniel Hall
Director of Legislative Affairs
Office of the Governor
Office of the Governor
Capitol Building, Room 216
Jefferson City, MO 65101
P: (573) 751-3222
F: (573) 526-3291

NEVADA
Ms. Stacy Woodbury
Legislative Director
Office of the Governor
State Capitol
101 North Carson Street
Carson City, NV 89701
P: (775) 684-5670
F: (775) 684-1000

NEW MEXICO
Mr. Eric Witt
Director of Legislative &
Political Affairs
Office of the Governor
State Capitol, Fourth Floor
Santa Fe, NM 87501
P: (505) 476-2200
F: (505) 476-2226

NEW YORK
Mr. Tony Giardina
Acting Deputy Secretary of
Intergovernmental Affairs
Office of the Governor
State Capitol
Albany, NY 12224
P: (518) 474-7516
F: (518) 474-8390

NORTH CAROLINA
Ms. Courtney Crowder
Legislative Director
Office of the Governor
20301 Mail Service Center
Raleigh, NC 27699
P: (919) 733-5811
F: (919) 733-2120

NORTH DAKOTA
Mr. Don Larson
Senior Policy Advisor
Office of the Governor
State Capitol, 600 East
Boulevard Avenue
Department 101
Bismarck, ND 58505
P: (701) 328-2200
F: (701) 328-2205

OHIO
Ms. Kris Long
Legislative Director
Office of the Governor
77 South High Street, 30th Floor
Columbus, OH 43215
P: (614) 466-0898
F: (614) 466-9354

OKLAHOMA
Ms. Kristi Ice
Director of Policy & Legislative
Liaison
Office of the Governor
State Capitol Building
2300 Lincoln Boulevard, Suite
212
Oklahoma, OK 73105
P: (405) 521-2342
F: (405) 521-3353

OREGON
Ms. Angi Dilkes
Legislative Director
Office of the Governor
900 Court Street Northeast,
Room 254
Salem, OR 97301
P: (503) 378-3111
F: (503) 378-8970

PENNSYLVANIA
Ms. Colleen Kopp
State-Legislative Relations
Office of the Governor
Room 225, Main Capitol
Building
Harrisburg, PA 17120
P: (717) 787-2500
F: (717) 772-8284

PUERTO RICO
Mr. Miguel Hernandez-Vivoni
State-Legislative Relations
Office of the Governor
La Fortaleza
P.O. Box 9020082
San Juan, PR 00902
P: (787) 721-7000

RHODE ISLAND
Mr. Mike Cronan
Director of Legislative Relations
Office of the Governor
State House
Providence, RI 02903
P: (401) 222-2080
F: (401) 273-5729

SOUTH CAROLINA
Ms. Marisa Crawford
Legislative Advisor - House &
Director of Special Projects
Office of the Governor
P.O. Box 12267
Columbia, SC 29211
P: (803) 734-2100
F: (803) 734-5167

Mr. Bob Frisina
Legislative Advisor - Senate
Office of the Governor
P.O. Box 12267
Columbia, SC 29211
P: (803) 734-2100
F: (803) 734-5167

SOUTH DAKOTA
Mr. Cody Bynum
State-Legislative Relations
Office of the Governor
500 East Capitol Avenue
Pierre, SD 57501
P: (605) 773-3212
F: (605) 773-3212

TENNESSEE
Mr. Pat Miller
Legislative Director
Office of the Governor
State Capitol
Nashville, TN 37243
P: (615) 741-2001
F: (615) 532-9711

TEXAS
Mr. Kenneth L. Armbrister
Director of Legislative Affairs
Office of the Governor
P.O. Box 12428
Austin, TX 78711
P: (512) 463-2000
F: (512) 463-5571

UTAH
Mr. Robert Spendlove
Policy Director
Office of the Governor
State Capitol, Suite 200
Salt Lake City, UT 84114
P: (801) 538-1000
F: (801) 538-1557

VERMONT
Ms. Dennise Casey
Deputy Chief of Staff
Office of the Governor
109 State Street, Pavilion
Montpelier, VT 05609
P: (802) 828-3339
F: (802) 828-1110

VIRGINIA
Mr. Andrew Lamar
State-Legislative Relations
Office of the Governor
Patrick Henry Building
1111 East Broad Street, 3rd Floor
Richmond, VA 23219
P: (804) 786-2211
F: (804) 371-6351

WASHINGTON
Mr. Jim Justin
Legislative Director
Office of the Governor
416 Sid Snyder Avenue, NW,
Ste. 200
P.O. Box 40002
Olympia, WA 98504
P: (360) 902-0486

WEST VIRGINIA
Mr. Jim L. Pitrolo
Legislative/Policy Director
Office of the Governor
Capitol Complex
Charleston, WV 25305
P: (304) 558-2000
F: (304) 342-7025

Governor's Legislative Director

WISCONSIN
Mr. Dan Kanninen
Legislative Director
Office of the Governor
115 East State Capitol
P.O. Box 7863
Madison, WI 53707
P: (608) 266-1212
F: (608) 267-8983

Governor's Media Contacts

Issues press releases on behalf of the governor, acts as a liaison with the media and public, and serves as the governor's spokesperson.

Information provided by:

National Governors Association
Ray Scheppach
Executive Director
Hall of the States
444 North Capitol Street
Suite 267
Washington, DC 20001
P: (202) 624-5300
F: (202) 624-5313
www.nga.org

ALABAMA
Ms. Rebekah Caldwell Mason
Communications Director
Office of the Governor
State Capitol, 600 Dexter Avenue
Montgomery, AL 36130
P: (334) 242-7150

ALASKA
Ms. Sharon Leighow
Press Secretary
Office of the Governor
State Capitol
P.O. Box 110001
Juneau, AK 99811
P: (907) 269-7450

AMERICAN SAMOA
Dr. Jacinta Galeai
Communications Director
Office of the Governor
Pago Pago, AS 96799
P: (684) 633-4116

ARIZONA
Mr. Matthew Benson
Communications Director
Office of the Governor
1700 West Washington
Phoenix, AZ 85007
P: (602) 542-4331
E: mbenson@az.gov

Mr. Paul Senseman
Deputy Chief of Staff, Communications
Office of the Governor
1700 West Washington
Phoenix, AZ 85007
P: (602) 542-4331

ARKANSAS
Mr. Grant Tennille
Communications Director
Office of the Governor
State Capitol, Room 250
Little Rock, AR 72201
P: (501) 682-3642

CALIFORNIA
Mr. Gil Duran
Press Secretary
Office of the Governor
State Capitol, First Floor
Sacramento, CA 95814
P: (916) 445-4571

COLORADO
Mr. Eric Brown
Communications Director
Office of the Governor
State Capitol, Room 127
Denver, CO 80203
P: (303) 866-6386

CONNECTICUT
Ms. Colleen Flanagan
Communications Director
Office of the Governor
State Capitol, 210 Capitol Avenue
Hartford, CT 06106
P: (860) 524-7313

DELAWARE
Ms. Catherine Rossi
Communications Director
Office of the Governor
Tatnall Building
William Penn Street
Dover, DE 19901
P: (302) 744-4101

FLORIDA
Mr. Brian Burgess
Communications Director
Office of the Governor
State Capitol, Room 206
Tallahassee, FL 32399
P: (850) 488-5394

GEORGIA
Mr. Brian Robinson
Deputy Chief of Staff for Communications
Office of the Governor
State Capitol, Room 100
Atlanta, GA 30334
P: (404) 651-7774

GUAM
Mr. Troy Torres
Communications Director
Office of the Governor
Executive Chamber
P.O. Box 2950
Hagatna, GU 96932
P: (671) 472-8931

HAWAII
Mr. Josh Levinson
Director of Communications
Office of the Governor
State Capitol
415 South Beretania Street
Honolulu, HI 96813
P: (808) 586-0034

IDAHO
Mr. Mark Warbis
Communications Director
Office of the Governor
State Capitol
700 West Jefferson, 2nd Floor
Boise, ID 83720
P: (208) 334-2100

ILLINOIS
Mica Matsoff
Director of Communications
Office of the Governor
James R. Thompson Center
100 West Randolph, Suite 16-100
Chicago, IL 60601
P: (217) 782-7355

INDIANA
Ms. Jane Jankowski
Press Secretary
Office of the Governor
206 State House
Indianapolis, IN 46204
P: (317) 232-4567

IOWA
Mr. Tim Albrecht
Communications Director
Office of the Governor
State Capitol
Des Moines, IA 50319
P: (515) 281-0173

KANSAS
Ms. Sherriene Jones-Sontag
Communications Director
Office of the Governor
State Capitol, Second Floor
Topeka, KS 66612
P: (785) 368-8500

KENTUCKY
Ms. Katie Allison Dailinger
Communications Director
Office of the Governor
State Capitol
700 Capitol Avenue, Suite 100
Frankfort, KY 40601
P: (502) 564-2611

LOUISIANA
Ms. Melissa Sellers
Director of Communications
Office of the Governor
P.O. Box 94004
Baton Rouge, LA 70804
P: (225) 342-7015

MAINE
Ms. Adrienne A. Bennett
Press Secretary
Office of the Governor
State House, Station 1
Augusta, ME 04333
P: (207) 287-2531

MARYLAND
Mr. Shaun Adamec
Press Secretary
Office of the Governor
State House
Annapolis, MD 21401
P: (410) 974-2316

MASSACHUSETTS
Mr. Brendan Ryan
Communications Director
Office of the Governor
State House, Room 265
Boston, MA 02133
P: (617) 725-4025

MICHIGAN
Ms. Geralyn Lasher
Communications Director
Office of the Governor
P.O. Box 30013
Lansing, MI 48909
P: (517) 335-6397

MINNESOTA
Ms. Katharine Tinucci
Press Secretary
Office of the Governor
State Capitol, Room 130
St. Paul, MN 55155
P: (651) 296-0001

MISSISSIPPI
Ms. Laura Hipp
Communications Director
Office of the Governor
P.O. Box 139
Jackson, MS 39205
P: (601) 576-2026

Governor's Media Contacts

MISSOURI
Ms. Christy Bertelson
Director of Communications
Office of the Governor
State Capitol
P.O. Box 720
Jefferson City, MO 65101
P: (573) 751-0290

MONTANA
Ms. Sarah Elliott
Communications Director
Office of the Governor
State Capitol
Helena, MT 59620
P: (406) 444-3111
F: (406) 444-5529

NEBRASKA
Ms. Jen Rae Hein
Communications Director
Office of the Governor
P.O. Box 94848
Lincoln, NE 68509
P: (402) 471-2244
F: (402) 471-6031

NEVADA
Mr. Dale Erquiaga
Communications Director
Office of the Governor
State Capitol
101 North Carson Street
Carson City, NV 89701
P: (775) 684-5670

NEW HAMPSHIRE
Mr. Colin Manning
Press Secretary
Office of the Governor
State House
Concord, NH 03301
P: (603) 271-2121

NEW JERSEY
Ms. Maria Comella
Director of Communications
Office of the Governor
125 West State Street
Governor's Office, P.O. Box 001
Trenton, NJ 08625
P: (609) 777-2600

NEW MEXICO
Mr. Scott Darnell
Communications Director
Office of the Governor
State Capitol, Fourth Floor
Santa Fe, NM 87501
P: (505) 476-2200

NORTH CAROLINA
Ms. Chrissy Pearson
Communications Director
Office of the Governor
20301 Mail Service Center
Raleigh, NC 27699
P: (919) 733-0098

NORTH DAKOTA
Ms. Jody Link
Senior Communications Advisor
Office of the Governor
600 East Boulevard Avenue
Department 101
Bismarck, ND 58505
P: (701) 328-2200
F: (701) 328-2205

NORTHERN MARIANA ISLANDS
Ms. Angel A. Demapan
Press Secretary
Office of the Governor
Capitol Hill
Saipan, MP 96950
P: (670) 664-2230

OHIO
Mr. Scott Milburn
Communications Director
Office of the Governor
South High Street, 30th Floor
Columbus, OH 43215
P: (614) 466-3555

OKLAHOMA
Mr. Alex Weintz
Communications Director
Office of the Governor
State Capitol
Oklahoma City, OK 73105
P: (405) 521-2342

OREGON
Mr. Tim Raphael
Communications Director
Office of the Governor
State Capitol, Room 254
900 Court Street, Northeast
Salem, OR 97310
P: (503) 378-4859

PENNSYLVANIA
Mr. Kevin Harley
Communications Director
Office of the Governor
Main Capitol Building, Room 308
Harrisburg, PA 17120
P: (717) 783-1116

PUERTO RICO
Mr. Eduardo Zayas
Press Secretary
Office of the Governor
La Fortaleza
San Juan, PR 00902
P: (787) 721-7000

RHODE ISLAND
Mr. Mike Trainor
Communications Director
Office of the Governor
State House
Providence, RI 02903
P: (401) 222-8134

SOUTH CAROLINA
Mr. Jeff Taillon
Press Assistant
Office of the Governor
P.O. Box 11829
Columbia, SC 29211
P: (803) 734-5254

SOUTH DAKOTA
Mr. Tony Venhuizen
Communications Director
Office of the Governor
500 East Capitol
Pierre, SD 57501
P: (605) 773-5706

TENNESSEE
Mr. Tom Griscom
Communications Consultant
Office of the Governor
State Capitol, Room G-9
Nashville, TN 37243
P: (615) 741-3763

TEXAS
Mr. Mark Miner
Communications Director
Office of the Governor
P.O. Box 12428
Austin, TX 78711
P: (512) 463-1826

U.S. VIRGIN ISLANDS
Mr. Jean P. Greaux Jr.
Communications Director
Office of the Governor
Government House, 21-22
Kongens Gade
Charlotte Amalie
St. Thomas, VI 00802
P: (340) 774-0294
F: (340) 774-1361

UTAH
Ms. Allyson Isom
Chief of Staff
Office of the Governor
210 State Capitol
Salt Lake City, UT 84114
P: (801) 538-1000

VERMONT
Ms. Bianca Slota
Press Secretary
Office of the Governor
109 State Street
Montpelier, VT 05609
P: (802) 828-3333

VIRGINIA
Mr. J. Tucker Martin
Director of Communications
Office of the Governor
Patrick Henry Building, 3rd Floor
1111 East Broad Street
Richmond, VA 23219
P: (804) 692-0145

WASHINGTON
Mr. Cory Curtis
Communications Director
Office of the Governor
416 4th Avenue, Southwest
Olympia, WA 98504
P: (360) 902-4136

WEST VIRGINIA
Ms. Jacqueline Proctor
Director of Communications
Office of the Governor
State Capitol
Charleston, WV 25305
P: (304) 558-2000

WISCONSIN
Mr. Chris Schrimpf
Communications Director
Office of the Governor
115 East, State Capitol
Madison, WI 53702
P: (608) 267-7303

WYOMING
Renny MacKay
Communications Director
Office of the Governor
State Capitol
Cheyenne, WY 82002
P: (307) 777-7437

Hazardous Waste Management

Develops and maintains a comprehensive hazardous waste management program in the state.

ALABAMA
Mr. Stephen Cobb
Chief
Governmental Hazardous Waste
P.O. Box 301463
Montgomery, AL 36130
P: (334) 271-7739
F: (334) 271-7950

ARIZONA
Ms. Amanda Stone
Waste Programs Division
Director
Department of Environmental
Quality
ADEQ Central Office
1110 West Washington Street
Phoenix, AZ 85007
P: (602) 771-4567
F: (602) 771-2302
E: stone.amanda@azdeq.gov

ARKANSAS
Mr. Clyde Rhodes
Chief
Hazardous Waste Division
P.O. Box 8913
Little Rock, AR 72209
P: (501) 682-0833
F: (501) 682-0565
E: rhodesc@adeq.state.ar.us

CALIFORNIA
Mr. Mark Leary
Acting Director
Department of Resources,
Recycling & Recovery
1001 I Street
P.O. Box 4025
Sacramento, CA 95812
P: (916) 341-6544
F: (916) 319-7319
E: Mark.Leary
   @CalRecycle.ca.gov

COLORADO
Mr. Gary Baughman
Director
Hazardous Materials & Waste
Management Division
Dept. of Public Health &
Environment
Denver, CO 80246
P: (303) 692-3320
F: (303) 759-5355
E: comments.hmwnd
   @state.co.us

CONNECTICUT
Mr. Daniel C. Esty
Commissioner
Department of Environmental
Protection
79 Elm Street
Hartford, CT 06106
P: (860) 424-3009
F: (860) 424-4054
E: daniel.esty@ct.gov

DELAWARE
Ms. Nancy C. Marker
Manager
Solid Waste & Hazardous
Management Branch
89 Kings Highway
Dover, DE 19901
P: (302) 739-9403
F: (302) 739-5060

DISTRICT OF COLUMBIA
Dr. Mohammad N. Akhter
Director
Department of Health
825 North Capitol Street,
Northeast
Washington, DC 20002
P: (202) 442-5999
F: (202) 442-4788
E: doh@dc.gov

FLORIDA
Mr. Jorge Caspary
Director
Division of Waste Management
Department of Environmental
Protection
2600 Blairstone Road, MS 4500
Tallahassee, FL 32399
P: (850) 245-8693
E: jorge.caspary
   @dep.state.fl.us

GEORGIA
Mr. Mark Smith
Branch Chief
Land Protection Branch
2 Martin Luther King, Jr. Drive,
SE
Suite 1154 East Tower
Atlanta, GA 30334
P: (404) 656-7802
F: (404) 651-9425

HAWAII
Mr. Steven Y.K. Chang
Branch Chief
Solid & Hazardous Waste
Branch
Department of Health
919 Ala Moana Boulevard, #212
Honolulu, HI 96814
P: (808) 586-4226
F: (808) 586-7509
E: schang
   @eha.health.state.hi.us

IDAHO
Mr. Orville Green
Administrator
Waste Management &
Remediation Division
DEQ State Office
1410 North Hilton
Boise, ID 83706
P: (208) 373-0148
F: (208) 373-0154
E: orville.green
   @deq.idaho.gov

ILLINOIS
Dr. Manohar R. Kulkarni
Director
Sustainable Technology Center
One Hazelwood Drive
Champaign, IL 61820
P: (217) 333-8569
F: (217) 333-8944
E: mkulkarni
   @istc.illinois.edu

INDIANA
Mr. Bruce Palin
Assistant Commissioner, Office
of Land Quality
Department of Environmental
Management
100 North Senate Avenue
Room IGCN 1154
Indianapolis, IN 46204
P: (317) 233-6591
F: (317) 233-6647
E: bpalin@idem.in.gov

IOWA
Mr. Brian J. Tormey
Bureau Chief
Land Quality Bureau
Wallace Building
502 East 9th Street
Des Moines, IA 50319
P: (515) 281-8927
F: (515) 281-8895
E: brian.tormey
   @dnr.iowa.gov

KANSAS
Mr. William L. Bider
Director
Bureau of Waste Management
1000 Southwest Jackson Street
Suite 320
Topeka, KS 66612
P: (785) 296-1600
F: (785) 296-8909

KENTUCKY
Mr. Anthony Hatton
Division Director
Division of Waste Management
Department for Environmental
Protection
200 Fair Oaks Lane
Frankfort, KY 40601
P: (502) 564-6716
F: (502) 564-4049
E: tony.hatton@ky.gov

LOUISIANA
Mr. Lourdes Iturralde
Administrator
Public Participation & Permits
Support Services
Department of Environmental
Quality
P.O. Box 4313
Baton Rouge, LA 70821
P: (225) 219-3180
F: (225) 219-3309

MAINE
Mr. Ron Dyer
Director
Bureau of Remediation & Waste
Management
Department of Environmental
Protection
17 State House Station
Augusta, ME 04333
P: (207) 287-7980
F: (207) 287-7826
E: ron.dyer@maine.gov

Hazardous Waste Management

MARYLAND
Mr. Horacio Tablada
Director
Land Management
Administration
Department of Environment
1800 Washington Boulevard
Baltimore, MD 21230
P: (410) 631-3304
F: (410) 631-3321
E: htablada@mde.state.md.us

MASSACHUSETTS
Mr. Kenneth Kimmell
Commissioner
Department of Environmental
Protection
One Winter Street, #1022
Boston, MA 02108
P: (617) 292-5856
F: (617) 574-6880
E: ken.kimmell@state.ma.us

MICHIGAN
Mr. George W. Bruchmann
Chief
Waste & Hazardous Materials
Division
525 West Allegan Street
P.O. Box 30241
Lansing, MI 48909
P: (517) 373-9523
F: (517) 373-4797
E: BRUCHMANNG@michigan.g

MINNESOTA
Mr. Paul Aasen
Commissioner
Pollution Control Agency
520 Lafayette Road North, 6th
Floor
St. Paul, MN 55155
P: (651) 757-2016
F: (651) 296-6334
E: paul.aasen@state.mn.us

MISSISSIPPI
Mr. Mark Williams
Chief
Solid Waste Policy, Planning &
Grants Branch
P.O. Box 2261
Jackson, MS 39225
P: (601) 961-5304
F: (601) 961-5785
E: mark_williams
    @deq.state.ms.us

MISSOURI
Mr. Bob Geller
Director
DEQ Hazardous Waste Program
P.O. Box 176
Jefferson City, MO 65102
P: (573) 751-3176
F: (573) 751-7869
E: bob.geller@dnr.mo.gov

MONTANA
Mr. Ed Tinsley
State Director
Disaster & Emergency Services,
Department of Military Affairs
1956 Mt. Majo Street
P.O. Box 4789
Fort Harrison, MT 59636
P: (406) 324-4777
F: (406) 841-3965
E: edtinsley@mt.gov

NEBRASKA
Mr. Michael J. Linder
Director
Department of Environmental
Quality
1200 N Street, Suite 400
P.O. Box 98922
Lincoln, NE 68509
P: (402) 471-3585
F: (402) 471-2909
E: mike.linder@nebraska.gov

NEVADA
Mr. Eric Noack
Bureau Chief
Bureau of Waste Management
Division of Environmental
Protection
901 South Stewart Street, Suite
4001
Carson City, NV 89701
P: (775) 687-9366
F: (775) 687-6396
E: enoack@ndep.nv.gov

NEW HAMPSHIRE
Mr. John Duclos
Bureau Administrator
Hazardous Waste Management
Bureau
29 Hazen Drive
P.O. Box 95
Concord, NH 03301
P: (603) 271-1998
F: (603) 271-0869
E: john.duclos@des.nh.gov

NEW MEXICO
Mr. John Kielng
Acting Bureau Chief
Hazardous Waste Bureau
2905 Rodeo Park Drive East,
Building 1
Santa Fe, NM 87505
P: (505) 476-6000
F: (505) 476-6030
E: john.kielng@state.nm.us

NEW YORK
Mr. Joe Martens
Commissioner
Department of Environmental
Conservation
625 Broadway, 14th Floor
Albany, NY 12233
P: (518) 402-8540
F: (518) 402-8541
E: joemartens
    @gw.dec.state.ny.us

NORTH CAROLINA
Ms. Elizabeth Cannon
Section Chief for Hazardous
Waste
Department of Environment &
Natural Resources
Division of Waste Management
1646 Mail Service Center
Raleigh, NC 27699
P: (919) 508-8534
F: (919) 715-3605
E: elizabeth.cannon
    @ncdenr.gov

NORTH DAKOTA
Mr. Scott Radig
Director
Division of Waste Management
Department of Health
918 East Divide Avenue, 3rd
Floor
Bismark, ND 58501
P: (701) 328-5166
F: (701) 328-5200
E: sradig@nd.gov

**NORTHERN MARIANA
ISLANDS**
Mr. Joaquin P. Omar
State Director
Emergency Management Office
Caller Box 10007
Saipan, MP 96950
P: (670) 322-8001
F: (670) 322-7743
E: jpomar@cnmiemo.gov.mp

OHIO
Mr. David A. Sholtis
Acting Division Chief
Division of Hazardous Waste
Management
50 West Town Street, Suite 700
P.O. Box 1049
Columbus, OH 43216
P: (614) 644-3778
F: (614) 728-3898
E: dave.sholtis
    @epa.state.oh.us

OKLAHOMA
Mr. Scott Thompson
Director
Land Protection Division
Department of Environmental
Quality
P.O. Box 1677
Oklahoma City, OK 73101
P: (405) 702-5100
F: (405) 702-5101
E: scott.thompson
    @deq.state.ok.us

OREGON
Ms. Karen Whisler
Organizational Improvement
Coordinator
Department of Environmental
Quality
811 Southwest 6th Avenue
Portland, OR 97204
P: (503) 229-5586
F: (503) 229-6524
E: karen.whisler
    @state.or.us

PUERTO RICO
Mr. Luis Bernal-Jimenez
Executive Director
Energy Affairs Administration
P.O. Box 41314
San Juan, PR 00940
P: (787) 999-2200 x2886
F: (787) 999-2246
E: lbernal@aae.gobierno.pr

Mr. Javier Quintana Mendez
Director
Solid Waste Management
Authority
P.O. Box 40285
San Juan, PR 00918
P: (787) 765-7575
F: (787) 753-2220

RHODE ISLAND
Ms. Janet Coit
Director
Department of Environmental
Management
235 Promenade Street, 4th Floor
Providence, RI 02908
P: (401) 222-2771
F: (401) 222-6802
E: janet.coit@dem.ri.gov

SOUTH CAROLINA
Ms. Daphne G. Neel
Bureau Chief
Bureau of Land & Waste
Management
Dept. of Health &
Environmental Control
2600 Bull Street
Columbia, SC 29201
P: (803) 896-4007
F: (803) 896-4001

SOUTH DAKOTA
Ms. Carrie Jacobson
Environmental Senior Scientist
Department of Environment &
Natural Resources
Waste Management Program
523 East Capitol Avenue
Pierre, SD 57501
P: (605) 773-3153
F: (605) 773-6035

TENNESSEE
Mr. Mike Apple
Director
Division of Solid & Hazardous
Waste Management
5th Floor, L & C Tower
401 Church Street
Nashville, TN 37243
P: (615) 532-0780
F: (615) 532-0886

TEXAS
Mr. Earl Lott
Director
Waste Permits Division
12100 Park 35 Circle
P.O. Box 13087
Austin, TX 78711
P: (512) 239-2047
F: (512) 239-2007

U.S. VIRGIN ISLANDS
Ms. Meliss C. McCall
Director
Division of Environmental
Protection
Cyril E. King Airport
Terminal Building, 2nd Floor
St. Thomas, VI 00802
P: (340) 774-3320
F: (340) 714-9549

UTAH
Mr. Scott Anderson
Director
Division of Solid & Hazardous
Waste
195 North 1950 West, 2nd Floor
P.O. Box 144880
Salt Lake City, UT 84114
P: (801) 536-0203
F: (801) 536-0222
E: standerson@utah.gov

VERMONT
Mr. George Desch
Director
Waste Management Division
103 South Main Street
West Office Building
Waterbury, VT 05671
P: (802) 241-3491
F: (802) 241-3296
E: george.desch@state.vt.us

VIRGINIA
Mr. David K. Paylor
Director
Department of Environmental
Quality
629 East Main Street
P.O. Box 1105
Richmond, VA 23218
P: (804) 698-4390
F: (804) 698-4019
E: dkpaylor
    @deq.virginia.gov

WASHINGTON
Mr. Darin Rice
Program Manager
Hazardous Waste & Toxic
Reduction Division
Department of Ecology
P.O. Box 47600
Olympia, WA 98504
P: (360) 407-6881
F: (360) 407-6715
E: dric461@ecy.wa.gov

WEST VIRGINIA
Mr. Ken Ellison
Director
Division of Land Restoration
601 57th Street, Southeast
Charleston, WV 25304
P: (304) 926-0455
E: ken.w.ellison@wv.gov

WISCONSIN
Mr. Al Shea
Air & Waste Division
Administrator
Air & Waste Division
P.O. Box 7921
Madison, WI 53707
P: (608) 266-5896
F: (608) 267-2768
E: Allen.Shea@Wisconsin.gov

WYOMING
Mr. John V. Corra
Director
Department of Environmental
Quality
Herschler Building
122 West 25th Street, 4th Floor,
West
Cheyenne, WY 82002
P: (307) 777-7937
F: (307) 777-7682
E: jcorra@wyo.gov

Health Services

Manages the development, administration and delivery of all health programs.

ALABAMA

Dr. Donald E. Williamson
State Health Officer
Department of Public Health
RSA Tower, 201 Monroe Street
P.O. Box 303017
Montgomery, AL 36130
P: (334) 206-5300
F: (334) 206-5609

ALASKA

Mr. Ward Hurlburt
Director
Division of Public Health
350 Main Street, Room 508
Juneau, AK 99801
P: (907) 465-3092
F: (907) 465-4632
E: ward.hurlburt@alaska.gov

AMERICAN SAMOA

Mr. Utoofili Asofa'afetai
   Maga
Director
Department of Health
American Samoa Government
Pago Pago, AS 96799
P: (684) 633-4606
F: (684) 633-5379

ARIZONA

Mr. Will Humble
Director
Department of Health Services
150 North 18th Avenue
Phoenix, AZ 85007
P: (602) 542-1025
F: (602) 542-1062

ARKANSAS

Dr. Paul Halverson
Director
Department of Health
4815 West Markham Street
Little Rock, AR 72205
P: (501) 280-4648
F: (501) 671-1450
E: paul.halverson
   @arkansas.gov

CALIFORNIA

Mr. Toby Douglas
Director
Department of Health Care
Services
1501 Capitol Avenue, Suite
6001
MS: 0000, P.O. Box 997413
Sacramento, CA 95899
P: (916) 440-7400
F: (916) 440-7404
E: toby.douglas@dhcs.ca.gov

COLORADO

Dr. Christopher E. Urbina
Executive Director
Department of Public Health &
Environment
4300 Cherry Creek Drive, South
Denver, CO 80246
P: (303) 692-2000
F: (303) 691-7702
E: christopher.urbina
   @state.co.us

CONNECTICUT

Dr. Jewel Mullen
Commissioner
Department of Public Health
410 Capitol Avenue
Hartford, CT 06134
P: (860) 509-8000
E: jewel.mullen@ct.gov

DELAWARE

Ms. Rita Landgraf
Secretary
Department of Health & Social
Services
Main Building
1901 North DuPont Highway
New Castle, DE 19720
P: (302) 255-9040
F: (302) 255-4429

DISTRICT OF COLUMBIA

Dr. Mohammad N. Akhter
Director
Department of Health
825 North Capitol Street,
Northeast
Washington, DC 20002
P: (202) 442-5999
F: (202) 442-4788
E: doh@dc.gov

FLORIDA

Dr. H. Frank Farmer Jr.
Surgeon General
Department of Health
4052 Bald Cypress Way, Bin
#A00
Tallahassee, FL 32399
P: (850) 245-4321
F: (850) 922-9453
E: health@doh.state.fl.us

GEORGIA

Dr. Brenda Fitzgerald
Director
Division of Public Health
Two Peachtree Street, Northwest
Atlanta, GA 30303
P: (404) 657-2700

HAWAII

Ms. Loretta J. Fuddy
Director
Department of Health
1250 Punchbowl Street
P.O. Box 3378
Honolulu, HI 96801
P: (808) 586-4410
F: (808) 586-4444

IDAHO

Mr. Richard Armstrong
Director
Department of Health &
Welfare
450 West State Street
Pete T. Cenarrusa Building
Boise, ID 83720
P: (208) 334-5500
F: (208) 334-6558
E: armstrongr@dhw.idaho.gov

ILLINOIS

Dr. Damon T. Arnold
Director
Department of Public Health
535 West Jefferson Street
Springfield, IL 62761
P: (217) 557-2556
F: (217) 785-3209

INDIANA

Mr. Gregory N. Larkin
State Health Commissioner
Department of Health
2 North Meridian Street, Room
2N3003
Indianapolis, IN 46204
P: (317) 233-7400
E: glarkin@isdh.in.gov

IOWA

Dr. Mariannette
   Miller-Meeks
Director
Department of Public Health
Lucas State Office Building
321 East 12th Street
Des Moines, IA 50319
P: (515) 281-8474
F: (515) 281-4958

KANSAS

Dr. Robert Moser
Secretary
Department of Health &
Environment
Curtis State Office Building
1000 Southwest Jackson Street
Topeka, KS 66612
P: (785) 296-1500
F: (785) 368-6368

KENTUCKY

Ms. Janie Miller
Secretary
Cabinet for Health & Family
Services
275 East Main Street
Mailstop 5W-A
Frankfort, KY 40621
P: (502) 564-7042
F: (502) 564-7091

LOUISIANA

Mr. Bruce D. Greenstein
Secretary
Department of Health &
Hospitals
628 North 4th Street
P.O. Box 629
Baton Rouge, LA 70821
P: (225) 342-9500
F: (225) 342-5568

MAINE

Ms. Mary Mayhew
Commissioner
Department of Health & Human
Services
221 State Street
Augusta, ME 04333
P: (207) 287-3707
F: (207) 287-3005
E: mary.mayhew@maine.gov

MARYLAND

Mr. Joshua Sharfstein
Secretary
Department of Health & Mental
Hygiene
201 West Preston Street
Baltimore, MD 21201
P: (410) 767-4639
F: (410) 767-6489
E: jsharfstein
   @dhmh.state.md.us

MASSACHUSETTS

Mr. John Auerbach
Commissioner
Department of Public Health
250 Washington Street
Boston, MA 02108
P: (617) 624-6000

MICHIGAN
Ms. Olga Dazzo
Department of Community
Health
Capitol View Building
201 Townsend Street, 7th Floor
Lansing, MI 48913
P: (517) 373-3500
F: (517) 373-4288

MINNESOTA
Dr. Edward Ehlinger
Commissioner
Department of Health
625 Robert Street North
Box 64975
St. Paul, MN 55164
P: (651) 201-5810
F: (651) 201-4986
E: edward.ehlinger
    @state.mn.us

MISSISSIPPI
Ms. Mary Currier M.D.
State Health Officer
State Department of Health
P.O. Box 1700
Jackson, MS 39215
P: (601) 576-7634
E: mary.currier
    @msdh.state.ms.us

MISSOURI
Ms. Margaret T. Donnelly
Director
Department of Health & Senior
Services
P.O. Box 570
Jefferson City, MO 65102
P: (573) 751-6400
F: (573) 751-6010
E: info@dhss.mo.gov

MONTANA
Ms. Anna Whiting Sorrell
Director
Department of Public Health &
Human Services
111 North Sanders, Room 301
P.O. Box 4210
Helena, MT 59604
P: (406) 444-5622
F: (406) 444-1970

NEBRASKA
Dr. Joann Schaefer
Director
Division of Public Health
Department of Health & Human
Services
P.O. Box 95007
Lincoln, NE 68509
P: (402) 471-8566
F: (402) 471-9449
E: joann.schaefer
    @nebraska.gov

NEVADA
Mr. Michael J. Willden
Director
Department of Health & Human
Services
4126 Technology Way, Room
100
Carson City, NV 89706
P: (775) 684-4000
F: (775) 684-4010
E: mwillden@dhhs.nv.gov

NEW HAMPSHIRE
Mr. Nicholas A. Toumpas
Commissioner
Department of Health & Human
Services
129 Pleasant Street
Concord, NH 03301
P: (603) 271-4331
F: (603) 271-4912
E: ntoumpas
    @dhhs.state.nh.us

NEW JERSEY
Ms. Mary E. O'Dowd
Acting Commissioner
Department of Health & Senior
Services
P.O. Box 360
Trenton, NJ 08625
P: (609) 292-7837
F: (609) 292-0053

NEW MEXICO
Dr. Catherine D. Torres
Secretary
Department of Health
1190 South St. Francis Drive
Santa Fe, NM 87502
P: (505) 827-2613
F: (505) 827-2530

NEW YORK
Dr. Nirav R. Shah
Commissioner
Department of Health
Corning Tower
Empire State Plaza
Albany, NY 12237
P: (518) 474-2011
F: (518) 474-1449

NORTH CAROLINA
Mr. Lanier Cansler
Secretary
Department of Health & Human
Services
2001 Mail Service Center
Raleigh, NC 27699
P: (919) 733-4534
F: (919) 715-4645
E: Lanier.Cansler
    @ncmail.net

NORTH DAKOTA
Dr. Terry Dwelle
State Health Officer
Department of Health
600 East Boulevard Avenue, 2nd
Floor
Judicial Wing
Bismarck, ND 58505
P: (701) 328-2372
F: (701) 328-4727
E: tdwelle@nd.gov

**NORTHERN MARIANA
ISLANDS**
Mr. Joseph P. Villagomez
Secretary of Public Health
Department of Public Health
P.O. Box 500409
Saipan, MP 96950
P: (670) 236-8201
F: (670) 234-8930
E: jkvsaipan@aol.com

OHIO
Dr. Theodore E. Wymyslo
Director of Health
Department of Health
246 North High Street
Columbus, OH 43215
P: (614) 466-2253
F: (614) 466-5866
E: director@odh.ohio.gov

OKLAHOMA
Dr. Terry L. Cline
Commissioner
Department of Health
1000 Northeast 10th Street
Oklahoma City, OK 73117
P: (405) 271-5600

OREGON
Dr. Mel Kohn
Acting Director/State Health
Officer
Public Health Division
Department Of Human Services
800 Northeast Oregon Street,
Suite 930
Portland, OR 97232
P: (971) 673-1300
F: (971) 673-1299
E: melvin.a.kohn
    @state.or.us

PENNSYLVANIA
Dr. Eli N. Avila
Secretary of Health
Department of Health
Health & Welfare Building
8th Floor West
Harrisburg, PA 17120
P: (717) 787-6436
F: (717) 787-0191

PUERTO RICO
Mr. Jose Rivera Dueño
Secretary
Department of Health
P.O. Box 70184
San Juan, PR 00936
P: (787) 274-7604
F: (787) 250-6547

RHODE ISLAND
Mr. Michael Fine
Director
Department of Health
3 Capitol Hill
Providence, RI 02908
P: (401) 222-5960
F: (401) 222-6548
E: health@ri.gov

SOUTH CAROLINA
Mr. Anthony Keck
Director
Department of Health & Human
Services
P.O. Box 8206
Columbia, SC 29202
P: (803) 898-2580
F: (803) 898-4515

SOUTH DAKOTA
Ms. Doneen Hollingsworth
Secretary
Department of Health
600 East Capitol Avenue
Pierre, SD 57501
P: (605) 773-3361
E: doneen.hollingsworth
    @state.sd.us

Health Services

TENNESSEE
Ms. Susan R. Cooper R.N.
Commissioner
Department of Health
425 Fifth Avenue, North
Cordell Hull Building, 3rd Floor
Nashville, TN 37243
P: (615) 741-3111
F: (615) 741-6230

TEXAS
Dr. David L. Lakey
Commissioner
Department of Health Services
1100 West 49th Street
P.O. Box 149347
Austin, TX 78714
P: (512) 458-7375
E: customer.service
    @dshs.state.tx.us

U.S. VIRGIN ISLANDS
Ms. Fern P. Clarke
Acting Commissioner
Department of Health
1303 Hospital Grounds, Suite 10
Charlotte Amalie
St. Thomas, VI 00802
P: (340) 774-9000

UTAH
Mr. David Patton
Executive Director
Department of Health
288 North 1460 West
P.O. Box 141000
Salt Lake City, UT 84114
P: (801) 538-6111
F: (801) 538-6306
E: david.patton@utah.gov

VERMONT
Dr. Harry L. Chen
Commissioner
Department of Health
108 Cherry Street
Burlington, VT 05402
P: (802) 863-7281
F: (802) 865-7754
E: hchen@vdh.state.vt.us

VIRGINIA
Ms. Karen Remley
Commissioner
Department of Health
109 Governor Street, 13th Floor
Richmond, VA 23219
P: (804) 864-7009
F: (804) 864-7022
E: karen.remley
    @vdh.virginia.gov

WASHINGTON
Ms. Mary C. Selecky
Secretary
Department of Health
P.O. Box 47890
Olympia, WA 98504
P: (360) 236-4030
F: (360) 586-7424
E: secretary@doh.wa.gov

WEST VIRGINIA
Mr. Michael J. Lewis
Cabinet Secretary
Department of Health & Human
Resources
One Davis Square, Suite 100
East
Charleston, WV 25301
P: (304) 558-0684
F: (304) 558-1130
E: DHHRSecretary@wv.gov

WISCONSIN
Mr. Dennis G. Smith
Secretary
Department of Health & Family
Services
1 West Wilson Street, Room 650
Madison, WI 53702
P: (608) 266-1865
E: dennis.smith
    @dhs.wisconsin.gov

WYOMING
Mr. Thomas O. Forslund
Director
Department of Health
Hathaway Building, 1st Floor
2300 Capitol Avenue
Cheyenne, WY 82002
P: (307) 777-7656
F: (307) 777-5648

Higher Education

Serves as coordinating and planning agency for state-supported post-secondary education.

Information provided by:

State Higher Education Executive Officers
Paul E. Lingenfelter
President
3035 Center Green Drive, Suite 100
Boulder, CO 80301
P: (303) 541-1600
F: (303) 541-1639
plingenfelter@sheeo.org
www.sheeo.org

ALABAMA
Mr. Gregory G. Fitch
Executive Director
Commission on Higher Education
P.O. Box 302000
100 North Union Street
Montgomery, AL 36130
P: (334) 242-2123
F: (334) 242-0268
E: gregory.fitch
@ache.alabama.gov

ALASKA
Ms. Diane Barrans
Executive Director
Commission on Postsecondary Education
707 A Street, Suite 206
P.O. Box 110505
Juneau, AK 99811
P: (907) 465-6740
F: (907) 465-3293
E: diane.barrans@alaska.gov

Mr. Patrick K. Gamble
President
University of Alaska System
202 Butrovich
P.O. Box 755000
Fairbanks, AK 99775
P: (907) 450-8009
F: (907) 450-8012
E: ua.president@alaska.edu

ARIZONA
Mr. Thomas K. Anderes
President
Board of Regents
2020 North Central Avenue, Suite 230
Phoenix, AZ 85004
P: (602) 229-2505
F: (602) 229-2555
E: tom.anderes
@azregents.edu

ARKANSAS
Mr. Shane Broadway
Interim Director
Department of Higher Education
114 East Capitol Avenue
Little Rock, AR 72201
P: (501) 371-2031
F: (501) 371-2003
E: Shane.Broadway@adhe.edu

CALIFORNIA
Ms. Karen Humphrey
Executive Director
Postsecondary Education Commission
770 L Street, Suite 1160
Sacramento, CA 95814
P: (916) 445-1504
F: (916) 324-6600
E: khumphrey@cpec.ca.gov

COLORADO
Hon. Joe Garcia (D)
Lieutenant Governor & Executive Director
Department of Higher Education
130 State Capitol
Denver, CO 80203
P: (303) 866-2087
F: (303) 866-5469

Mr. David A. Longanecker
President
Commission for Higher Education
3035 Center Green Drive, Suite 200
Boulder, CO 80301
P: (303) 541-0201
F: (303) 541-0291
E: dlonganecker@wiche.edu

CONNECTICUT
Mr. Michael P. Meotti
Commissioner
Department of Higher Education
61 Woodland Street
Hartford, CT 06105
P: (860) 947-1801
F: (860) 947-1310
E: meotti@ctdhe.org

DELAWARE
Ms. Maureen Laffey
Director
Higher Education Office
Carvel State Office Building, 5th Floor
820 North French Street
Wilmington, DE 19801
P: (302) 577-5240
F: (302) 577-6765
E: mlaffey@doe.k12.de.us

DISTRICT OF COLUMBIA
Ms. Emily Durso
Interim Asst. Superintendent of Postsecondary Education & Workforce Readiness
Office of the State Superintendent of Education, Postsecondary Education & Workforce Readiness
Government of the District of Columbia
810 First Street, Northeast, 2nd Floor
Washington, DC 20002
P: (202) 741-5529
F: (202) 741-0229
E: Emily.durso@dc.gov

FLORIDA
Mr. Frank T. Brogan
Chancellor
Board of Governors
State University System of Florida
325 West Gaines Street, Suite 1614
Tallahassee, FL 32399
P: (850) 245-0466
F: (850) 245-9685
E: frank.brogan@flbog.edu

GEORGIA
Mr. Erroll B. Davis Jr.
Chancellor
Board of Regents of the University System of Georgia
270 Washington Street, Southwest
Suite 7025
Atlanta, GA 30334
P: (404) 656-2202
F: (404) 657-6979
E: chancellor@usg.edu

HAWAII
Dr. M.R.C. Greenwood
President
University of Hawaii System
2444 Dole Street, Bachman Hall 202
Honolulu, HI 96822
P: (808) 956-9704
F: (808) 956-9943
E: mrcgreenwood@hawaii.edu

IDAHO
Mr. Michael Rush
Executive Director
State Board of Education
650 West State Street, Room 307
P.O. Box 83720
Boise, ID 83720
P: (208) 332-1565
F: (208) 334-2632
E: mike.rush@osbe.idaho.gov

ILLINOIS
G.W. Reid
Executive Director
Board of Higher Education
431 East Adams, 2nd Floor
Springfield, IL 62701
P: (217) 782-2551
F: (217) 782-8548
E: reid@ibhe.org

INDIANA
Ms. Teresa S. Lubbers
Commissioner
Commission for Higher Education
101 West Ohio Street, Suite 550
Indianapolis, IN 46204
P: (317) 464-4400
F: (317) 464-4410
E: teresal@che.in.gov

IOWA
Mr. Robert Donley
Executive Director
Board of Regents
11260 Aurora Avenue
Urbandale, IA 50322
P: (515) 281-6426
F: (515) 281-6420
E: bdonley@iastate.edu

KANSAS
Mr. Andy Tompkins
President & CEO
Board of Regents
Curtis State Office Building
1000 Southwest Jackson Street, Suite 520
Topeka, KS 66612
P: (785) 296-3421
F: (785) 296-0983
E: atompkins@ksbor.org

KENTUCKY
Mr. Robert L. King
President
Council on Postsecondary Education
1024 Capital Center Drive, Suite 320
Frankfort, KY 40601
P: (502) 573-1652
F: (502) 573-1535
E: robert.king@ky.gov

Higher Education

LOUISIANA
Mr. James Purcell
Commissioner of Higher
Education
Board of Regents
1201 North Third Street
P.O. Box 3677
Baton Rouge, LA 70821
P: (225) 342-4253
F: (225) 342-9318
E: jim.purcell@la.gov

MAINE
Mr. Richard Pattenaude
Chancellor
University of Maine System
16 Central Street
Bangor, ME 04401
P: (207) 973-3205
F: (207) 973-3221
E: pattenaude@maine.edu

MARYLAND
Ms. Elisabeth A. Sachs
Interim Secretary of Higher
Education
Higher Education Commission
839 Bestgate Road, Suite 400
Annapolis, MD 21401
P: (410) 260-4516
F: (410) 260-3204
E: esachs@mhec.state.md.us

MASSACHUSETTS
Mr. Richard Freeland
Commissioner
Department of Higher Education
One Ashburton Place, Room
1401
Boston, MA 02108
P: (617) 994-6901
F: (617) 727-6656
E: rfreeland@bhe.mass.edu

Mr. Michael K. Thomas
President & CEO
New England Board of Higher
Education
45 Temple Place
Boston, MA 02111
P: (617) 357-9620
F: (617) 338-1692
E: mthomas@nebhe.org

MINNESOTA
Mr. James H. McCormick
Chancellor
State Colleges & Universities
Wells Fargo Place
30-7th Street East, Suite 350
St. Paul, MN 55101
P: (651) 201-1696
F: (651) 297-7465
E: james.mccormick
    @so.mnscu.edu

Ms. Lana Oleen
Interim President
Midwestern Higher Education
Compact
1300 South Second Street, Suite
130
Minneapolis, MN 55454
P: (612) 626-8292
F: (612) 626-8290
E: lanao@mhec.org

Ms. Sheila Wright
Director
Office of Higher Education
1450 Energy Park Drive, Suite
350
St. Paul, MN 55108
P: (651) 259-3900
F: (651) 642-0597
E: Sheila.wright
    @state.mn.us

MISSISSIPPI
Dr. Hank M. Bounds
Commissioner of Higher
Education
Institutions of Higher Learning
3825 Ridgewood Road
Jackson, MS 39211
P: (601) 432-6198
F: (601) 432-6972
E: hbounds@ihl.state.ms.us

MISSOURI
Mr. David R. Russell
Commissioner of Higher
Education
Department of Higher Education
205 Jefferson Street
P.O. Box 1469
Jefferson City, MO 65102
P: (573) 751-1876
F: (573) 526-0984
E: David.Russell@dhe.mo.gov

MONTANA
Ms. Sheila Stearns
Commissioner of Higher
Education
University System
2500 Broadway Street
P.O. Box 203201
Helena, MT 59620
P: (406) 444-0374
F: (406) 444-1469
E: sstearns@montana.edu

NEBRASKA
Dr. Marshall A. Hill
Executive Director
Coordinating Commission for
Postsecondary Education
140 North 8th Street, Suite 300
P.O. Box 95005
Lincoln, NE 68509
P: (402) 471-2847
F: (402) 471-2886
E: Marshall.Hill
    @nebraska.gov

NEVADA
Mr. Daniel J. Klaich
Chancellor
System of Higher Education
2601 Enterprise Road
Reno, NV 89512
P: (775) 784-3222
F: (775) 784-1127
E: daniel_klaich
    @nshe.nevada.edu

NEW HAMPSHIRE
Ms. Kathryn G. Dodge
Executive Director
Postsecondary Education
Commission
3 Barrell Court, Suite 300
Concord, NH 03301
P: (603) 271-2555
F: (603) 271-2696
E: kdodge@pec.state.nh.us

Mr. Edward R. MacKay
Chancellor
University System
25 Concord Road
Dunlap Center
Durham, NH 03824
P: (603) 862-0918
F: (603) 862-0908
E: ed.mackay@usnh.edu

NEW JERSEY
Ms. Marguerite Beardsley
Acting Executive Director
Commission on Higher
Education
20 West State Street
P.O. Box 542
Trenton, NJ 08625
P: (609) 292-2955
F: (609) 292-7225
E: marguerite.beardsley
    @che.state.nj.us

Mr. Glenn B. Lang
Acting Executive Director
Commission on Higher
Education
20 West State Street
P.O. Box 542
Trenton, NJ 08625
P: (609) 984-2709
F: (609) 633-8420
E: glang@che.state.nj.us

NEW MEXICO
Mr. Jose Garcia
Cabinet Secretary
Higher Education Department
2048 Galisteo Street
Santa Fe, NM 87505
P: (505) 476-8404
F: (505) 476-8454
E: jose.garcia@state.nm.us

NEW YORK
Mr. James Baldwin
Chief of Staff/Interim Deputy
Commissioner
State Education Department,
Office of Higher Education
Room 977, Education Building
Annex
89 Washington Avenue
Albany, NY 12234
P: (518) 486-3633
F: (518) 486-2254
E: jbaldwin@mail.nysed.gov

NORTH CAROLINA
Mr. Thomas W. Ross
President
University of North Carolina
910 Raleigh Road
P.O. Box 2688
Chapel Hill, NC 27514
P: (919) 962-4622
F: (919) 843-9695
E: tomross
    @northcarolina.edu

Mr. Tom Ross
President
University of North Carolina
General Administration 910
Raleigh Road
P.O. Box 2688
Chapel Hill, NC 27515
P: (919) 962-4622
F: (919) 843-9695
E: tross@northcarolina.edu

NORTH DAKOTA
Mr. William G. Goetz
Chancellor
University System
600 East Boulevard Avenue
Department 215,10th Floor,
State Capitol
Bismarck, ND 58505
P: (701) 328-2963
F: (701) 328-2961
E: william.goetz@ndus.edu

OHIO
Mr. James Petro
Chancellor
Board of Regents
30 East Broad Street, 36th Floor
Columbus, OH 43215
P: (614) 466-0965
F: (614) 466-5866
E: jpetro
@regents.state.oh.us

OKLAHOMA
Mr. Glen D. Johnson Jr.
Chancellor
State Regents for Higher
Education
655 Research Parkway, Suite
200
Oklahoma City, OK 73104
P: (405) 225-9100
F: (405) 225-9230
E: gjohnson@osrhe.edu

OREGON
Mr. George Pernsteiner
Chancellor
University System
P.O. Box 3175, 1431 Johnson
Lane
111 Susan Campbell Hall
Eugene, OR 97403
P: (541) 346-5703
F: (541) 346-5764
E: george_pernsteiner
@ous.edu

PENNSYLVANIA
Dr. John C. Cavanaugh
Chancellor
State System of Higher
Education
Dixon University Center
2986 North Second Street
Harrisburg, PA 17110
P: (717) 720-4010
F: (717) 720-4011
E: jcavanaugh@passhe.edu

Ms. Sandra O. Edmunds
Deputy Secretary for
Postsecondary & Higher
Education
Department of Education
333 Market Street, 12th Floor
Harrisburg, PA 17126
P: (717) 787-5041
F: (717) 772-3622
E: sedmunds@state.pa.us

PUERTO RICO
Mr. David A. Baez-Davila
Acting Executive Director
Council on Higher Education
P.O. Box 19900
San Juan, PR 00910
P: (787) 641-7100
F: (787) 641-2573
E: Vda_baez@ces.gobierno.pr

RHODE ISLAND
Mr. Raymond M. Di Pasquale
Commissioner & President of
Community College
Board of Governors for Higher
Education
The Shepard Building
80 Washington Street, Suite 450
Providence, RI 02903
P: (401) 456-6002
F: (401) 456-6028
E: rmdipasquale@ccri.edu

SOUTH CAROLINA
Dr. E. Garrison Walters
Executive Director
Commission on Higher
Education
1333 Main Street, Suite 200
Columbia, SC 29201
P: (803) 737-2275
F: (803) 737-2297
E: gwalters@che.sc.gov

SOUTH DAKOTA
Dr. Jack R. Warner
Executive Director & CEO
Board of Regents
306 East Capitol Avenue, Suite
200
Pierre, SD 57501
P: (605) 773-3455
F: (605) 773-5320
E: JackW@sdbor.edu

TENNESSEE
Dr. Richard G. Rhoda
Executive Director
Higher Education Commission
404 James Robertson Parkway
Parkway Towers, Suite 1900
Nashville, TN 37243
P: (615) 741-7561
F: (615) 741-6230
E: richard.rhoda@tn.gov

TEXAS
Dr. Raymund Paredes
Commissioner of Higher
Education
Higher Education Coordinating
Board
P.O. Box 12788
1200 East Anderson Lane
Austin, TX 78752
P: (512) 427-6101
F: (512) 427-6127
E: raymund.paredes
@thecb.state.tx.us

UTAH
Mr. William A. Sederburg
Commissioner
System of Higher Education
60 South 400 West
Salt Lake City, UT 84101
P: (801) 321-7103
F: (801) 321-7199
E: wsederburg@utahsbr.edu

VERMONT
Mr. Timothy J. Donovan
Chancellor
State Colleges
P.O. Box 359
Park Street, Stanley Hall
Waterbury, VT 05676
P: (802) 241-3378
F: (802) 241-3369
E: tim.donovan@vsc.edu

Mr. Daniel Mark Fogel
President
University of Vermont
350 Waterman Building
85 South Prospect Street
Burlington, VT 05405
P: (802) 656-3186
F: (802) 656-1363
E: daniel.fogel@uvm.edu

VIRGINIA
Mr. Andy Fogarty
Interim Director
State Council of Higher
Education
101 North 14th Street, 9th Floor
Richmond, VA 23219
P: (804) 225-2611
F: (804) 225-2604
E: andrewfogarty@schev.edu

WASHINGTON
Mr. Don Bennett
Executive Director
Higher Education Coordinating
Board
917 Lakeridge Way, Southwest
P.O. Box 43430
Olympia, WA 98504
P: (360) 753-7831
F: (360) 753-7808
E: donb@hecb.wa.gov

WEST VIRGINIA
Dr. Brian Noland
Chancellor
Higher Education Policy
Commission
1018 Kanawha Boulevard, East,
Suite 700
Charleston, WV 25301
P: (304) 558-0699
F: (304) 558-1011
E: noland@hepc.wvnet.edu

WISCONSIN
Mr. Kevin P. Reilly
President
University of Wisconsin System
1220 Linden Drive, 1720 Van
Hise Hall
Madison, WI 53706
P: (608) 262-2321
F: (608) 262-3985
E: kreilly@uwsa.edu

Higher Education

WYOMING
Mr. Thomas Buchanan
President
University of Wyoming
Old Main Room 206,
Department 3434
1000 East University Avenue
Laramie, WY 82071
P: (307) 766-4121
F: (307) 766-4126
E: tombuch@uwyo.edu

Dr. James O. Rose
Executive Director
Community College
Commission
2020 Carey Avenue, 8th Floor
Cheyenne, WY 82002
P: (307) 777-7763
F: (307) 777-6567
E: jrose@commission.wcc.edu

Historic Preservation

Surveys, restores and preserves structures and/or sites of historical or architectural significance in the state.

ALABAMA
Mr. Frank White
Executive Director
Historical Commission
468 South Perry Street
Montgomery, AL 36130
P: (334) 242-3184
F: (334) 240-3477
E: frank.white
   @preserveala.org

ALASKA
Ms. Judith Bittner
State Historic Preservation
Officer
Office of History & Archeology
Department of Natural
Resources
550 West 7th Avenue, Suite 1310
Anchorage, AK 99501
P: (907) 269-8721
F: (907) 269-8908
E: judy.bittner@alaska.gov

AMERICAN SAMOA
Mr. David J. Herdrich
Historic Preservation Officer
Historic Preservation Office
Executive Offices of the
Governor
Pago Pago, AS 96799
P: (684) 699-2316
F: (684) 699-2276
E: david_j_herdrich
   @samoatelco.com

ARIZONA
Mr. James W. Garrison
State Historic Preservation
Officer
State Parks
1300 West Washington
Phoenix, AZ 85007
P: (602) 542-4174
F: (602) 542-4180
E: jwg2@azstateparks.gov

ARKANSAS
Ms. Cathie Matthews
Director
Department of Arkansas
Heritage
323 Center Street
Suite 1500
Little Rock, AR 72201
P: (501) 324-9150
F: (501) 324-9154
E: cathie
   @arkansasheritage.org

CALIFORNIA
Mr. Milford Wayne Donaldson
State Historic Preservation
Officer
Office of Historic Preservation
Department of Parks &
Recreation
P.O. Box 942896
Sacramento, CA 94296
P: (916) 653-6624
F: (916) 653-9824
E: mwdonaldson@parks.ca.gov

COLORADO
Mr. Edward C. Nichols
State Historic Preservation
Officer
Historical Society
1300 Broadway
Denver, CO 80203
P: (303) 866-3355
F: (303) 866-4464
E: ed.nichols
   @chs.state.co.us

CONNECTICUT
Ms. Karen J. Senich
State Historic Preservation
Officer
Commission on Culture &
Tourism
One Constitution Plaza
Hartford, CT 06103
P: (860) 256-2753
F: (860) 256-2811
E: karen.senich@ct.gov

DELAWARE
Mr. Timothy A. Slavin
State Historic Preservation
Officer
Division of Historical &
Cultural Affairs
21 The Green
Dover, DE 19901
P: (302) 739-5313
F: (302) 739-6711
E: timothy.slavin
   @state.de.us

DISTRICT OF COLUMBIA
Mr. David Maloney
State Historic Preservation
Officer
Historic Preservation Office
Reeves Center
2000 14th Street, Northwest,
#400
Washington, DC 20009
P: (202) 442-8800
F: (202) 741-5246
E: david.maloney@dc.gov

FLORIDA
Mr. Scott M. Stroh III
State Historic Preservation
Officer
Division of Historical Resources
Department of State
500 South Bronough Street,
Room 305
Tallahassee, FL 32399
P: (850) 245-6300
E: smstroh@dos.state.fl.us

GEORGIA
Mr. Chris Clark
State Historic Preservation
Officer
Historic Preservation
Division/DNR
254 Washington Street,
Southwest
Ground Level
Atlanta, GA 30334
P: (404) 656-2840
F: (404) 651-8739

GUAM
Ms. Lynda Aguon
State Historic Preservation
Officer
Historic Preservation Office
Department of Parks &
Recreation
490 Chalan Palasyo
Agana Heights, GU 96910
P: (671) 475-6294
F: (671) 477-2822
E: lynda.aguon@dpr.guam.gov

HAWAII
Ms. Laura H. Thielen
Chairperson
Department of Land & Natural
Resources
1151 Punchbowl Street
P.O. Box 621
Kapolei, HI 96809
P: (808) 587-0400
F: (808) 587-0390
E: dlnr@hawaii.gov

IDAHO
Ms. Janet Gallimore
Executive Director
State Historical Society
2205 Old Penitentiary Road
Boise, ID 83712
P: (208) 334-2682

ILLINOIS
Ms. Jan Grimes
State Historic Preservation
Officer
Historic Preservation Agency
1 Old State Capitol Plaza
Springfield, IL 62701
P: (217) 782-4836
F: (217) 524-7525
E: Jan.Grimes@Illinois.gov

INDIANA
Mr. Robert E. Carter Jr.
Director
Department of Natural
Resources
402 West Washington Street,
Room W256
Indianapolis, IN 46204
P: (317) 232-4020
F: (317) 233-6811
E: rcarter@dnr.IN.gov

IOWA
Mr. Jerome Thompson
Interim Administrator
Historical Society of Iowa
Capitol Complex
East 6th & Locust Street
Des Moines, IA 50319
P: (515) 281-4221
F: (515) 242-6498
E: Jerome.Thompson@Iowa.gov

KANSAS
Ms. Jennie Chinn
State Historic Preservation
Officer & Executive Director
State Historical Society
6425 Southwest 6th Avenue
Topeka, KS 66615
P: (785) 272-8681 Ext. 205
F: (785) 272-8682
E: jchinn@kshs.org

KENTUCKY
Mr. Mark Dennen
Interim Executive Director
Heritage Council
300 Washington Street
Frankfort, KY 40601
P: (502) 564-7005
F: (502) 564-5820
E: mark.dennen@ky.gov

Historic Preservation

LOUISIANA
Ms. Pam Breaux
State Historic Preservation
Officer
Department of Culture,
Recreation & Tourism
P.O. Box 44247
Baton Rouge, LA 70804
P: (225) 342-8200
F: (225) 342-8173

MAINE
Mr. Earle G.
    Shettleworth Jr.
State Historic Preservation
Officer
Historic Preservation
Commission
55 Capitol Street
Station 65
Augusta, ME 04333
P: (207) 287-2132
F: (207) 287-2335
E: earle.shettleworth
    @maine.gov

MARYLAND
Mr. J. Rodney Little
State Historic Preservation
Officer
State Historical Trust
100 Community Place, 3rd Floor
Crownsville, MD 21032
P: (410) 514-7600
F: (410) 514-7678
E: rlittle@mdp.state.md.us

MASSACHUSETTS
Ms. Brona Simon
State Historic Preservation
Officer & Executive Director
Historical Commission
220 Morrissey Boulevard
Boston, MA 02125
P: (617) 727-8470
F: (617) 727-5128
E: Brona.Simon@state.ma.us

MICHIGAN
Mr. Brian D. Conway
State Historic Preservation
Officer
State Historical Center
702 West Kalamazoo Street
P.O. Box 30740
Lansing, MI 48909
P: (517) 373-1630
F: (517) 335-0348
E: conwaybd@michigan.gov

MINNESOTA
Mr. Michael J. Fox
State Historic Preservation
Officer
Historical Society
345 Kellogg Boulevard West
St. Paul, MN 55102
P: (651) 259-3100
F: (651) 282-2374

MISSISSIPPI
Mr. H.T. Holmes
State Historic Preservation
Officer
Department of Archives &
History
P.O. Box 571
Jackson, MS 39205
P: (601) 576-6850
F: (601) 576-6975

MISSOURI
Mr. Kip Setzler
State Historic Preservation
Officer
Department of Natural
Resources
P.O. Box 176
Jefferson City, MO 65102
P: (573) 751-4732
F: (573) 751-7627

MONTANA
Dr. Mark F. Baumler
State Historic Preservation
Officer
State Historic Preservation
Office
1410 8th Avenue
P.O. Box 201202
Helena, MT 59620
P: (406) 444-7719
F: (406) 444-6575
E: mbaumler@mt.gov

NEBRASKA
Mr. Michael Smith
Director & State Historic
Preservation Officer
State Historical Society
P.O. Box 82554
1500 R Street
Lincoln, NE 68501
P: (402) 471-4745
F: (402) 471-3100
E: michael.smith
    @nebraska.gov

NEVADA
Mr. Ronald James
State Historic Preservation
Officer
Historic Preservation Office
100 North Stewart Street
Capitol Complex
Carson City, NV 89701
P: (775) 684-3440
F: (775) 684-3442
E: rjames@nevadaculture.org

NEW HAMPSHIRE
Ms. Elizabeth H. Muzzey
State Historic Preservation
Officer & Director
Division of Historical Resources
19 Pillsbury Street, 2nd Floor
Concord, NH 03301
P: (603) 271-8850
F: (603) 271-3433
E: elizabeth.muzzey
    @dcr.nh.gov

NEW JERSEY
Mr. Bob Martin
Commissioner
Department of Environmental
Protection
401 East State Street
P.O. Box 402
Trenton, NJ 08625
P: (609) 292-2885
F: (609) 292-7695

NEW MEXICO
Ms. Jan Biella
Interim State Historic
Preservation Officer
Historic Preservation Division
Bataan Memorial Building
407 Galisteo Street, Suite 236
Santa Fe, NM 87501
P: (505) 827-6320
F: (505) 827-6338
E: jan.biella@state.nm.us

NEW YORK
Ms. Carol Ash
Commissioner & State Historic
Preservation Officer
Office of Parks, Recreation &
Historic Preservation
Empire State Plaza
Agency Building No.1
Albany, NY 12238
P: (518) 474-0443
F: (518) 474-1365

NORTH CAROLINA
Dr. Jeffrey J. Crow
State Historic Preservation
Officer
Division of Archives & History
4610 Mail Service Center
Raleigh, NC 27699
P: (919) 807-7280
F: (919) 733-8807
E: jeff.crow@ncdcr.gov

NORTH DAKOTA
Mr. Merlan E. Paaverud Jr.
State Historical Preservation
Officer
State Historical Society
612 East Boulevard Avenue
Bismarck, ND 58505
P: (701) 328-2666
F: (701) 328-3710
E: mpaaverud@nd.gov

**NORTHERN MARIANA
ISLANDS**
Mr. Epiphanio E.
    Cabrera Jr.
Historic Preservation Officer
Department of Community &
Cultural Affairs
Division of Historic
Preservation
Airport Road
Saipan, MP 96950
P: (670) 664-2120
F: (670) 664-2139
E: epicabrera@cnmihpo.com

OHIO
Mr. Burt Logan
Director
Historical Society
1982 Velma Avenue
Columbus, OH 43211
P: (614) 297-2350
F: (614) 297-2352
E: blogan@ohiohistory.org

OKLAHOMA
Dr. Bob L. Blackburn
State Historic Preservation
Officer
State Historic Preservation
Office
Historical Society, History
Center
2401 North Laird Avenue
Oklahoma City, OK 73105
P: (405) 521-6249
F: (405) 522-0816
E: bblackburn@okhistory.org

OREGON
Mr. Tim Wood
Director
Parks & Recreation Department
725 Summer Street, Northeast
Salem, OR 97301
P: (503) 986-0718
F: (503) 986-0796
E: tim.wood@state.or.us

PENNSYLVANIA
Ms. Barbara Franco
Executive Director
Historical & Museum
Commission
300 North Street
Harrisburg, PA 17120
P: (717) 787-2891
F: (717) 783-9924

PUERTO RICO
Mr. Carlos A.
   Rubio-Cancelar
State Historic Preservation
Officer
State Historic Preservation
Office
P.O. Box 9066581
San Juan, PR 00906
P: (787) 721-3737
F: (787) 721-3773
E: carubio
   @prshpo.gobierno.pr

RHODE ISLAND
Mr. Edward Sanderson
Executive Director
Historic Preservation &
Heritage Commission
Old State House
150 Benefit Street
Providence, RI 02903
P: (401) 222-4130
F: (401) 222-2968
E: esanderson
   @preservation.ri.gov

SOUTH CAROLINA
Mr. Eric Emerson
State Historic Preservation
Officer
Department of Archives &
History
8301 Parklane Road
Columbia, SC 29223
P: (803) 896-6100
F: (803) 896-6167
E: eemerson
   @scdah.state.sc.us

SOUTH DAKOTA
Mr. Jay D. Vogt
Director
State Historical Society
Cultural Heritage Center
900 Governors Drive
Pierre, SD 57501
P: (605) 773-3458
F: (605) 773-6041
E: jay.vogt@state.sd.us

TENNESSEE
Mr. Patrick McIntyre Jr.
Executive Director & State
Historic Preservation Officer
State Historical Commission
2941 Lebanon Road
Nashville, TN 37243
P: (615) 532-1550
F: (615) 532-1549
E: patrick.mcintyre
   @state.tn.us

TEXAS
Mr. Mark S. Wolfe
State Historic Preservation
Officer
State Historical Commission
P.O. Box 12276
Austin, TX 78711
P: (512) 463-6100
F: (512) 463-8222
E: mark.wolfe
   @thc.state.tx.us

U.S. VIRGIN ISLANDS
Mr. Robert Mathes
State Historic Preservation
Officer
Department of Planning &
Natural Resources
Cyril E. King Airport
Terminal Building - 2nd Floor
St. Thomas, VI 00802
P: (340) 776-8605
F: (340) 776-7236

UTAH
Mr. Wilson Martin
State Historic Preservation
Officer
State History
300 Rio Grande
Salt Lake City, UT 84101
P: (801) 533-3500
F: (801) 533-3503
E: wmartin@utah.gov

VERMONT
Ms. Giovanna Peebles
State Historic Preservation
Officer
State Division for Historic
Preservation
National Life North Building
One National Life Drive, 2nd
Floor
Montpelier, VT 05620
F: (802) 828-3206
E: giovanna.peebles
   @state.vt.us

VIRGINIA
Ms. Kathleen Kilpatrick
State Historic Preservation
Officer
Department of Historic
Resources
2801 Kensington Avenue
Richmond, VA 23221
P: (804) 367-2323
F: (804) 367-2391
E: Kathleen.Kilpatrick
   @dhr.virginia.gov

WASHINGTON
Dr. Allyson Brooks
State Historic Preservation
Officer
Office of Archaeology &
Historic Preservation
1063 South Capitol Way, Suite
106
P.O. Box 48343
Olympia, WA 98504
P: (360) 586-3065
F: (360) 586-3067
E: allyson.brooks
   @dahp.wa.gov

WEST VIRGINIA
Mr. Randall Reid-Smith
State Historic Preservation
Officer
State Division of Culture &
History
Historic Preservation Office
1900 Kanawha Boulevard East
Charleston, WV 25305
P: (304) 558-0220
F: (304) 558-2779

WISCONSIN
Dr. Michael E. Stevens
State Historic Preservation
Officer
State Historical Society
816 State Street
Madison, WI 53706
P: (608) 264-6464
F: (608) 264-6504
E: michael.stevens
   @wisconsinhistory.org

WYOMING
Ms. Mary Hopkins
Interim State Historic
Preservation Officer
State Historic Preservation
Office
2301 Central Avenue, 3rd Floor
Cheyenne, WY 82002
P: (307) 777-7697
F: (307) 777-6421
E: hopkins@uwyo.edu

Housing Finance

Administers the state's housing assistance programs, provides low and moderate income housing by financing low interest loans.

ALABAMA
Mr. Robert Strickland
Executive Director
Housing Finance Authority
P.O. Box 242967
Montgomery, AL 36124
P: (334) 244-9200
F: (334) 244-9214

ALASKA
Mr. Dan R. Fauske
Executive Director/CEO
Housing Finance Corporation
4300 Boniface Parkway
P.O. Box 101020
Anchorage, AK 99510
P: (907) 330-8452
F: (907) 338-9218
E: dfauske@ahfc.state.ak.us

AMERICAN SAMOA
Mr. Lolo M. Moliga
President
Development Bank of American
Samoa
P.O. Box 9
Pago Pago, AS 96799
P: (684) 633-4565
F: (684) 633-1163

ARKANSAS
Mr. Mac Dodson
Director
Development Finance Authority
423 Main Street, Suite 500
Little Rock, AR 72201
P: (501) 682-5900
F: (501) 682-5939
E: mdodson@adfa.state.ar.us

CALIFORNIA
Ms. Claudia Cappio
Executive Director
Housing Finance Agency
500 Capitol Mall, Suite 1400
Sacramento, CA 95814
P: (916) 326-8000
F: (916) 324-8640

COLORADO
Ms. Pat Coyle
Director
Division of Housing
Department of Local Affairs
1313 Sherman, Room 518
Denver, CO 80203
P: (303) 866-4977
F: (303) 866-4077
E: pat.coyle@state.co.us

DELAWARE
Mr. Anas Ben Addi
Director
State Housing Authority
18 The Green
Dover, DE 19901
P: (302) 739-4263
F: (302) 739-6122

DISTRICT OF COLUMBIA
Ms. Leila Funucane Edmonds
Director
Department of Housing &
Community Development
1800 Martin Luther King Jr.
Avenue
Southeast
Washington, DC 20020
P: (202) 442-7200
F: (202) 442-8391
E: dhcd@dc.gov

FLORIDA
Mr. J. Thomas Cardwell
Commissioner
Office of Financial Regulation
200 East Gaines Street
Tallahassee, FL 32399
P: (850) 410-9601
F: (850) 410-9663
E: OFR@flofr.com

GEORGIA
Ms. Carmen Chubb
Assistant Commissioner
Housing Finance Division
60 Executive Park South,
Northeast
Atlanta, GA 30329
P: (404) 679-0607
F: (404) 679-4837
E: carmen.chubb@dca.ga.gov

GUAM
Mr. Jose Guevara
President
Housing Corporation
590 S. Marine Corps Drive
Suite 214, ITC Building
Tamuning, GU 96931
P: (671) 647-4143
F: (674) 649-4144

HAWAII
Ms. Karen Seddon
Executive Director
Housing Finance &
Development Corporation
677 Queen Street, Suite 300
Honolulu, HI 96813
P: (808) 587-0680
F: (808) 587-3416

IDAHO
Mr. Gerald M. Hunter
Executive Director
Housing & Finance Association
P.O. Box 7899
Boise, ID 83707
P: (208) 331-4889
F: (208) 331-4804
E: geraldh@ihfa.org

ILLINOIS
Ms. Mary Kenney
Executive Director
Housing Development Authority
401 North Michigan Avenue,
Suite 700
Chicago, IL 60611
P: (312) 836-5314
F: (312) 832-2170
E: mkenney@IHDA.org

INDIANA
Ms. Sherry Seiwert
Executive Director
Housing & Community
Development Authority
30 South Meridian Street, Suite
1000
Indianapolis, IN 46204
P: (317) 234-3873
F: (317) 232-7778
E: sseiwert@ihcda.in.gov

IOWA
Mr. Dave Jamison
Executive Director
Finance Authority
2015 Grand Avenue
Des Moines, IA 50312
P: (515) 725-4900
F: (515) 725-4901
E: dave.jamison@iowa.gov

KANSAS
Mr. Timothy M.
    Shallenburger
President
Development Finance Authority
555 South Kansas Avenue, Suite
202
Topeka, KS 66603
P: (785) 357-4445
F: (785) 357-4478
E: tshallenburger@kdfa.org

KENTUCKY
Mr. Richard L. McQuady
Chief Executive Officer
Housing Corporation
1231 Louisville Road
Frankfort, KY 40601
P: (502) 564-7630 Ext. 218
F: (502) 564-5708
E: rmcquady@kyhousing.org

MAINE
Ms. Dale McCormick
Director
State Housing Authority
353 Water Street
Augusta, ME 04330
P: (207) 626-4600
F: (207) 626-4678
E: dmccormick
    @mainehousing.org

MARYLAND
Mr. Raymond A. Skinner
Secretary
Department of Housing &
Community Development
100 Community Place
Crownsville, MD 21032
P: (410) 514-7001
E: skinner@mdhousing.org

MASSACHUSETTS
Mr. Thomas R. Gleason
Executive Director
MassHousing
One Beacon Street
Boston, MA 02108
P: (617) 854-1000
F: (617) 854-1029

MICHIGAN
Mr. Gary Heidel
Executive Director
State Housing Development
Authority
735 East Michigan Avenue
P.O. Box 30044
Lansing, MI 48909
P: (517) 373-8370
F: (517) 335-4797

MINNESOTA
Ms. Mary Tingerthal
Commissioner
Housing Finance Agency
400 Sibley Street, Suite 300
St. Paul, MN 55101
P: (651) 296-5738
F: (651) 296-8139
E: Mary.Tingerthal
    @state.mn.us

MISSISSIPPI
Ms. Diane Bolen
Executive Director
Home Corporation
P.O. Box 23369
Jackson, MS 39225
P: (601) 718-4600
F: (601) 354-7076
E: dbolen@mshc.com

MISSOURI
Ms. Margaret Lineberry
Executive Director
Housing Development
Commission
3435 Broadway
Kansas City, MO 64111
P: (816) 759-6600
F: (816) 759-6608

MONTANA
Mr. Dore Schwinden
Director
Department of Commerce
301 South Park
P.O. Box 200501
Helena, MT 59620
P: (406) 841-2704
F: (406) 841-2701
E: dschwinden@mt.gov

NEBRASKA
Mr. Richard Baier
Director
Department of Economic
Development
P.O. Box 94666
Lincoln, NE 68509
P: (402) 471-3111
F: (402) 471-3778
E: richard.baier
   @nebraska.gov

NEVADA
Mr. Charles L. Horsey III
Administrator
Housing Division
Department of Business &
Industry
1535 Old Hot Springs Road, #50
Carson City, NV 89706
P: (775) 687-2031
F: (775) 687-4040
E: chorsey
   @nvhousing.state.nv.us

NEW HAMPSHIRE
Mr. Dean J. Christon
Executive Director
Housing Finance Authority
P.O. Box 5087
Bedford, NH 03108
P: (603) 472-8623
F: (603) 472-2663
E: dean.christon@nhhfa.org

NEW JERSEY
Mr. Anthony L. Marchetta
Executive Director
Housing & Mortgage Finance
Agency
637 South Clinton Avenue
P.O. Box 18550
Trenton, NJ 08650
P: (609) 278-7400
F: (609) 278-1754

NEW MEXICO
Mr. Jay Czar
Executive Director
Mortgage Finance Authority
334 Fourth Street Southwest
Albuquerque, NM 87102
P: (505) 767-2210
F: (505) 243-3289
E: jczar@housingnm.org

NEW YORK
Mr. Darryl C. Towns
Commissioner/CEO
State Homes & Community
Renewal
641 Lexington Avenue, 4th
Floor
New York, NY 10022
P: (212) 688-4000
F: (518) 872-0789

NORTH CAROLINA
Mr. Bob Kucab
Executive Director
Housing Finance Agency
3508 Bush Street
Raleigh, NC 27609
P: (919) 877-5600
F: (919) 877-5701
E: arkucab@nchfa.com

NORTH DAKOTA
Mr. Mike Anderson
Executive Director
Housing Finance Agency
2624 Vermont Avenue
P.O. Box 1535
Bismarck, ND 58502
P: (701) 328-8080
F: (701) 328-8090
E: maanders@ndhfa.org

**NORTHERN MARIANA
ISLANDS**
Mr. Thomas C. Duenas
Executive Director
Housing Corporation
P.O. Box 502149
Saipan, MP 96950
P: (670) 234-6245
F: (670) 234-7144
E: administration
   @cda.gov.mp

OHIO
Mr. Michael Hiler
Chief
Office of Housing &
Community Partnerships
77 South High Street, 25th Floor
P.O. Box 1001
Columbus, OH 43216
P: (614) 466-2285
F: (614) 466-7408
E: michael.hiler
   @development.ohio.gov

OKLAHOMA
Mr. Dennis Shockley
Executive Director
Housing Finance Agency
100 Northwest 63rd Street, Suite
200
P.O. Box 26720
Oklahoma City, OK 73126
P: (405) 848-1144
F: (405) 840-1109

OREGON
Mr. Rick Crager
Acting Director
Housing & Community Services
725 Summer Street, Northeast,
Suite B
Salem, OR 97301
P: (503) 986-2096
F: (503) 986-2020
E: richard.w.crager
   @state.or.us

PENNSYLVANIA
Mr. Brian A. Hudson Sr.
Executive Director & CEO
Housing Finance Agency
211 North Front Street
P.O. Box 8029
Harrisburg, PA 17105
P: (717) 780-3911
F: (717) 780-1865
E: bhudson@phfa.org

PUERTO RICO
Mr. Jose Cestero Casanova
Executive Director
Housing Finance Authority
235 Arterial Hostos
Suite 1201, North Tower
Hato Rey, PR 00918
P: (787) 765-7577 Ext. 4573
F: (787) 620-3521

RHODE ISLAND
Mr. Michael Tondra
Executive Director
Housing Resources Commission
One Capitol Hill, 3rd Floor
Providence, RI 02903
P: (401) 222-6490
F: (401) 222-2803
E: mtondra@doa.ri.gov

SOUTH CAROLINA
Ms. Valarie Williams
Executive Director
State Housing Finance &
Development Authority
300-C Outlet Point Boulevard
Columbia, SC 29210
P: (803) 896-9005
F: (803) 551-4876
E: Valarie.Williams
   @schousing.com

SOUTH DAKOTA
Mr. Mark Lauseng
Executive Director
Housing Development Authority
P.O. Box 1237
3060 E. Elizabeth Street
Pierre, SD 57501
P: (605) 773-3181
F: (605) 773-5154
E: mark@sdhda.org

TENNESSEE
Mr. Ted R. Fellman
Executive Director
Housing Development Agency
404 James Robertson Parkway,
Suite 1200
Nashville, TN 37243
P: (615) 815-2015
F: (615) 564-2700
E: tfellman@thda.org

TEXAS
Mr. Michael Gerber
Executive Director
Department of Housing &
Community Affairs
221 East 11th Street
P.O. Box 13941
Austin, TX 78711
P: (512) 475-3930

U.S. VIRGIN ISLANDS
Mr. Clifford Graham
Executive Director
Housing Finance Authority
3202 Demarara #3
Frenchtown Plaza, Suite 200
St. Thomas, VI 00802
P: (340) 774-4432
F: (340) 775-7913
E: vihfa@vihfa.gov

Housing Finance

UTAH
Mr. Grant S. Whitaker
President & CEO
Housing Corporation
2479 South Lake Park
Boulevard
West Valley City, UT 84120
P: (801) 902-8200
F: (801) 902-8325
E: GWHITAKER@uthc.org

VERMONT
Ms. Sarah E. Carpenter
Executive Director
Housing Finance Agency
164 St. Paul Street
P.O. Box 408
Burlington, VT 05402
P: (802) 864-5743
F: (802) 864-8081

VIRGINIA
Ms. Susan F. Dewey
Executive Director
Housing Development Authority
600 South Belvidere Street
Richmond, VA 23230
P: (804) 343-5701
F: (804) 783-6704
E: susan.dewey@vhda.com

Mr. William C. Shelton
Director
Department of Housing &
Community Development
The Jackson Center
501 North 2nd Street
Richmond, VA 23219
P: (804) 371-7002
F: (804) 371-6524
E: bill.shelton
    @dhcd.virginia.gov

WASHINGTON
Mr. Kim Herman
Executive Director
Housing Finance Commission
1000 2nd Avenue, Suite 2700
Seattle, WA 98104
P: (206) 464-7139
F: (206) 587-5113

WEST VIRGINIA
Mr. Joe Hatfield
Executive Director
Housing Development Fund
814 Virginia Street, East
Charleston, WV 25301
P: (304) 345-6475
F: (304) 345-4828

WISCONSIN
Mr. Wyman B. Winston
Executive Director
Housing & Economic
Development Authority
201 West Washington Avenue,
Suite 700
P.O. Box 1728
Madison, WI 53703
P: (608) 266-2893
F: (608) 267-1099
E: wyman.winston@wheda.com

WYOMING
Mr. Dave Haney
Executive Director
Community Development
Authority
P.O. Box 634
Casper, WY 82601
P: (307) 265-0603
F: (307) 266-5414
E: haney@wyomingcda.com

Human Services

Manages the development, administration, and delivery of all human and social service programs.

ALABAMA
Ms. Nancy T. Buckner
Commissioner
Department of Human Resources
50 North Ripley Street
Montgomery, AL 36130
P: (334) 242-1160
F: (334) 242-0198
E: Nancy.Buckner @dhr.alabama.gov

ALASKA
Mr. William Streur
Commissioner
Department of Health and Social Services
3601 C Street
Suite 902
Anchorage, AK 99503
P: (907) 465-3030
F: (907) 465-3068
E: william.streur @alaska.gov

AMERICAN SAMOA
Ms. Leilua Stevenson
Director
Department of Human & Social Services
American Samoa Government
P.O. Box 997534
Pago Pago, AS
P: (684) 633-7506
F: (684) 633-7449

ARIZONA
Mr. Will Humble
Director
Department of Health Services
150 North 18th Avenue
Phoenix, AZ 85007
P: (602) 542-1025
F: (602) 542-1062

ARKANSAS
Mr. John Selig
Director
Department of Human Services
P.O. Box 1437, Slot S201
Little Rock, AR 72203
P: (501) 682-8650
F: (501) 682-6836
E: John.Selig@arkansas.gov

CALIFORNIA
Ms. Diana Dooley
Secretary
Health & Human Services Agency
1600 Ninth Street, Room 460
Sacramento, CA 95814
P: (916) 654-3454
F: (916) 654-3343

COLORADO
Mr. Reginald L. Bicha
Executive Director
Department of Human Services
1575 Sherman Street
Denver, CO 80203
P: (303) 866-5700
F: (303) 866-4740

CONNECTICUT
Mr. Roderick L. Bremby
Commissioner
Department of Social Services
25 Sigourney Street
Hartford, CT 06106
P: (860) 424-5053
E: roderick.bremby@ct.gov

DELAWARE
Ms. Rita Landgraf
Secretary
Department of Health & Social Services
Main Building
1901 North DuPont Highway
New Castle, DE 19720
P: (302) 255-9040
F: (302) 255-4429

DISTRICT OF COLUMBIA
Mr. David A. Berns
Director
Department of Human Services
64 New York Avenue, Northeast
6th Floor
Washington, DC 20002
P: (202) 671-4200
E: dhs@dc.gov

FLORIDA
Mr. David Wilkins
Secretary
Department of Children & Families
1317 Winewood Boulevard
Building 1, Room 202
Tallahassee, FL 32399
P: (850) 487-1111
F: (850) 922-2993
E: david_wilkins @dcf.state.fl.us

GEORGIA
Mr. Clyde Reese
Commissioner
Department of Human Services
2 Peachtree Street, Northwest
Room 29-250
Atlanta, GA 30303
P: (404) 463-3390
F: (404) 651-8669

HAWAII
Ms. Patricia McManaman
Director
Department of Human Services
1390 Miller Street, Room 209
Honolulu, HI 96813
P: (808) 586-4997
F: (808) 586-4890
E: dhs@dhs.hawaii.gov

IDAHO
Mr. Richard Armstrong
Director
Department of Health & Welfare
450 West State Street
Pete T. Cenarrusa Building
Boise, ID 83720
P: (208) 334-5500
F: (208) 334-6558
E: armstrongr@dhw.idaho.gov

ILLINOIS
Ms. Michelle R.B. Saddler
Director
Department of Human Services
100 South Grand Avenue, East
Springfield, IL 62762
P: (217) 557-1601
F: (217) 557-1647

INDIANA
Mr. Mike Carr
Director, Division of Family Resources
Family & Social Services Administration
402 West Washington Street, Room W392
P.O. Box 7083
Indianapolis, IN 46207
P: (317) 233-4450
E: michael.carr@fssa.in.gov

IOWA
Mr. Kevin Concannon
Director
Department of Human Services
Hoover Building
1305 East Walnut Street
Des Moines, IA 50319
P: (515) 281-5454
F: (515) 281-4980

Mr. Charles M. Palmer
Director
Department of Human Services
Hoover State Office Building
1305 East Walnut Street
Des Moines, IA 50319
P: (515) 281-5452
F: (515) 281-4980
E: cpalmer1@dhs.state.ia.us

KANSAS
Mr. Robert Siedlecki
Secretary
Department of Social & Rehabilitation Services
915 Southwest Harrison Street, 6th Floor
Topeka, KS 66612
P: (785) 296-3271
F: (785) 296-2173

KENTUCKY
Ms. Janie Miller
Secretary
Cabinet for Health & Family Services
275 East Main Street
Mailstop 5W-A
Frankfort, KY 40621
P: (502) 564-7042
F: (502) 564-7091

LOUISIANA
Ms. Ruth Johnson
Secretary
Department of Children & Family Services
627 North 4th Street
P.O. Box 3776
Baton Rouge, LA 70821
P: (225) 342-0286
F: (225) 342-8636

MAINE
Ms. Mary Mayhew
Commissioner
Department of Health & Human Services
221 State Street
Augusta, ME 04333
P: (207) 287-3707
F: (207) 287-3005
E: mary.mayhew@maine.gov

MARYLAND
Mr. Theodore Dallas
Interim Secretary
Department of Human Resources
311 West Saratoga Street
Baltimore, MD 21201
P: (410) 767-7109

Human Services

MASSACHUSETTS
Dr. JudyAnn Bigby
Secretary
Executive Office of Health &
Human Services
One Ashburton Place, Room
1109
Boston, MA 02108
P: (617) 727-7600
F: (617) 727-5134

MICHIGAN
Ms. Maura D. Corrigan
Director
Department of Human Services
235 South Grand Avenue
P.O. Box 30037
Lansing, MI 48909
P: (517) 373-2035
F: (517) 335-6101
E: dhsweb@michigan.gov

MISSISSIPPI
Ms. Mary Currier M.D.
State Health Officer
State Department of Health
P.O. Box 1700
Jackson, MS 39215
P: (601) 576-7634
E: mary.currier
    @msdh.state.ms.us

Mr. Donald Thompson
Executive Director
Department of Human Services
750 North State Street
Jackson, MS 39202
P: (601) 359-4500

MISSOURI
Ms. Margaret T. Donnelly
Director
Department of Health & Senior
Services
P.O. Box 570
Jefferson City, MO 65102
P: (573) 751-6400
F: (573) 751-6010
E: info@dhss.mo.gov

MONTANA
Ms. Anna Whiting Sorrell
Director
Department of Public Health &
Human Services
111 North Sanders, Room 301
P.O. Box 4210
Helena, MT 59604
P: (406) 444-5622
F: (406) 444-1970

NEVADA
Mr. Michael J. Willden
Director
Department of Health & Human
Services
4126 Technology Way, Room
100
Carson City, NV 89706
P: (775) 684-4000
F: (775) 684-4010
E: mwillden@dhhs.nv.gov

NEW HAMPSHIRE
Mr. Nicholas A. Toumpas
Commissioner
Department of Health & Human
Services
129 Pleasant Street
Concord, NH 03301
P: (603) 271-4331
F: (603) 271-4912
E: ntoumpas
    @dhhs.state.nh.us

NEW JERSEY
Ms. Jennifer Velez
Commissioner
Department of Human Services
222 South Warren Street
P.O. Box 700
Trenton, NJ 08625
P: (609) 292-3717

NEW MEXICO
Ms. Sidonie Squier
Secretary
Human Services Department
P.O. Box 2348
Santa Fe, NM 87504
P: (505) 827-7750
F: (505) 827-3185

NEW YORK
Ms. Elizabeth R. Berlin
Executive Deputy Secretary
Office of Temporary &
Disability Assistance
40 North Pearl Street
Albany, NY 12243
P: (518) 474-4152
F: (518) 486-9179

NORTH CAROLINA
Mr. Lanier Cansler
Secretary
Department of Health & Human
Services
2001 Mail Service Center
Raleigh, NC 27699
P: (919) 733-4534
F: (919) 715-4645
E: Lanier.Cansler
    @ncmail.net

NORTH DAKOTA
Ms. Carol K. Olson
Executive Director
Department of Human Services
State Capitol, Judicial Wing
600 East Boulevard Avenue,
Dept. 325
Bismarck, ND 58505
P: (701) 328-2538
F: (701) 328-1545
E: colson@nd.gov

**NORTHERN MARIANA
ISLANDS**
Mr. Joseph P. Villagomez
Secretary of Public Health
Department of Public Health
P.O. Box 500409
Saipan, MP 96950
P: (670) 236-8201
F: (670) 234-8930
E: jkvsaipan@aol.com

OHIO
Mr. Michael B. Colbert
Director
Department of Job & Family
Services
30 East Broad Street, 32nd Floor
Columbus, OH 43215
P: (614) 466-6283
F: (614) 466-2815

OKLAHOMA
Mr. Howard H. Hendrick
Secretary
Department of Human Services
2400 North Lincoln Boulevard
P.O. Box 25352
Oklahoma City, OK 73125
P: (405) 521-3646

OREGON
Ms. Erinn L. Kelley-Siel
Acting Director
Department of Human Services
500 Summer Street, Northeast,
E-62
Salem, OR 97301
P: (503) 945-5944
F: (503) 378-2897
E: erinn.kelley-siel
    @state.or.us

PENNSYLVANIA
Mr. Gary D. Alexander
Acting Secretary
Department of Public Welfare
P.O. Box 2675
Harrisburg, PA 17105
P: (717) 787-2600
F: (717) 772-2062

PUERTO RICO
Ms. Yanitsia Irizarry
    Mendez
Secretary
Department of the Family
P.O. Box 11398
San Juan, PR 00910
P: (787) 294-4900
F: (787) 294-0732

RHODE ISLAND
Ms. Sandra M. Powell
Director
Department of Human Services
Louis Pasteur Building
600 New London Avenue
Cranston, RI 02920
P: (401) 462-2121
F: (401) 462-3677
E: Director@dhs.ri.gov

SOUTH CAROLINA
Ms. Lillian B. Koller
Director
Department of Social Services
1535 Confederate Avenue
Extension
P.O. Box 1520
Columbia, SC 29202
P: (803) 898-7360
F: (803) 898-7277

SOUTH DAKOTA
Ms. Amy Iversen-Pollreisz
Director
Department of Human Services
3800 E. Hwy 34, Hillsview
Properties Pl.
C/o 500 East Capitol Avenue
Pierre, SD 57501
P: (605) 773-5990
F: (605) 773-5483

TENNESSEE
Dr. Raquel Hatter
Commissioner
Department of Human Services
400 Deaderick Street, 15th Floor
Nashville, TN 37243
P: (615) 313-4700
F: (615) 741-4165

TEXAS
Mr. Thomas Suehs
Executive Commissioner
Health & Human Services
Commission
4900 North Lamar
P.O. Box 13247
Austin, TX 78711
P: (512) 424-6502
F: (512) 424-6587

Mr. Chris Traylor
Commissioner
Department of Aging &
Disability Services
701 West 51st Street
P.O. Box 149030
Austin, TX 78714
P: (512) 438-3011
F: (512) 438-4220

U.S. VIRGIN ISLANDS
Mr. Christopher Finch
Commissioner
Department of Human Services
Knud Hansen Complex,
Building A
1303 Hospital Grounds
St. Thomas, VI 00802
P: (340) 774-0930
F: (340) 774-3466

UTAH
Mr. Palmer DePaulis
Executive Director
Department of Human Services
195 North 1950 West
Salt Lake City, UT 84116
P: (801) 538-4171
F: (801) 538-4016
E: palmer@utah.gov

VERMONT
Mr. Douglas A. Racine
Secretary
Agency of Human Services
103 South Main Street
Waterbury, VT 05671
P: (802) 241-2220
F: (802) 241-2979

VIRGINIA
Mr. Bill Hazel
Secretary
Office of the Secretary of
Health & Human Services
1111 East Broad Street
Patrick Henry Building
Richmond, VA 23219
P: (804) 786-7765
F: (804) 786-3389
E: bill.hazel
   @governor.virginia.gov

WASHINGTON
Ms. Susan N. Dreyfus
Secretary
Department of Social & Health
Services
P.O. Box 45130
Olympia, WA 98504
P: (360) 902-7800

WEST VIRGINIA
Mr. Michael J. Lewis
Cabinet Secretary
Department of Health & Human
Resources
One Davis Square, Suite 100
East
Charleston, WV 25301
P: (304) 558-0684
F: (304) 558-1130
E: DHHRSecretary@wv.gov

WISCONSIN
Mr. Dennis G. Smith
Secretary
Department of Health & Family
Services
1 West Wilson Street, Room 650
Madison, WI 53702
P: (608) 266-1865
E: dennis.smith
   @dhs.wisconsin.gov

WYOMING
Mr. Steve Corsi
Director of Family Services
Department of Family Services
Hathaway Building, 3rd Floor
2300 Capitol Avenue
Cheyenne, WY 82002
P: (307) 777-7564
F: (307) 777-7747

Information Systems

Provides statewide computer services or coordinates the operation of various data processing systems within state government.

ALABAMA
Mr. Jack Doane
Director
Information Services Division
Folsom Administrative Building
64 North Union Street
Montgomery, AL 36130
P: (334) 242-3658
F: (334) 242-7002
E: jack.doane
@isd.alabama.gov

ALASKA
Mr. Pat Shier
Director
Division of Enterprise
Technology Services
333 Willoughby Avenue
State Office Building, 5th Floor
Juneau, AK 99801
P: (907) 382-3512
F: (907) 465-3450
E: pat.shier@alaska.gov

AMERICAN SAMOA
Hon. Magalei Logovi'i
Treasurer
Department of the Treasury
American Samoa Government
Pago Pago, AS 96799
P: (684) 633-4155
F: (684) 633-4100

Mr. Faleseu Eliu Paopao
Director
Department of Commerce
American Samoa Government
Executive Office Building,
Utulei
Pago Pago, AS 96799
P: (684) 633-5155
F: (684) 633-4195

ARIZONA
Ms. Lori Boak
Interim Assistant Director &
CIO
Information Services Division
Department of Administration
100 North 15th Avenue
Phoenix, AZ 85007
P: (602) 542-2250
F: (602) 542-4272
E: lori.boak@azdoa.gov

ARKANSAS
Ms. Claire Bailey
Chief Technology Officer
Department of Information
Systems
#1 Capitol Mall, 3rd Floor
Little Rock, AR 72203
P: (501) 682-9990
F: (501) 682-9465
E: claire.bailey
@arkansas.gov

CALIFORNIA
Mr. Adrian Farley
Acting Director
Office of Technology Services
P.O. Box 1810
Rancho Cordova, CA 95741
P: (916) 464-7547
F: (916) 464-4025

COLORADO
Ms. Kristin Russell
Chief Information Officer
Governor's Office of
Information Technology
601 East 18th Avenue, Suite 250
Denver, CO 80203
P: (303) 764-7700
F: (303) 764-7725
E: kristin.russell
@state.co.us

CONNECTICUT
Mr. Mark Raymond
Chief Information Officer
Department of Information
Technology
101 East River Drive
East Hartford, CT 06108
P: (860) 622-2200
F: (860) 291-8665
E: mark.raymond@ct.gov

DISTRICT OF COLUMBIA
Mr. Brian Sivak
Chief Technology Officer
Office of the Chief Technology
Officer
441 4th Street, Northwest
Washington, DC 20001
P: (202) 727-2277
F: (202) 727-6857
E: octo@dc.gov

FLORIDA
Mr. David W. Taylor
Executive Director & Chief
Information Officer
Agency for Enterprise
Information Technology
4030 Esplanade Way, Suite 135
Tallahassee, FL 32399
P: (850) 922-7502
F: (850) 487-9937
E: David.Taylor
@aeit.myflorida.com

GEORGIA
Mr. Calvin Rhodes
Executive Director
Technology Authority
47 Trinity Avenue, Southwest
Atlanta, GA 30334
P: (404) 463-2340
F: (404) 463-2380
E: calvn.rhodes@gta.ga.gov

GUAM
Ms. Lourdes M. Perez
Director
Department of Administration
P.O. Box 884
Hagatna, GU 96932
P: (671) 475-1122
F: (671) 475-1243
E: lou.perez@doa.guam.gov

HAWAII
Ms. Debra A. Gagne
Administrator
Information & Communications
Services Division
1151 Punchbowl Street
Honolulu, HI 96813
P: (808) 586-1920
F: (808) 586-1922

IDAHO
Ms. Teresa Luna
Director
Department of Administration
650 West State Street, Room
100
P.O. Box 83720
Boise, ID 83720
P: (208) 332-1827
F: (208) 334-2307
E: teresa.luna
@adm.idaho.gov

ILLINOIS
Ms. Lana Kains
Division Manager
Office of Communication &
Information
120 West Jefferson
Communication Center, 3rd
Floor
Springfield, IL 62702
P: (217) 524-6895

INDIANA
Mr. Brian Arrowood
Office of Technology
1000 North Senate Avenue,
Room N551
Indianapolis, IN 46204
P: (317) 234-3843
F: (317) 234-0917
E: barrowood@iot.in.gov

KANSAS
Mr. Morey Sullivan
Director
Division of Information Systems
& Communications
900 Southwest Jackson, Room
751S
Topeka, KS 66612
P: (785) 296-3463
F: (785) 296-1168
E: morey.sullivan
@da.state.ks.us

KENTUCKY
Ms. Lori Flanery
Cabinet Secretary
Finance & Administration
Cabinet
Room 383, Capitol Annex
Frankfort, KY 40601
P: (502) 564-4240
F: (502) 564-5856
E: Lori.Flanery@ky.gov

LOUISIANA
Mr. Edward J. Driesse
Chief Information Officer
Office of Information
Technology
Division of Administration
P.O. Box 94095
Baton Rouge, LA 70804
P: (225) 342-7105
F: (225) 219-4994
E: cio@la.gov

MAINE
Mr. Greg McNeal
Chief Information Officer
Office of Information
Technology
26 Edison Drive
145 State House Station
Augusta, ME 04333
P: (207) 624-8800

MARYLAND
Mr. Elliot H. Schlanger
Secretary
Department of Information
Technology
45 Calvert Street
Annapolis, MD 21401
P: (410) 260-2994
F: (410) 974-5615
E: Elliot.Schlanger
@doit.state.md.us

Information Systems

MASSACHUSETTS
Mr. John Letchford
Assistant Secretary for
Information Technology & CIO
Information Technology
Division
One Ashburton Place, Room 804
Boston, MA 02108
P: (617) 727-2040
F: (617) 727-2779

MICHIGAN
Mr. David Behen
Director & CIO
Department of Technology,
Management & Budget
320 South Walnut Street, 2nd
Floor
Lansing, MI 48933
P: (517) 373-1006
F: (517) 373-8213

MINNESOTA
Mr. Spencer Cronk
Commissioner
Department of Administration
50 Sherburne Avenue
200 Administration Building
St. Paul, MN 55155
P: (651) 201-2555
F: (651) 297-7909
E: Spencer.Cronk
@state.mn.us

MISSISSIPPI
Mr. David L. Litchliter
Executive Director
Department of Information
Technology Services
301 North Lamar Street, Suite
508
Jackson, MS 39201
P: (601) 359-1395
F: (601) 354-6016
E: david.litchliter
@its.state.ms.us

MISSOURI
Mr. Doug Young
Chief Information Officer
Information Technology
Services Division
301 West High Street, Room
280
P.O. Box 809
Jefferson City, MO 65102
P: (573) 526-7746
F: (573) 751-3299
E: Doug.Young@oa.mo.gov

MONTANA
Mr. Richard Clark
Chief Information Officer
Information Technology
Services Division
Department of Administration
P.O. Box 200113
Helena, MT 59620
P: (406) 444-2700
F: (406) 444-2701
E: dclark@mt.gov

NEBRASKA
Ms. Brenda L. Decker
Chief Information Officer
Office of the Chief Information
Officer
501 South 14th Street
P.O. Box 95045
Lincoln, NE 68509
P: (402) 471-2761
F: (402) 471-4864
E: brenda.decker
@nebraska.gov

NEVADA
Mr. David Gustafson
Acting Director
Department of Information
Technology
400 West King Street, Room
300
Carson City, NV 89703
P: (775) 684-5849
F: (775) 684-5846

NEW HAMPSHIRE
Mr. Bill Rogers
Chief Information Officer
Department of Information
Technology
27 Hazen Drive
Concord, NH 03301
P: (603) 223-5703
F: (603) 271-6531

NEW JERSEY
Mr. Adel W. Ebeid
Chief Technology Officer
Office of Information
Technology
200/300 Riverview Plaza
P.O. Box 212
Trenton, NJ 08625
P: (609) 984-4082
F: (609) 633-9100
E: abel.ebeid
@oit.state.nj.us

NEW MEXICO
Mr. Darryl Ackley
Secretary
Department of Information
Technology
P.O. Box 22550
Santa Fe, NM 87502
P: (505) 827-0000

NORTH CAROLINA
Mr. Gerald L. Fralick
Chief Information Officer
Information Technology
Services
P.O. Box 17209
Raleigh, NC 27619
P: (919) 754-6575
E: jerry.fralick@nc.gov

NORTH DAKOTA
Dr. Lisa Feldner
Chief Information Officer
Information Technology
Department
600 East Boulevard Avenue
Department 112
Bismarck, ND 58505
P: (701) 328-1000
F: (701) 328-3000
E: lfeldner@nd.gov

**NORTHERN MARIANA
ISLANDS**
Mr. Joe I. Quitugua
Director
Commonwealth of Northern
Mariana Islands
P.O. Box 5234 CHRB
Saipan, MP 96950
P: (670) 664-1400
F: (670) 664-1415
E: finanedp02
@gtepacifica.net

OHIO
Mr. Stuart R. Davis
Chief Information Officer
Office of Information
Technology
30 East Broad Street, 40th Floor
Columbus, OH 43215
P: (614) 644-6446
F: (614) 644-9152
E: stu.davis@oit.ohio.gov

OKLAHOMA
Mr. Alex Pettit
Chief Information Officer
Office of State Finance
3115 North Lincoln Boulevard
Oklahoma City, OK 73105
P: (405) 522-4667
E: alex.pettit@osf.ok.gov

OREGON
Mr. Dugan Petty
Division Administrator & State
Chief Information Officer
Enterprise Information Strategy
& Policy Division
Department of Administrative
Services
955 Center Street, Northeast,
Room 470
Salem, OR 97301
P: (503) 378-2128
F: (503) 378-4351
E: dugan.a.petty
@state.or.us

PENNSYLVANIA
Mr. George White
Chief Information Officer
Office of Information
Technology
209 Finance Building
Harrisburg, PA 17120
P: (717) 787-5440
F: (717) 787-4523

RHODE ISLAND
Mr. John E. Landers
Chief Information Officer
Division of Information
Technology
Department of Administration
One Capitol Hill
Providence, RI 02908
P: (401) 222-4444
F: (401) 422-4260
E: John.Landers@doit.ri.gov

SOUTH CAROLINA
Mr. Jimmy Earley
Division Director
Division of Information
Technology
4430 Broad River Road
Columbia, SC 29210
P: (803) 896-0222
F: (803) 896-0789
E: jimmy.earley@cio.sc.gov

SOUTH DAKOTA
Mr. Dom Bianco
Commissioner & Chief
Information Officer
Bureau of Information &
Telecommunications
Kneip Building
700 Governors Drive
Pierre, SD 57501
P: (605) 773-5110
F: (605) 773-6040
E: dom.bianco@state.sd.us

Information Systems

TENNESSEE
Mr. Mark Bengel
Chief Information Officer
Office for Information
Resources
312 Rosa L. Parks Avenue
16th Floor, Tennessee Tower
Nashville, TN 37343
P: (615) 741-7951
F: (615) 532-0471

TEXAS
Ms. Karen W. Robinson
Chief Technology Officer
Department of Information
Resources
300 West 15th Street, Suite 1300
P.O. Box 13564
Austin, TX 78711
P: (512) 475-4720
F: (512) 475-4759

U.S. VIRGIN ISLANDS
Mr. John George
Director, Chief Information
Technology Officer
Information Technology
1050 Norre Gade, #5
Charlotte Amalie, VI 00801
P: (340) 774-1013
F: (340) 774-1490

UTAH
Mr. Stephen Fletcher
Chief Information Officer /
Executive Director
Department of Technology
Services
1 State Office Building, Floor 6
Salt Lake City, UT 84114
P: (801) 538-3298
F: (801) 538-3622
E: sfletcher@utah.gov

VERMONT
Ms. Ruthann Sullivan
Interim Commissioner & Chief
Information Officer
Department of Information &
Innovation
Agency of Administration
133 State Street
Montpelier, VT 05633
P: (802) 828-4141
F: (802) 828-3398
E: ruthann.sullivan
   @state.vt.us

VIRGINIA
Mr. Jim Duffey
Secretary of Technology
Office of the Secretary of
Technology
1111 East Broad Street
Patrick Henry Building
Richmond, VA 23219
P: (804) 786-9579
F: (804) 786-9584
E: jim.duffey
   @virginia.goveror.gov

WASHINGTON
Mr. Mike Ricchio
Acting Director
Department of Information
Services
1110 Jefferson Street, Southeast
Olympia, WA 98504
P: (360) 902-3500
F: (360) 586-5885
E: mike.ricchio@dis.wa.gov

WEST VIRGINIA
Mr. Ron Bolin
Director of Information Services
Office of Technology
1900 Kanawha Boulevard, East
Capitol Complex, Building 5,
10th Floor
Charleston, WV 25301
P: (304) 558-8601
E: Ronald.S.Bolin@wv.gov

WISCONSIN
Ms. Diane Kohn
Acting Chief Information
Officer
Division of Enterprise
Technology
Department of Administration
P.O. Box 7844
Madiso, WI 53707
P: (608) 264-9502
F: (608) 267-0626
E: dian.kohn@wisconsin.gov

WYOMING
Mr. John Hartwig
Administrator
Information Technology
Division
Dept. of Administration &
Information
2001 Capitol Avenue
Cheyenne, WY 82002
P: (307) 777-5600
F: (307) 777-6725

Insurance

Licenses and regulates insurance agents and insurance and title companies in the state.

ALABAMA
Mr. Jim L. Ridling
Commissioner
Department of Insurance
201 Monroe Street, Suite 1700
P.O. Box 303351
Montgomery, AL 36130
P: (334) 269-3550
F: (334) 241-4192

ALASKA
Ms. Linda S. Hall
Director
Department of Commerce,
Community & Economic
Development
Division of Insurance
550 West 7th Avenue, Suite 1560
Anchorage, AK 99501
P: (907) 269-7900
F: (907) 269-7910
E: linda.hall@alaska.gov

AMERICAN SAMOA
Mr. Aoomalo Manupo Turituri
Insurance Commissioner
Office of the Governor
American Samoa Government
Pago Pago, AS 96799
P: (684) 633-4116
F: (684) 633-2269

ARIZONA
Ms. Christina Urias
Director
Department of Insurance
2910 North 44th Street, 2nd
Floor
Ste. 210
Phoenix, AZ 85018
P: (602) 364-3100

ARKANSAS
Mr. Jay Bradford
Commissioner
Department of Insurance
1200 West Third Street
Little Rock, AR 72201
P: (501) 371-2600
F: (501) 371-2618

CALIFORNIA
Mr. Dave Jones
Commissioner
Department of Insurance
300 Capitol Mall, 17th Floor
Sacramento, CA 95814
P: (916) 492-3500
F: (916) 445-5280

COLORADO
Mr. John Postolowski
Interim Commissioner
Division of Insurance
Department of Regulatory
Agencies
1560 Broadway, Suite 850
Denver, CO 80202
P: (303) 894-7499
F: (303) 894-7455

CONNECTICUT
Mr. Thomas B. Leonardi
Commissioner
Insurance Department
153 Market Street
P.O. Box 816
Hartford, CT 06142
P: (860) 297-3800
F: (860) 566-7410

DELAWARE
Hon. Karen Weldin
   Stewart (D)
Commissioner
Insurance Department
841 Silver Lake Boulevard
Dover, DE 19904
P: (302) 674-7305
E: karen.stewart
   @state.de.us

DISTRICT OF COLUMBIA
Mr. William P. White
Commissioner
Department of INsurance,
Securities & Banking
810 First Street, Northeast, Suite
70
Washington, DC 20002
P: (202) 727-8000
F: (202) 535-1196

FLORIDA
Mr. Kevin M. McCarty
Commissioner
Office of Insurance Regulation
Department of Financial
Services
200 East Gaines Street
Tallahassee, FL 32399
P: (850) 413-3140
E: kevin.mccarty@fldfs.com

GEORGIA
Hon. Ralph T. Hudgens (R)
Commissioner
Office of Insurance & Safety
Fire Commissioner
2 Martin Luther King Jr. Drive
West Tower, Suite 704
Atlanta, GA 30334
P: (404) 656-2070
F: (404) 657-8542

GUAM
Mr. John Camacho
Banking & Insurance
Commissioner
Department of Revenue &
Taxation
Regulatory Division
P.O. Box 23607 GMF
Barrigada, GU 96921
P: (671) 635-1817
F: (671) 633-2643

HAWAII
Mr. Gordon Ito
Commissioner
Division of Insurance
Commerce & Consumer Affairs
P.O. Box 3614
Honolulu, HI 96811
P: (808) 586-2799
F: (808) 586-2806
E: insurance
   @dcca.hawaii.gov

IDAHO
Mr. Bill Deal
Director
Department of Insurance
700 West State Street
P.O. Box 83720
Boise, ID 83720
P: (208) 334-4250
F: (208) 334-4398

ILLINOIS
Mr. Michael T. McRaith
Director
Department of Insurance
320 West Washington Street
Springfield, IL 62767
P: (217) 782-4515
F: (217) 782-5020
E: DOI.Director
   @illinois.gov

INDIANA
Mr. Stephen W. Robertson
Commissioner
Department of Insurance
311 West Washington Street,
Suite 300
Indianapolis, IN 46204
P: (317) 232-3520
F: (317) 232-5251

IOWA
Ms. Susan E. Voss
Commissioner
Insurance Division
330 Maple Street
Des Moines, IA 50319
P: (515) 281-5705
F: (515) 281-3059

KANSAS
Hon. Sandy Praeger (R)
Commissioner of Insurance
Insurance Department
420 Southwest 9th Street
Topeka, KS 66612
P: (785) 296-3071
F: (785) 296-7805
E: commissioner
   @ksinsurance.org

KENTUCKY
Ms. Sharon P. Clark
Commissioner
Department of Insurance
P.O. Box 517
Frankfort, KY 40602
P: (502) 564-3630
F: (502) 564-1453
E: Debbie.Stamper@ky.gov

LOUISIANA
Hon. James J. Donelon (R)
Commissioner
Department of Insurance
P.O. Box 94214
Baton Rouge, LA 70804
P: (225) 342-5900
F: (225) 342-8622

MAINE
Ms. Mila Kofman
Superintendent
Department of Professional &
Financial Regulation
Bureau of Insurance
34 State House Station
Augusta, ME 04333
P: (207) 624-8475
F: (207) 624-8599
E: Mila.Kofman@maine.gov

MARYLAND
Ms. Beth Sammis
Acting Insurance Commissioner
Insurance Administration
200 Saint Paul Place, Suite 2700
Baltimore, MD 21202
P: (410) 468-2002
F: (410) 468-2020
E: bsammis
   @mdinsurance.state.md.us

MASSACHUSETTS
Mr. Joseph Murphy
Commissioner
Division of Insurance
Consumer Affairs & Business
Regulation
One South Station, 5th Floor
Boston, MA 02110
P: (617) 521-7794

Insurance

MICHIGAN
Mr. R. Kevin Clinton
Commissioner
Office of Financial & Insurance
Regulation
P.O. Box 30220
Lansing, MI 48909
P: (517) 373-0220
F: (517) 373-4978

MINNESOTA
Mr. Mike Rothman
Commissioner of Commerce
Department of Commerce
85 7th Place East, Suite 500
St. Paul, MN 55101
P: (651) 296-6025
F: (651) 297-1959
E: commerce.commissioner
    @state.mn.us

MISSISSIPPI
Hon. Mike Chaney (R)
Commissioner & State Fire
Marshal
Insurance Department
1001 Woolfolk State Office
Building
501 North West Street, P.O. Box
79
Jackson, MS 39205
P: (601) 359-3569
F: (601) 359-2543
E: mike.chaney
    @mid.state.ms.us

MISSOURI
Mr. John Huff
Director
Department of Insurance,
Financial Institutions &
Professional Registration
301 West High Street, Room
530
P.O. Box 690
Jefferson City, MO 65102
P: (573) 751-1927

MONTANA
Hon. Monica J. Lindeen (D)
State Auditor
Office of the Auditor
840 Helena Avenue
Helena, MT 59601
P: (406) 444-2006
F: (406) 444-3497
E: monica@lindeen.net

NEBRASKA
Mr. Bruce Ramge
Director
Department of Insurance
941 O Street, Suite 400
Lincoln, NE 68508
P: (402) 471-2201
F: (402) 471-4610

NEVADA
Mr. Brett J. Barratt
Commissioner
Division of Insurance
Department of Buisness &
Industry
788 Fairview Drive, Suite 300
Carson City, NV 89701
P: (775) 687-0700
F: (775) 687-0787

NEW HAMPSHIRE
Mr. Roger A. Sevigny
Commissioner
Department of Insurance
21 South Fruit Street, Suite 14
Concord, NH 03301
P: (603) 271-7973
F: (603) 271-1406
E: roger.sevigny@ins.nh.gov

NEW JERSEY
Mr. Thomas B. Considine
Commissioner
Department of Banking &
Insurance
20 West State Street
P.O. Box 325
Trenton, NJ 08625
P: (609) 292-7272
F: (609) 663-3601
E: commissioner
    @dobi.state.nj.us

NEW MEXICO
Mr. John G. Fanchini
Superintendent of Insurance
Insurance Division
Public Regulation Commission
P.O. Box 1269
Santa Fe, NM 87504
P: (505) 827-4601
F: (505) 827-4734

NEW YORK
Mr. James Wynn
Superintendent
Insurance Department
One Commerce Plaza
Albany, NY 12257
P: (518) 474-4567

NORTH CAROLINA
Hon. Wayne Goodwin (D)
Insurance Commissioner & State
Fire Marshal
Department of Insurance
430 North Salisbury Street
Raleigh, NC 27603
P: (919) 807-6750

NORTH DAKOTA
Hon. Adam Hamm (R)
Commissioner
Insurance Department
State Capitol, 5th Floor
600 East Boulevard Avenue
Bismarck, ND 58505
P: (701) 328-2440
F: (701) 328-4880
E: insurance@nd.gov

**NORTHERN MARIANA
ISLANDS**
Mr. Sixto Igisomar
Acting Secretary
Department of Commerce
Caller Box 10007
Saipan, MP 96950
P: (670) 664-3064
F: (670) 664-3067

OHIO
Hon. Mary Taylor (R)
Lieutenant Governor
Department of Insurance
77 South High Street, 30th Floor
Columbus, OH 43215
P: (614) 644-0935
F: (614) 466-9354

OKLAHOMA
Hon. John Doak
Insurance Commissioner
Insurance Department
3625 Northwest 56th, Suite 100
P.O. Box 53408
Oklahoma City, OK 73152
P: (405) 521-2828
F: (405) 521-6635

OREGON
Ms. Teresa Miller
Insurance Administrator
Insurance Division
P.O. Box 14480
350 Winter Street, Northeast
Salem, OR 97309
P: (503) 947-7980
F: (503) 378-4351
E: teresa.d.miller
    @state.or.us

PENNSYLVANIA
Mr. Michael F. Consedine
Acting Insurance Commissioner
Insurance Department
13th Floor, Strawberry Square
Harrisburg, PA 17120
P: (717) 783-0442
F: (717) 772-1969

PUERTO RICO
Mr. Ramon Cruz-Colon
Commissioner
Office of the Insurance
Commissioner
B5 Tabonuco Street, Suite 216
PMB 356
Guaynabo, PR 00968
P: (787) 722-8686
F: (787) 273-6082

RHODE ISLAND
Mr. Joseph Torti III
Associate Director &
Superintendent
Department of Business
Regulation
Insurance Regulation Division
1511 Pontiac Avenue
Cranston, RI 02920
P: (401) 462-9520
F: (401) 462-9602
E: InsuranceInquiry
    @dbr.state.ri.us

SOUTH CAROLINA
Mr. David Black
Director
Department of Insurance
1201 Main Street, Suite 1000
P.O. Box 100105
Columbia, SC 29202
P: (803) 737-6160
F: (803) 737-6205
E: info@doi.sc.gov

SOUTH DAKOTA
Mr. Merle Scheiber
Director
Division of Insurance
Department of Revenue &
Regulation
445 East Capitol Avenue
Pierre, SD 57501
P: (605) 773-3563
F: (605) 773-5369
E: insurance@state.sd.us

TENNESSEE
Ms. Julie Mix McPeak
Commissioner
Department of Commerce &
Insurance
500 James Robertson Parkway
Davy Crockett Tower
Nashville, TN 37243
P: (615) 741-2176
F: (615) 532-6934
E: ask.tdci@tn.gov

TEXAS
Mr. Mike Geeslin
Commissioner of Insurance
Department of Insurance
333 Guadalupe
P.O. Box 149104
Austin, TX 78714
P: (512) 463-6468
F: (512) 475-2005

U.S. VIRGIN ISLANDS
Mr. John McDonald
Director
Division of Banking &
Insurance
#18 Kongens Gade
St. Thomas, VI 00802
P: (340) 774-7166
F: (340) 774-9458

UTAH
Mr. Neal Gooch
Commissioner
Department of Insurance
3110 State Office Building
Salt Lake City, UT 84114
P: (801) 538-3800
F: (801) 538-3829
E: ngooch@utah.gov

VERMONT
Mr. Steve Kimbell
Commissioner
Department of Banking,
Insurance, Securities & Health
Care Administration
89 Main Street
Montpelier, VT 05620
P: (802) 828-3301
F: (802) 828-3306
E: steve.kimbell
@state.vt.us

VIRGINIA
Ms. Jacqueline K.
Cunningham
Commissioner
Bureau of Insurance
State Corporation Commission
1300 East Main Street, P.O. Box
1157
Richmond, VA 23218
P: (804) 371-9741
F: (804) 371-9348

WASHINGTON
Hon. Mike Kreidler (D)
Commissioner
Office of the Insurance
Commissioner
302 Sid Snyder Avenue,
Southwest
Suite 200
Olympia, WA 98504
P: (360) 725-7000
E: askMike@oic.wa.gov

WEST VIRGINIA
Ms. Jane L. Cline
Commissioner
Insurance Commission
1124 Smith Street
Charleston, WV 25301
P: (304) 558-3029
F: (304) 558-0412
E: jane.cline
@wvinsurance.gov

WISCONSIN
Mr. Ted Nickel
Commissioner
Office of the Commissioner of
Insurance
125 South Webster Street
Madison, WI 53703
P: (608) 266-3585
F: (608) 266-9935

WYOMING
Mr. Ken Vines
Commissioner of Insurance
Insurance Department
106 East 6th Avenue
Cheyenne, WY 82002
P: (307) 777-7401
F: (307) 777-2446

International Trade

Promotes state exports, attracts overseas investments in the state and directs trade and investment missions.

ALABAMA
Mr. Seth Hammett
Director
Development Office
401 Adams Avenue, 6th Floor
Montgomery, AL 36130
P: (334) 242-0400
F: (334) 242-5669
E: seth.hammett
@ado.alabama.gov

AMERICAN SAMOA
Mr. Faleseu Eliu Paopao
Director
Department of Commerce
American Samoa Government
Executive Office Building,
Utulei
Pago Pago, AS 96799
P: (684) 633-5155
F: (684) 633-4195

ARIZONA
Ms. Sandra Watson
Chief Operating Officer
Commerce Authority
1700 West Washington, Suite
600
Phoenix, AZ 85007
P: (602) 771-1215
F: (602) 771-1200
E: commerce@azcommerce.com

ARKANSAS
Ms. Becky Thompson
Deputy Director, Global
Business
Economic Development
Commission
900 West Capital Avenue
Little Rock, AR 72201
P: (501) 682-7350
F: (501) 682-7394
E: bthompson
@arkansas.edc.com

CALIFORNIA
Ms. Traci Stevens
Acting Undersecretary
Business, Transportation &
Housing Agency
980 9th Street, Suite 2450
Sacramento, CA 95814
F: (916) 323-5440

COLORADO
Ms. Sandi Moilanen
Interim Division Director
International Trade Office
1625 Broadway, Suite 2700
Denver, CO 80202
P: (303) 892-3840
F: (303) 892-3840
E: sandi.moilanen
@state.co.us

Ms. Pam Reichert
Office of Economic
Development & International
Trade
1625 Broadway, Suite 2700
Denver, CO 80202
P: (303) 892-3840
F: (303) 892-3840

Mr. Dwayne Romero
Director
Office of Economic
Development & International
Trade
1625 Broadway, Suite 2700
Denver, CO 80202
P: (303) 892-3840
F: (303) 892-3848
E: dwayne.romero
@state.co.us

CONNECTICUT
Ms. Catherine Smith
Commissioner
Department of Economic &
Community Development
505 Hudson Street
Hartford, CT 06106
P: (860) 270-8010
E: catherine.smith@ct.gov

DELAWARE
Mr. John Pastor
Director
International Trade &
Development
820 North French Street
Wilmington, DE 19801
P: (302) 577-8466
F: (302) 577-1176
E: john.pastor@state.de.us

DISTRICT OF COLUMBIA
Mr. Victor L. Hoskins
Deputy Mayor for Planning and
Economic Development
Office of the Deputy Mayor for
Planning & Economic
Development
John A. Wilson Building, Suite
317
1350 Pennsylvania Avenue,
Northwest
Washington, DC 20004
P: (202) 727-6365
F: (202) 727-6703
E: dmped.eom@dc.gov

FLORIDA
Chris Hart
Director
Office of Tourism, Trade &
Economic Development
Office of the Governor
The Capitol, Suite 2001
Tallahassee, FL 32399
P: (850) 487-2568
F: (850) 487-3014
E: chris.hart
@eog.myflorida.com

GEORGIA
Mr. Chris Cummiskey
Commissioner
Department of Economic
Development
75 Fifth Street, Northwest
Suite 1200
Atlanta, GA 30308
P: (404) 962-4003
F: (404) 962-4009
E: ccummiskey@geogia.org

HAWAII
Mr. Richard C. Lim
Director
Department of Business,
Economic Development &
Tourism
P.O. Box 2359
Honolulu, HI 96804
P: (808) 586-2355
F: (808) 586-2377
E: director
@dbedt.hawaii.gov

IDAHO
Hon. Brad Little (R)
Lieutenant Governor
Office of the Lieutenant
Governor
State Capitol
Boise, ID 83720
P: (208) 334-2200
F: (208) 334-3259

ILLINOIS
Ms. Mary Roberts
Deputy Director
Office of Trade & Investment
100 West Randolph Street, Suite
3-401
Chicago, IL 60601
P: (312) 814-2828
F: (312) 814-6581
E: MRoberts@ildceo.net

INDIANA
Mr. Stephen Akard
Director, International Business
Development
Economic Development
Corporation
One North Capitol Avenue,
Suite 700
Indianapolis, IN 46204
P: (317) 234-2083
F: (317) 232-4146
E: sakard@iedc.in.gov

IOWA
Ms. Debi Durham
Director
Department of Economic
Development
200 East Grand Avenue
Des Moines, IA 50309
P: (515) 725-3022
F: (515) 725-3010
E: debi.durham@iowa.gov

KANSAS
Mr. John Watson
Director
Trade Development Division
Curtis State Office Building
1000 Southwest Jackson Street,
Suite 100
Topeka, KS 66612
P: (785) 296-1866
F: (785) 296-5263
E: jwatson
@kansascommerce.com

KENTUCKY
Mr. Erik Dunnigan
Commissioner
Department for Business
Development
Old Capitol Annex, 300 West
Broadway
Frankfort, KY 40601
P: (502) 564-7140
F: (502) 564-3256
E: Erik.Dunnigan@ky.gov

International Trade

LOUISIANA
Mr. Larry Collins
International Services Director
International Services Division
Economic Development
1051 North Third Street
Baton Rouge, LA 70802
P: (225) 342-4323
F: (225) 342-5349
E: lcollins@la.gov

MAINE
Ms. Janine Bisaillon-Cary
President & State Director of
International Trade
International Trade Center
511 Congress Street, Suite 100
Portland, ME 04101
P: (207) 541-7400
F: (207) 541-7420
E: jbcary@mitc.com

MARYLAND
Mr. Robert Walker
Assistant Secretary
Department of Business &
Economic Development
International Trade and
Investment
401 East Pratt Street
Baltimore, MD 21202
P: (410) 767-0680
E: RWalker
@choosemaryland.org

MICHIGAN
Mr. Michael A. Finney
President & CEO
Economic Development
Corporation
300 North Washington Square
Lansing, MI 48913
P: (517) 241-1400
F: (517) 241-3683

MINNESOTA
Ms. Kathryn Clark
Director
Trade Office
1st National Bank Building,
Suite E200
332 Minnesota Street
St. Paul, MN 55101
P: (651) 259-7489
F: (651) 296-3555
E: kathryn.clark
@state.mn.us

MISSISSIPPI
Mr. Griff Salmon
Director, Global Business
Division
Development Authority
P.O. Box 849
Jackson, MS 39205
P: (601) 359-3155
F: (601) 359-4339
E: gsalmon@mississippi.org

MISSOURI
Ms. Sally Hemenway
Division Director
Division of Business &
Community Services
301 West High Street
P.O. Box 1157
Jefferson City, MO 65102
P: (573) 751-8497
E: missouridevelopment
@ded.mo.gov

MONTANA
Mr. Dore Schwinden
Director
Department of Commerce
301 South Park
P.O. Box 200501
Helena, MT 59620
P: (406) 841-2704
F: (406) 841-2701
E: dschwinden@mt.gov

NEBRASKA
Mr. Richard Baier
Director
Department of Economic
Development
P.O. Box 94666
Lincoln, NE 68509
P: (402) 471-3111
F: (402) 471-3778
E: richard.baier
@nebraska.gov

NEVADA
Mr. Alan Di Stefano
Director, Global Business
Development
Commission on Economic
Development
808 West Nye Lane
Carson City, NV 89703
P: (775) 687-4325
F: (775) 687-9924
E: ccintl
@diversifynevada.com

NEW HAMPSHIRE
Ms. Dawn M. Wivell
Administrator
Office of International
Commerce
172 Pembroke Road
Portsmouth, NH 03301
P: (603) 271-8444
F: (603) 271-6784
E: dwivell@dred.state.nh.us

NEW JERSEY
Ms. Caren S. Franzini
Chief Executive Officer
Economic Development
Authority
36 West State Street
P.O. Box 990
Trenton, NJ 08625
P: (609) 292-1800
F: (609) 292-0885
E: njeda@njeda.com

NEW YORK
Mr. Kenneth Adams
President & CEO
Empire State Development
Corporation
633 Third Avenue
New York, NY 10017
P: (212) 803-3700
F: (212) 803-3715

NORTH CAROLINA
Ms. Jean Davis
Director of International Trade
Department of Commerce
4301 Mail Service Center
Raleigh, NC 27699
P: (919) 715-5746
F: (919) 733-0110
E: jdavis@nccommerce.com

NORTH DAKOTA
Mr. Al Anderson
Commissioner
Department of Commerce
1600 East Century Avenue,
Suite 2
P.O. Box 2057
Bismarck, ND 58503
P: (701) 328-7284
F: (701) 328-5320
E: alrandeson@nd.gov

**NORTHERN MARIANA
ISLANDS**
Mr. Sixto Igisomar
Acting Secretary
Department of Commerce
Caller Box 10007
Saipan, MP 96950
P: (670) 664-3064
F: (670) 664-3067

OHIO
Mr. Scott Kuehn
Director
Global Markets Division
Department of Development
77 South High Street
Columbus, OH 43215
P: (614) 466-5800
E: scott.kuehn
@development.ohio.gov

Ms. Deborah A.
Scherer Mullen
Director
International Trade Division
Department of Development
77 South High Street
Columbus, OH 43215
P: (614) 466-5017
F: (614) 463-1540

OKLAHOMA
Ms. Dessie Apostolova
Director, International Trade
Department of Commerce
Global Business Services
700 N. Greenwood Avenue,
Suite 1400
Tulsa, OK 74106
P: (918) 594-8412
F: (405) 605-2988

Mr. Barry Clark
Director, Global Business
Services
Global Business Services
900 North Stiles Avenue
P.O. Box 26980
Oklahoma City, OK 73126
P: (918) 594-8588
F: (918) 594-8413

OREGON
Ms. Karen Goddin
Business Innovation and Trade
Manager
Business Innovation & Trade
Division
Business Development
Department
775 Summer Street Northeast,
Suite 200
Salem, OR 97301
P: (503) 229-6054
F: (503) 581-5115
E: karen.goddin@state.or.us

International Trade

PENNSYLVANIA
Mr. Peter O'Neill
Executive Director
Office of International Business
Development
Commonwealth Keystone
Building
4th Floor
Harrisburg, PA 17120
P: (717) 720-7374
F: (717) 772-5106

PUERTO RICO
Mr. Jose R. Perez Riera
Executive Director
Industrial Development
Company
#355 FD Roosevelt Avenue
Suite 404
Hato Rey, PR 00918
P: (787) 758-4747
F: (787) 764-1415

RHODE ISLAND
Ms. Katherine Tufts
International Trade Director
Economic Development
Corporation
315 Iron Horse Way, Suite 101
Providence, RI 02908
P: (401) 278-9100 Ext. 139
F: (401) 273-8270
E: ktufts@riedc.com

SOUTH CAROLINA
Mr. Clarke Thompson
Manager, International
Department
Department of Commerce
1201 Main Street, Suite 1600
Columbia, SC 29201
P: (803) 737-0438
F: (803) 806-3508

SOUTH DAKOTA
Mr. Pat Costello
Commissioner
Governor's Office of Economic
Development
711 East Wells Avenue
Pierre, SD 57501
P: (605) 773-3301
F: (605) 773-3256
E: goedinfo@state.sd.us

TENNESSEE
Mr. Kingsley Brock
Assistant Commissioner,
Business Development
Department of Economic &
Community Development
312 Rosa L. Parks Avenue, 11th
Floor
Nashville, TN 37243
P: (615) 532-9821
F: (615) 741-7306
E: kingsley.brock@tn.gov

TEXAS
Mr. Aaron Demerson
Director
Economic Development &
Tourism Division
Office of the Governor
P.O. Box 12428
Austin, TX 78711
P: (512) 936-0101
F: (512) 936-0303

U.S. VIRGIN ISLANDS
Mr. Percival Clouden
Chief Executive Officer
Economic Development
Authority
1050 Norre Gade
P.O. Box 305038
St. Thomas, VI 00803
P: (340) 714-1700

UTAH
Mr. Craig Peterson
Program Director
International Trade &
Diplomacy
Office of Economic
Development
324 South State Street, Suite 500
Salt Lake City, UT 84111
P: (801) 538-8778
F: (801) 538-8888
E: cepeterson@utah.gov

VERMONT
Ms. Noelle MacKay
Commissioner
Department of Economic
Development
1 National Life Drive
Montpelier, VT 05620
P: (802) 828-3080
F: (802) 828-3258
E: noelle.mackay
  @state.vt.us

VIRGINIA
Mr. Jeffrey R. Anderson
Executive Director
Economic Development
Partnership
901 East Byrd Street
P.O. Box 798
Richmond, VA 23218
P: (804) 545-5612
F: (804) 371-6524
E: janderson
  @yesvirginia.org

WASHINGTON
Ms. Patti Brooke
Assistant Director
Business Services Division
P.O. Box 42525
Olympia, WA 98504
P: (360) 725-4035
E: patti.brooke
  @commerce.wa.gov

WEST VIRGINIA
Mr. J. Keith Burdette
Secretary of Commerce
Department of Commerce
Capitol Complex Building 6,
Room 525
1900 Kanawha Boulevard East
Charleston, WV 25305
P: (304) 558-2234
F: (304) 558-1189
E: J.Keith.Burdette@wv.gov

WISCONSIN
Ms. Mary Regel
Director, Bureau of Export
Development
Division of International
Exports
201 West Washington Ave.
Madison, WI 53703
P: (608) 266-1767
F: (608) 266-5551
E: mregel@wisconsin.gov

WYOMING
Mr. Bob Jensen
Chief Executive Officer
Business Council
214 West 15th Street
Cheyenne, WY 82002
P: (307) 777-2800
F: (307) 777-2837
E: bob.jensen
  @wybusiness.org

Juvenile Rehabilitation

Administers rehabilitative facilities and programs for delinquent youth committed by the courts.

ALABAMA

Mr. J. Walter Wood Jr.
Executive Director
Department of Youth Services
P.O. Box 66
Mount Meigs, AL 36057
P: (334) 215-3800
F: (334) 215-1453
E: walter.wood
@dys.alabama.gov

ALASKA

Ms. Barbara Henjum
Director
Division of Juvenile Justice
Department of Health & Social
Services
P.O. Box 110635
Juneau, AK 99811
P: (907) 465-2212
F: (907) 465-2333
E: Hss.djj@alaska.gov

AMERICAN SAMOA

Mr. Tuaolo M. Fruean
Commissioner
Department of Public Safety
American Samoa Government
P.O. Box 3699
Pago Pago, AS 96799
P: (684) 633-1111
F: (684) 633-7296

ARIZONA

Mr. Michael D. Branham
Director
Department of Juvenile
Corrections
Central Administration Office
1624 West Adams
Phoenix, AZ 85007
P: (602) 364-4051
F: (602) 542-5156

ARKANSAS

Mr. Ron Angel
Director
Division of Youth Services
P.O. Box 1437, Slot S501
Little Rock, AR 72203
P: (501) 682-8755
F: (501) 682-1351
E: ron.angel@arkansas.gov

CALIFORNIA

Ms. Rachel Rios
Chief Deputy Secretary
Division of Juvenile Justice
4241 Williamsbourgh Drive,
Suite 201
Sacramento, CA 95823
P: (916) 262-1470
F: (916) 262-1767

COLORADO

Mr. John Gomez
Director
Division of Youth Corrections
4255 S. Knox Court
Denver, CO 80236
P: (303) 866-7390
F: (303) 866-7344

CONNECTICUT

Mr. Leo Arnone
Director
Department of Correction
24 Wolcott Hill Road
Wethersfield, CT 06106
P: (860) 692-7480

DELAWARE

Ms. Carlyse Giddins
Director
Division of Youth Rehabilitative
Services
1825 Faulkland Road
Wilmington, DE 19805
P: (302) 633-2620
F: (302) 633-2636

DISTRICT OF COLUMBIA

Mr. Robert A. Hildum
Interim Director
Department of Youth
Rehabilitation Services
1000 Mt. Olivet Road, Northeast
Washington, DC 20002
P: (202) 576-8175
F: (202) 576-8457
E: dyrs@dc.gov

FLORIDA

Ms. Wansley Waters Jr.
Secretary
Department of Juvenile Justice
2737 Centerview Drive
Knight Building
Tallahassee, FL 32399
P: (850) 488-1850
F: (850) 922-2992
E: Secretary.DJJ
@djj.state.fl.us

GEORGIA

Ms. Amy Howell
Commissioner
Department of Juvenile Justice
3408 Covington Highway
Decatur, GA 30032
P: (404) 508-7200
F: (404) 508-7340
E: amyhowell
@djj.state.ga.us

HAWAII

Mr. David Hipp
Executive Director
Office of Youth Services
820 Mililani Street, Suite 817
Honolulu, HI 96813
P: (808) 587-5706
F: (808) 587-5734

IDAHO

Ms. Sharon Harrigfeld
Director
Department of Juvenile
Corrections
954 West Jefferson Street
P.O. Box 83720
Boise, ID 83720
P: (208) 334-5100
F: (208) 334-5120
E: sharon.harrigfeld
@idjc.idaho.gov

INDIANA

Ms. Ashley Barnett
Youth Division Director
Youth Division
Criminal Justice Institute, Suite
1170
101 West Washington Street,
East Tower
Indianapolis, IN 46204
P: (317) 233-3340
F: (317) 232-4979
E: abarnett@cji.in.gov

IOWA

Ms. Wendy Rickman
Administrator
Division of Adult, Children &
Family Services
Department of Human Services
1305 East Walnut
Des Moines, IA 50319
P: (515) 281-5521
F: (515) 242-6036
E: wrickma@dhs.state.ia.us

KANSAS

Mr. Curtis Whitten
Commissioner
Juvenile Justice Authority
714 Southwest Jackson Avenue,
Suite 300
Topeka, KS 66603
P: (785) 296-4213
F: (785) 296-1412

KENTUCKY

Mr. J. Ronald Haws
Commissioner
Department of Juvenile Justice
1025 Capital Center Drive
Frankfort, KY 40601
P: (502) 573-2738
F: (502) 573-4308

LOUISIANA

Dr. Mary L. Livers
Deputy Secretary
Office of Juvenile Justice
7919 Independence Boulevard
P.O. Box 66458
Baton Rouge, LA 70896
P: (225) 287-7900
F: (225) 287-7987
E: Debbie.Linder@la.gov

MAINE

Mr. Bartlett H. Stoodley
Associate Commissioner
Juvenile Services Division
111 State House Station
Augusta, ME 04333
P: (207) 287-4362
F: (207) 287-4370
E: bartlett.h.stoodley
@maine.gov

MARYLAND

Mr. Sam Abed
Secretary
Department of Juvenile Services
One Center Plaza
120 West Fayette Street
Baltimore, MD 21201
P: (410) 230-3100
F: (410) 333-4199
E: AbedS@djs.state.md.us

MASSACHUSETTS

Ms. Jane E. Tewksbury
Commissioner
Department of Youth Services
27 Wormwood Street, Suite 400
Boston, MA 02110
P: (617) 727-7575
F: (617) 727-0696

Juvenile Rehabilitation

MICHIGAN
Ms. Maura D. Corrigan
Director
Department of Human Services
235 South Grand Avenue
P.O. Box 30037
Lansing, MI 48909
P: (517) 373-2035
F: (517) 335-6101
E: dhsweb@michigan.gov

Mr. Kurt Warner
Acting Director
Bureau of Juvenile Justice
235 South Grand Avenue
P.O. Box 30037
Lansing, MI 48909
P: (517) 335-3489
F: (517) 241-5632
E: WarnerK5@michigan.gov

MINNESOTA
Mr. Tom Roy
Commissioner
Department of Corrections
1450 Energy Park Drive, Suite 200
St. Paul, MN 55108
P: (651) 361-7226
F: (651) 642-0414
E: tom.roy@state.mn.us

MISSOURI
Mr. Tim Decker
Director
Division of Youth Services
3418 Knipp, Suite A-1
P.O. Box 447
Jefferson City, MO 65102
P: (573) 751-3324
F: (573) 526-4494
E: tim.decker@dss.mo.gov

MONTANA
Mr. Mike Ferriter
Director
Department of Corrections
1539 11th Avenue
P.O. Box 201301
Helena, MT 59620
P: (406) 444-3930
F: (406) 444-4920
E: mferriter@asca.net

NEBRASKA
Mr. Todd Reckling
Director
Division of Children & Family Services
Department of Health & Human Services
P.O. Box 95026
Lincoln, NE 60509
P: (402) 471-1878

NEVADA
Ms. Diane J. Comeaux
Administrator
Division of Child & Family Services
Department of Health & Human Services
4126 Technology Way, Room 100
Carson City, NV 89706
P: (775) 684-4000
F: (775) 684-4010
E: dcomeaux@dcfs.nv.gov

NEW HAMPSHIRE
Mr. Jay Apicelli
Interim Director
Division for Juvenile Justice Services
Department of Health & Human Services
1056 North River Road
Manchester, NH 03104
P: (603) 625-5471
F: (603) 625-1110
E: jay.a.apicelli
   @dhhs.state.nh.us

NEW JERSEY
Ms. Veleria N. Lawson
Executive Director
Juvenile Justice Commission
1001 Spruce Street, Suite 202
P.O. Box 107
Trenton, NJ 08625
P: (609) 292-1400
F: (609) 943-4611

NEW MEXICO
Ms. Yolanda Berumen-Deines
Secretary
Children, Youth & Families Department
P.O. Drawer 5160
Santa Fe, NM 87502
P: (505) 827-7602

NEW YORK
Ms. Gladys Carrion
Commissioner
Office of Children & Family Services
Capitol View Office Park
52 Washington Street
Rensselaer, NY 12144
P: (518) 473-7793
F: (518) 486-7550

NORTH CAROLINA
Ms. Linda Hayes
Secretary
Department of Juvenile Justice & Delinquency Prevention
1801 Mail Service Center
Raleigh, NC 27699
P: (919) 733-3388

NORTH DAKOTA
Ms. Lisa Bjergaard
Director
Department of Corrections & Rehabilitation
Division of Juvenile Services
3100 Railroad Avenue
Bismarck, ND 58501
P: (701) 328-6362
F: (701) 328-6651
E: lbjergaa@nd.gov

NORTHERN MARIANA ISLANDS
Ms. Debra Inos
Director
Division of Youth Services
Caller Box 10007, Capital Hill
Saipan, MP 96950
P: (670) 664-2550
F: (670) 664-2560

OHIO
Mr. Harvey J. Reed
Director
Department of Youth Services
51 North High Street
Columbus, OH 43215
P: (614) 466-4314
F: (614) 752-9078

OKLAHOMA
Mr. Robert E. Christian
Executive Director
Office of Juvenile Affairs
3812 North Santa Fe, Suite 400
P.O. Box 268812
Oklahoma City, OK 73126
P: (405) 530-2806
F: (405) 530-2890
E: gene.christian
   @oja.ok.gov

OREGON
Ms. Colette S. Peters
Director
Youth Authority
530 Center Street, Northeast, Suite 200
Salem, OR 97301
P: (503) 373-7212
F: (503) 373-7622
E: Colette.Peters
   @oya.state.or.us

PUERTO RICO
Mr. Miguel A.
   Pereira Castillo
Administrator
Juvenile Institutions Administration
P.O. Box 19175
San Juan, PR 00910
P: (787) 767-9600
F: (787) 765-3394

RHODE ISLAND
Mr. Warren Hurlbut
Superintendent
Juvenile Correctional Services
101 Friendship Street
Providence, RI 02903
P: (401) 462-7200

SOUTH CAROLINA
Ms. Margaret Barber
Director
Department of Juvenile Justice
4900 Broad River Road
P.O. Box 21069
Columbia, SC 29221
P: (803) 896-9749
F: (803) 896-9767

SOUTH DAKOTA
Mr. Doug Herrmann
Director, Juvenile Services
Department of Corrections
Juvenile Community Corrections
1600 Sedivy Lane
Rapid City, SD 57701
P: (605) 394-6645
F: (605) 394-6649
E: doug.herrmann
   @state.sd.us

TENNESSEE
Dr. Viola Miller
Commissioner
Department of Children's Services
Cordell Hull Building, 7th Floor
436 Sixth Avenue, North
Nashville, TN 37243
P: (615) 741-9699
F: (615) 532-8079

Ms. Kate O'Day
Commissioner
Department of Children's Services
Cordell Hull Building, 7th Floor
436 Sixth Avenue, North
Nashville, TN 37243
P: (615) 741-9699
F: (615) 532-8079

TEXAS
Ms. Vicki Spriggs
Executive Director
Juvenile Probation Commission
4900 North Lamar
P.O. Box 13547
Austin, TX 78711
P: (512) 424-6682
F: (512) 424-6717

U.S. VIRGIN ISLANDS
Mr. Christopher Finch
Commissioner
Department of Human Services
Knud Hansen Complex,
Building A
1303 Hospital Grounds
St. Thomas, VI 00802
P: (340) 774-0930
F: (340) 774-3466

UTAH
Mr. Dan Maldonado
Director
Division of Juvenile Justice
Services
Department of Human Services
195 North 1950 West
Salt Lake City, UT 84116
P: (801) 538-4330
F: (801) 538-4334
E: lschauer@utah.gov

VERMONT
Ms. Cindy K. Walcott
Deputy Commissioner
Family Services Division
Department for Children &
Families
103 South Main Street, Osgood 3
Waterbury, VT 05671
P: (802) 241-2131
F: (802) 241-2407
E: Cindy.Walcott
   @ahs.state.vt.us

VIRGINIA
Ms. Helivi L. Holland
Executive Director
Department of Juvenile Justice
700 East Franklin Street
Richmond, VA 23219
P: (804) 371-0704
F: (804) 371-0773
E: helivi.holland
   @djj.virginia.gov

WASHINGTON
Mr. John Clayton
Assistant Secretary
Juvenile Rehabilitation
Administration
14th & Jefferson Street
P.O. Box 45045
Olympia, WA 98504
P: (360) 902-7804
F: (360) 902-7848

WEST VIRGINIA
Mr. Dale Humphreys
Director
Division of Juvenile Services
1200 Quarrier Street
Charleston, WV 25301
P: (304) 558-9800
F: (304) 558-6032
E: dhumphreys
   @djs.state.wv.us

WISCONSIN
Mr. Margaret Carpenter
Administrator
Division of Juvenile Corrections
3099 East Washington Avenue
P.O. Box 8930
Madison, WI 53708
P: (608) 240-5901
E: margaret.carpenter
   @wisconsin.gov

WYOMING
Mr. Steve Corsi
Director of Family Services
Department of Family Services
Hathaway Building, 3rd Floor
2300 Capitol Avenue
Cheyenne, WY 82002
P: (307) 777-7564
F: (307) 777-7747

Labor

Overall responsibility for administering and enforcing the state's labor laws.

ALABAMA
Mr. Jim Bennett
Commissioner
Department of Labor
P.O. Box 303500
Montgomery, AL 36130
P: (334) 242-3460
F: (334) 240-3417
E: jbennett
@alalabor.alabama.gov

ALASKA
Mr. Click Bishop
Commissioner
Department of Labor &
Workforce Development
P.O. Box 21149
Juneau, AK 99802
P: (907) 465-2700
F: (907) 465-2784
E: commissioner.labor
@ak.gov

ARIZONA
Ms. Laura L. McGrory
Director
Industrial Commission
800 West Washington Street
Phoenix, AZ 85007
P: (602) 542-4411
F: (602) 542-7889
E: lmcgrory@ica.state.az.us

ARKANSAS
Mr. James L. Salkeld
Director
Department of Labor
10421 West Markham Street
Suite 100
Little Rock, AR 72205
P: (501) 682-4541
F: (501) 682-4535
E: james.salkeld
@arkansas.gov

CALIFORNIA
Ms. Julie Su
Commissioner
Division of labor Standards &
Enforcement
455 Golden Gate Avenue, 9th
Floor
San Francisco, CA 94102
P: (415) 703-4810
F: (415) 703-4807

COLORADO
Ms. Ellen Golombek
Executive Director
Department of Labor &
Employment
633 17th Street, Suite 201
Denver, CO 80202
P: (303) 318-8000
F: (303) 318-8048
E: egolombek@state.co.us

CONNECTICUT
Mr. Glenn Marshall
Commissioner
Department of Labor
200 Folly Brook Boulevard
Wethersfield, CT 06109
P: (860) 263-6505
F: (860) 263-6529
E: glenn.marshall@ct.gov

DELAWARE
Mr. John McMahon
Secretary of Labor
Department of Labor
4425 North Market Street, 4th
Floor
Wilmington, DE 19802
P: (302) 761-8000
F: (302) 761-6621
E: john.mcmahon@state.de.us

DISTRICT OF COLUMBIA
Ms. Lisa Maria Mallory
Acting Director
Department of Employment
Services
4058 Minnesota Avenue,
Northeast
Washington, DC 20019
P: (202) 724-7000
F: (202) 673-6993
E: does@dc.gov

FLORIDA
Ms. Cynthia R. Lorenzo
Director
Agency for Workforce
Innovation
107 East Madison Street
MSC 110, Caldwell Building
Tallahassee, FL 32399
P: (850) 245-7298
F: (850) 921-3223
E: cynthia.lorenzo
@flaawi.com

GEORGIA
Hon. Mark Butler (R)
Commissioner
Department of Labor
148 International Boulevard
Northeast
Atlanta, GA 30303
P: (404) 232-7300
F: (404) 656-2683
E: mark.butler
@dol.state.ga.us

GUAM
Ms. Leah Beth Naholowaa
Director
Department of Labor
Government of Guam
P.O. Box 9970
Tamuning, GU 96931
P: (671) 647-6510
F: (671) 674-6517

HAWAII
Mr. Dwight Y. Takamine
Director
Department of Labor &
Industrial Relations
830 Punchbowl Stree, Room
321
Honolulu, HI 96813
P: (808) 586-8865
F: (808) 586-9099

IDAHO
Mr. Roger B. Madsen
Director
Department of Labor
317 West Main Street
Boise, ID 83735
P: (208) 332-3579
F: (208) 334-6430
E: rmadsen@cl.idaho.gov

ILLINOIS
Ms. Catherine M. Shannon
Director
Department of Labor
160 North LaSalle Street, Suite
C-1300
Chicago, IL 60601
P: (312) 793-1808
F: (312) 793-5257
E: catherine.shannon
@illinois.gov

INDIANA
Ms. Lori A. Torres
Commissioner
Department of Labor
Indiana Government
Center-South
402 West Washington Street,
Room W-195
Indianapolis, IN 46204
P: (317) 232-2655
F: (317) 974-2001
E: ltorres@dol.in.gov

IOWA
Mr. David Neil
Commissioner
Division of Labor Services
1000 East Grand Avenue
Des Moines, IA 50319
P: (515) 281-3447
F: (515) 281-4698
E: dave.neil@iwd.iowa.gov

KANSAS
Ms. Karin Brownlee
Secretary
Department of Labor
401 Southwest Topeka
Boulevard
Topeka, KS 66603
P: (785) 296-5058
F: (785) 368-5286
E: karin.brownlee
@dol.ks.gov

KENTUCKY
Mr. Mark Brown
Secretary
Labor Cabinet
1047 US Highway 127 South
Frankfort, KY 40601
P: (502) 564-3070
F: (502) 696-5205
E: marks.brown@ky.gov

LOUISIANA
Mr. Curt Eysink
Executive Director
Workforce Commission
1001 North 23rd Street
Baton Rouge, LA 70802
P: (225) 342-3111
F: (225) 342-3778
E: ceysink@lwc.la.gov

MAINE
Ms. Laura Boyett
Acting Commissioner
Department of Labor
P.O. Box 259
Augusta, ME 04332
P: (207) 287-3787
F: (207) 623-7934
E: luara.l.boyett@maine.gov

MARYLAND
Mr. Alexander M. Sanchez
Secretary
Department of Labor, LIcensing
& Regulation
500 North Calvert Street #401
Balitmore, MD 21201
P: (410) 230-6020
F: (410) 333-0853
E: asanchez
@dllr.state.md.us

MASSACHUSETTS
Ms. Joanne F. Goldstein
Secretary
Executive Office of Labor &
Workforce Development
One Ashburton Place
Suite 2112
Boston, MA 02108
P: (617) 626-7122
F: (617) 727-1090
E: joanne.goldstein
@state.ma.us

Mr. George E. Noel
Director
Department of Labor
1 Ashburton Place, Room 2112
Boston, MA 02108
P: (617) 626-7122
F: (617) 727-1090
E: george.noel@state.ma.us

MICHIGAN
Mr. Steven Hilfinger
Director
Department of Licensing &
Regulatory Affairs
P.O. Box 30004
Lansing, MI 48909
P: (517) 373-1820
F: (517) 373-2129
E: bcslic@michigan.gov

MINNESOTA
Mr. Ken Peterson
Commissioner
Department of Labor & Industry
443 Lafayette Road North
St. Paul, MN 55155
P: (651) 284-5010
F: (651) 284-5721
E: dli.commissioner
@state.mn.us

MISSISSIPPI
Mr. Les Range
Executive Director
Department of Employment
Security
1235 Echelon Parkway
P.O. Box 1699
Jackson, MS 39215
P: (601) 321-6100
F: (601) 321-6104
E: lrange@mdes.ms.gov

MISSOURI
Mr. Lawrence G. Rebman
Director
Department of Labor &
Industrial Relations
P.O. Box 504
Jefferson City, MO 65102
P: (573) 751-4091
F: (573) 751-4945
E: larry.rebman
@labor.mo.gov

MONTANA
Mr. Keith Kelly
Commissioner
Department of Labor & Industry
P.O. Box 1728
Helena, MT 59624
P: (406) 444-9091
F: (406) 444-1394
E: dliquestions@mt.gov

NEBRASKA
Ms. Catherine D. Lang
Commissioner of Labor
Department of Labor
P.O. Box 94600
Lincoln, NE 68509
P: (402) 471-9000
F: (402) 471-2318
E: catherine.lang
@nebraska.gov

NEVADA
Mr. Michael J. Tanchek
Commissioner
Office of the Labor
Commissioner
675 Fairview Drive, Suite 226
Carson City, NV 89701
P: (775) 687-4850
F: (775) 687-6409
E: mail1
@laborcommissioner.com

NEW HAMPSHIRE
Mr. George N. Copadis
Commissioner of Labor
Department of Labor
95 Pleasant Street
Concord, NH 03301
P: (603) 271-3171
F: (603) 271-6852
E: gcopadis
@labor.state.nh.us

NEW JERSEY
Mr. Harold Wirths
Commissioner
Department of Labor &
Workforce Development
P.O. Box 110
Trenton, NJ 08625
P: (609) 292-2323
F: (609) 633-9271
E: hal.wirths
@dol.state.nj.us

NEW MEXICO
Ms. Celina Bussey
Secretary
Department of Workforce
Solutions
401 Broadway Northeast
Albuquerque, NM 87103
P: (505) 841-8405
F: (505) 841-8491

NEW YORK
Ms. Colleen C. Gardner
Commissioner
Department of Labor
W. Averell Harriman State
Office Campus
Building 12
Albany, NY 12240
P: (518) 457-9000
F: (518) 485-6297
E: colleen.gardner
@labor.state.ny.us

NORTH CAROLINA
Hon. Cherie K. Berry (R)
Commissioner
Department of Labor
1101 Mail Service Center
Raleigh, NC 27699
P: (919) 733-0359
F: (919) 733-7640
E: commissioners.office
@nclabor.com

NORTH DAKOTA
Mr. Tony Weiler
Commissioner of Labor
Department of Labor
600 East Boulevard Avenue
Department 406
Bismarck, ND 58505
P: (701) 328-2660
F: (701) 328-2031
E: tjweiler@nd.gov

OHIO
Mr. Randall Weber
Chief
Bureau of Labor & Worker
Safety
Department of Commerce
P.O. Box 4009
Reynoldsburg, OH 43068
P: (614) 644-2450

OKLAHOMA
Hon. Mark Costello
Commissioner of Labor
Department of Labor
3017 North Stiles, Suite 100
Oklahoma City, OK 73105
P: (405) 521-6100
F: (405) 521-6018

OREGON
Hon. Brad Avakian (D)
Commissioner
Bureau of Labor & Industries
800 Northeast Oregon Street
Suite 1045
Portland, OR 97232
P: (503) 731-4070
F: (503) 731-4103
E: brad.avakian@state.or.us

PENNSYLVANIA
Ms. Julia Hearthway
Acting Secretary
Department of Labor & Industry
651 Boas Street, Room 1700
Harrisburg, PA 17121
P: (717) 787-5279
F: (717) 787-8826

PUERTO RICO
Mr. Miguel Romero
Director
Department of Labor & Human
Resources
P.O. Box 191020
San Juan, PR 00919
P: (787) 754-5353
F: (787) 756-1149

Labor

RHODE ISLAND
Mr. Charles J. Fogarty
Director
Department of Labor & Training
1511 Pontiac Avenue
Cranston, RI 02920
P: (401) 462-8000
F: (401) 462-8872
E: director-dlt@dlt.ri.gov

SOUTH CAROLINA
Ms. Catherine Templeton
Director
Department of Labor, Licensing
& Regulation
P.O. Box 11329
Columbia, SC 29211
P: (803) 896-4390
F: (803) 896-4393
E: templetonc@llr.sc.gov

SOUTH DAKOTA
Ms. Pamela S. Roberts
Secretary
Department of Labor
700 Governors Drive
Pierre, SD 57501
P: (605) 773-3101
F: (605) 773-4211
E: pamela.roberts
    @state.sd.us

TENNESSEE
Ms. Karla Davis
Commissioner
Department of Labor &
Workforce Development
Andrew Johnson Tower
710 James Robertson Parkway
Nashville, TN 37243
P: (615) 741-6642
F: (615) 741-5078
E: karla.davis@state.tn.us

TEXAS
Mr. Ronald G. Congleton
Commissioner Representing
Labor
Workforce Commission
101 East 15th Street, Room 674
Austin, TX 78778
P: (512) 463-2829
F: (512) 475-2152
E: ronald.congleton
    @twc.state.tx.us

Mr. Larry E. Temple
Executive Director
Workforce Commission
101 East 15th Street
Austin, TX 78778
P: (512) 463-0735
F: (512) 475-2321
E: larry.temple
    @twc.state.tx.us

U.S. VIRGIN ISLANDS
Mr. Albert Bryan Jr.
Commissioner of Labor
Department of Labor
2203 Church Street,
Christiansted
St. Croix, VI 00820
P: (340) 773-1994
F: (340) 773-0094
E: abryan@vidol.gov

UTAH
Ms. Sherrie M. Hayashi
Commissioner
Labor Commission
160 East 300 South, 3rd Floor
P.O. Box 146600
Salt Lake City, UT 84114
P: (801) 530-6848
F: (801) 530-6390
E: shayashi@utah.gov

VERMONT
Ms. Annie Noonan
Commissioner
Department of Labor
P.O. Box 488
Montpelier, VT 05602
P: (802) 828-4301
F: (802) 828-4022
E: annie.noonan@state.vt.us

VIRGINIA
Mr. Courtney Malveaux
Commissioner
Department of Labor & Industry
13 South 13th Street
Richmond, VA 23219
P: (804) 786-2377
F: (804) 371-6524
E: courtney.malveaux
    @doli.virginia.gov

WASHINGTON
Ms. Judy Schurke
Director
Department of Labor &
Industries
P.O. Box 44001
Olympia, WA 98504
P: (360) 902-4203
F: (360) 902-4202
E: scju235@lni.wa.gov

WEST VIRGINIA
Mr. David W. Mullins
Commissioner
Division of Labor
Bureau of Commerce
Capitol Complex, Building 6,
Room B-749
Charleston, WV 25305
P: (304) 558-7890
F: (304) 558-3797
E: david.w.mullins@wv.gov

WISCONSIN
Mr. Manny Perez
Secretary
Department of Workforce
Development
P.O. Box 7946
Madison, WI 53707
P: (608) 267-9692
F: (608) 266-1784
E: manuel.perez
    @dwd.wisconsin.gov

WYOMING
Ms. Joan Evans
Director
Department of Workforce
Services
122 West 25th Street
Herschler Building, 2 East
Cheyenne, WY 82002
P: (307) 777-8650
E: jevans1@state.wy.us

Law Enforcement

Conducts state-level criminal investigations.

ALABAMA
Colonel Hugh B. McCall
Director
Department of Public Safety
301 South Ripley Street
P.O. Box 1511
Montgomery, AL 36102
P: (334) 242-4394
F: (334) 242-0512
E: director@alalinc.net

ALASKA
Mr. Joseph A. Masters
Commissioner
Department of Public Safety
5700 East Tudor Road
P.O. Box 111200
Anchorage, AK 99811
P: (907) 269-5086
F: (907) 269-4543
E: joseph.masters
     @alaska.gov

AMERICAN SAMOA
Mr. Tuaolo M. Fruean
Commissioner
Department of Public Safety
American Samoa Government
P.O. Box 3699
Pago Pago, AS 96799
P: (684) 633-1111
F: (684) 633-7296

ARIZONA
Mr. Robert Halliday
Director
Department of Public Safety
2102 West Encanto Boulevard
P.O. Box 6638
Phoenix, AZ 85005
P: (602) 223-2000
F: (602) 223-2917

CALIFORNIA
Hon. Kamala Harris (D)
Attorney General
Office of the Attorney General
1300 I Street, Suite 1740
Sacramento, CA 95814
P: (916) 445-9555

COLORADO
Mr. Ron Sloan
Director
Bureau of Investigation
Department of Public Safety
690 Kipling Street
Lakewood, CO 80215
P: (303) 239-4201
F: (303) 235-0568

CONNECTICUT
Mr. Kevin T. Kane
Chief State's Attorney
Division of Criminal Justice
300 Corporate Place
Rocky Hill, CT 06067
P: (860) 258-5800
F: (860) 258-5858
E: conndcj@po.state.ct.us

DELAWARE
Colonel Robert M. Coupe
Superintendent
State Police
1441 North DuPont Highway
Dover, DE 19901
P: (302) 739-5960
F: (302) 739-5966

DISTRICT OF COLUMBIA
Ms. Cathy L. Lanier
Chief of Police
Metropolitan Police Department
300 Indiana Avenue, Northwest
Washington, DC 20001
P: (202) 727-4218
F: (202) 727-9524
E: cathy.lanier@dc.gov

FLORIDA
Mr. Gerald M. Bailey
Commissioner
Department of Law
Enforcement
2331 Phillips Road
P.O. Box 1489
Tallahassee, FL 32302
P: (850) 410-7001
E: GeraldBailey
     @fdle.state.fl.us

GEORGIA
Mr. Vernon M. Keenan
Director
Bureau of Investigation
3121 Panthersville Road
P.O. Box 370808
Decatur, GA 30037
P: (404) 244-2501
F: (404) 270-8352
E: vernon.keenan@gbi.ga.gov

GUAM
Mr. Paul Suba
Commander
Police Department
233 Central Avenue
Tiyan, GU 96913
P: (671) 475-8512
F: (671) 472-2825

HAWAII
Mr. Keith Kamita
Deputy Director for Law
Enforcement
Department of Public Safety
919 Ala Moana Boulevard,
Room 400
Honolulu, HI 96814
P: (808) 587-2562
F: (808) 587-1282

IDAHO
Col. Jerry Russell
Director
State Police
P.O. Box 700
Meridian, ID 83680
P: (208) 884-7003
F: (208) 884-7090
E: jerry.russell
     @isp.idaho.gov

ILLINOIS
Mr. Hiram Grau
State Director
State Police
2200 South Dirksen Parkway
Springfield, IL 62703
P: (217) 782-7263
E: hiram.grau@illinois.gov

INDIANA
Dr. Paul Whitesell
Superintendent
State Police
100 North Senate Avenue, Room
IGCN N340
Indianapolis, IN 46204
P: (317) 232-8241
E: pwhitesell@isp.in.gov

IOWA
Mr. Larry L. Noble
Commissioner
Department of Public Safety
215 East 7th Street
Des Moines, IA 50319
P: (515) 725-6182
E: noble@dps.state.ia.us

KANSAS
Mr. Robert E. Blecha
Director
Bureau of Investigation
1620 Southwest Tyler Street
Topeka, KS 66612
P: (785) 296-8200

KENTUCKY
Mr. Rodney Brewer
Commissioner
State Police
919 Versailles Road
Frankfort, KY 40601
P: (502) 695-6300
F: (502) 573-1479

LOUISIANA
Lt. Col. Val Penouilh
Deputy Superintendent
Bureau of Investigations
7919 Independence Boulevard
Baton Rouge, LA 70806
P: (225) 922-1467

MAINE
Hon. William J.
     Schneider (R)
Attorney General
Office of the Attorney General
State House Station 6
Augusta, ME 04333
P: (207) 626-8800

MARYLAND
Colonel Terrence Sheridan
Superintendent
Department of State Police
1201 Reisterstown Road
Pikesville, MD 21208
P: (410) 653-4219
F: (410) 653-4269
E: superintendent@mdsp.org

MASSACHUSETTS
Colonel Marian McGovern
Superintendent
State Police
470 Worcester Road
Framingham, MA 01702
P: (508) 820-2300
F: (617) 727-6874

MICHIGAN
Colonel Kriste Kibbey Etue
Director
State Police
714 South Harrison Road
East Lansing, MI 48823
P: (517) 336-6157
F: (517) 336-6551

MINNESOTA
Ms. Ramona Dohman
Commissioner
Department of Public Safety
Bremer Tower, Suite 1000
445 Minnesota Street
St. Paul, MN 55101
P: (651) 201-7160
F: (651) 297-5728
E: Mona.Dohman@state.mn.us

Law Enforcement

MISSISSIPPI
Mr. Albert Santa Cruz
Commissioner
Department of Public Safety
P.O. Box 958
Jackson, MS 39205
P: (601) 987-1212
F: (601) 987-1488
E: commissioner
  @mdps.state.ms.us

MISSOURI
Mr. George Lombardi
Director
Department of Corrections
2729 Plaza Drive
Jefferson City, MO 65109
P: (573) 751-2389
F: (573) 751-4099

MONTANA
Hon. Steve Bullock (D)
Attorney General
Department of Justice
215 North Sanders, Third Floor
Helena, MT 59620
P: (406) 444-2026
F: (404) 444-3549
E: contactdoj@mt.gov

NEBRASKA
Colonel David Sankey
Superintendent of Law
Enforcement & Public Safety
State Police
P.O. Box 94907
Lincoln, NE 68509
P: (402) 471-4545
F: (402) 479-4002

NEVADA
Ms. Elizabeth Conboy
Chief
Investigations Division
Department of Public Safety
555 Wright Way
Carson City, NV 89711
P: (775) 684-7412
F: (775) 687-4405

NEW HAMPSHIRE
Colonel Robert L. Quinn
Director
Division of State Police
Department of Safety
33 Hazen Drive
Concord, NH 03305
P: (603) 271-2450
F: (603) 271-1153
E: robert.quinn@dos.nh.gov

NEW JERSEY
Col. Rick Fuentes
Superintendent
State Police
P.O. Box 7068
West Trenton, NJ 08628
P: (609) 882-2000
F: (609) 530-4383

NEW MEXICO
Mr. Robert Shilling
State Police Chief
Department of Public Safety
4491 Cerrillos Road
P.O. Box 1628
Santa Fe, NM 87504
P: (505) 827-9219
F: (505) 827-3395
E: robert.shilling
  @state.nm.us

NEW YORK
Mr. Joseph D'Amico
Superintendent
State Police
1220 Washington Avenue,
Building 22
Albany, NY 12226
P: 518) 457-6721

NORTH CAROLINA
Mr. Greg McLeod
Director
State Bureau of Investigation
P.O. Box 29500
Raleigh, NC 27626
P: (919) 662-4500
F: (919) 662-4523

NORTH DAKOTA
Mr. Jerry Kemmet
Director
Bureau of Criminal
Investigation
Office of Attorney General
P.O. Box 1054
Bismark, ND 58502
P: (701) 328-5500
F: (701) 328-5510
E: jkemmet@nd.gov

Colonel James Prochniak
Superintendent
Highway Patrol
600 East Boulevard Avenue
Department 504
Bismarck, ND 58505
P: (701) 328-2455
F: (701) 328-1717
E: jprochni@nd.gov

OHIO
Mr. Thomas P. Charles
Director
Department of Public Safety
1970 West Broad Street
P.O. Box 182081
Columbus, OH 43223
P: (614) 466-3383
F: (614) 466-0433

OKLAHOMA
Mr. Michael C. Thompson
Secretary of Safety & Security
Department of Public Safety
P.O. Box 11415
Oklahoma City, OK 73136
P: (405) 425-2424

PENNSYLVANIA
Mr. Frank Noonan
Commissioner
State Police
3rd Floor, Department
Headquarters
1800 Elmerton Avenue
Harrisburg, PA 17110
P: (717) 783-5558
F: (717) 787-2948

PUERTO RICO
Mr. Jose Figueroa Sancha
Superintendent
Puerto Rico Police
P.O. Box 70166
San Juan, PR 00936
P: (787) 793-1234
F: (787) 781-0080

RHODE ISLAND
Colonel Steven G. O'Donnell
Superintendent
State Police
311 Danielson Pike
North Scituate, RI 02857
P: (401) 444-1000
F: (401) 444-1105
E: sodonnell
  @risp.state.ri.us

Lt. Col. Raymond S. White
Acting Superintendent & Interim
Commissioner
Department of Public Safety
Headquarters
311 Danielson Pike
Scituate, RI 02857
P: (401) 444-1010
F: (401) 444-1105
E: rwhite@risp.dps.ri.gov

SOUTH CAROLINA
Mr. Reginald I. Lloyd
Director
State Law Enforcement Division
4400 Broad River Road
P.O. Box 21398
Columbia, SC 29221
P: (803) 737-9000
F: (803) 896-7041

SOUTH DAKOTA
Mr. Bryan Gortmaker
Director
Division of Criminal
Investigation
1302 East Highway 14, Suite 5
Pierre, SD 57501
P: (605) 773-3331
F: (605) 773-4629
E: atghelp@state.sd.us

TENNESSEE
Mr. Mark Gwyn
Director
Bureau of Investigation
901 R.S. Gass Boulevard
Nashville, TN 37216
P: (615) 744-4000

TEXAS
Mr. Timothy Braaten
Executive Director
Commission on Law
Enforcement Officer Standards
& Education
6330 East Highway 290, Suite
200
Austin, TX 78723
P: (512) 936-7700
F: (512) 936-7714
E: timothyb
  @tcleose.state.tx.us

U.S. VIRGIN ISLANDS
Mr. Novelle E. Francis Jr.
Commissioner
Police Department
Alexander Farrelly Criminal
Justice Ctr.
Charlotte Amalie
St. Thomas, VI 00802
P: (340) 774-2211
F: (340) 715-5517

UTAH
Col. Daniel Fuhr
Superintendent
Department of Public Safety
Utah Highway Patrol
4501 South 2700 West, P.O. Box
141775
Salt Lake City, UT 84114
P: (801) 965-4379
F: (801) 965-4716
E: dfuhr@utah.gov

VIRGINIA
Col. W. Steven Flaherty
Superintendent
Department of State Police
7700 Midlothian Turnpike
P.O. Box 27472
Richmond, VA 23235
P: (804) 674-2087
F: (804) 674-2132
E: steve.flaherty
    @vsp.virginia.gov

WASHINGTON
Mr. John R. Batiste
Chief
State Patrol
General Administration Building
P.O. Box 42600
Olympia, WA 98504
P: (360) 596-4101

WEST VIRGINIA
Colonel Timothy S. Pack
Superintendent
State Police
725 Jefferson Road
South Charleston, WV 25309
P: (304) 746-2111
F: (304) 746-2230
E: tspack@wvsp.state.wv.us

WISCONSIN
Mr. Edward F. Wall
Administrator
Division of Criminal
Investigation
17 West Main Street
P.O. Box 7865
Madison, WI 53707
P: (608) 266-1221
F: (608) 267-2779
E: edward.wall
    @wisconsin.gov

WYOMING
Mr. Forrest Bright
Director
Division of Criminal
Investigation
316 West 22nd Street
Cheyenne, WY 82002
P: (307) 777-7181
F: (307) 777-7252

Law Library

Legal resource for the state's highest court.

ALABAMA
Mr. Timothy A. Lewis
Director & State Law Librarian
State Law Library
300 Dexter Avenue
Montgomery, AL 36104
P: (334) 229-0560
F: (334) 242-4484
E: director@alalinc.net

ALASKA
Ms. Catherine Lemann
Law Librarian
State Court Law Library
303 K Street
Anchorage, AK 99501
P: (907) 264-0583
F: (907) 264-0733
E: clemann
@courts.state.ak.us

AMERICAN SAMOA
Hon. Fepulea'i A.
Ripley Jr.
Attorney General
Office of the Attorney General
American Samoa Government
Executive Office Building,
Utulei
Pago Pago, AS 96799
P: (684) 633-4163
F: (684) 633-1838

ARIZONA
Ms. Janet Fisher
Acting Director
State Library, Archives &
Public Records
1700 West Washington Street,
Suite 200
Phoenix, AZ 85007
P: (602) 926-4035
F: (602) 256-7983

ARKANSAS
Ms. Ava Hicks
Director
Supreme Court Library
Justice Building, 1st Floor North
625 Marshall
Little Rock, AR 72201
P: (501) 682-2147
F: (501) 682-6877
E: ava.hicks
@mail.state.ar.us

CALIFORNIA
Mr. Mark Linneman
Manager
Witkin State Law Library
P.O. Box 942837
Sacramento, CA 94237
P: (916) 653-3883
E: mlinneman@library.ca.gov

COLORADO
Mr. Dan Cordova
Librarian
State Law Library, Judicial
Branch
State Judicial Building, #B112
2 East 14th Avenue
Denver, CO 80203
P: (303) 837-3720
F: (303) 864-4510

CONNECTICUT
Ms. Maureen Well
Deputy Director
Law Libraries
Judicial Branch
90 Washington Street, Third
Floor
Hartford, CT 06106
P: (860) 706-5145
F: (860) 706-5086
E: maureen.well@jud.ct.gov

DELAWARE
Ms. Karen Parrott
Law Librarian
State Law Library
414 Federal Street, #100
Dover, DE 19901
P: (302) 739-5467
F: (302) 739-6721

DISTRICT OF COLUMBIA
Ms. Letty Limbach
Librarian
Court of Appeals
500 Indiana Avenue, Northwest
Washington, DC 20001
P: (202) 879-2767

FLORIDA
Ms. Billie J. Blaine
Librarian
Supreme Court Library
500 South Duvall Street
Tallahassee, FL 32399
P: (850) 488-8919
F: (850) 922-5219

GUAM
Mr. Andrew Quenga
Executive Director/Librarian
Law Library
141 San Ramon Street
Hagatna, GU 96910
P: (671) 477-7623
F: (671) 472-1246
E: gllexecdir@teleguam.net

HAWAII
Ms. Jenny Fujinaka
Law Librarian
Supreme Court Law Library
Ali'iolani Hale, Room 115
417 South King Street
Honolulu, HI 96813
P: (808) 539-4964
F: (808) 539-4974
E: jenny.r.fujinaka
@courts.state.hi.us

IDAHO
Mr. John Keay
Acting Director
Law Library
702 West Idaho
P.O. Box 83720
Boise, ID 83720
P: (208) 334-2117
F: (208) 334-2467
E: jkeaye@idcourts.net

ILLINOIS
Ms. Brenda Larison
Librarian
Courts of Illinois
Supreme Court Building
200 East Capitol Avenue
Springfield, IL 62701
P: (217) 782-2424
F: (217) 782-5287

INDIANA
Ms. Terri Ross
Law Librarian
Supreme Court Law Library
200 West Washington Street
State House 316
Indianapolis, IN 46204
P: (317) 232-2557
F: (317) 233.8693
E: tross@courts.state.in.us

IOWA
Mr. Cory Quist
Law Librarian
State Law Library
State Library
1007 East Grand Avenue
Des Moines, IA 50319
P: (515) 281-4307
F: (515) 281-5405
E: cory.quist
@lib.state.ia.us

KENTUCKY
Ms. Jennifer Frazier
Manager
State Law Library
State Capitol, Suite 200
700 Capitol Avenue
Frankfort, KY 40601
P: (502) 564-4848
F: (502) 564-5041

LOUISIANA
Ms. Georgia Chadwick
Director
Law Library
Supreme Court
400 Royal Street, 2nd Floor
New Orleans, LA 70130
P: (504) 310-2400
F: (504) 310-2419
E: library@lasc.org

MAINE
Mr. John R. Barden
Director
State Law & Legislative
Reference Library
43 State House Station
Augusta, ME 04333
P: (207) 287-1600
F: (207) 287-6467
E: john.barden
@legislature.maine.gov

MARYLAND
Mr. Steve P. Anderson
Director
State Law Library
Murphy Courts of Appeal
Building
361 Rowe Boulevard
Annapolis, MD 21401
P: (410) 260-1432
F: (410) 974-2063

MICHIGAN
Ms. Susan Adamczak
Administrator
State Law Library
702 West Kalamazoo Street
P.O. Box 30007
Lansing, MI 48909
P: (517) 373-0630
F: (517) 373-7130
E: AdamczakS@michigan.gov

MINNESOTA
Ms. Judy Rehak
Acting State Law Librarian
State Law Library
Room G25, Judicial Center
25 Rev. Dr. Martin Luther King
Jr. Dr.
St. Paul, MN 55155
P: (651) 297-7800
F: (651) 296-6740
E: judy.rehak
@courts.state.mn.us

MISSISSIPPI
Ms. Clara Joorfetz
State Librarian
State Law Library
P.O. Box 1040
Jackson, MS 39215
P: (601) 359-3672
F: (601) 359-2912
E: cjoorfetz
@mssc.state.ms.us

MISSOURI
Mr. Bryan Dunlap
Assistant Librarian
Supreme Court Library
207 West High Street
P.O. Box 150
Jefferson City, MO 65102
P: (573) 751-2636
F: (573) 751-2573

MONTANA
Ms. Judith A. Meadows
Director & State Law Librarian
State Law Library
P.O. Box 203004
Helena, MT 59620
P: (406) 444-3660
F: (406) 444-3603
E: jmeadows@mt.gov

NEBRASKA
Ms. Janice K. Walker
State Court Administrator
Supreme Court
1445 "K" Street, 1213 State
Capitol
P.O. Box 98910
Lincoln, NE 68509
P: (402) 471-3730
F: (402) 471-2197
E: nsc.info@nebraska.gov

NEVADA
Ms. Kathleen L. Harrington
Law Librarian
Supreme Court Law Library
201 South Carson Street
Carson City, NV 89701
P: (775) 684-1671
F: (775) 684-1662
E: harrington
@nvcourts.nv.gov

NEW HAMPSHIRE
Ms. Mary S. Searles
Director, Cataloging
State Law Library
Supreme Court Building
One Charles Doe Drive
Concord, NH 03301
P: (603) 271-3777
F: (603) 513-5450
E: msearles
@courts.state.nh.us

NEW MEXICO
Mr. Robert Mead
State Law Librarian
Supreme Court Law Library
237 Don Gaspar
Santa Fe, NM 87501
P: (505) 827-4850
F: (505) 827-4852

NORTH CAROLINA
Mr. Tom Davis
Librarian
Supreme Court Library
500 Justice Building
2 East Morgan Street
Raleigh, NC 27601
P: (919) 831-5709
E: tpd@sc.state.nc.us

NORTH DAKOTA
Mr. Ted Smith
Law Librarian
Supreme Court Law Library
600 East Boulevard Avenue, 2nd
Floor
Judicial Wing
Bismarck, ND 58505
P: (701) 328-4594
F: (701) 328-3609
E: TSmith@ndcourts.gov

**NORTHERN MARIANA
ISLANDS**
Ms. Margarita M. Palacios
Court Administrator
Supreme Court
P.O. Box 2165
Saipan, MP 96950
P: (670) 236-9800
F: (670) 236-9701
E: supreme.court@saipan.com

OHIO
Mr. Kenneth Kozlowski
Director
Law Library
Supreme Court of Ohio
65 South Front Street, 11th Floor
Columbus, OH 43215
P: (614) 387-9650
F: (614) 387-9689
E: libref@sc.ohio.gov

OKLAHOMA
Ms. Susan Gilley
Administrator
Cartwright Memorial Library
2300 North Lincoln Boulevard,
Room B-8
Oklahoma City, OK 73105
P: (405) 522-3213
F: (405) 521-2753

OREGON
Mr. Joe Stephens
Law Librarian
State Law Library
1163 State Street
Salem, OR 97301
P: (503) 986-5644
F: (503) 986-5623
E: joe.k.stephens
@ojd.state.or.us

PENNSYLVANIA
Ms. Alice Lubrecht
Director
Bureau of State Library
333 Market Street
Harrisburg, PA 17126
P: (717) 783-5968
F: (717) 772-8258
E: alubrecht@state.pa.us

RHODE ISLAND
Ms. Karen Quinn
Chief Law Librarian
State Law Library
Frank Licht Judicial Complex
250 Benefit Street
Providence, RI 02903
P: (401) 222-3275
F: (401) 222-3865
E: kquinn
@courts.state.ri.us

SOUTH CAROLINA
Ms. Janet Meyer
Librarian
Supreme Court Library
Supreme Court Building
1231 Gervais Street
Columbia, SC 29211
P: (803) 734-1080
F: (803) 734-0519

SOUTH DAKOTA
Ms. Sheridan Anderson
Director
Supreme Court Law Library
500 East Capitol Avenue
Pierre, SD 57501
P: (605) 773-4898
F: (605) 773-6128
E: sheri.anderson
@ujs.state.sd.us

TEXAS
Mr. Dale W. Propp
Director
State Law Library
205 West 14th , Room G01
P.O. Box 12367
Austin, TX 78711
P: (512) 463-1722
F: (512) 463-1728

U.S. VIRGIN ISLANDS
Ms. Janet Lloyd
Law Librarian
Law Library
5400 Veteran's Drive
St. Thomas, VI 00802
P: (340) 774-6680
F: (340) 776-9889

UTAH
Ms. Jessica Van Buren
Director
State Law Library
450 South State Street
Salt Lake City, UT 84114
P: (801) 238-7991
F: (801) 238-7993
E: JESSICAVB
@email.utcourts.gov

VERMONT
Ms. Martha Reid
State Librarian
Department of Libraries
Agency of Adminstration
109 State Street
Montpelier, VT 05609
P: (802) 828-3265
F: (802) 828-2199
E: martha.reid@state.vt.us

VIRGINIA
Mr. Karl Hade
Executive Secretary
Supreme Court
Supreme Court of Virginia
100 North Ninth Street
Richmond, VA 23219
P: (804) 786-6455
F: (804) 786-4542
E: khade@courts.state.va.us

Law Library

WASHINGTON

Ms. Kay E. Newman
State Law Librarian
State Law Library
415 12th Avenue, Southwest
P.O. Box 40751
Olympia, WA 98504
P: (360) 357-2136
E: kay.newman@courts.wa.gov

WEST VIRGINIA

Ms. Kaye L. Maerz
State Law Librarian
State Law Library
State Capitol, Room E-404
1900 Kanawha Boulevard, East
Charleston, WV 25305
P: (304) 558-2607
F: (304) 558-3673
E: kaye.maerz@courtswv.gov

WISCONSIN

Ms. Jane Colwin
State Law Librarian
State Law Library
120 Martin Luther King Jr.
Boulevard
Madison, WI 53703
P: (608) 266-1600
F: (608) 267-2319
E: jane.colwin@wicourts.gov

WYOMING

Ms. Kathy Carlson
State Law Librarian
State Law Library
Supreme Court & Library
Building
2301 Capitol Avenue
Cheyenne, WY 82002
P: (307) 777-7509
F: (307) 777-7040
E: kcarls@state.wy.us

Licensing (Occupational and Professional)

Licenses and regulates the function of various professions in the state. Since there are hundreds of autonomous boards in the states, it is the centralized agencies that are represented in this listing.

Information provided by:

Council on Licensure, Enforcement and Regulation
Adam Parfitt
Executive Director
403 Marquis Avenue
Suite 200
Lexington, KY 40502
P: (859) 269-1289
F: (859) 269-1943
aparfitt@mis.net
www.clearhq.org

ALASKA
Mr. Don Habeger
Director
Division of Corporations,
Business & Professional
Licensing
P.O. Box 110806
Juneau, AK 99811
P: (907) 465-2534
F: (907) 465-2974
E: don.habeger@alaska.gov

CALIFORNIA
Mr. Brian Stiger
Director
Department of Consumer
Affairs
1625 North Market Boulevard,
Suite S-308
Sacramento, CA 95834
P: (916) 574-8200
F: (916) 574-8613
E: brian.stiger@dca.ca.gov

COLORADO
Ms. Rosemary McCool
Division Director
Division of Registrations
Department of Regulatory
Agencies
1560 Broadway, Suite 1350
Denver, CO 80202
P: (303) 894-7711
F: (303) 894-7693
E: rose.mccool
    @dora.state.co.us

CONNECTICUT
Ms. Jennifer Filippone
Section Chief
Department of Public Health
410 Capitol Avenue
P.O. Box 340308
Hartford, CT 06134
P: (860) 509-7405
F: (860) 509-7539
E: jennifer.filippone
    @ct.gov

DELAWARE
Mr. James L. Collins
Director
Division of Professional
Regulation
Cannon Building, Suite 203
861 Silver Lake Boulevard
Dover, DE 19904
P: (302) 744-4501
F: (302) 739-2711
E: james.l.collins
    @state.de.us

DISTRICT OF COLUMBIA
Mr. Clifford Cooks
Program Manager
Department of Consumer &
Regulatory Affairs
1100 Fourth Street, Southwest
Washington, DC 20024
P: (202) 442-4320
F: (202) 698-4329
E: clifford.cooks@dc.gov

Feseha Woldu
Administrator
Health Regulation & Licensing
Administration
Department of Health
899 North Capitol Street,
Northeast
Washington, DC 20002
P: (202) 724-4900
F: (202) 442-4788
E: feseha.woldu@dc.gov

FLORIDA
Ms. Lucy C. Gee
Division Director
Division of Medical Quality
Assurance
Department of Health
4052 Bald Cypress Way, Bin
#C01
Tallahassee, FL 32399
P: (850) 488-0595
F: (850) 414-7613
E: lucy_gee@doh.state.fl.us

Mr. Ken Lawson
Secretary
Department of Business &
Professional Regulation
1940 North Monroe Street
Tallahassee, FL 32399
P: (850) 413-0755
F: (850) 921-4094
E: ken_lawson
    @dbpr.state.fl.us

GEORGIA
Mr. Randall D. Vaughn
Division Director
Professional Licensing Boards
Division
Office of Secretary of State
237 Coliseum Drive
Macon, GA 31217
P: (478) 207-1320
F: (478) 207-1363
E: rvaughn@sos.state.ga.us

HAWAII
Ms. Celia Suzuki
Acting Licensing Administrator
Professional Licensing Division
Dept. of Commerce &
Consumer Affairs
P.O. Box 3469
Honolulu, HI 96801
P: (808) 586-2690
F: (808) 586-2689
E: pvl@dcca.hawaii.gov

IDAHO
Ms. Tana Cory
Bureau Chief
Bureau of Occupational
Licenses
1109 Main Street, Suite 220
Boise, ID 83702
P: (208) 334-3233
F: (208) 334-3945
E: tcory@ibol.idaho.gov

ILLINOIS
Mr. Daniel E. Bluthardt
Division Director
Division of Professional
Regulation
320 West Washington Street, 3rd
Floor
Springfield, IL 62786
P: (217) 782-9405
F: (217) 558-6001
E: jody.watson@illinois.gov

Mr. Donald W. Seasock
Acting Division Director
Division of Professional
Regulation
320 West Washington, 3rd Floor
Springfield, IL 62786
P: (217) 782-9405
F: (217) 558-6001

INDIANA
Frances L. Kelly
Executive Director
Professional Licensing Agency
402 West Washington Street,
Room W072
Indianapolis, IN 46204
P: (317) 232-2960
F: (317) 232-2312
E: fkelly@pla.in.gov

IOWA
Ms. Shari Fett
Bureau Chief
Professional Licensing Division
Department of Commerce
1920 Southeast Hulsizer Road
Ankeny, IA 50021
P: (515) 281-7447
F: (515) 281-7411
E: shari.fett@iowa.gov

Ms. Barbara Huey
Bureau Chief
Bureau of Professional
Licensure
Lucas State Office Building
321 East 12th Street, 5th Floor
Des Moines, IA 50266
P: (515) 281-0254
F: (515) 281-3121
E: barbara.huey
    @idph.iowa.gov

KENTUCKY
Shannon Tivitt
Executive Director
Office of Occupations &
Professions
P.O. Box 1360
Frankfort, KY 40601
P: (502) 564-3296 Ext. 224
F: (502) 564-4818
E: shannon.tivitt@ky.gov

Licensing (Occupational and Professional)

MAINE
Ms. Anne L. Head
Director
Office of Licensing &
Registration
Professional & Financial
Regulation
35 State House Station, Gardiner
Annex
Augusta, ME 04333
P: (207) 624-8633
F: (207) 624-8637
E: anne.l.head@maine.gov

MARYLAND
Mr. Harry Loleas
Deputy Commissioner
Department of Labor, Licensing
& Regulation
Occupational & Professional
Licensing
500 North Calvert Street, 3rd
Floor
Baltimore, MD 21202
P: (410) 230-6226
F: (410) 333-6314
E: hloleas@dllr.state.md.us

Mr. Joshua Sharfstein
Secretary
Department of Health & Mental
Hygiene
201 West Preston Street
Baltimore, MD 21201
P: (410) 767-4639
F: (410) 767-6489
E: jsharfstein
  @dhmh.state.md.us

MASSACHUSETTS
Ms. Jean Pontikas
Director
Division of Health Professions
Licensure
Department of Public Health
239 Causeway Street, Suite 200
Boston, MA 02114
P: (617) 973-0948
F: (617) 973-0983
E: jean.pontikas
  @state.ma.us

Mr. George K. Weber
Director
Division of Professional
Licensure
Office of Consumer Affairs
1000 Washington Street, Suite
710
Boston, MA 02118
P: (617) 727-3074
F: (617) 727-2197
E: george.k.weber
  @state.ma.us

MICHIGAN
Mr. Steven Hilfinger
Director
Department of Licensing &
Regulatory Affairs
P.O. Box 30004
Lansing, MI 48909
P: (517) 373-1820
F: (517) 373-2129
E: bcslic@michigan.gov

Mr. Nick Lyon
Deputy Director
Bureau of Health Professions
611 West Ottawa, 1st Floor
P.O. Box 30670
Lansing, MI 48909
P: (517) 373-8068
F: (517) 241-3082
E: griffithsc@michigan.gov

MISSOURI
Ms. Jane A. Rackers
Division Director
Division of Professional
Regulation
P.O. Box 1335
Jefferson City, MO 65102
P: (573) 751-1081
F: (573) 751-4176
E: jane.rackers@pr.mo.gov

MONTANA
Mr. Jack Kane
Division Administrator
Business Standards Division
Department of Labor & Industry
P.O. Box 200513
Helena, MT 59620
P: (406) 841-2042
F: (406) 841-2050
E: dliquestions@mt.gov

NEBRASKA
Ms. Helen L. Meeks
Administrator
Health & Human Services
Regulation & Licensure
301 Centennial Mall South
P.O. Box 94986
Lincoln, NE 68509
P: (402) 471-0179
F: (402) 471-3577
E: helen.meeks@hhss.ne.gov

NEW JERSEY
Mr. Thomas R. Calcagni
Acting Director
Division of Consumer Affairs
124 Halsey Street
Newark, NJ 07102
P: (973) 504-6200
F: (973) 273-8035
E: askconsumeraffairs
  @lps.state.nj.us

NEW MEXICO
Mr. J. Dee Dennis Jr.
Superintendent
Regulation & Licensing
Department
2550 Cerrillos Road
Sante Fe, NM 87504
P: (505) 476-4508
F: (505) 476-4511
E: dee.dennis@state.nm.us

NEW YORK
Mr. Frank Munoz
Deputy Commissioner
State Education Department
Office of the Professions
89 Washington Avenue
Albany, NY 12234
P: (518) 474-3862
F: (518) 474-1449
E: fmunoz@mail.nysed.gov

OREGON
Mr. Randall Everitt
Director
Health Licensing Agency
700 Summer Street, Northeast
Suite 320
Salem, OR 97301
P: (503) 378-8667
F: (503) 585-9114
E: randy.l.everitt
  @state.or.us

PENNSYLVANIA
Ms. Katie True
Commissioner
Bureau of Professional &
Occupational Affairs
Department of State
P.O. Box 2649
Harrisburg, PA 17105
P: (717) 783-7192
F: (717) 783-0510
E: ra-bpoa@state.pa.us

RHODE ISLAND
Mr. Charles Alexandre
Chief
Office of Health Professions
Regulation
Department of Health
3 Capitol Hill, Room 205
Providence, RI 02908
P: (401) 222-5700
F: (401) 222-3352
E: charlie.alexandre
  @doh.state.ri.us

SOUTH CAROLINA
Ms. Catherine Templeton
Director
Department of Labor, Licensing
& Regulation
 P.O. Box 11329
Columbia, SC 29211
P: (803) 896-4390
F: (803) 896-4393
E: templetonc@llr.sc.gov

TENNESSEE
Mr. Steven Majchrzak
Assistant Commissioner
Division of Regulatory Boards
Department of Commerce &
Insurance
500 James Robertson Parkway,
2nd Floor
Nashville, TN 37243
P: (615) 741-3449
F: (615) 741-6470
E: steven.majchrzak
  @state.tn.us

Ms. Elizabeth Miller
Director
Division of Health Related
Boards
Department of Health
227 French Landing, Suite 300
Nashville, TN 37243
P: (615) 741-2040
F: (615) 532-5369
E: elizabeth.miller
  @state.tn.us

TEXAS
Mr. William H. Kuntz
Executive Director
Department of Licensing &
Regulation
P.O. Box 12157
Austin, TX 78711
P: (512) 463-3173
F: (512) 475-2874
E: executive.director
  @license.state.tx.us

Ms. Kathryn Perkins
Assistant Commissioner
Division of Regulatory Services
Department of State Health
Services
1100 West 49th Street
Austin, TX 78756
P: (512) 834-6660
F: (512) 834-6635
E: debbie.peterson
   @dshs.state.tx.us

UTAH
Mr. Mark B. Steinagel
Director
Division of Occupational &
Professional Licensing
160 East 300, South
P.O. Box 146741
Salt Lake City, UT 84114
P: (801) 530-6292
F: (801) 530-6511
E: msteinagel@utah.gov

VERMONT
Mr. Christopher D. Winters
Director
Office of Professional
Regulation
Secretary of State's Office
National Life Building, North,
Floor 2
Montpelier, VT 05620
P: (802) 828-2458
F: (802) 828-2496
E: cwinters@sec.state.vt.us

VIRGINIA
Mr. Gordon Dixon
Director
Department of Professional &
Occupational Regulation
9960 Mayland Drive, Suite 400
Richmond, VA 23233
P: (804) 367-8519
F: (804) 367-9537
E: director
   @dpor.virginia.gov

Ms. Dianne Reynolds-Cane
Director
Department of Health
Professions
9960 Mayland Drive, Suite 300
Richmond, VA 23233
P: (804) 662-9919
F: (804) 662-9114
E: dianne.cane
   @dhp.virginia.gov

WASHINGTON
Ms. Karen Jensen
Assistant Secretary
State Health Systems Quality
Assurance
P.O. Box 47850
Olympia, WA 98504
P: (360) 236-4600
F: (360) 236-4626
E: karen.jensen@doh.wa.gov

Ms. Liz Luce
Director
Department of Licensing
1125 Washington Street,
Southeast
P.O. Box 9020
Olympia, WA 98507
P: (360) 902-3933
F: (360) 902-4042
E: doldirector@dol.wa.gov

WISCONSIN
Mr. Dave Ross
Secretary
Department of Regulation &
Licensing
1400 East Washington Avenue
P.O. Box 8935
Madison, WI 53708
P: (608) 266-1352
F: (608) 261-2381
E: DRLOfficeOfTheSecretary
   @wisconsin.gov

Lieutenant Governor

The statewide elected official who is next in line of succession to the governorship. (In Maine, New Hampshire, New Jersey, Tennessee and West Virginia, the presidents (or speakers) of the Senate are the next in line of succession to the governorship. In Tennessee, the speaker of the Senate bears the statutory title of lieutenant governor. In Arizona, Oregon, and Wyoming, the secretary of state is next in line of succession to the governorship.)

Information provided by:

National Lieutenant Governors Association
Julia Nienaber Hurst
Executive Director
71 Cavalier Boulevard
Suite 226
Florence, KY 41042
P: (859) 283-1400
F: (859) 244-8001
jhurst@csg.org
www.nlga.us

ALABAMA
Hon. Kay Ivey (R)
Lieutenant Governor
Office of the Lieutenant
Governor
11 South Union Street, Suite 725
Montgomery, AL 36130
P: (334) 242-7900
F: (334) 242-4661

ALASKA
Hon. Mead Treadwell (R)
Lieutenant Governor
Office of the Lieutenant
Governor
550 West 7th Street, Suite 1700
Anchorage, AK 99501
P: (907) 269-7460
F: (907) 269-0263

AMERICAN SAMOA
Hon. Ipulasi Aito Sunia (D)
Lieutenant Governor
Office of the Lieutenant
Governor
Territory of American Samoa
Pago Pago, AS 96799
P: (684) 633-4116
F: (684) 633-2269

ARKANSAS
Hon. Mark Darr (R)
Lieutenant Governor
Office of the Lieutenant
Governor
270 Capitol Avenue
Little Rock, AR 72201
P: (501) 682-2144
F: (501) 682-2894

CALIFORNIA
Hon. Gavin Newsom (D)
Lieutenant Governor
Office of the Lieutenant
Governor
State Capitol, Room 1114
Sacramento, CA 98514
P: (916) 445-8994
F: (916) 323-4998

COLORADO
Hon. Joe Garcia (D)
Lieutenant Governor &
Executive Director
Office of the Lieutenant
Governor
130 State Capitol
Denver, CO 80203
P: (303) 866-2087
F: (303) 866-5469

CONNECTICUT
Hon. Nancy Wyman (D)
Lieutenant Governor
Office of the Lieutenant
Governor
State Capitol, Room 304
210 Capitol Avenue
Hartford, CT 06106
P: (860) 524-7384
F: (860) 524-7304

DELAWARE
Hon. Matthew Denn (D)
Lieutenant Governor
Office of the Lieutenant
Governor
Tatnall Building, 3rd Floor
Dover, DE 19901
P: (302) 744-4333
F: (302) 739-6965
E: matthew.denn@state.de.us

FLORIDA
Hon. Jennifer Carroll (R)
Lieutenant Governor
Office of the Lieutenant
Governor
The State Capitol
Tallahassee, FL 32399
P: (850) 488-7146
F: (850) 488-0801

GEORGIA
Hon. Casey Cagle (R)
Lieutenant Governor
Office of the Lieutenant
Governor
240 State Capitol
Atlanta, GA 30334
P: (404) 656-5030
F: (404) 656-6739

GUAM
Hon. Ray Tenorio (R)
Lieutenant Governor
Office of the Lieutenant
Governor
R.J. Bordallo Governor's
Complex
P.O. Box 2950
Hagatna, GU 96932
P: (671) 475-9380
F: (671) 477-2007
E: webmaster
    @guamletgovernor.net

HAWAII
Hon. Brian Schatz (D)
Lieutenant Governor
Office of the Lieutenant
Governor
Executive Chambers
Hawaii State Capitol
Honolulu, HI 96813
P: (808) 586-0255
F: (808) 586-0231

IDAHO
Hon. Brad Little (R)
Lieutenant Governor
Office of the Lieutenant
Governor
State Capitol
Boise, ID 83720
P: (208) 334-2200
F: (208) 334-3259

ILLINOIS
Hon. Sheila Simon
Lieutenant Governor
Office of the Lieutenant
Governor
214 State House
Springfield, IL 62706
P: (217) 558-3085
F: (217) 558-3086

INDIANA
Hon. Becky Skillman (R)
Lieutenant Governor
Office of the Lieutenant
Governor
State Capitol, Room 333
Indianapolis, IN 46204
P: (317) 232-4545
F: (317) 232-4788

IOWA
Hon. Kim Reynolds (R)
Lieutenant Governor
Office of the Lieutenant
Governor
State Capitol, Room 9
Des Moines, IA 50319
P: (515) 281-5211
F: (515) 725-3527

KANSAS
Hon. Jeff Colyer (R)
Lieutenant Governor
Office of the Lieutenant
Governor
State Capitol, 2nd Floor
300 Southwest 10th Avenue
Topeka, KS 66612
P: (785) 296-2214
F: (785) 296-5669

KENTUCKY
Hon. Daniel Mongiardo (D)
Lieutenant Governor
Office of the Lieutenant
Governor
700 Capital Avenue, Suite 142
Frankfort, KY 40601
P: (502) 564-2611
F: (502) 564-2849

LOUISIANA
Hon. Jay Dardenne (R)
Lieutenant Governor
Office of the Lieutenant
Governor
1051 North 3rd Street
P.O. Box 44243
Baton Rouge, LA 70804
P: (225) 342-7009
F: (225) 342-1949

MARYLAND
Hon. Anthony G. Brown (D)
Lieutenant Governor
Office of the Lieutenant
Governor
100 State Circle
Annapolis, MD 21401
P: (410) 974-2804
F: (410) 974-5882
E: ltgov@gov.state.md.us

MASSACHUSETTS
Hon. Timothy Murray (D)
Lieutenant Governor
Office of the Lieutenant
Governor
Room 360
Boston, MA 02133
P: (617) 725-4005
F: (617) 727-9725

Lieutenant Governor

MICHIGAN
Hon. Brian Calley (R)
Lieutenant Governor
Office of the Lieutenant Governor
P.O. Box 30013
Lansing, MI 48909
P: (517) 373-6800
F: (517) 241-5026

MINNESOTA
Hon. Yvonne Prettner Solon (DFL)
Lieutenant Governor
Office of the Lieutenant Governor
130 State Capitol
75 Rev. Martin Luther King Jr. Boulevard
St. Paul, MN 55155
P: (651) 201-3400
F: (651) 797-1850

MISSISSIPPI
Hon. Phil Bryant (R)
Lieutenant Governor
Office of the Lieutenant Governor
New Capitol, Room 315
P.O. Box 1018
Jackson, MS 39215
P: (601) 359-3200
F: (601) 359-4054

MISSOURI
Hon. Peter Kinder (R)
Lieutenant Governor
Office of the Lieutenant Governor
State Capitol, Room 224
Jefferson City, MO 65101
P: (573) 751-4727
F: (573) 751-9422
E: ltgovinfo@mail.mo.gov

MONTANA
Hon. John C. Bohlinger (R)
Lieutenant Governor
Office of the Lieutenant Governor
Capitol Station, Room 207
P.O. Box 200801
Helena, MT 59620
P: (406) 444-5665
F: (406) 444-4648

NEBRASKA
Hon. Rick Sheehy (R)
Lieutenant Governor
Office of the Lieutenant Governor
State Capitol, Room 2315
P.O. Box 94863
Lincoln, NE 68509
P: (402) 471-2256
F: (402) 471-6031

NEVADA
Hon. Brian K. Krolicki (R)
Lieutenant Governor
Office of the Lieutenant Governor
101 North Carson Street, Suite 2
Carson City, NV 89701
P: (775) 684-7111
F: (775) 684-7110
E: ltgov@ltgov.nv.gov

NEW JERSEY
Hon. Kim Guadagno (R)
Lieutenant Governor/Secretary of State
Office of the Secretary of State
125 West 8th Street
P.O. Box 300
Trenton, NJ 08625
P: (609) 292-6000
F: (609) 292-3454

NEW MEXICO
Hon. John A. Sanchez (R)
Lieutenant Governor
Office of the Lieutenant Governor
State Capitol, Suite 417
Santa Fe, NM 87501
P: (505) 476-2250
F: (505) 476-2257

NEW YORK
Hon. Robert Duffy (D)
Lieutenant Governor
Office of the Lieutenant Governor
State Capitol
Albany, NY 12224
P: (518) 474-8390
F: (518) 474-1513

NORTH CAROLINA
Hon. Walter H. Dalton (D)
Lieutenant Governor
Office of the Lieutenant Governor
310 North Blount Street
Raleigh, NC 27601
P: (919) 733-7350
F: (919) 733-6595
E: ltgovernor@ncmail.net

NORTH DAKOTA
Hon. Drew Wrigley (R)
Lieutenant Governor
Office of the Lieutenant Governor
State Capitol
Bismarck, ND 58505
P: (701) 328-2200
F: (701) 328-2205

NORTHERN MARIANA ISLANDS
Hon. Eloy S. Inos
Lieutenant Governor
Office of the Governor
Caller Box 10007
Capitol Hill
Saipan, MP 96950
P: (670) 664-2300
F: (670) 664-2311

OHIO
Hon. Mary Taylor (R)
Lieutenant Governor
Office of the Lieutenant Governor
77 South High Street, 30th Floor
Columbus, OH 43215
P: (614) 644-0935
F: (614) 466-9354

OKLAHOMA
Hon. Todd Lamb (R)
Lieutenant Governor
Office of the Lieutenant Governor
State Capitol, Room 211
Oklahoma City, OK 73105
P: (405) 521-2161
F: (405) 522-8694

PENNSYLVANIA
Hon. Jim Cawley (R)
Lieutenant Governor
Office of the Lieutenant Governor
200 Main Capitol Building
Harrisburg, PA 17120
P: (717) 787-3300
F: (717) 783-0150

RHODE ISLAND
Hon. Elizabeth H. Roberts (D)
Lieutenant Governor
Office of the Lieutenant Governor
116 State House
Providence, RI 02903
P: (401) 222-2371
F: (401) 222-2012
E: riltgov@ltgov.ri.gov

SOUTH CAROLINA
Hon. Ken Ard (R)
Lieutenant Governor
Office of the Lieutenant Governor
P.O. Box 142
Columbia, SC 29202
P: (803) 734-2080
F: (803) 734-2082

SOUTH DAKOTA
Hon. Matthew Michels (R)
Lieutenant Governor
Office of the Lieutenant Governor
500 East Capitol Avenue
Pierre, SD 57501
P: (605) 773-3661
F: (605) 773-4711

TENNESSEE
Hon. Ron Ramsey (R)
(elected by the Senate)
Lieutenant Governor/Senate President
Office of the Lieutenant Governor
One Legislative Plaza
Nashville, TN 37243
P: (615) 741-4524
F: (615) 253-0197
E: lt.gov.ron.ramsey @capitol.tn.gov

TEXAS
Hon. David Dewhurst (R)
Lieutenant Governor
Office of the Lieutenant Governor
Capitol Station
P.O. Box 12068
Austin, TX 78711
P: (512) 463-0001
F: (512) 463-0677

U.S. VIRGIN ISLANDS
Hon. Gregory Francis (D)
Lieutenant Governor
Office of the Lieutenant Governor
1131 Kings Street, Suite 101
St. Croix, VI 00802
P: (340) 773-6449
F: (340) 773-0330

UTAH
Hon. Gregory S. Bell (R)
Lieutenant Governor
Office of the Lieutenant Governor
P.O. Box 142325
Salt Lake City, UT 84114
P: (801) 538-1041
F: (801) 538-1133
E: gregbell@utah.gov

Lieutenant Governor

VERMONT
Hon. Phil Scott (R)
Lieutenant Governor
Office of the Lieutenant
Governor
115 State Street
Montpelier, VT 05633
P: (802) 828-2226
F: (802) 828-3198
E: pscott14@aol.com

VIRGINIA
Hon. William T. Bolling (R)
Lieutenant Governor
Office of the Lieutenant
Governor
102 Governor Street
Richmond, VA 23219
P: (804) 786-2078
F: (804) 786-7514
E: bill.bolling
   @ltgov.virginia.gov

WASHINGTON
Hon. Brad Owen (D)
Lieutenant Governor
Office of the Lieutenant
Governor
416 14th Avenue, Southwest
P.O. Box 40400
Olympia, WA 98504
P: (360) 786-7700
F: (360) 786-7749
E: ltgov@leg.wa.gov

WEST VIRGINIA
Hon. Earl Ray Tomblin (D)
Governor
West Virginia Legislature
State Capitol Complex
Charleston, WV 25305
P: (304) 558-2000
F: (304) 342-7025
E: senate.president
   @wvsenate.gov

WISCONSIN
Hon. Rebecca Kleefisch (R)
Lieutenant Governor
Office of the Lieutenant
Government
Room 19, East State Capitol
P.O. Box 2043
Madison, WI 53702
P: (608) 266-3516
F: (608) 267-3571

Lobby Law Administration

Administers registration and reporting requirements for lobbyists.

ALABAMA
Hon. Beth Chapman (R)
Secretary of State
Office of the Secretary of State
P.O. Box 5616
Montgomery, AL 36103
P: (334) 242-7200
F: (334) 242-4993
E: Beth.Chapman
@sos.alabama.gov

ALASKA
Mr. Paul Dauphinais
Director
Public Offices Commission
2221 East Northern Lights
Boulevard
Room 128
Anchorage, AK 99508
P: (907) 276-4176
F: (907) 276-7018
E: Paul.Dauphinais
@alaska.gov

ARKANSAS
Hon. Mark Martin (R)
Secretary of State
Office of the Secretary of State
256 State Capitol Building
Little Rock, AR 72201
P: (501) 682-1010
F: (501) 682-3510
E: sos@sos.arkansas.gov

CALIFORNIA
Ms. Cathy Mitchell
Chief
Elections Division
1500 11th Street, 5th Floor
Sacramento, CA 95814
P: (916) 657-2166
F: (916) 653-3214
E: cmitchel@sos.ca.gov

COLORADO
Hon. Scott Gessler (R)
Secretary of State
Office of the Secretary of State
1700 Broadway, Suite 250
Denver, CO 80290
P: (303) 894-2200
F: (303) 869-4860
E: secretary
@sos.state.co.us

CONNECTICUT
Ms. Carol Carson
Executive Director
Office of State Ethics
18-20 Trinity Street, Suite 205
Hartford, CT 06106
P: (860) 263-2384
F: (860) 263-2402
E: carol.carson@ct.gov

DELAWARE
Ms. Janet Wright
Attorney
Public Integrity Commission
Margaret O'Neill Building
410 Federal Street, Suite 3
Dover, DE 19901
P: (302) 739-2399
F: (302) 739-2398

DISTRICT OF COLUMBIA
Ms. Cecily E.
    Collier-Montgomery
Director
Office of Campaign Finance
Frank D. Reeves Municipal
Building
2000 14th Street, Northwest,
Suite 433
Washington, DC 20009
P: (202) 671-0547
F: (202) 671-0658
E: ocf@dc.gov

FLORIDA
Mr. Phillip Claypool
Executive Director & General
Counsel
Commission on Ethics
P.O. Drawer 15709
Tallahassee, FL 32317
P: (904) 488-7864
F: (904) 488-3077
E: Claypool.Phil
    @leg.state.fl.us

Mr. W. Pierce Schuessler
Legislative Affairs Director
Office of Legislative Affairs
R. A. Gray Building, Suite 115
500 South Bronough Street
Tallahassee, FL 32399
P: (850) 245-6509
F: (850) 245-6125
E: WPSchuessler
    @dos.state.fl.us

GEORGIA
Ms. Stacy Kalberman
Executive Secretary
State Ethics Commission
200 Piedmont Avenue, Southeast
Suite 1402, West Tower
Atlanta, GA 30334
P: (404) 463-1980
F: (404) 463-1988
E: gaethics@ethics.ga.gov

HAWAII
Mr. Les Kondo
Executive Director & General
Counsel
State Ethics Commission
P.O. Box 616
Honolulu, HI 96809
P: (808) 587-0460
F: (808) 587-0470
E: ethics@hawaiiethics.org

IDAHO
Hon. Ben T. Ysursa (R)
Secretary of State
Office of the Secretary of State
P.O. Box 83720
Boise, ID 83720
P: (208) 334-2300
F: (208) 334-2282
E: secstate@sos.idaho.gov

ILLINOIS
Ms. Jacqueline Price
Director
Department of Index
111 East Monroe Street
Springfield, IL 62756
P: (217) 782-7017
F: (217) 524-0930

INDIANA
Mr. Charles W. Harris
Executive Director & General
Counsel
Lobby Registration Commission
10 West Market Street, Suite
1760
Indianapolis, IN 46204
P: (317) 232-9860
F: (317) 233-0077
E: CHarris@lrc.IN.gov

IOWA
Mr. Michael E. Marshall
Secretary of the Senate
General Assembly
State Capitol
1007 East Grand Avenue
Des Moines, IA 50319
P: (515) 281-5307
E: Mike.Marshall
    @legis.state.ia.us

KANSAS
Mr. Brad Bryant
Deputy Assistant for Elections
Office of the Secretary of State -
Elections & Legislative Matters
120 Southwest 10th Avenue
Memorial Hall, 1st Floor
Topeka, KS 66612
P: (785) 296-4561
F: (785) 368-8033

KENTUCKY
Hon. Elaine Walker (D)
Secretary of State
Office of the Secretary of State
700 Capital Avenue, Suite 152
Frankfort, KY 40601
P: (502) 564-3490
F: (502) 564-5687
E: sos.secretary@ky.gov

LOUISIANA
Ms. Kathleen Allen
Ethics Administrator
Ethics Administration
617 North Third Street, Suite
10-36
P.O. Box 4368
Baton Rouge, LA 70821
P: (225) 219-5600
F: (225) 381-7271

MAINE
Mr. Jonathan Wayne
Executive Director
Commission on Governmental
Ethics & Election Practices
135 State House Station
Augusta, ME 04333
P: (207) 287-4179
F: (207) 287-6775
E: Jonathan.Wayne@maine.gov

MARYLAND
Mr. Robert A. Hahn
Executive Director
State Ethics Commission
Executive Department
45 Calvert Street, 3rd Floor
Annapolis, MD 21401
P: (410) 260-7770
F: (410) 260-7746
E: rhahn@gov.state.md.us

MASSACHUSETTS
Hon. William Francis
    Galvin (D)
Secretary of the Commonwealth
Office of the Secretary of the
Commonwealth
State House, Room 337
Boston, MA 02133
P: (617) 727-9180
F: (617) 742-4722
E: cis@sec.state.ma.us

Lobby Law Administration

MICHIGAN
Mr. Christopher M. Thomas
Director
Bureau of Elections
Richard H. Austin Building,
First Floor
430 West Allegan Street
Lansing, MI 48918
P: (517) 373-2450
F: (517) 241-4785
E: ChristopherT
  @michigan.gov

MINNESOTA
Mr. Gary Goldsmith
Executive Director
Campaign Finance & Public
Disclosure Board
Centennial Office Building,
Suite 190
658 Cedar Street
St. Paul, MN 55155
P: (651) 296-1721
F: (651) 296-1722
E: gary.goldsmith
  @state.mn.us

Hon. Mark Ritchie (DFL)
Secretary of State
Office of the Secretary of State
180 State Office Building
100 Martin Luther King Jr.
Boulevard
St. Paul, MN 55155
P: (651) 201-1328
F: (651) 215-0682
E: secretary.state
  @state.mn.us

MISSISSIPPI
Mr. W. Heath Hillman
Assistant Secretary of State for
Elections
Elections Division
401 Mississippi Street
P.O. Box 136
Jackson, MS 39205
P: (601) 359-6368
F: (601) 359-5019

MISSOURI
Ms. Julie A. Allen
Executive Director
Ethics Commission
3411A Knipp Drive
Jefferson City, MO 65109
P: (573) 751-2020
F: (573) 526-4506
E: helpdesk@mec.mo.gov

MONTANA
Ms. Jennifer L. Hensley
Commissioner
Commissioner of Political
Practices
1205 Eighth Avenue
P.O. Box 202401
Helena, MT 59620
P: (406) 444-2942
F: (406) 444-1643
E: JLHensley@mt.gov

NEBRASKA
Mr. Patrick J. O'Donnell
Clerk of the Legislature
State Legislature
State Capitol, Room 2018
P.O. Box 94604
Lincoln, NE 68509
P: (402) 471-2271
F: (402) 471-2126
E: podonnell@leg.ne.gov

NEVADA
Mr. Lorne J. Malkiewich
Director
Legislative Counsel Bureau
Legislative Building
401 South Carson Street
Carson City, NV 89701
P: (775) 684-6800
F: (775) 684-6600
E: malkiewich
  @lcb.state.nv.us

NEW HAMPSHIRE
Hon. William M. Gardner (D)
Secretary of State
Office of the Secretary of State
State House, Room 204
Concord, NH 03301
P: (603) 271-3242
F: (603) 271-6316
E: kladd@sos.state.nh.us

NEW JERSEY
Mr. Jeffrey M. Brindle
Executive Director
Election Law Enforcement
Commission
P.O. Box 185
Trenton, NJ 08625
P: (609) 292-8700
F: (609) 777-1448

NEW MEXICO
Hon. Dianna J. Duran (R)
Secretary of State
Office of the Secretary of State
325 Don Gaspar, Suite 300
Capitol Annex
Santa Fe, NM 87503
P: (505) 827-3600
F: (505) 827-3634
E: diannaj.duran
  @state.nm.us

NEW YORK
Mr. Barry Ginsberg
Executive Director
Commission on Public Integrity
540 Broadway
Albany, NY 12207
P: (518) 408-3976

NORTH CAROLINA
Hon. Elaine F. Marshall (D)
Secretary of State
Office of the Secretary of State
P.O. Box 29622
Raleigh, NC 27626
P: (919) 807-2005
F: (919) 807-2010
E: emarshal@sosnc.com

NORTH DAKOTA
Hon. Alvin A. Jaeger (R)
Secretary of State
Office of the Secretary of State
600 East Boulevard
Department 108
Bismarck, ND 58505
P: (701) 328-2900
F: (701) 328-2992
E: sos@nd.gov

OHIO
Mr. Tony W. Bledsoe
Legislative Inspector
General/Executive Director
Office of the Legislative
Inspector General
50 West Broad Street, Suite
1308
Columbus, OH 43215
P: (614) 728-5100
F: (614) 728-5074
E: info
  @jlec-olig.state.oh.us

OKLAHOMA
Ms. Marilyn Hughes
Executive Director
Ethics Commission
2300 North Lincoln Boulevard,
Room B-5
Oklahoma City, OK 73105
P: (405) 521-3451
F: (405) 521-4905

OREGON
Mr. Ronald A. Bersin
Executive Director
Government Ethics Commission
3218 Pringle Road, Southeast,
Suite 220
Salem, OR 97302
P: (503) 378-5108
F: (503) 373-1456
E: ron.a.bersin@state.or.us

PENNSYLVANIA
Mr. Mark R. Corrigan
Secretary-Parliamentarian of the
Senate
State Legislature
462 Capitol Building
Senate Box 203053
Harrisburg, PA 17120
P: (717) 787-5920
E: mcorrigan@os.pasen.gov

SOUTH CAROLINA
Hon. Mark Hammond (R)
Secretary of State
Office of the Secretary of State
P.O. Box 11350
Columbia, SC 29211
P: (803) 734-2170
F: (803) 734-1661
E: rdaggerhart@sos.sc.gov

Mr. Herbert R. Hayden Jr.
Executive Director
State Ethics Commission
5000 Thurmond Mall, Suite 250
Columbia, SC 29201
P: (803) 253-4192
F: (803) 253-7539
E: herb@ethics.state.sc.us

SOUTH DAKOTA
Hon. Jason M. Gant (R)
Secretary of State
Office of the Secretary of State
500 East Capitol Avenue, Suite
204
Pierre, SD 57501
P: (605) 773-3537
F: (605) 773-6580
E: sdsos@state.sd.us

TENNESSEE
Mr. Stephen Rawlins
Executive Director
Registry of Elections Finance
404 James Robertson Parkway,
Suite 104
Nashville, TN 37243
P: (615) 741-7959
F: (615) 532-8905
E: registry.info
  @state.tn.us

TEXAS
Ms. Ann McGeehan
Division Director
Elections Division
Office of the Secretary of State
P.O. Box 12697
Austin, TX 78711
P: (512) 463-9871
F: (512) 475-2811

VERMONT
Hon. Jim Condos (D)
Secretary of State
Office of the Secretary of State
26 Terrace Street
Montpelier, VT 05609
P: (802) 828-2148
F: (802) 828-2496
E: jim.condos
    @sec.state.vt.us

WASHINGTON
Mr. Doug Ellis
Interim Executive Director
Public Disclosure Commission
711 Capitol Way, #206
P.O. Box 40908
Olympia, WA 98504
P: (360) 664-2735
F: (360) 753-1112
E: Dellis@pdc.wa.gov

WISCONSIN
Mr. Jonathan Becker
Division Administrator
Ethics Division
P.O. Box 7984
Madison, WI 53707
P: (608) 267-0647
E: jonathan.becker@wi.gov

WYOMING
Hon. Max Maxfield (R)
Secretary of State
Office of the Secretary of State
State Capitol Building
200 West 24th
Cheyenne, WY 82002
P: (307) 777-7378
F: (307) 777-6217
E: Secofstate@state.wy.us

Lottery

Administers the state lottery system.

ARIZONA
Mr. Jeff Hatch Miller
Director
State Lottery
4740 East University Drive
Phoenix, AZ 85034
P: (480) 921-4400
F: (480) 921-4488

ARKANSAS
Mr. Ernie Passailaigue
Director
State Scholarship Lottery
124 West Capitol, Suite 1400
Little Rock, AR 72201
P: (501) 683-2000

CALIFORNIA
Mr. Linh Nguyen
Acting Director
State Lottery
600 North 10th Street
Sacramento, CA 95814
P: (916) 323-0403
F: (916) 323-7087

COLORADO
Mr. Abel J. Tapia
Director
State Lottery
212 West 3rd Street, Suite 210
Pueblo, CO 81003
P: (719) 546-2400
E: colorado.lottery
  @state.co.us

CONNECTICUT
Ms. Anne M. Noble
President & CEO
State Lottery Corporation
777 Brook Street
Rocky Hill, CT 06067
P: (860) 713-2800
F: (860) 713-2805
E: ctlottery@ctlottery.org

DELAWARE
Mr. Wayne Lemons
Director
State Lottery
McKee Business Park
1575 McKee Road, Suite 102
Dover, DE 19904
P: (302) 739-5291
F: (302) 739-6706
E: brian.peters@state.de.us

DISTRICT OF COLUMBIA
Mr. Buddy Roogow
Executive Director
Lottery & Charitable Games
Control Board
2101 Martin Luther King Jr.
Avenue
Southeast
Washington, DC 20020
P: (202) 645-8000
F: (202) 645-7914
E: lcgcb@dc.gov

FLORIDA
Ms. Cynthia F. O'Connell
Secretary
State Lottery
250 Marriott Dirve
Tallahassee, FL 32301
P: (850) 487-7777
F: (850) 487-7709

GEORGIA
Ms. Margaret DeFrancisco
President & CEO
State Lottery Corporation
Suite 3000, 250 Williams Street
Atlanta, GA 30303
P: (404) 215-5000
F: (404) 215-8871
E: glottery@galottery.org

IDAHO
Mr. Jeffrey R. Anderson
Executive Director
State Lottery
1199 Shoreline Lane, Suite 100
P.O. Box 6537
Boise, ID 83707
P: (208) 334-2600
E: janderson
  @lottery.idaho.gov

ILLINOIS
Ms. Jodie Winnett
Acting Superintendent
State Lottery
100 West Randolph
Mail Code 7-901
Chicago, IL 60601
P: (312) 793-1681
F: (312) 793-5514

INDIANA
Ms. Kathryn Densborn
Executive Director
Hoosier Lottery
Pan Am Plaza
201 South Capitol Avenue, Suite
1100
Indianapolis, IN 46225
P: (317) 264-4800
F: (317) 264-4908
E: playersupport
  @hoosierlottery.com

IOWA
Mr. Terry Rich
President & CEO
State Lottery
2323 Grand Avenue
Des Moines, IA 50312
P: (515) 725-7900
F: (515) 725-7905
E: wmaster@ialottery.com

KANSAS
Mr. Ed Van Petten
Executive Director
State Lottery
128 North Kansas Avenue
Topeka, KS 66603
P: (785) 296-5700
F: (785) 296-5712
E: lotteryinfo
  @kslottery.net

KENTUCKY
Mr. Arch Gleason
President & CEO
State Lottery
1011 West Main Street
Louisville, KY 40202
P: (502) 560-1500
F: (502) 560-1532
E: custsrvs@kylottery.com

LOUISIANA
Ms. Rose Hudson
President/CEO
State Lottery Corporation
555 Laurel Street
Baton Rouge, LA 70801
P: (225) 297-2000
F: (225) 297-2005
E: info
  @louisianalottery.com

MAINE
Mr. Dan Gwadosky
Director
Bureau of Alcoholic Beverages
& Lottery Operations
8 State House Station
Augusta, ME 04333
P: (207) 287-3721
F: (207) 287-6769
E: dgwadosky@maine.gov

MARYLAND
Mr. Stephen L. Martino
Director
State Lottery Agency
Montgomery Park Business
Center
1800 Washington Boulevard,
Suite 330
Baltimore, MD 21230
P: (410) 230-8790

MASSACHUSETTS
Mr. Paul Sternburg
Executive Director
State Lottery
60 Columbian Street
Braintree, MA 02184
P: (781) 849-5555
F: (781) 849-5546

MICHIGAN
Mr. Scott Bowen
Lottery Commissioner
Bureau of State Lottery
101 East Hillsdale
Lansing, MI 48909
P: (517) 335-5600
F: (517) 335-5651
E: milottery@michigan.gov

MINNESOTA
Mr. Clint Harris
Executive Director
State Lottery
2645 Long Lake Road
Roseville, MN 55113
P: (651) 635-8100
F: (651) 297-7496
E: lottery@mnlottery.com

MISSOURI
Ms. May Scheve Reardon
Executive Director
State Lottery
1823 Southridge Drive
Jefferson City, MO 65109
P: (573) 751-4050

MONTANA
Ms. Angela Wong
Director
State Lottery
2525 North Montana Avenue
Helena, MT 59601
P: (406) 444-5825
F: (406) 444-5830

NEBRASKA
Mr. Jim Haynes
Director
State Lottery
1800 "O" Street, Suite 101
Lincoln, NE 68509
P: (402) 471-6100
F: (402) 471-6108

NEW HAMPSHIRE
Mr. Charles McIntyre
Executive Director
State Lottery Commission
14 Integra Drive
Concord, NH 03301
P: (603) 271-3391

NEW JERSEY
Ms. Carole Hedinger
Executive Director
State Lottery
One Lawrence Park Complex
Brunswick Avenue Circle
Lawrenceville, NJ 08648
P: (609) 599-5800
E: publicinfo
   @lottery.state.nj.us

NEW MEXICO
Mr. Tom Romero
CEO
State Lottery
4511 Osuna Road, Northeast
P.O. Box 93130
Albuquerque, NM 87109
P: (505) 342-7600
F: (505) 342-7512
E: custservice
   @nmlottery.com

NEW YORK
Mr. Gordon Medenica
Director
State Lottery
One Broadway Center
P.O. Box 7500
Schenectady, NY 12301
P: (518) 388-3300
F: (518) 388-3403
E: questions
   @lottery.state.ny.us

NORTH CAROLINA
Ms. Alice Garland
Executive Director
Education Lottery
2100 Yonkers Road
Raleigh, NC 27604
P: (919) 301-3601
F: (919) 715-8825
E: playerinfo@lotterync.net

NORTH DAKOTA
Mr. Randy Miller
Director
State Lottery
600 East Boulevard Avenue
Department 125
Bismarck, ND 58505
P: (701) 328-1574

OHIO
Mr. Dennis Berg
Acting Executive Director
State Lottery
615 West Superior Avenue
Cleveland, OH 44113
P: (216) 774-5900

OKLAHOMA
Mr. Jim Scroggins
Executive Director
Lottery Commission
3817 North Santa Fe
Oklahoma City, OK 73112
P: (405) 522-7700
F: (405) 521-0528

OREGON
Mr. Larry Niswender
Director
State Lottery
P.O. Box 12649
Salem, OR 97309
P: (503) 540-1000
E: webcenter@state.or.us

PENNSYLVANIA
Mr. Drew Svitko
Executive Director
State Lottery
1200 Fulling Mill Road, Suite 1
Middletown, PA 17057
P: (717) 702-8000
F: (717) 702-8024
E: info@palottery.com

PUERTO RICO
Ms. Carmen Diaz Marrero
Auxiliary Director
Electronic Lottery
383 Roosevelt Avenue, Suite 107
Fundacion Angel Ramos Building
San Juan, PR 00918
P: (787) 250-8150, Ext. 223
E: info
   @loteriaelectronicapr.com

RHODE ISLAND
Mr. Gerald Aubin
Director
State Lottery
1425 Pontiac Avenue
Cranston, RI 02920
P: (401) 463-6500
F: (401) 463-5669
E: mferriola@rilot.ri.gov

SOUTH CAROLINA
Ms. Paula Harper-Bethea
Executive Director
State Education Lottery Commission
1333 Main Street, Suite 400
Columbia, SC 29201
P: (803) 737-2002
F: (803) 737-2005
E: questions@sclot.com

SOUTH DAKOTA
Mr. Norman Lingle
Executive Director
State Lottery
207 East Capitol, Suite 200
Pierre, SD 57501
P: (605) 773-5770
F: (605) 773-5786
E: lottery@state.sd.us

TENNESSEE
Ms. Rebecca Paul Hargrove
President & CEO
Education Lottery Corporation
Plaza Tower, MetroCenter
200 Athens Way, Suite 200
Nashville, TN 37228
P: (615) 324-6500
F: (615) 324-6512

TEXAS
Mr. Gary Grief
Executive Director
Lottery Commission
611 East 6th Street
P.O.Box 16630
Austin, TX 78761
P: (512) 344-5160
F: (512) 478-3682
E: gary.grief
   @lottery.state.tx.us

U.S. VIRGIN ISLANDS
Mr. Conrad Francois
Executive Director
State Lottery
8A Ross Estate
Barbel Plaza
St. Thomas, VI 00802
P: (340) 774-2502, Ext. 25

VERMONT
Mr. Alan R. Yandow
Executive Director
Lottery Commission
1311 U.S. Route 302 - Suite 100
Barre, VT 05641
P: (802) 479-5686
F: (802) 479-4294
E: ayandow@vtlottery.com

VIRGINIA
Ms. Paula I. Otto
Executive Director
State Lottery
900 East Main Street
Richmond, VA 23219
P: (804) 692-7000
F: (804) 692-7102
E: info@valottery.com

WASHINGTON
Mr. Bill Hanson
Director
State Lottery
P.O. Box 43000
Olympia, WA 98504
P: (360) 664-4800
F: (360) 586-1039
E: director's_office
   @walottery.com

WEST VIRGINIA
Mr. John Musgrave
Executive Director
State Lottery
P.O. Box 2067
Charleston, WV 25327
P: (304) 558-0500
F: (304) 558-3321
E: jmusgrave
   @tax.state.wv.us

WISCONSIN
Mr. Michael Edmonds
Director
State Lottery
2135 Rimrock Road #231
Madison, WI 53713
P: (608) 261-8800
F: (608) 264-6644

Medicaid

Administers the medical assistance program that finances medical care for income assistance recipients and other eligible medically needy persons.

ALABAMA
Mr. R. Bob Mullins
Commissioner
Medicaid Agency
501 Dexter Avenue
P.O. Box 5624
Montgomery, AL 36103
P: (334) 242-5600
E: bob.mullins
	@medicaid.alabama.gov

ALASKA
Mr. Ron Kreher
Director
Division of Public Assistance
Department of Health & Social Services
P.O. Box 110640
Juneau, AK 99811
P: (907) 465-5847
F: (907) 465-5154
E: ron.kreher@alaska.gov

AMERICAN SAMOA
Mr. Andy Puletasi
Medicaid Program Director
Medicaid Program
LBJ Tropical Medical Center
Pago Pago, AS 96799
P: (684) 633-4590
F: (684) 633-1869

ARIZONA
Mr. Tom J. Betlach
Director
Health Care Cost Containment System
801 East Jefferson Street, MD 4100
Phoenix, AZ 85034
P: (602) 417-4000
F: (602) 252-6536

ARKANSAS
Mr. Eugene Gessow
Director
Division of Medicaid Services
P.O. Box 1437, Slot S401
Little Rock, AR 72203
P: (501) 682-8740
F: (501) 682-1197
E: eugene.gessow
	@arkansas.gov

CALIFORNIA
Mr. Toby Douglas
Director
Department of Health Care Services
1501 Capitol Avenue, Suite 6001
MS: 0000, P.O. Box 997413
Sacramento, CA 95899
P: (916) 440-7400
F: (916) 440-7404
E: toby.douglas@dhcs.ca.gov

COLORADO
Ms. Laurel Karabatsos
Acting Medicaid Director
Department of Health Care
1570 Grant Street
Denver, CO 80203
P: (303) 866-5920
F: (303) 866-4411

CONNECTICUT
Mr. Mark Schaefer
Director, Medical Care Administration
Department of Social Services
25 Sigourney Street
Hartford, CT 06106
P: (860) 424-5067
E: mark.schaefer@ct.gov

DELAWARE
Ms. Rosanne Mahaney
Director
Division of Medicaid & Medical Assistance
Department of Health & Social Services
1901 North DuPont Highway
New Castle, DE 19720
P: (302) 255-9535

DISTRICT OF COLUMBIA
Mr. Wayne Turnage
Director
Department of Health Care Finance
825 North Capitol Street, Northeast
Suite 6037
Washington, DC 20001
P: (202) 442-5988
F: (202) 442-4790
E: dhcf@dc.gov

FLORIDA
Ms. Roberta K. Bradford
Deputy Secretary
Agency for Healthcare Administration
2727 Mahan Drive
Tallahassee, FL 32308
P: (850) 412-4007
F: (850) 488-2520
E: Bradforr
	@ahca.myflorida.com

GEORGIA
Dr. Jerry Dubberly
Chief
Medicaid Division
Department of Community Health
Two Peachtree Street, Northwest
Atlanta, GA 30303
P: (404) 651-8681
F: (404) 283-0128

GUAM
Ms. Tess Arcangel
Administrator
Department of Public Health & Social Services
123 Chalan Kareta
Mangilcio, GU 96913
P: (671) 735-7282

HAWAII
Dr. Kenneth S. Fink
Administrator
Med-Quest Division
Department of Human Services
601 Kamokila Boulevard, Rooms 506 & 518
Kapolei, HI 96707
P: (808) 692-8050
F: (808) 692-8155

IDAHO
Ms. Leslie Clement
Administrator
Division of Medicaid
Department of Health & Welfare
3232 Elder Street
Boise, ID 83705
P: (208) 364-1804
F: (208) 364-1811

ILLINOIS
Ms. Theresa Eagleson
Administrator
Division of Medical Programs
Dept. of Healthcare & Family Services
201 South Grand Avenue, East
Springfield, IL 62763
P: (217) 782-2570
F: (217) 782-5672

INDIANA
Ms. Pat Casanova
Director of Medicaid
Office of Medicaid Policy & Planning
402 West Washington Street, Room W461
P.O. Box 7083
Indianapolis, IN 46207
P: (317) 234-2407
F: (317) 233-4693
E: Pat.Casanova@fssa.in.gov

IOWA
Ms. Jennifer Vermeer
Medicaid Director
Department of Human Services
100 Army Post Road
Des Moines, IA 50315
P: (515) 256-4621
F: (515) 725-1360
E: jvermee@dhs.state.ia.us

KANSAS
Dr. Andrew Allison
Executive Director
Health Policy Authority
Landon State Office Building, Room 900-N
900 Southwest Jackson Street
Topeka, KS 66612
P: (785) 296-3981
F: (785) 296-4813

KENTUCKY
Mr. Neville Wise
Acting Commissioner
Department for Medicaid Services
275 East Main Street, 6W-A
Frankfort, KY 40621
P: (502) 564-4321
F: (502) 564-0509

LOUISIANA
Mr. Don Gregory
Director
Bureau of Health Services Financing
628 North 4th Street
P.O. Box 91030
Baton Rouge, LA 70821
P: (225) 342-5774
F: (225) 342-3893
E: medweb@dhh.la.gov

MAINE
Ms. Stefanie Nadeau
Acting Director
Office of MaineCare Services
11 State House Station
Augusta, ME 04333
P: (207) 287-2093
F: (207) 287-2675
E: Stefanie.Nadeau
	@maine.gov

MARYLAND
Mr. Chuck Milligan
Deputy Secretary, Health Care Financing
Department of Health & Mental Hygiene
201 West Preston Street, 5th Floor
Baltimore, MD 21201
P: (410) 767-4639
F: (410) 767-6489

MASSACHUSETTS
Ms. Terry Dougherty
Medicaid Director
Office of Medicaid
One Ashburton Place, Room 1109
Boston, MA 02108
P: (617) 573-1770
F: (617) 573-1894

MICHIGAN
Mr. Stephen Filton
Medicaid Director
Department of Community Health
400 South Pine Street
Lansing, MI 48913
P: (517) 241-7882
F: (517) 335-5007

MINNESOTA
Mr. David Godfrey
Medicaid Director
Department of Human Services
P.O. Box 64983
540 Cedar Street
St. Paul, MN 55164
P: (651) 431-2182
F: (651) 431-7421

MISSISSIPPI
Dr. Bob Robinson
Medicaid Director
Division of Medicaid
550 High Street, Suite 1000
Jackson, MS 39201
P: (601) 359-9562

MISSOURI
Dr. Ian McCaslin
Director
HealthNet Division
615 Howerton Court
P.O. Box 6500
Jefferson City, MO 65102
P: (573) 751-3425
F: (573) 751-6564
E: Ask.MHD@dss.mo.gov

MONTANA
Ms. Mary Dalton
Medicaid and Health Services Branch Manager
Department of Public Health & Human Services
111 North Sanders, Room 301
P.O. Box 4210
Helena, MT 59604
P: (406) 444-4084
F: (406) 444-1970
E: mary.dalton@mt.gov

NEBRASKA
Ms. Vivianne M. Chaumont
Director
Division of Medicaid & Long Term Care
P.O. Box 95026
Lincoln, NE 68509
P: (402) 471-2135
F: (402) 471-9449

NEVADA
Mr. Charles C. Duarte
Administrator
Division of Health Care Financing & Policy
Department of Health & Human Services
100 East William Street, Suite 101
Carson City, NV 89701
P: (775) 684-3677
F: (775) 684-3893
E: cduarte@dhcfp.nv.gov

NEW HAMPSHIRE
Ms. Kathleen A. Dunn
Assistant Medicaid Director
Office of Medicaid Business & Policy
Department of Health & Human Services
129 Pleasant Street
Concord, NH 03301
P: (603) 271-5258
F: (603) 271-4727
E: kdunn@dhhs.state.nh.us

NEW JERSEY
Ms. Valerie Harr
Director
Division of Medical Assistance & Health Services
P.O. Box 712
Trenton, NJ 08625
P: (609) 588-2600
F: (609) 588-3583

NEW MEXICO
Ms. Julie Weinberg
Acting Division Director
Medical Assisance Division
Department of Human Services
P.O. Box 2348
Santa Fe, NM 87504
P: (505) 827-6253

NEW YORK
Ms. Deborah Bachrach
Deputy Commissioner
Office of Health Insurance Programs
Corning Tower
Empire State Plaza
Albany, NY 12237
P: (518) 474-3018

NORTH CAROLINA
Dr. Craigan L. Gray
Director
Division of Medical Assistance
1985 Umstead Drive
2501 Mail Service Center
Raleigh, NC 27699
P: (919) 855-4100
F: (919) 733-6608

NORTH DAKOTA
Ms. Maggie D. Anderson
Director
Medical Services
600 East Boulevard Avenue
Bismarck, ND 58505
P: (701) 328-1603
F: (701) 328-1544

NORTHERN MARIANA ISLANDS
Ms. Helen Sablan
Administrator
Medicaid Program
Department of Public Health
P.O. Box 500409
Saipan, MP 96950
P: (670) 664-4884
F: (670) 664-4885
E: dlnrgov@vzpacifica.net

OHIO
Mr. John McCarthy
Medicaid Director
Department of Job & Family Services
50 West Town Street, 4th Floor
Columbus, OH 43215
P: (614) 466-4443

OKLAHOMA
Dr. Gartin Splinter
Medicaid Director
Health Care Authority
2401 Northwest 23rd Street, Suite 1A
Oklahoma City, OK 73105
P: (405) 522-7365
F: (405) 530-3218

OREGON
Ms. Judy Mohr Peterson
Assistant Director
Medical Assistance Programs
Department Of Human Services
500 Summer Street, Northeast, E-49
Salem, OR 97301
P: (503) 945-5772
F: (503) 373-7689
E: dhs.info@state.or.us

PENNSYLVANIA
Mr. Michael Nardone
Deputy Secretary
Office of Medical Assistance Programs
515 Health & Welfare Building
P.O. Box 2675
Harrisburg, PA 17110
P: (717) 787-1870
F: (717) 787-4639

PUERTO RICO
Mr. Miguel Negron-Rivera
Executive Director
Department of Health, Medicaid Program
P.O. Box 70184
San Juan, PR 00936
P: (787) 250-0453
F: (787) 250-0990

RHODE ISLAND
Ms. Elena Nicolella
Medicaid Director
Department of Human Services
600 New London Avenue
Cranston, RI 02920
P: (401) 462-3575

SOUTH CAROLINA
Mr. Anthony Keck
Director
Department of Health & Human Services
P.O. Box 8206
Columbia, SC 29202
P: (803) 898-2580
F: (803) 898-4515

SOUTH DAKOTA
Mr. Larry Iversen
Division Director
Office of Medical Services
700 Governors Drive
Pierre, SD 57501
P: (605) 773-3495
F: (605) 773-5246
E: Medical@state.sd.us

TENNESSEE
Mr. Darin Gordon
Deputy Commissioner
Bureau of TennCare
Department of Finance & Administration
310 Great Circle Drive
Nashville, TN 37243
P: (800) 342-3145
F: (615) 253-5607

Medicaid

TEXAS

Mr. Billy Millwee
Associate Commissioner for
Medicaid
Department of State Health
Services
11209 Metric Boulevard,
Building H
P.O. Box 85200
Austin, TX 78758
P: (512) 491-1867

U.S. VIRGIN ISLANDS

Mr. Paul Ritzma
Executive Director
Bureau of Health Insurance &
Medical Assistance
3730 Estate Altona
Frostco Center, Suite 302
St. Thomas, VI 00802
P: (340) 774-4624
F: (340) 774-4918

UTAH

Mr. Michael Hales
Director
Division of Medicaid & Health
Care Financing
288 North 1460 West
Salt Lake City, UT 84116
P: (801) 538-6689
F: (801) 538-6099
E: mthales@utah.gov

VERMONT

Dr. Susan Besio
Director
Office of Vermont Health
Access
Agency of Human Services
312 Hurricane Lane, Suite 201
Williston, VT 05495
P: (802) 879-5901
F: (802) 879-5962
E: susan.besio
   @ahs.state.vt.us

VIRGINIA

Dr. Gregg A. Pane
Director
Department of Medical
Assistance Services
600 East Broad Street, Suite
1300
Richmond, VA 23219
P: (804) 786-8099
E: gregg.pane
   @dmas.virginia.gov

WASHINGTON

Mr. Doug Porter
Assistant Secretary
Health & Recovery Services
Administration
Department of Social & Health
Services
P.O. Box 45505
Olympia, WA 98504
P: (360) 725-1863
F: (360) 902-7885

WEST VIRGINIA

Ms. Nancy V. Atkins
Commissioner
Bureau for Medical Services
Department of Health & Human
Services
350 Capitol Street, Room 251
Charleston, WV 25301
P: (304) 558-1703
F: (304) 558-1451
E: dhhrmedicaidcomm@wv.gov

WISCONSIN

Mr. Brett H. Davis
Medicaid Director
Division of Health Care
Financing
1 West Wilson Street, Room 350
Madison, WI 53701
P: (608) 266-1271
F: (608) 266-1096

WYOMING

Ms. Teri Green
Administrator
Office of Health Care Financing
6101 Yellowstone Road, Suite
210
Cheyenne, WY 82009
P: (307) 777-7531
F: (307) 777-6964

Mental Health and Mental Retardation

Administers the mental services of the state and/or plans and coordinates programs for persons with mental illness.

ALABAMA
Ms. Zelia Baugh
Commissioner
Department of Mental Health
100 North Union Street
P.O. Box 301410
Montgomery, AL 36130
P: (334) 242-3640
F: (334) 242-0684
E: zelia.baugh
   @mh.alabama.gov

ALASKA
Ms. Melissa Witzler-Stone
Director, Behavioral Health
Division of Behavioral Health
3601 C Street, Suite 934
Anchorage, AK 99503
P: (907) 269-3410
F: (907) 269-8166
E: melissa.stone@alaska.gov

AMERICAN SAMOA
Ms. Leilua Stevenson
Director
Department of Human & Social Services
American Samoa Government
P.O. Box 997534
Pago Pago, AS
P: (684) 633-7506
F: (684) 633-7449

ARIZONA
Dr. Laura Nelson
Acting Deputy Director
Division of Behavioral Health Services
Department of Health Services
150 North 18th Avenue, Suite 200
Phoenix, AZ 85007
P: (602) 364-4566
F: (602) 364-4570
E: nelsonla@azdhs.gov

ARKANSAS
Mr. David Laffoon
Director
Division of Behavioral Health Services
Department of Human Services
305 South Palm Street
Little Rock, AR 72205
P: (501) 686-9164
F: (501) 686-9182
E: david.laffoon
   @arkansas.gov

CALIFORNIA
Mr. Cliff Allenby
Acting Director
Department of Mental Health
1600 9th Street, Room 151
Sacramento, CA 95814
P: (916) 654-2309
F: (916) 654-3198
E: cliff.allenby@dmh.ca.gov

COLORADO
Ms. Joscelyn Gay
Deputy Executive Director
Division of Behavorial Health Services
1575 Sherman Street
Denver, CO 80203
P: (303) 866-2806
F: (303) 866-2362
E: joscelyn.gay@state.co.us

CONNECTICUT
Ms. Patricia Rehmer
Commissioner
Department of Mental Health & Addiction Services
410 Capitol Avenue
P.O. Box 341431
Hartford, CT 06134
P: (860) 418-7000
F: (860) 418-6691
E: Pat.Rehmer
   @po.state.ct.us

DELAWARE
Ms. Kevin Huckshorn
Director
Division of Substance Abuse & Mental Health
Department of Health & Social Services
1901 North DuPont Highway
New Castle, DE 19720
P: (302) 255-9398
F: (302) 255-4427
E: Kevin.Huckshorn
   @state.de.us

DISTRICT OF COLUMBIA
Mr. Stephen T. Baron
Director
Department of Mental Health
64 New York Avenue, Northeast, 4th Floor
Washington, DC 20002
P: (202) 673-2200
F: (202) 673-3433
E: steve.baron@dc.gov

FLORIDA
Mr. David A. Sofferin
Assistant Secretary for Substance Abuse & Mental Health
Department of Children & Families
1317 Winewood Boulevard
Tallahassee, FL 32399
P: (850) 414-9063
F: (850) 487-2239
E: david_sofferin
   @dcf.state.fl.us

GEORGIA
Dr. Frank E. Shelp
Commissioner
Department of Behavioral Health & Developmental Disabilities
2 Peachtree Street, Northwest
24th Floor
Atlanta, GA 30303
P: (404) 463-7946
F: (770) 408-5480

HAWAII
Ms. Michelle R. Hill
Deputy Director
Behavioral Health Administration
Department of Health
1250 Punchbowl Street, P.O. Box 3378
Honolulu, HI 96801
P: (808) 586-4419
F: (808) 586-4444
E: michelle.hill
   @doh.hawaii.gov

IDAHO
Ms. Kathleen Allyn
Commissioner
Division of Behavioral Health
P.O. Box 83720
450 West State, 3rd Floor
Boise, ID 83720
P: (208) 334-6997
F: (208) 332-7291
E: allynk@dhw.idaho.gov

ILLINOIS
Dr. Lorrie Rickman Jones
Director
Division of Mental Health
160 North LaSalle Street
10th Floor, S-1000
Chicago, IL 60601
P: (312) 814-3784
F: (312) 814-2964
E: LorrieRickman.Jones
   @illinois.gov

INDIANA
Ms. Gina Eckart
Director
Division of Mental Health & Addiction
Family & Social Services Administration
402 West Washington Street, Room W353
Indianapolis, IN 46204
P: (317) 232-7860
F: (317) 233-3472
E: gina.eckart@fssa.in.gov

IOWA
Ms. Jeanne Nesbit
Division Administrator
Division of Mental Health & Disability Services
1305 East Walnut Street
Des Moines, IA 50319
P: (515) 281-8580
F: (515) 242-6036
E: jnesbit@dhs.state.ia.us

KANSAS
Mr. Rick Shults
Director of Mental Health Disability & Behavioral Health Services
Docking State Office Building
915 Southwest Harrison Avenue, 9th Floor
Topeka, KS 66612
P: (785) 296-7272
F: (785) 296-6142
E: rick.shults@srs.ks.gov

KENTUCKY
Mr. Stephen Hall
Commissioner
Department for Behavioral Health, Developmental & Intellectual Disabilities
100 Fair Oaks Lane, 4E-B
Frankfort, KY 40621
P: (502) 564-4527
E: Stephen.Hall@ky.gov

Mental Health and Mental Retardation

LOUISIANA
Mr. Peter Calamari
Interim Assistant Secretary
Office of Behavioral Health
Department of Health &
Hospitals
P.O. Box 4049
Baton Rouge, LA 70821
P: (225) 342-2540
F: (225) 342-5066
E: pete.calamari@la.gov

MAINE
Mr. Ron Welch
Director
Office of Adult Mental Health
#11 State House Station
Marquardt Building, 2nd Floor
Augusta, ME 04333
P: (207) 287-2991
F: (207) 287-1022
E: Ron.Welch@maine.gov

MARYLAND
Dr. Brian Hepburn
Executive Director
Mental Hygiene Administration
Spring Grove Hospital Center
55 Wade Avenue, Dix Building
Catonsville, MD 21228
P: (410) 402-8457
F: (410) 402-8441
E: bhepburn
   @dhmh.state.md.us

MASSACHUSETTS
Ms. Barbara Leadholm
Commissioner
Department of Mental Health
25 Staniford Street
Boston, MA 02114
P: (617) 626-8123
F: (617) 626-8131
E: Barbara.Leadholm
   @state.ma.us

MINNESOTA
Ms. Maureen O'Connell
Assistant Commissioner
Chemical & Mental Health
Services Administration
P.O. Box 0988
St. Paul, MN 55164
P: (651) 431-2323
F: (651) 431-7455
E: maureen.oconnell
   @state.mn.us

MISSISSIPPI
Mr. Edwin C. LeGrand III
Executive Director
Department of Mental Health
1101 Robert E. Lee Building
239 North Lamar Street
Jackson, MS 39201
P: (601) 359-1288
F: (601) 359-5069
E: ed.legrand
   @dmh.state.ms.us

MISSOURI
Mr. Keith Schafer
Director
Department of Mental Health
1706 East Elm Street
Jefferson City, MO 65102
P: (573) 751-4970
F: (573) 751-7814
E: keith.schafer@dmh.mo.gov

MONTANA
Ms. Lou Thompson
Administrator
Addictive & Mental Disorders
Division
555 Fuller Avenue
P.O. Box 202905
Helena, MT 59620
P: (406) 444-3969
F: (406) 444-4435
E: lothompson@mt.gov

NEBRASKA
Dr. Scot L. Adams
Director
Division of Behavioral Health
Department of Health & Human
Services
301 Centennial Mall South, 3rd
Floor
Lincoln, NE 68509
P: (402) 471-8553
F: (402) 471-9449
E: scot.adams@nebraska.gov

NEVADA
Dr. Harold Cook
Administrator
Division of Mental Health &
Developmental Services
Department of Health & Human
Services
4126 Technology Way, 2nd
Floor
Carson City, NV 89706
P: (775) 684-5943
F: (775) 684-5966
E: hcook@mhds.nv.gov

NEW HAMPSHIRE
Ms. Nancy Rollins
Director
Division for Children, Youth &
Families
Department of Health & Human
Services
105 Pleasant Street, Main
Building
Concord, NH 03301
P: (603) 271-8560
F: (603) 271-5058
E: nrollins
   @dhhs.state.nh.us

NEW JERSEY
Ms. Valerie Larosiliere
Acting Commissioner
Division of Mental Health
Services
P.O. Box 727
Trenton, NJ 08625
P: (609) 777-0702
F: (609) 777-0662

NEW MEXICO
Ms. Linda Roebuck
CEO
Behavioral Health Collaborative
Human Services Department
37 Plaza La Prensa, P.O. Box
26110
Santa Fe, NM 87507
P: (505) 476-9257
F: (505) 476-9272
E: linda.roebuck
   @state.nm.us

NEW YORK
Dr. Michael F. Hogan
Commissioner
Office of Mental Health
Commissioner's Office
44 Holland Avenue
Albany, NY 12229
P: (518) 474-4403
F: (518) 474-2149
E: cocomfh@omh.state.ny.us

NORTH CAROLINA
Mr. Steve Jordan
Director
Division of Mental Health,
Developmental Disabilities &
Substance Abuse Services
Department of Health & Human
Services
3001 Mail Service Center
Raleigh, NC 27699
P: 9919) 733-7011
F: (919) 508-0951
E: steve.jordan@dhhs.nc.gov

**NORTHERN MARIANA
ISLANDS**
Ms. Josephine T. Sablan
Director
Mental Health & Social
Services
P.O. Box 500409
Saipan, MP 96950
P: (670) 232-6560
F: (670) 323-6580
E: cgcl@dphcgc.com

OHIO
Ms. Tracy J. Plouck
Director
Department of Mental Health
30 East Broad Street, 8th Floor
Columbus, OH 43215
P: (614) 466-2337
F: (614) 752-9453
E: tracy.plouck@mh.ohio.gov

OKLAHOMA
Ms. Terri White
Commissioner
Department of Mental Health &
Substance Abuse Services
Executive Department, P.O. Box
53277
1200 Northeast 13th
Oklahoma City, OK 73152
P: (405) 522-3877
F: (405) 522-0637
E: tlwhite@odmhsas.org

OREGON
Mr. Richard L. Harris
Assistant Director
Addictions & Mental Health
Division
Department of Human Services
500 Summer Street, Northeast,
E86
Salem, OR 97301
P: (503) 945-9708
F: (503) 373-7327
E: Richard.Harris
   @state.or.us

PENNSYLVANIA
Ms. Sherry Snyder
Acting Deputy Secretary
Office of Mental Health &
Substance Abuse Services
P.O. Box 2675, Administration
Building
DGS Complex Annex
Harrisburg, PA 17105
P: (717) 787-5450
F: (717) 787-5394
E: shersnyder@state.pa.us

PUERTO RICO
Dr. Jose Luis
   Galarza Arbona
Administrator
Mental Health &
Anti-Addiction Services
Administration
Ave Barbosa 414
P.O. Box 21414
San Juan, PR 00928
P: (787) 764-3760
F: (787) 765-5888
E: jgalarza
   @assmca.gobierno.pr

RHODE ISLAND
Dr. Craig S. Stenning
Director
Department of Behavioral
Healthcare, Developmental
Disabilities & Hospitals
Barry Hall
14 Harrington Road
Cranston, RI 02920
P: (401) 462-2339
F: (401) 462-6636
E: cstenning@mhrh.ri.gov

SOUTH CAROLINA
Mr. John H. Magill
State Director
Department of Mental Health
2414 Bull Street, Suite 321
P.O. Box 485
Columbia, SC 29202
P: (803) 898-8319
F: (803) 898-8586
E: jhm03@scdmh.org

SOUTH DAKOTA
Ms. Shawna Fullerton
Interim Director
Division of Mental Health
C/o 500 East Capitol
Pierre, SD 57501
P: (605) 773-5991
F: (605) 773-7076
E: shawna.fullerton
   @state.sd.us

TENNESSEE
Mr. E. Douglas Varney
Commissioner
Department of Mental Health &
Developmental Disabilities
Cordell Hull Building, 3rd Floor
425 Fifth Avenue, North
Nashville, TN 37243
P: (615) 532-6500
F: (615) 532-6514
E: Doug.Varney@tn.gov

TEXAS
Mr. Michael D. Maples
Assistant Commissioner for
Mental Health Substance Abuse
Services
Mental Health & Substance
Abuse Services
1100 West 49th Street
P.O.Box 149347
Austin, TX 78714
P: (512) 206-5968
F: (512) 206-5718
E: mike.maples
   @dshs.state.tx.us

UTAH
Ms. Lana Stohl
Director
Division of Substance Abuse &
Mental Health
Department of Human Services
195 North 1950 West
Salt Lake City, UT 84116
P: (801) 538-3939
F: (801) 538-4696
E: lstohl@utah.gov

VERMONT
Ms. Christine Oliver
Commissioner
Department of Mental Health
103 South Main Street
Wasson Hall
Waterbury, VT 05671
P: (802) 241-4008
F: (802) 241-4009
E: christine.oliver
   @dhs.state.vt.us

VIRGINIA
Mr. James Stewart
Commissioner
Department of Behavioral
Health & Developmental
Services
1220 Bank Street
P.O. Box 1797
Richmond, VA 23218
P: (804) 786-3921
F: (804) 371-6638
E: jim.stewart
   @dbhds.virginia.gov

WASHINGTON
Mr. David Dickinson
Director
Division of Behavioral Health &
Recovery
Department of Social & Health
Services
P.O. Box 45320
Olympia, WA 98504
P: (360) 725-3700
F: (360) 586-9551
E: david.dickinson
   @dshs.wa.gov

WEST VIRGINIA
Ms. Victoria L. Jones
Commissioner
Bureau for Behavioral Health &
Health Facilities
Department of Health & Human
Resources
350 Capitol Street, Room 350
Charleston, WV 25301
P: (304) 558-0736
F: (304) 558-2230
E: Victoria.L.Jones@wv.gov

WISCONSIN
Ms. Joyce Bohn Allen
Director
Division of Mental Health &
Substance Abuse Services
1 West Wilson Street, Room 850
P.O. Box 7851
Madison, WI 53707
P: (608) 266-1351
F: (608) 266-2579
E: joyce.allen
   @wisconsin.gov

WYOMING
Ms. Chris Newman
Interim Administrator
Mental Health & Substance
Abuse Division
Department of Health
6101 Yellowstone Road, Room
220
Cheyenne, WY 82002
P: (307) 777-8763
F: (307) 777-5580
E: chris.newman
   @health.wyo.gov

Minority Affairs

Serves as an advocate for state minority communities and promotes minority business enterprises within the state.

AMERICAN SAMOA
Ms. Leilua Stevenson
Director
Department of Human & Social Services
American Samoa Government
P.O. Box 997534
Pago Pago, AS
P: (684) 633-7506
F: (684) 633-7449

ARIZONA
Ms. Sandra Watson
Chief Operating Officer
Commerce Authority
1700 West Washington, Suite 600
Phoenix, AZ 85007
P: (602) 771-1215
F: (602) 771-1200
E: commerce@azcommerce.com

CONNECTICUT
Mr. Martin W. Anderson
Commissioner
Department of Administrative Services
165 Capitol Avenue
Room 491
Hartford, CT 06106
P: (860) 713-5100
F: (860) 713-7481
E: martin.anderson@ct.gov

ILLINOIS
Mr. N. Keith Chambers
Executive Director
Human Rights Commission
James R. Thompson Center
100 West Randolph Street, Suite 5-100
Chicago, IL 60601
P: (312) 814-6269
F: (312) 814-6517
E: Keith.Chambers
   @Illinois.gov

INDIANA
Ms. Felecia Roseburgh
Deputy Commissioner
Minority & Women's Business Enterprises
Department of Administration
402 West Washington Street, Room W-469
Indianapolis, IN 46204
P: (317) 232-3061
F: (317) 233-6921
E: froseburgh@idoa.in.gov

IOWA
Mr. Ralph Rosenberg
Executive Director
Civil Rights Commission
Grimes State Office Building
400 East 14th Street
Des Moines, IA 50319
P: (515) 242-6537
F: (515) 242-5840
E: ralph.rosenberg@iowa.gov

KANSAS
Dr. Mildred Edwards
Executive Director
African-American Affairs Commission
900 Southwest Jackson, Room 100
Topeka, KS 66612
P: (785) 296-1904
F: (785) 296-1795
E: Mildred.Edwards@ks.gov

Ms. Adrienne Foster
Executive Director
Hispanic & Latin American Affairs Commission
900 Southwest Jackson, Room 100
Topeka, KS 66612
P: (785) 296-3465
F: (785) 296-8118

KENTUCKY
Mr. Delquan Dorsey
Executive Director
Governor's Office of Minority Empowerment
700 Capital Avenue, Suite 132
Frankfort, KY 40601
P: (502) 564-2611
F: (502) 564-0437
E: kyome@ky.gov

LOUISIANA
Mr. Patrick Bell
Deputy Commissioner of Minority Affairs
Department of Insurance
1702 North Third Street
P.O. Box 94214
Baton Rouge, LA 70804
P: (225) 342-8395
E: pbell@ldi.state.la.us

MAINE
Ms. Laurel J. Shippee
State Equal Employment Opportunity Coordinator
Department of Professional & Financial Regulation
Bureau of Human Resources
4 State House Station
Augusta, ME 04333
P: (207) 624-7761
F: (207) 287-4414
E: Laurel.J.Shippee
   @maine.gov

MARYLAND
Ms. Luwanda W. Jenkins
Special Secretary
Governor's Office of Minority Affairs
6 Saint Paul Street, Suite 1502
Baltimore, MD 21202
P: (410) 767-8232
F: (410) 333-7568
E: ljenkins
   @mdminoritybusiness.com

MASSACHUSETTS
Ms. Sandra E. Borders
Director
Office of Diversity & Equal Opportunity
One Ashburton Place, Room 213
Boston, MA 02108
P: (617) 727-7441
F: (617) 727-0568

MICHIGAN
Mr. Daniel Krichbaum
Director
Department of Civil Rights
Capitol Tower Building
110 West Michigan Avenue, Suite 900
Lansing, MI 48933
P: (517) 335-3164
F: (517) 335-6513
E: krichbaumd@michigan.gov

MINNESOTA
Mr. Kevin Lindsey
Commissioner
Department of Human Rights
190 East 5th Street, Suite 700
St. Paul, MN 55101
P: (651) 296-5675
F: (651) 296-9042
E: Kevin.Lindsey
   @state.mn.us

MISSOURI
Mr. Alan Green
Director
Office of Supplier & Workforce Diversity
Harry S. Truman Building
301 West High Street, Room 630
Jefferson City, MO 65101
P: (573) 751-8130
F: (573) 522-8078
E: alan.green@oa.mo.gov

MONTANA
Mr. Dore Schwinden
Director
Department of Commerce
301 South Park
P.O. Box 200501
Helena, MT 59620
P: (406) 841-2704
F: (406) 841-2701
E: dschwinden@mt.gov

NORTH DAKOTA
Mr. Tony Weiler
Commissioner of Labor
Department of Labor
600 East Boulevard Avenue
Department 406
Bismarck, ND 58505
P: (701) 328-2660
F: (701) 328-2031
E: tjweiler@nd.gov

OHIO
Mr. G. Michael Payton
Executive Director
Civil Rights Commission
Rhodes State Office Tower
30 East Broad Street, 5th Floor
Columbus, OH 43215
P: (614) 466-2785
F: (614) 466-7742
E: paytonm@ocrc.state.oh.us

OKLAHOMA
Mr. Oscar B. Jackson Jr.
Administrator & Cabinet Secretary
Office of Personnel Management
Human Resources & Administration
2101 North Lincoln Boulevard, Room G-80
Oklahoma City, OK 73105
P: (405) 521-6301
F: (405) 522-0694
E: oscar.jackson@opm.ok.gov

OREGON
Mr. Frank Garcia Jr.
Director of Diversity &
Inclusion
Governor's Office
225 Capitol Street, Northeast
Salem, OR 97301
P: (503) 986-6543
F: (503) 378-3225
E: frank.garcia@state.or.us

SOUTH CAROLINA
Mr. Thomas Smith
Executive Director
Commission for Minority
Affairs
6904 North Main Street, Suite
107
Columbia, SC 29203
P: (803) 333-9621
F: (803) 333-9627
E: tsmith@cfma.state.sc.us

SOUTH DAKOTA
Mr. Leroy LaPlante
Secretary of Tribal Relations
Department of Tribal
Governmental Relations
Capitol Lake Plaza
711 East Wells Avenue
Pierre, SD 57501
P: (605) 773-3415
F: (605) 773-6592

VIRGINIA
Ms. Ida McPherson
Director
Department of Minority
Business Enterprise
1100 East Main Street, Suite 300
Richmond, VA 23219
P: (804) 371-6228
F: (804) 371-7359
E: ida.mcpherson
    @dmbe.virginia.gov

WEST VIRGINIA
Ms. Ivin B. Lee
Executive Director
Human Rights Commission
1321 Plaza East
Room 108A
Charleston, WV 25301
P: (304) 558-2616
F: (304) 558-0085
E: ivinlee@wvdhhr.org

WISCONSIN
Ms. Claire Dehnert
Division of Affirmative Action
P.O. Box 7855
Madison, WI 53707
P: (608) 267-1005
E: claire.dehnert
    @wisconsin.gov

Motor Vehicle Administration

Issues and maintains all records related to motor vehicle registration, operators' licenses and certificates of titles in the state.

ALABAMA
Colonel Hugh B. McCall
Director
Department of Public Safety
301 South Ripley Street
P.O. Box 1511
Montgomery, AL 36102
P: (334) 242-4394
F: (334) 242-0512
E: director@alalinc.net

ALASKA
Ms. Whitney Brewster
Director
Division of Motor Vehicles
Department of Administration
1300 West Benson Boulevard, Suite 300
Anchorage, AK 99503
P: (907) 269-5559
F: (907) 269-3762
E: whitney.brewster
@alaska.gov

Colonel Keith Mallard
Director
State Troopers
5700 East Tudor Road
Anchorage, AK 99507
P: (907) 269-0316
F: (907) 337-2059
E: keith.mallard@alaska.gov

AMERICAN SAMOA
Mr. Tuaolo M. Fruean
Commissioner
Department of Public Safety
American Samoa Government
P.O. Box 3699
Pago Pago, AS 96799
P: (684) 633-1111
F: (684) 633-7296

ARIZONA
Mr. Robert Halliday
Director
Department of Public Safety
2102 West Encanto Boulevard
P.O. Box 6638
Phoenix, AZ 85005
P: (602) 223-2000
F: (602) 223-2917

Ms. Stacey K. Stanton
Assistant Director
Motor Vehicle Division
Department of Transportation
P.O. Box 2100
Phoenix, AZ 85001
P: (602) 712-8152
F: (602) 712-6539
E: sstanton@azdot.gov

ARKANSAS
Mr. Roger Duren
Administrator of Motor Vehicles
Revenue Division
P.O. Box 1272
Little Rock, AR 72203
P: (501) 682-4630
F: (501) 682-1116
E: roger.duren
@rev.state.ar.us

Mr. Mike Munns
Assistant Commissioner of Revenue
Revenue Division
P.O. Box 1272
Little Rock, AR 72203
P: (501) 682-7052
F: (501) 682-1683
E: mike.munns
@rev.state.ar.us

Ms. Tonie Shields
Administrator of Driver Services
Office of Driver Services
P.O. Box 1272
Little Rock, AR 72203
P: (501) 682-7060
F: (501) 682-7688
E: tonie.shields
@rev.state.ar.us

Mr. John H. Theis
Assistant Commissioner of Revenue
Department of Finance & Administration
P.O. Box 1272
Little Rock, AR 72203
P: (501) 682-7000
F: (501) 682-1161
E: john.theis
@rev.state.ar.us

CALIFORNIA
Mr. J.A. Farrow
Commissioner
Highway Patrol
601 North 7th Street
P.O. Box 942898
Sacramento, CA 94298
P: (916) 843-3001
F: (916) 843-3264

Mr. George Valverde
Director
Department of Motor Vehicles
2415 1st Avenue, Mail Station F101
Sacramento, CA 95818
P: (916) 657-6940
F: (916) 657-7393

COLORADO
Ms. Roxy Huber
Executive Director
Department of Revenue
1375 Sherman Street
Denver, CO 80261
P: (303) 866-5610
F: (303) 866-2400

DELAWARE
Ms. Jennifer L. Cohan
Director
Division of Motor Vehicles
303 Transportation Circle
P.O. Box 698
Dover, DE 19903
P: (302) 744-2500
F: (302) 739-3152

Colonel Robert M. Coupe
Superintendent
State Police
1441 North DuPont Highway
Dover, DE 19901
P: (302) 739-5960
F: (302) 739-5966

DISTRICT OF COLUMBIA
Ms. Lucinda M. Babers
Director
Department of Motor Vehicles
P.O. Box 90120
Washington, DC 20090
P: (202) 737-4404
E: dmv@dc.gov

FLORIDA
Ms. Julie Jones
Executive Director
Department of Highway Safety & Motor Vehicles
Neil Kirkman Building
2900 Apalachee Parkway
Tallahassee, FL 32399
P: (850) 487-3132
F: (850) 922-6274
E: executivedirector
@flhsmv.gov

GEORGIA
Mr. Greg C. Dozier
Commissioner
Department of Driver Services
2206 East View Parkway
P.O. Box 80447
Conyers, GA 30013
P: (678) 413-8654
F: (678) 413-8661

Mr. Tim Shields
Director
Motor Vehicle Division
1200 Tradeport Boulevard
Hapeville, GA 30354
P: (404) 968-3800
E: motorvehicleinquiry
@dor.ga.gov

GUAM
Mr. Steve Aguon
Supervisor, Vehicle Registration Branch
Department of Revenue & Taxation
Motor Vehicle Division
P.O. Box 23607
GMF, GU 96921
P: (671) 635-7652
E: saguon@revtax.gov.gu

HAWAII
Dr. Glenn M. Okimoto
Director
Department of Transportation
869 Punchbowl Street
Honolulu, HI 96813
P: (808) 587-2150
F: (808) 587-2167

IDAHO
Mr. Alan Frew
Administrator
Motor Vehicles Division
3311 West State Street
P.O. Box 7129
Boise, ID 83707
P: (208) 334-4443
F: (208) 334-8739
E: alan.frew@itd.idaho.gov

Col. Jerry Russell
Director
State Police
P.O. Box 700
Meridian, ID 83680
P: (208) 884-7003
F: (208) 884-7090
E: jerry.russell
@isp.idaho.gov

ILLINOIS
Mr. Ernie Dannenberger
Director
Vehicle Services Department
Michael J. Howlett Building
501 South Second Street, Room 312
Springfield, IL 62756
P: (217) 785-3000
F: (217) 785-4727
E: edannenberger@ilsos.net

Mr. Hiram Grau
State Director
State Police
2200 South Dirksen Parkway
Springfield, IL 62703
P: (217) 782-7263
E: hiram.grau@illinois.gov

Mr. Gary Hannig
Secretary
Department of Transportation
2300 South Dirksen Parkway
Springfield, IL 62764
P: (217) 782-5597
F: (217) 782-6828

Mr. Gary Lazzerini
Director, Metro Operation
Driver Services Department
17 North State Street
Suite 1100
Chicago, IL 60602
P: (312) 793-1010
F: (312) 814-2974
E: glazzerini@ilsos.net

Mr. Michael J. Mayer
Director, Downstate Operations
Driver Services Department
2701 South Dirksen Parkway
Springfield, IL 62723
P: (217) 782-6212
F: (217) 785-2472
E: mmayer@lisos.net

INDIANA
Mr. Scott Waddell
Commissioner
Bureau of Motor Vehicles
100 North Senate Avenue,
IGCN, Room N440
Indianapolis, IN 46204
P: (317) 232-2915
F: (317) 233-3135
E: swaddell@bmv.IN.gov

Dr. Paul Whitesell
Superintendent
State Police
100 North Senate Avenue, Room IGCN N340
Indianapolis, IN 46204
P: (317) 232-8241
E: pwhitesell@isp.in.gov

IOWA
Col. Patrick J. Hoye
Colonel
State Patrol Division
Department of Public Safety
215 East 7th Street
Des Moines, IA 50319
P: (515) 725-6090
E: hoye@dps.state.ia.us

Mr. Mark Lowe
Director
Motor Vehicle Division
6310 Southeast Convenience Boulevard
Des Moines, IA 50306
P: (515) 244-9124
F: (515) 237-3152
E: mark.lowe@dot.iowa.gov

Mr. Larry L. Noble
Commissioner
Department of Public Safety
215 East 7th Street
Des Moines, IA 50319
P: (515) 725-6182
E: noble@dps.state.ia.us

KANSAS
Colonel Ernest E. Garcia
Superintendent
Highway Patrol
122 Southwest 7th Street
Topeka, KS 66603
P: (785) 296-6800
F: (785) 296-3049

Mr. Nick Jordan
Secretary
Department of Revenue
Docking State Office Building, Room 230
915 Southwest Harrison Street
Topeka, KS 66612
P: (785) 296-3909
F: (785) 296-7928

KENTUCKY
Mr. Mike Hancock
Secretary
Transportation Cabinet
200 Mero Street
Frankfort, KY 40622
P: (502) 564-4890
F: (502) 564-4809

Mr. Thomas Zawacki
Commissioner
Department of Vehicle Regulation
200 Mero Street
Frankfort, KY 40601
P: (502) 564-7000

LOUISIANA
Col. Michael D. Edmonson
Superintendent of State Police
Public Safety Services
7919 Independence Boulevard
Baton Rouge, LA 70806
P: (225) 925-6118
F: (225) 925-6006

Mr. Nick Gautreaux
Commissioner
Motor Vehicle Administration
7979 Independence Boulevard
P.O. Box 64886
Baton Rouge, LA 70896
P: (225) 925-6146
F: (225) 925-6735

MAINE
Mr. Thomas Arnold
Deputy Secretary of State
Bureau of Motor Vehicles
29 State House Station
Augusta, ME 04333
P: (207) 624-9000
F: (207) 624-9013
E: thomas.arnold@maine.gov

Col. Patrick J. Fleming
Chief
State Police
42 State House Station
45 Commerce Drive
Augusta, ME 04333
P: (207) 624-7200
E: patrick.j.fleming
   @maine.gov

MARYLAND
Mr. John T. Kuo
Administrator
Motor Vehicle Administration
Department of Transportation
Room 200, MVA Building
Glen Burnie, MD 21062
P: (410) 768-7274
F: (410) 768-7506
E: jkuo@marylandmva.com

Colonel Terrence Sheridan
Superintendent
Department of State Police
1201 Reisterstown Road
Pikesville, MD 21208
P: (410) 653-4219
F: (410) 653-4269
E: superintendent@mdsp.org

MASSACHUSETTS
Mr. Thomas G. Gatzunis
Commissioner
Department of Public Safety
One Ashburton Place, Suite 2133
Boston, MA 02108
P: (617) 727-7775
F: (617) 727-4764
E: thomas.gatzunis
   @state.ma.us

Ms. Rachel Kaprielian
Registrar
Registry of Motor Vehicles
One Copley Place
Boston, MA 02116
P: (617) 351-9992
F: (617) 351-9971

MICHIGAN
Colonel Kriste Kibbey Etue
Director
State Police
714 South Harrison Road
East Lansing, MI 48823
P: (517) 336-6157
F: (517) 336-6551

Hon. Ruth Johnson (R)
Secretary of State
Office of the Secretary of State
430 West Allegan Street
Lansing, MI 48918
P: (517) 373-2510
F: (517) 373-0727
E: secretary@michigan.gov

MINNESOTA
Col. Mark A. Dunaski
Chief
State Patrol
444 Cedar Street
Suite 130, Town Square
St. Paul, MN 55101
P: (651) 201-7100
E: mark.dunaski@state.mn.us

Motor Vehicle Administration

Ms. Patricia McCormack
Director
Driver & Vehicle Services
Division
445 Minnesota Street
Suite 195
St. Paul, MN 55101
P: (651) 201-7580
F: (651) 296-3141
E: patricia.mccormack
@state.mn.us

MISSISSIPPI
Mr. Ed Morgan
Commissioner
Department of Revenue
P.O. Box 1033
Jackson, MS 39215
P: (601) 923-7000
F: (601) 923-7423

Mr. Albert Santa Cruz
Commissioner
Department of Public Safety
P.O. Box 958
Jackson, MS 39205
P: (601) 987-1212
F: (601) 987-1488
E: commissioner
@mdps.state.ms.us

MISSOURI
Ms. Alana M. Barragan-Scot
Director
Department of Revenue
301 West High Street
P.O. Box 311
Jefferson City, MO 65105
P: (573) 751-4450
F: (573) 751-7150
E: dormail@dor.mo.gov

MONTANA
Ms. Brenda Nordlund
Administrator
Motor Vehicle Division
Scott Hart Building, 2nd Floor
303 North Roberts, P.O. Box
201430
Helena, MT 59620
P: (406) 444-0295
F: (406) 444-2086
E: mvd@mt.gov

Mr. Duane Williams
Administrator
Motor Carrier Services Division
2701 Prospect Avenue
P.O. Box 201001
Helena, MT 59620
P: (406) 444-7312
E: duwilliams@mt.gov

NEBRASKA
Ms. Beverly Neth
Director
Department of Motor Vehicles
301 Centennial Mall South
Lincoln, NE 68509
P: (402) 471-3900
F: (402) 471-9594
E: beverly.neth
@nebraska.gov

NEVADA
Mr. Tony Alvarez
Chief
Highway Patrol
Department of Public Safety
555 Wright Way
Carson City, NV 89711
P: (775) 684-4867
E: talmaraz@dps.state.nv.us

Mr. Bruce H. Breslow
Director
Department of Motor Vehicles
555 Wright Way
Carson City, NV 89711
P: (775) 684-4549
F: (775) 684-4692
E: breslow@dmv.nv.gov

Col. Chris Perry
Acting Director
Department of Public Safety
555 Wright Way
Carson City, NV 89711
P: (775) 684-4808
F: (775) 684-4809
E: cperry@dps.state.nv.us

NEW HAMPSHIRE
Mr. John J. Barthelmes
Commissioner
Department of Safety
James H. Hayes Safety Building
33 Hazen Drive
Concord, NH 03305
P: (603) 271-2791
F: (603) 271-3903
E: john.barthelmes
@dos.nh.gov

NEW JERSEY
Mr. Raymond P. Martinez
Chief Administrator
Motor Vehicle Commission
P.O. Box 403
Trenton, NJ 08666
P: (609) 292-6500
F: (609) 777-4171
E: raymond.martinez
@dot.state.nj.us

NEW MEXICO
Ms. Demesia Padilla
Secretary
Taxation & Revenue
Department
1100 South St. Francis Drive
Santa Fe, NM 87504
P: (505) 827-0700
F: (505) 827-1759

NEW YORK
Mr. Joseph D'Amico
Superintendent
State Police
1220 Washington Avenue,
Building 22
Albany, NY 12226
P: 518) 457-6721

Ms. Barbara J. Fiala
Acting Commissioner
Department of Motor Vehicles
6 Empire State Plaza
Albany, NY 12228
P: (518) 474-0841
F: (518) 474-9578

NORTH CAROLINA
Mr. Michael Robertson
Commissioner
Department of Transportation
Division of Motor Vehicles
3101 Mail Service Center
Raleigh, NC 27699
P: (919) 861-3015
F: (919) 733-0126
E: mdrobertson1@ncdot.gov

NORTH DAKOTA
Ms. Linda Butts
Deputy Director
Driver and Vehicle Services
Department of Transportation
608 East Boulevard Avenue
Bismarck, ND 58505
P: (701) 328-2500
F: (701) 328-0310
E: lnbutts@nd.gov

Mr. Francis G. Ziegler
Director
Department of Transportation
608 East Boulevard Avenue
Bismarck, ND 58505
P: (701) 328-2500
F: (701) 328-0310
E: fziegler@nd.gov

NORTHERN MARIANA ISLANDS
Mr. Ramon Mafnas
Commissioner
Department of Public Safety
Caller Box 10007, Capitol Hill
Caller Box 10007, Capitol Hill
Saipan, MP 96950
P: (670) 664-9022
F: (670) 664-9027

OHIO
Colonel John Born
Superintendent
State Highway Patrol
1970 West Broad Street
P.O. Box 182074
Columbus, OH 43218
P: (614) 644-5837

Mr. Thomas P. Charles
Director
Department of Public Safety
1970 West Broad Street
P.O. Box 182081
Columbus, OH 43223
P: (614) 466-3383
F: (614) 466-0433

Mr. Mike Rankin
Registrar
Bureau of Motor Vehicles
1970 West Broad Street
P.O. Box 16520
Columbus, OH 43216
P: (614) 752-7500
F: (614) 261-9601

OKLAHOMA
Mr. Russ Nordstrom
Director
Motor Vehicle Division
2501 North Lincoln Boulevard
Oklahoma City, OK 73194
P: (405) 521-3221
F: (405) 521-6937
E: rnordstrom
@eris.oktax.state.ok.us

OREGON
Mr. Gregg Dal Ponte
Administrator
Motor Carrier Transportation
Division
Department Of Transportation
550 Capitol Street, Northeast
Salem, OR 97301
P: (503) 378-6351
F: (503) 373-1940
E: gregg.l.dalponte
@odot.state.or.us

Mr. Thomas McClellan
Administrator
Driver & Motor Vehicle
Services Division
1905 Lana Avenue, Northeast
Salem, OR 97314
P: (503) 945-5100
F: (503) 945-0893
E: thomas.l.mcclellan
    @state.or.us

PENNSYLVANIA

Mr. Frank Noonan
Commissioner
State Police
3rd Floor, Department
Headquarters
1800 Elmerton Avenue
Harrisburg, PA 17110
P: (717) 783-5558
F: (717) 787-2948

Mr. Barry J. Schoch
Secretary
Department of Transportation
Keystone Building
400 North Street
Harrisburg, PA 17120
P: (717) 787-3154
F: (717) 787-5491

PUERTO RICO

Mr. Jose Figueroa Sancha
Superintendent
Puerto Rico Police
P.O. Box 70166
San Juan, PR 00936
P: (787) 793-1234
F: (787) 781-0080

RHODE ISLAND

Ms. Sara R. Strachan
Administrator
Division of Motor Vehicles
Department of Revenue
100 Main Street
Pawtucket, RI 02860
P: (401) 462-4368
F: (401) 462-5784

SOUTH CAROLINA

Ms. Marcia S. Adams
Executive Director
Department of Motor Vehicles
10311 Wilson Boulevard,
Building C
P.O. Box 1498
Blythewood, SC 29016
P: (803) 896-8924
F: (803) 737-1785
E: marcia.adams@scdmv.net

Mr. Mark A. Keel
Director
Department of Public Safety
P.O. Box 1993
10311 Wilson Boulevard
Blythewood, SC 29016
P: (803) 896-7979
F: (803) 896-7881

Colonel F. K. Lancaster Jr.
Commander
Highway Patrol
10311 Wilson Boulevard
P.O. Box 1993
Blythewood, SC 29016
P: (803) 896-7920
F: (803) 896-7922

SOUTH DAKOTA

Ms. Debra Hillmer
Director
Motor Vehicles Division
Department of Revenue
445 East Capitol Avenue
Pierre, SD 57501
P: (605) 773-5747
F: (605) 773-5129
E: motorv@state.sd.us

TENNESSEE

Mr. Leon Stribling
Executive Director
Motor Vehicle Commission
500 James Robertson Parkway
Nashville, TN 37243
P: (615) 741-2711
F: (615) 741-0651
E: Leon.Stribling
    @state.tn.us

Colonel Tracy Trott
Director
Highway Patrol
1150 Foster Avenue
Nashville, TN 37249
P: (615) 251-5175

TEXAS

Dr. Rebecca Davio
Director
Vehicle Titles & Registration
Division
Department of Transportation
4000 Jackson Avenue
Austin, TX 78731
P: (512) 465-7570
F: (512) 467-5909

Mr. Steve McCraw
Director
Department of Public Safety
5805 North Lamar Boulevard
P.O. Box 4087
Austin, TX 78773
P: (512) 424-2000
F: (512) 475-0876

U.S. VIRGIN ISLANDS

Mr. Novelle E. Francis Jr.
Commissioner
Police Department
Alexander Farrelly Criminal
Justice Ctr.
Charlotte Amalie
St. Thomas, VI 00802
P: (340) 774-2211
F: (340) 715-5517

UTAH

Mr. Brad L. Simpson
Division Director
Division of Motor Vehicles
Tax Commission
P.O. Box 30412
Salt Lake City, UT 84130
P: (801) 297-7687
F: (801) 297-7697
E: bsimpson@utah.gov

VERMONT

Mr. Robert Ide
Commissioner
Department of Motor Vehicles
Agency of Transportation
120 State Street
Montpelier, VT 05603
P: (802) 828-2011
F: (802) 828-2170
E: robert.ide@state.vt.us

Mr. Thomas L'Esperance
Director
State Police
103 South Main Street
Waterbury, VT 05671
P: (802) 244-7345

VIRGINIA

Mr. Richard D. Holcomb
Commissioner
Department of Motor Vehicles
P.O. Box 27412
Richmond, VA 23269
P: (804) 367-6606
F: (804) 367-2296
E: richard.holcomb
    @dmv.virginia.gov

WASHINGTON

Mr. John R. Batiste
Chief
State Patrol
General Administration Building
P.O. Box 42600
Olympia, WA 98504
P: (360) 596-4101

Ms. Liz Luce
Director
Department of Licensing
1125 Washington Street,
Southeast
P.O. Box 9020
Olympia, WA 98507
P: (360) 902-3933
F: (360) 902-4042
E: doldirector@dol.wa.gov

WEST VIRGINIA

Mr. Joe E. Miller
Commissioner
Division of Motor Vehicles
Capitol Complex Building 5,
Room A-137
1900 Kanawha Boulevard, East
Charleston, WV 25305
P: (304) 558-2723
F: (304) 558-1987
E: dot.dmvcommissioner
    @wv.gov

WISCONSIN

Mr. David L. Collins
Superintendent
Division of State Patrol
4802 Sheboygan Avenue, Room
551
P.O. Box 7912
Madison, WI 53707
P: (608) 266-0454
F: (608) 267-4495
E: david.collins
    @dot.state.wi.us

Ms. Lynne Judd
Administrator
Division of Motor Vehicles
4802 Sheboygan Avenue
Madison, WI 53702
P: (608) 266-7079
F: (608) 267-6974
E: lynne.judd@dot.wi.gov

WYOMING

Mr. John F. Cox
Director
Department of Transportation
5300 Bishop Boulevard
Cheyenne, WY 82009
P: (307) 777-4484
F: (307) 777-4163

Motor Vehicle Administration

Lt. Col. Jess Oyler
Administrator
Highway Patrol
5300 Bishop Boulevard
Cheyenne, WY 82009
P: (307) 777-4301

Natural Resources

Formulates and coordinates policies to protect, develop, utilize, restore and enhance the state's natural resources.

ALABAMA
Mr. M. Barnett Lawley
Commissioner of Conservation
Department of Conservation &
Natural Resources
64 North Union Street
Montgomery, AL 36130
P: (334) 242-3486
F: (334) 242-3489
E: commissioner
    @dcnr.state.al.us

AMERICAN SAMOA
Mr. Ufagafa Ray Tulafono
Director
Department of Marine &
Wildlife Resources
American Samoa Government
Pago Pago, AS 96799
P: (684) 633-4456
F: (684) 633-5590

ARIZONA
Mr. Stephen Williams
Director
State Land Department, Natural
Resources
1616 West Adams Street
Phoenix, AZ 85007
P: (602) 542-2693

ARKANSAS
Mr. Randy Young
Executive Director
Natural Resources Commission
101 East Capitol, Suite 350
Little Rock, AR 72201
P: (501) 682-1611
F: (501) 682-3991
E: randy.young@arkansas.gov

CALIFORNIA
Mr. Mark W. Cowin
Director
Department of Water Resources
1416 Ninth Street
P.O. Box 942836
Sacramento, CA 94236
P: (916) 653-7007
F: (916) 653-5028
E: mcowin@water.ca.gov

COLORADO
Mr. Mike King
Executive Director
Department of Natural
Resources
1313 Sherman Street
Centennial Building, 7th Floor
Denver, CO 80203
P: (303) 866-3311
F: (303) 866-2115
E: Mike.King@state.co.us

CONNECTICUT
Mr. Daniel C. Esty
Commissioner
Department of Environmental
Protection
79 Elm Street
Hartford, CT 06106
P: (860) 424-3009
F: (860) 424-4054
E: daniel.esty@ct.gov

DISTRICT OF COLUMBIA
Mr. Christophe A. G. Tulou
Acting Director
Department of the Environment
1200 First Street, Northeast, 5th
Floor
Washington, DC 20002
P: (202) 535-2600
F: (202) 535-2881
E: ddoe@dc.gov

FLORIDA
Ms. Mimi Drew
Interim Secretary
Department of Environmental
Protection
3900 Commonwealth Boulevard
Mail Station 49
Tallahassee, FL 32399
P: (850) 245-2011
F: (850) 245-2128
E: mimi.drew
    @dep.state.fl.us

Mr. Herschel T. Vinyard
Secretary
Department of Environmental
Protection
3900 Commonwealth Boulevard
Mail Station 49
Tallahassee, FL 32399
P: (850) 245-2011
F: (850) 245-2128
E: herschel.vinyard
    @dep.state.fl.us

GEORGIA
Mr. Mark Williams
Commissioner
Department of Natural
Resources
2 Martin Luther King Jr. Drive
Southeast
Floyd Towers, Suite 1252 East
Atlanta, GA 30334
P: (404) 656-3500
F: (404) 656-0770
E: mark@markwilliams.com

GUAM
Mr. Paul C. Bassler
Director
Department of Agriculture
163 Dairy Road
Mangilao, GU 96913
P: (671) 734-3942
F: (671) 734-6569

HAWAII
Mr. William J. Aila Jr.
Chairperson
Department of Land & Natural
Resources
1151 Punchbowl Street
P.O. Box 621
Kapolei, HI 96809
P: (808) 587-0400
F: (808) 587-0390
E: dlnr@hawaii.gov

IDAHO
Ms. Toni Hardesty
Director
Department of Environmental
Quality
1410 North Hilton
Boise, ID 83706
P: (208) 373-0240
F: (208) 373-0417
E: toni.hardesty
    @deq.idaho.gov

ILLINOIS
Mr. Marc Miller
Director
Department of Natural
Resources
One Natural Resources Way
Springfield, IL 62702
P: (217) 785-0075
F: (217) 785-9236

INDIANA
Mr. Robert E. Carter Jr.
Director
Department of Natural
Resources
402 West Washington Street,
Room W256
Indianapolis, IN 46204
P: (317) 232-4020
F: (317) 233-6811
E: rcarter@dnr.IN.gov

IOWA
Mr. Roger L. Lande
Director
Department of Natural
Resources
East Ninth & Grand Avenue
Des Moines, IA 50319
P: (515) 281-5385
F: (515) 281-6794
E: roger.lande@dnr.iowa.gov

KANSAS
Mr. Greg Foley
Executive Director
State Conservation Commission
109 Southwest 9th Street
Suite 500, Mills Building
Topeka, KS 66612
P: (785) 296-3600
F: (785) 296-6172
E: greg.foley@scc.ks.gov

KENTUCKY
Mr. Carl Campbell
Commissioner
Department for Natural
Resources
#2 Hudson Hollow
Frankfort, KY 40601
P: (502) 564-6940
F: (502) 564-5698
E: carl.campbell@ky.gov

LOUISIANA
Mr. Scott A. Angelle
Secretary
Department of Natural
Resources
617 North Third Street
P.O. Box 94396
Baton Rouge, LA 70804
P: (225) 342-2710
F: (225) 342-4313
E: info@dnr.state.la.us

MAINE
Mr. Bill Beardsley
Commissioner
Department of Conservation
22 State House Station
Augusta, ME 04333
P: (207) 287-4900
F: (207) 287-2400

MARYLAND
Mr. John R. Griffin
Secretary
Department of Natural
Resources
Tawes State Office Building, C4
580 Taylor Avenue
Annapolis, MD 21401
P: (410) 260-8101
E: jgriffin@dnr.state.md.us

Natural Resources

MASSACHUSETTS
Mr. Edward M. Lambert Jr.
Commissioner
Department of Conservation &
Recreation
20 Somerset Street
Boston, MA 02108
P: (617) 722-5500
F: (617) 727-0891

MINNESOTA
Mr. Tom Landwehr
Commissioner
Department of Natural
Resources
500 Lafayette Road
P.O. Box 37
St. Paul, MN 55155
P: (651) 259-5022
F: (651) 296-4799
E: Tom.Landwehr@state.mn.us

MISSISSIPPI
Ms. Trudy H. Fisher
Executive Director
Department of Environmental
Quality
2380 Highway 80 West
P.O. Box 2369
Jackson, MS 39289
P: (601) 961-5001
F: (601) 961-5093
E: trudy_fisher
   @deq.state.ms.us

MISSOURI
Ms. Sara Parker Pauley
Director
Department of Natural
Resources
P.O. Box 176
Jefferson City, MO 65102
P: (573) 751-4732
F: (573) 751-7627
E: sara.pauley@dnr.mo.gov

Mr. Kip Setzler
State Historic Preservation
Officer
Department of Natural
Resources
P.O. Box 176
Jefferson City, MO 65102
P: (573) 751-4732
F: (573) 751-7627

MONTANA
Mr. Joe Maurier
Director
Department of Fish, Wildlife &
Parks
1420 East Sixth Avenue
P.O. Box 200701
Helena, MT 59620
P: (406) 444-3186
F: (406) 444-4952

Ms. Mary Sexton
Director
Department of Natural
Resources & Conservation
1625 11th Avenue
P.O. Box 201601
Helena, MT 59620
P: (406) 444-2074
F: (406) 444-2684
E: msexton@mt.gov

NEBRASKA
Mr. Brian Dunnigan
Director
Department of Natural
Resources
P.O. Box 94676
Lincoln, NE 68509
P: (402) 471-2366
F: (402) 471-2900
E: brian.dunnigan
   @nebraska.gov

NEVADA
Mr. Leo Drozdoff
Director
Department of Conservation &
Natural Resources
901 South Stewart, Suite 5001
Carson City, NV 89701
P: (775) 684-2710
F: (775) 684-2715
E: ldrozdoff@dcnr.nv.gov

NEW HAMPSHIRE
Mr. George Bald
Commissioner
Department of Resources &
Economic Development
172 Pembroke Road
P.O. Box 1856
Concord, NH 03302
P: (603) 271-2411
F: (603) 271-2629
E: gbald@dred.state.nh.us

NEW JERSEY
Mr. John Sacco
Acting Chief
Office of Natural Resource
Restoration
P.O. Box 404, Station Plaza 5
Trenton, NJ 08625
P: (609) 984-5475
F: (609) 984-0836
E: Onrr@dep.state.nj.us

NEW MEXICO
Mr. John Bernis
Secretary
Energy, Minerals & Natural
Resources Department
1220 South St. Francis Drive
Santa Fe, NM 87505
P: (505) 476-3200
F: (505) 476-3220

NEW YORK
Mr. Joe Martens
Commissioner
Department of Environmental
Conservation
625 Broadway, 14th Floor
Albany, NY 12233
P: (518) 402-8540
F: (518) 402-8541
E: joemartens
   @gw.dec.state.ny.us

NORTH DAKOTA
Mr. Paul Schadewald
Chief
Conservation &
Communications Division
Game & Fish Department
100 North Bismarck Expressway
Bismarck, ND 58501
P: (701) 328-6328
F: (701) 328-6352
E: pschadew@nd.gov

**NORTHERN MARIANA
ISLANDS**
Dr. Ignacio T. Dela Cruz
Secretary
Department of Lands & Natural
Resources
Caller Box 10007, Capitol Hill
Saipan, MP 96950
P: (670) 322-9830
F: (670) 322-2633
E: dlnrgov@vzpacifica.net

OHIO
Mr. David Mustine
Director
Department of Natural
Resources
2045 Morse Road
Columbus, OH 43229
P: (614) 265-6565
F: (614) 261-9601

OKLAHOMA
Mr. Gary Sherrer
Secretary of the Environment
Office of the Secretary of the
Environment
3800 North Classen Boulevard
Oklahoma City, OK 73118
P: (405) 530-8995
F: (405) 530-8999

OREGON
Mr. Roy Elicker
Director
Department of Fish & Wildlife
3406 Cherry Avenue, Northeast
Salem, OR 97303
P: (503) 947-6044
F: (503) 947-6042
E: roy.elicker@state.or.us

PENNSYLVANIA
Mr. Richard J. Allan
Acting Secretary
Department of Conservation &
Natural Resources
Rachel Carson State Office
Building
7th Floor, P.O. Box 8767
Harrisburg, PA 17105
P: (717) 772-9084
F: (717) 705-2832

PUERTO RICO
Mr. Daniel J. Galan Kercado
Secretary
Department of Natural &
Environmental Resources
P.O. Box 366147
San Juan, PR 00936
P: (787) 999-2000
F: (787) 999-2303

RHODE ISLAND
Mr. Larry Mouradjian
Associate Director
Department of Environmental
Management
Bureau of Natural Resources
235 Promenade Street
Providence, RI 02908
P: (401) 222-4700 Ext. 2414
F: (401) 222-3162
E: larry.mouradjian
   @dem.ri.gov

SOUTH CAROLINA

Mr. John E. Frampton
Director
Department of Natural
Resources
P.O. Box 167
Columbia, SC 29202
P: (803) 734-4007
F: (803) 734-6310
E: framptonj@dnr.sc.gov

SOUTH DAKOTA

Mr. Steve M. Pirner
Secretary
Department of Environment &
Natural Resources
Joe Foss Building
523 East Capital Avenue
Pierre, SD 57501
P: (605) 773-3151
F: (605) 773-6035
E: steve.pirner@state.sd.us

TENNESSEE

Mr. Mike Carlton
Assistant Commissioner
State Parks & Conservation
401 Church Street
21st Floor, L & C Tower
Nashville, TN 37243
P: (615) 532-0025
F: (615) 741-8858

TEXAS

Dr. Bryan W. Shaw
Chairman
Commission on Environmental
Quality
12100 Park 35 Circle
P.O. Box 13087
Austin, TX 78711
P: (512) 239-5510
F: (512) 239-6377

U.S. VIRGIN ISLANDS

Mr. Robert Mathes
State Historic Preservation
Officer
Department of Planning &
Natural Resources
Cyril E. King Airport
Terminal Building - 2nd Floor
St. Thomas, VI 00802
P: (340) 776-8605
F: (340) 776-7236

UTAH

Mr. Michael R. Styler
Executive Director
Department of Natural
Resources
1594 West North Temple
P.O. Box 145610
Salt Lake City, UT 84114
P: (801) 538-7201
F: (801) 538-7315
E: mikestyler@utah.gov

VERMONT

Ms. Deborah L. Markowitz
Secretary
Agency of Natural Resources
103 South Main Street
Center Building
Waterbury, VT 05671
P: (802) 241-3600
F: (802) 244-1102
E: deb.markowitz
    @state.vt.us

VIRGINIA

Mr. Doug Domenech
Secretary
Office of the Secretary of
Natural Resources
1111 East Broad Street
Patrick Henry Building
Richmond, VA 23219
P: (804) 786-0044
F: (804) 371-8333
E: doug.domenech
    @governor.virginia.gov

WASHINGTON

Hon. Peter J. Goldmark (D)
Commissioner of Public Lands
Department of Natural
Resources
1111 Washington Street,
Southeast
P.O. Box 47000
Olympia, WA 98504
P: (360) 902-1004
F: (360) 902-1775
E: cpl@dnr.wa.gov

WEST VIRGINIA

Mr. Frank Jezioro
Director
Natural Resources
324 Fourth Avenue, Building 74
South Charleston, WV 25303
P: (304) 558-2754
F: (304) 558-2768
E: Frank.J.Jezioro@wv.gov

WISCONSIN

Ms. Cathy Stepp
Secretary
Department of Natural
Resources
101 South Webster Street
P.O. Box 7921
Madison, WI 53707
P: (608) 267-7556
F: (608) 266-6983
E: cathy.stepp
    @wisconsin.gov

Occupational Safety

Enforces safety standards for the protection of employees in places of employment.

ALABAMA
Mr. Jim Bennett
Commissioner
Department of Labor
P.O. Box 303500
Montgomery, AL 36130
P: (334) 242-3460
F: (334) 240-3417
E: jbennett
  @alalabor.alabama.gov

ALASKA
Mr. Grey Mitchell
Director
Department of Labor &
Workforce Development
Division of Labor Standards &
Safety
P.O. Box 111149
Juneau, AK 99811
P: (907) 465-4855
F: (907) 465-6012
E: grey.mitchell@alaska.gov

AMERICAN SAMOA
Lt. Col. Evelyn Vaiautolu
  Langford
Director
Department of Human
Resources
American Samoa Government
Pago Pago, AS 96799
P: (684) 644-4485
F: (684) 633-1139

ARIZONA
Ms. Laura L. McGrory
Director
Industrial Commission
800 West Washington Street
Phoenix, AZ 85007
P: (602) 542-4411
F: (602) 542-7889
E: lmcgrory@ica.state.az.us

ARKANSAS
Mr. James L. Salkeld
Director
Department of Labor
10421 West Markham Street
Suite 100
Little Rock, AR 72205
P: (501) 682-4541
F: (501) 682-4535
E: james.salkeld
  @arkansas.gov

CALIFORNIA
Ms. Ellen Widess
Chief
Division of Occupational Safety
& Health
Department of Industrial
Relations
1515 Clay Street, Suite 1901
Oakland, CA 94612
P: (510) 286-7000
F: (510) 286-7037

CONNECTICUT
Mr. Glenn Marshall
Commissioner
Department of Labor
200 Folly Brook Boulevard
Wethersfield, CT 06109
P: (860) 263-6505
F: (860) 263-6529
E: glenn.marshall@ct.gov

DELAWARE
Mr. James G. Cagle Jr.
Director
Division of Industrial Affairs
4425 North Market Street
Wilmington, DE 19802
P: (302) 761-8176
F: (302) 761-6601

DISTRICT OF COLUMBIA
Ms. Lisa Maria Mallory
Acting Director
Department of Employment
Services
4058 Minnesota Avenue,
Northeast
Washington, DC 20019
P: (202) 724-7000
F: (202) 673-6993
E: does@dc.gov

FLORIDA
Mr. Tanner Holloman
Director
Division of Workers'
Compensation
200 East Gaines Street
Tallahassee, FL 32399
P: (850) 413-1600
E: Tanner.Holloman
  @myfloridacfo.com

GEORGIA
Mr. Earl Everett
Director of Safety &
Engineering
Safety Engineering Division
1700 Century Circle, Suite 100
Atlanta, GA 30345
P: (404) 679-0687
F: (404) 982-3405
E: earl.everett
  @dol.state.ga.us

GUAM
Ms. Leah Beth Naholowaa
Director
Department of Labor
Government of Guam
P.O. Box 9970
Tamuning, GU 96931
P: (671) 647-6510
F: (671) 674-6517

HAWAII
Mr. Dwight Y. Takamine
Director
Department of Labor &
Industrial Relations
830 Punchbowl Stree, Room
321
Honolulu, HI 96813
P: (808) 586-8865
F: (808) 586-9099

ILLINOIS
Mr. Mitch Weisz
Acting Chair
Workers' Compensation
Commission
100 West Randolph Street,
#8-200
Chicago, IL 60601
P: (312) 814-6560

INDIANA
Ms. Lori A. Torres
Commissioner
Department of Labor
Indiana Government
Center-South
402 West Washington Street,
Room W-195
Indianapolis, IN 46204
P: (317) 232-2655
F: (317) 974-2001
E: ltorres@dol.in.gov

IOWA
Mr. David Neil
Commissioner
Division of Labor Services
1000 East Grand Avenue
Des Moines, IA 50319
P: (515) 281-3447
F: (515) 281-4698
E: dave.neil@iwd.iowa.gov

KANSAS
Ms. Karin Brownlee
Secretary
Department of Labor
401 Southwest Topeka
Boulevard
Topeka, KS 66603
P: (785) 296-5058
F: (785) 368-5286
E: karin.brownlee
  @dol.ks.gov

Mr. Clifford Morris
Acting Director
Industrial Safety & Health
Section
700 Southwest Jackson, Room
420
Topeka, KS 66603
P: (785) 296-4386
F: (785) 296-1775
E: indsafetyhealth
  @dol.ks.gov

KENTUCKY
Mr. Mike Dixon
Executive Director
Office of Occupational Safety &
Health
1047 US Highway 127 South
Suite 4
Frankfort, KY 40601
P: (502) 564-3070
F: (502) 696-1902

LOUISIANA
Mr. Jay Augustine
Deputy Executive Director
Workforce Commission
1001 North 23rd Street
Baton Rouge, LA 70802
P: (225) 342-3111
F: (225) 342-3778

MAINE
Mr. David Wacker
Director
Workplace Safety Division
Department of Labor
45 State House Station
Augusta, ME 04333
P: (207) 623-7900
F: (207) 624-6449
E: david.e.wacker@maine.gov

MARYLAND
Mr. Roger Campbell
Assistant Commissioner
Department of Labor, Licensing
& Regulation
MOSH Administration
1100 North Eutaw Street, Room
606
Baltimore, MD 21201
P: (410) 767-2190
E: campbell.roger@dol.gov

MASSACHUSETTS
Ms. Mary Elizabeth
  Heffernan
Secretary
Executive Office of Public
Safety
One Ashburton Place, Suite
2133
Boston, MA 02108
P: (617) 727-7775
F: (617) 727-4764

MICHIGAN
Mr. Douglas J. Kalinowski
Director
Occupational Safety & Health
Administration
P.O. Box 30643
Lansing, MI 48909
P: (517) 322-1817
F: (517) 322-1775
E: kalinowskid@michigan.gov

MINNESOTA
Mr. Ken Peterson
Commissioner
Department of Labor & Industry
443 Lafayette Road North
St. Paul, MN 55155
P: (651) 284-5010
F: (651) 284-5721
E: dli.commissioner
    @state.mn.us

MISSOURI
Mr. Lawrence G. Rebman
Director
Department of Labor &
Industrial Relations
P.O. Box 504
Jefferson City, MO 65102
P: (573) 751-4091
F: (573) 751-4945
E: larry.rebman
    @labor.mo.gov

MONTANA
Mr. Keith Kelly
Commissioner
Department of Labor & Industry
P.O. Box 1728
Helena, MT 59624
P: (406) 444-9091
F: (406) 444-1394
E: dliquestions@mt.gov

NEBRASKA
Ms. Catherine D. Lang
Commissioner of Labor
Department of Labor
P.O. Box 94600
Lincoln, NE 68509
P: (402) 471-9000
F: (402) 471-2318
E: catherine.lang
    @nebraska.gov

NEVADA
Mr. Donald E. Jayne
Administrator
Division of Industrial Relations
Department of Business &
Industry
400 West King Street, Suite 400
Carson City, NV 89703
P: (775) 684-7260
F: (775) 687-6305
E: djayne@business.nv.gov

NEW HAMPSHIRE
Mr. George N. Copadis
Commissioner of Labor
Department of Labor
95 Pleasant Street
Concord, NH 03301
P: (603) 271-3171
F: (603) 271-6852
E: gcopadis
    @labor.state.nh.us

NEW JERSEY
Dr. Christina Tan
Assistant Commissioner
Division of Epidemiology,
Environmental & Occupational
Health
P.O. Box 369
Trenton, NJ 08625
P: (609) 588-7463
E: epi@doh.state.nj.us

NEW MEXICO
Ms. Mary Uhl
Bureau Chief
Occupational Safety & Health
Bureau
525 Camino De Los Marquez,
Suite 3
P.O. Box 5469
Santa Fe, NM 87502
P: (505) 476-8787
F: (505) 476-8734
E: mary.uhl@state.nm.us

NEW YORK
Ms. Colleen C. Gardner
Commissioner
Department of Labor
W. Averell Harriman State
Office Campus
Building 12
Albany, NY 12240
P: (518) 457-9000
F: (518) 485-6297
E: colleen.gardner
    @labor.state.ny.us

NORTH CAROLINA
Mr. Allen McNeely
Deputy Commissioner
Department of Labor
Occupational Safety & Health
Division
1101 Mail Service Center
Raleigh, NC 27699
P: (919) 807-2860
E: allen.mcneely
    @labor.nc.gov

NORTH DAKOTA
Mr. Wally Kalmbach
Director
Loss Prevention
Workers Compensation Bureau
500 East Front Avenue
Bismarck, ND 58504
P: (701) 328-3886
F: (701) 328-3820
E: wkalmbac@nd.gov

**NORTHERN MARIANA
ISLANDS**
Mr. Gil M. San Nicolas
Secretary
Department of Labor
Caller Box 10007
Saipan, MP 96950
P: (670) 322-9834
F: (670) 322-2633

OHIO
Mr. David Goodman
Director
Department of Commerce
77 South High Street, 23rd Floor
Columbus, OH 43266
P: (614) 466-3636
F: (614) 752-5078
E: Directorsoffice
    @com.state.oh.us

OKLAHOMA
Ms. Diana Jones
Director of OSHA
Department of Labor
3017 North Stiles, Suite 100
Oklahoma City, OK 73105
P: (405) 521-6139
F: (405) 521-6018
E: diana.jones@labor.ok.gov

OREGON
Mr. Michael Wood
Division Administrator
Occupational Safety & Health
Division
Labor & Industries Building
350 Winter Street, Northeast,
Room 430
Salem, OR 97301
P: (503) 947-7400
F: (503) 947-7461
E: michael.wood@state.or.us

PENNSYLVANIA
Mr. Edward L. Leister
Director
Bureau of Occupational &
Industrial Safety
1613 Labor & Industry Building
Harrisburg, PA 17121
P: (717) 783-6304
F: (717) 787-8363

PUERTO RICO
Mr. Miguel Romero
Director
Department of Labor & Human
Resources
P.O. Box 191020
San Juan, PR 00919
P: (787) 754-5353
F: (787) 756-1149

RHODE ISLAND
Mr. Charles J. Fogarty
Director
Department of Labor & Training
1511 Pontiac Avenue
Cranston, RI 02920
P: (401) 462-8000
F: (401) 462-8872
E: director-dlt@dlt.ri.gov

SOUTH CAROLINA
Ms. Catherine Templeton
Director
Department of Labor, Licensing
& Regulation
P.O. Box 11329
Columbia, SC 29211
P: (803) 896-4390
F: (803) 896-4393
E: templetonc@llr.sc.gov

SOUTH DAKOTA
Mr. James E. Marsh
Director
Division of Human Rights
700 Governors Drive
Pierre, SD 57501
P: (605) 773-3681
F: (605) 773-4211
E: james.marsh@state.sd.us

Occupational Safety

TENNESSEE
Mr. John Winkler
Administrator
Division of Occupational Safety
& Health
Dept. of Labor and Workforce
Development
220 French Landing Drive
Nashville, TN 37243
P: (615) 741-2793
F: (615) 741-3325

TEXAS
Dr. David L. Lakey
Commissioner
Department of Health Services
1100 West 49th Street
P.O. Box 149347
Austin, TX 78714
P: (512) 458-7375
E: customer.service
   @dshs.state.tx.us

U.S. VIRGIN ISLANDS
Mr. Albert Bryan Jr.
Commissioner of Labor
Department of Labor
2203 Church Street,
Christiansted
St. Croix, VI 00820
P: (340) 773-1994
F: (340) 773-0094
E: abryan@vidol.gov

UTAH
Mr. Louis Silva
UOSH Administrator
Occupational Safety & Health
Division
160 East 300 South, 3rd Floor
P.O. Box 146650
Salt Lake City, UT 84114
P: (801) 530-6898
F: (801) 530-7606
E: LSILVA@utah.gov

VERMONT
Mr. Robert P. McLeod
VOSHA & Passenger Tramway
Manager
Occupational Safety & Health
Administration
Department of Labor
North Building, National Life
Montpelier, VT 05620
P: (802) 828-5084
F: (802) 828-2748
E: robert.mcleod
   @state.vt.us

VIRGINIA
Mr. Courtney Malveaux
Commissioner
Department of Labor & Industry
13 South 13th Street
Richmond, VA 23219
P: (804) 786-2377
F: (804) 371-6524
E: courtney.malveaux
   @doli.virginia.gov

WASHINGTON
Dr. Michael Silverstein
Assistant Director
Division of Occupational Safety
& Health
P.O. Box 44810
Olympia, WA 98504
P: (360) 902-4805
F: (360) 902-5529

WEST VIRGINIA
Mr. David W. Mullins
Commissioner
Division of Labor
Bureau of Commerce
Capitol Complex, Building 6,
Room B-749
Charleston, WV 25305
P: (304) 558-7890
F: (304) 558-3797
E: david.w.mullins@wv.gov

WISCONSIN
Mr. Tom Nardelli
Division Administrator
Safety & Buildings Division
Department of Commerce
P.O. Box 2599
Madison, WI 53701
P: (608) 266-1816
F: (608) 266-9946
E: thomas.nardelli@wi.gov

Oil & Gas Regulation

Regulates the drilling, operation, maintenance and abandonment of oil and gas wells in the state.

ALABAMA
Mr. Berry H. Tew Jr.
State Geologist & Oil and Gas Supervisor
Geological Survey of Alabama
P.O. Box 869999
420 Hackberry Lane
Tuscaloosa, AL 35486
P: (205) 349-2852
F: (205) 349-2861
E: ntew@gsa.state.al.us

ALASKA
Mr. Kevin Banks
Division Director
Division of Oil & Gas
Department of Natural Resources
550 West 7th Avenue, Suite 800
Anchorage, AK 99501
P: (907) 269-8800
F: (907) 269-8938
E: kevin.banks@alaska.gov

ARIZONA
Dr. M. Lee Allison
Director & State Geologist
Geological Survey
416 West Congress Street, Suite 100
Tucson, AZ 85701
P: (520) 770-3500
F: (520) 770-3505
E: Lee.Allison@azgs.az.gov

ARKANSAS
Mr. Larry Bengal
Director
Oil & Gas Commission
301 Natural Resources Drive, Suite 102
Little Rock, AR 72205
P: (501) 683-5816
F: (501) 683-5818
E: Larry.Bengal
@aogc.state.ar.us

CALIFORNIA
Ms. Elena Miller
Oil & Gas Supervisor
Division of Oil, Gas & Geothermal Resources
801 K Street, MS 20-20
Sacramento, CA 95814
P: (916) 323-1777
F: (916) 323-0424
E: elena.miller
@conservation.ca.gov

COLORADO
Mr. David Neslin
Director
Oil & Gas Conservation Commission
1120 Lincoln Street, Suite 801
Denver, CO 80203
P: (303) 894-2100 Ext. 122
F: (303) 894-2109
E: david.neslin
@cogcc.state.co.us

CONNECTICUT
Mr. Kevin DelGobbo
Chair
Department of Public Utility Control
10 Franklin Square
New Britain, CT 06051
P: (860) 827-2809
F: (334) 242-0921
E: kevin.delgobbo
@po.state.ct.us

FLORIDA
Mr. Ed Garrett
Professional Geologist/Administrator
Geological Survey - Oil & Gas Section
Bureau of Mining & Minerals Regulation
2051 East Paul Dirac Drive, M.S. 715
Tallahassee, FL 32310
P: (850) 488-8217 Ext. 12
F: (850) 488-1254
E: Ed.Garrett
@dep.state.fl.us

GEORGIA
Mr. William G. Smith
Program Manager
Regulatory Support Program
4220 International Parkway, Suite 101
Atlanta, GA 30354
P: (404) 656-3214
F: (404) 463-6432

GUAM
Ms. Joanne Brown
Director
Department of Public Works
542 North Marine Drive
Tamuning, GU 96913
P: (671) 646-3131
F: (671) 649-6178
E: joanne.brown
@dpw.guam.gov

IDAHO
Mr. George Bacon
Director
Department of Lands
300 North 6th Street, Suite 103
P.O. Box 83720
Boise, ID 83720
P: (208) 334-0242
F: (208) 334-2339
E: gbacon@idl.idaho.gov

ILLINOIS
Mr. Duane Pulliam
Interim Supervisor
Division of Oil & Gas
One Natural Resources Way
Springfield, IL 62702
P: (217) 782-7756
E: duane.pulliam
@illinois.gov

INDIANA
Mr. Herschel McDivitt
Director
Oil & Gas Division
402 West Washington Street, Room W293
Indianapolis, IN 46204
P: (317) 232-4058
F: (317) 232-1550
E: hmcdivitt@dnr.in.gov

IOWA
Ms. Libby Jacobs
Chair
Utilities Board
1375 East Court Avenue, RM 69
Des Moines, IA 50319
P: (515) 725-7300
F: (515) 725-7399
E: libby.jacobs
@iub.iowa.gov

KANSAS
Mr. Doug Louis
Director
Conservation Division
Finney State Office Building
130 South Market, Room 2078
Wichita, KS 67202
P: (316) 337-6200
F: (316) 337-6211

KENTUCKY
Kim Collings
Environmental Scientist & Geologist/Permit Reviewer
Division of Oil & Gas Conservation
1025 Capital Center Drive
Frankfort, KY 40601
P: (502) 573-0147
F: (502) 573-1099
E: Kim.Collings@ky.gov

LOUISIANA
Dr. Madhurendu B. Kumar
Director
Geological Oil & Gas Division
617 North Third Street
P.O. Box 94396
Baton Rouge, LA 70804
P: (225) 342-5501
F: (225) 342-8199
E: Madhurendu.Kumar@la.gov

MAINE
Mr. Ron Dyer
Director
Bureau of Remediation & Waste Management
Department of Environmental Protection
17 State House Station
Augusta, ME 04333
P: (207) 287-7980
F: (207) 287-7826
E: ron.dyer@maine.gov

MARYLAND
Mr. Horacio Tablada
Director
Land Management Administration
Department of Environment
1800 Washington Boulevard
Baltimore, MD 21230
P: (410) 631-3304
F: (410) 631-3321
E: htablada@mde.state.md.us

MASSACHUSETTS
Mr. Kenneth Kimmell
Commissioner
Department of Environmental Protection
One Winter Street, #1022
Boston, MA 02108
P: (617) 292-5856
F: (617) 574-6880
E: ken.kimmell@state.ma.us

Oil & Gas Regulation

MICHIGAN
Mr. Harold R. Fitch
State Geologist
Office of Geological Survey
Constitution Hall
525 West Allegan Street, Box 30256
Lansing, MI 48909
P: (517) 241-1548
F: (517) 241-1601
E: fitchh@michigan.gov

MINNESOTA
Ms. Ellen Anderson
Chair
Public Utilities Commission
121 Seventh Place East, Suite 350
St. Paul, MN 55101
P: (651) 201-2250
F: (651) 297-7073
E: ellen.anderson
    @state.mn.us

MISSISSIPPI
Ms. Lisa Ivshin
Executive Director
Oil & Gas Board
500 Greymont Avenue, Suite E
Jackson, MS 39202
P: (601) 354-7112
F: (601) 354-6873
E: livshin@ogb.state.ms.us

MONTANA
Mr. Tom Richmond
Division Administrator &
Petroleum Engineer
Board of Oil & Gas
Billings Technical Office
2535 St. Johns Avenue
Billings, MT 59102
P: (406) 656-0040
F: (406) 655-6015

NEBRASKA
Mr. William H. Sydow
Director
Oil & Gas Conservation
Commission
P.O. Box 399
Sidney, NE 69162
P: (308) 254-6919
F: (308) 254-6922

NEVADA
Mr. Alan R. Coyner
Administrator
Division of Minerals
Commission on Mineral
Resources
400 West King Street, Suite 106
Carson City, NV 89703
P: (775) 684-7040
F: (775) 684-7052
E: acoyner
    @govmail.state.nv.us

NEW JERSEY
Mr. James P. Giuliano
Director
Division of Reliability &
Security
Board of Public Utilities
2 Gateway Center, 8th Floor
Newark, NJ 07102
P: (973) 648-3875
F: (201) 648-2242

NEW MEXICO
Jami Bailey
Director
Oil, Gas & Minerals Division
310 Old Santa Fe Trail
P.O. Box 1148
Santa Fe, NM 87504
P: (505) 827-5745
F: (505) 827-4739
E: jbailey@slo.state.nm.us

NEW YORK
Mr. Joe Martens
Commissioner
Department of Environmental
Conservation
625 Broadway, 14th Floor
Albany, NY 12233
P: (518) 402-8540
F: (518) 402-8541
E: joemartens
    @gw.dec.state.ny.us

NORTH DAKOTA
Mr. Lynn D. Helms
Director
Oil & Gas Division
Industrial Commission,
Department 405
600 East Boulevard Avenue
Bismarck, ND 58505
P: (701) 328-8020
F: (701) 328-8022
E: lhelms@nd.gov

OHIO
Mr. David Goodman
Director
Department of Commerce
77 South High Street, 23rd Floor
Columbus, OH 43266
P: (614) 466-3636
F: (614) 752-5078
E: Directorsoffice
    @com.state.oh.us

OKLAHOMA
Ms. Lori Wrotenbery
Director
Corporation Commission
Oil & Gas Conservation
Division
2100 N. Lincoln Blvd., P.O. Box 52000
Oklahoma City, OK 73152
P: (405) 521-2302

OREGON
Mr. Robert A. Houston
Oil, Gas and Geothermal
Specialist
Mineral Land Regulation &
Reclamation
229 Broadalbin Street,
Southwest
Albany, OR 97321
P: (541) 967-2080
F: (541) 967-2075
E: Robert.A.Houston
    @mlrr.oregongeology.com

PENNSYLVANIA
Mr. Ronald P. Gilius
Director
Bureau of Oil & Gas
Management
Rachael Carson Office Building
5th Floor, P.O. Box 8765
Harrisburg, PA 17105
P: (717) 772-2199
F: (717) 772-2291

PUERTO RICO
Mr. Luis Bernal-Jimenez
Executive Director
Energy Affairs Administration
P.O. Box 41314
San Juan, PR 00940
P: (787) 999-2200 x2886
F: (787) 999-2246
E: lbernal@aae.gobierno.pr

Mr. Javier Mendez Quintana
Administrator
Energy Affairs Administration
P.O. Box 366147
Puerta De Tierra
San Juan, PR 00936
P: (787) 999-2200 Ext. 2888
F: (787) 753-2220
E: mvillanueva
    @drna.gobierno.pr

RHODE ISLAND
Mr. Elia Germani
Chair
Public Utilities Commission
89 Jefferson Boulevard
Warwick, RI 02888
P: (401) 941-4500
F: (401) 941-1691
E: egermani@puc.state.ri.us

SOUTH CAROLINA
Mr. Joe Gellici
Section Chief
Hydrology Section
Land, Water & Conservation
Division
1000 Assembly Street
Columbia, SC 29201
P: (803) 734-6428
F: (803) 734-9200
E: gellicij@dnr.sc.gov

SOUTH DAKOTA
Mr. Fred Steece
Oil & Gas Supervisor
Department of Environment &
Natural Resources
Minerals & Mining Program
2050 W. Main, Suite 1
Rapid City, SD 57702
P: (605) 394-2229
F: (605) 394-5317
E: fred.steece@state.sd.us

TENNESSEE
Mr. Mike Burton
Assistant Supervisor
Oil & Gas Board
401 Church Street
1st Floor, L & C Annex
Nashville, TN 37243
P: (615) 532-0166
F: (615) 532-1517
E: Michael.K.Burton
    @state.tn.us

UTAH
Mr. John R. Baza
Director
Division of Oil, Gas & Mining
1594 West North Temple, Suite 1210
P.O. Box 145801
Salt Lake City, UT 84114
P: (801) 538-5334
F: (801) 359-3940
E: johnbaza@utah.gov

VERMONT
Ms. Deborah L. Markowitz
Secretary
Agency of Natural Resources
103 South Main Street
Center Building
Waterbury, VT 05671
P: (802) 241-3600
F: (802) 244-1102
E: deb.markowitz
   @state.vt.us

VIRGINIA
Mr. Conrad T. Spangler III
Director
Department of Mines, Minerals & Energy
Washington Building, 8th Floor
1100 Bank Street
Richmond, VA 23219
P: (804) 692-3202
F: (804) 692-3237
E: conrad.spangler
   @dmme.virginia.gov

WEST VIRGINIA
Mr. James Martin
Chief
Office of Oil & Gas
601 57th Street, Southeast
Charleston, WV 25304
P: (304) 926-0450
F: (304) 926-0452
E: James.A.Martin@wv.gov

WISCONSIN
Mr. Robert Norcross
Administrator
Electric Division
P.O. Box 7839
Madison, WI 53707
P: (608) 266-0699
F: (608) 267-1381
E: robert.norcross
   @psc.state.wi.us

WYOMING
Mr. Thomas E. Doll
State Oil & Gas Supervisor
Oil & Gas Conservation Commission
P.O. Box 2640
777 West 1st Street
Casper, WY 82602
P: (307) 234-7147
F: (307) 234-5306

Ombudsman

Investigates citizens' complaints about the administrative acts of any state agency.

ALABAMA
Ms. Patricia Simpkins
Director of Constituent Services
Office of the Governor
600 Dexter Avenue
Montgomery, AL 36130
P: (334) 242-7100
F: (334) 353-0004

ALASKA
Ms. Linda Lord-Jenkins
Ombudsman
Office of the Ombudsman
State Legislature
P.O. Box 101140
Anchorage, AK 99510
P: (907) 269-5290
F: (907) 269-5291
E: ombudsman
    @legis.state.ak.us

ARIZONA
Mr. Patrick Shannahan
Ombudsman-Citizens' Aide
Office of the Ombudsman -
Citizen's Aide
3737 North 7th Street, Suite 209
Phoenix, AZ 85014
P: (602) 277-7292
F: (602) 277-7312
E: ombuds@azoca.org

ARKANSAS
Mr. Chris Masingill
Director of Agency &
Constituency Affairs
Office of the Governor
State Capitol, Suite 120
Little Rock, AR 72201
P: (501) 682-2345
F: (501) 682-3596
E: chris.masingill
    @governor.arkansas.gov

CALIFORNIA
Hon. Elaine M. Howle
State Auditor
Bureau of State Audits
555 Capitol Mall, Suite 300
Sacramento, CA 95814
P: (916) 445-0255
F: (916) 323-0913
E: elaineh@bsa.ca.gov

COLORADO
Ms. Karen Schaefer
Ombuds
Department of Personnel &
Administration
633 17th Street, Suite 1337
Denver, CO 80203
P: (866) 484-7270
F: (303) 866-4027
E: ombuds@state.co.us

DELAWARE
Mr. Bo McDowell
Constituent Relations
Office of the Governor
Tatnall Building
William Penn Street, 2nd Floor
Dover, DE 19901
P: (302) 744-4101
F: (302) 744-2775

DISTRICT OF COLUMBIA
Mr. Chris Taylor
Director of Community
Relations and Services
Mayor's Office of Community
Relations & Services
1350 Pennsylvania Avenue,
Northwest
Suite 211
Washington, DC 20004
P: (202) 727-8195
F: (202) 727-5931
E: chris.taylor@dc.gov

FLORIDA
Mr. Warren Davis
Director of Citizen Services
Office of the Governor
The Capitol
400 South Monroe Street
Tallahassee, FL 32399
P: (850) 488-7146
F: (850) 487-0801
E: Warren.Davis
    @eog.myflorida.com

HAWAII
Mr. Robin K. Matsunaga
Ombudsman
Office of the Ombudsman
465 South King Street, 4th Floor
Honolulu, HI 96813
P: (808) 587-0770
F: (808) 587-0773

IDAHO
Ms. Megan Olmstead
Constituent Services
Representative
Office of the Governor
P.O. Box 83720
Boise, ID 83720
P: (208) 334-2100
F: (208) 334-3454
E: megan.olmstead
    @gov.idaho.gov

IOWA
Ms. Ruth H. Cooperrider
Acting Ombudsman
Office of Citizen's
Aide/Ombudsman
Ola Babcock Miller Building
1112 East Grand
Des Moines, IA 50319
P: (515) 281-3592
F: (515) 242-6007
E: ombudsman
    @legis.state.ia.us

KENTUCKY
Mr. Edward C. Monahan
Public Advocate
Department of Public Advocacy
100 Fair Oaks Lane, Suite 302
Frankfort, KY 40601
P: (502) 564-8006
F: (502) 564-7890

MAINE
Ms. Patricia A. Condon
Director of Constituent Services
Office of the Governor
#1 State House Station
Augusta, ME 04333
P: (207) 287-3531
F: (207) 287-1034

MARYLAND
Mr. Jeremy C. Rosendale
Deputy Director
Correspondence & Constituent
Services
Office of the Governor
State House
Annapolis, MD 21401
P: (410) 974-3901
F: (410) 260-3830
E: jrosendale
    @gov.state.md.us

MASSACHUSETTS
Mr. Thomas Reece
Constituent Services
Office of the Governor
State House, Room 280
Boston, MA 02133
P: (617) 725-4005
F: (617) 727-9725

MISSISSIPPI
Ms. Anniece McLemore
State LTC Ombudsman
Division of Aging
Department of Human Services
750 North State Street
Jackson, MS 39202
P: (601) 359-4927

MISSOURI
Hon. Peter Kinder (R)
Lieutenant Governor
Office of the Lieutenant
Governor
State Capitol, Room 224
Jefferson City, MO 65101
P: (573) 751-4727
F: (573) 751-9422
E: ltgovinfo@mail.mo.gov

MONTANA
Mr. Bob Schleicher
Citizens' Advocate
Citizens' Advocate Office
State Capitol, Room 232
P.O. Box 200803
Helena, MT 59620
P: (406) 444-3468
F: (406) 444-4151
E: citizensadvocate@mt.gov

NEBRASKA
Mr. Marshall Lux
Ombudsman
State Legislature
P.O. Box 94604
Lincoln, NE 68509
P: (402) 471-2035

NEW HAMPSHIRE
Mr. Charles H. Weatherill
Ombudsman
Department of Health & Human
Services
129 Pleasant Street
Concord, NH 03301
P: (603) 271-5573
F: (603) 271-4632
E: cweather
    @dhhs.state.nh.us

NORTH DAKOTA
Ms. Barb Peske
Director
Constituent Services
Office of the Governor
600 East Boulevard Avenue
Bismarck, ND 58505
P: (701) 328-2208
F: (701) 328-2205
E: govservices@nd.gov

NORTHERN MARIANA ISLANDS
Mr. James Benedetto
Office of the Attorney General
P.O. Box 502452
Saipan, MP 96950
P: (670) 664-2333
F: (670) 664-2349
E: ombudsman@federal.com

OREGON
Ms. Ramona Perrault
Citizens' Representative
Office of the Governor
900 Court Street, Northeast
State Capitol, Room 160
Salem, OR 97301
P: (503) 373-1027
F: (503) 378-6827
E: ramona.perrault
  @state.or.us

PUERTO RICO
Mr. Carlos Lopez-Nieves
Ombudsman
Office of the Ombudsman
P.O. Box 41088
San Juan, PR 00940
P: (787) 724-7373
F: (787) 724-7386

SOUTH DAKOTA
Ms. Kelsey Webb
Constituent Services Director
Office of the Governor
State Capitol
500 East Capitol Avenue
Pierre, SD 57501
P: (605) 773-3212
F: (605) 773-4711

TEXAS
Mr. Gregory S. Davidson
Director
Constituent Communication
Division
Office of the Governor
P.O. Box 12428
Austin, TX 78711
P: (512) 463-1800
F: (512) 463-0039

U.S. VIRGIN ISLANDS
Mr. Julien Harley
St. John Administrator
Office of the Governor
P.O. Box 488
Cruz Bay
St. Johns, VI 00830
P: (340) 776-6484
F: (340) 776-6992

UTAH
Ms. Gloria Hunt
Constituent Services Director
Office of the Governor
350 North State Street, Suite 200
P.O. Box 142220
Salt Lake City, UT 84114
P: (801) 538-1000
F: (801) 538-1528
E: GHUNT@utah.gov

WASHINGTON
Hon. Brian Sonntag (D)
State Auditor
Office of the State Auditor
P.O. Box 40021
Olympia, WA 98504
P: (360) 902-0370
F: (360) 753-0646
E: sonntagb@sao.wa.gov

WEST VIRGINIA
Ms. Jennifer Ferrell
Director of Constituent Services
Office of the Governor
1900 Kanawha Boulevard, East
Charleston, WV 25305
P: (304) 558-2000
F: (304) 342-7025
E: Jennifer.L.Ferrell
  @wv.gov

Parks and Recreation

Manages the state's parks, historical sites and recreational areas.

Information provided by:

National Association of State Park Directors
Philip McKnelly
Executive Director
8829 Woodyhill Road
Raleigh, NC 27613
P: (919) 676-8365
F: (919) 676-8365
NASPD@me.com
www.naspd.org

ALABAMA
Mr. Mark Easterwood
Director
State Parks
64 North Union Street
Montgomery, AL 36130
P: (334) 242-3334
F: (334) 353-8629

ALASKA
Mr. Ben Ellis
Director
Division of Parks & Outdoor Recreation
550 West 7th Avenue, Suite 1380
Anchorage, AK 99501
P: (907) 269-8700
F: (907) 269-8907

ARIZONA
Ms. Renee Bahl
Executive Director
State Parks
1300 West Washington
Phoenix, AZ 85007
P: (602) 542-4174
F: (602) 542-4188

ARKANSAS
Mr. Greg Butts
Director
State Parks
One Capitol Mall
Little Rock, AR 72201
P: (501) 682-7743
F: (501) 682-1364

CALIFORNIA
Ms. Ruth Coleman
Director
Department of Parks & Recreation
1416 Ninth Street, Room 1405
Sacramento, CA 95814
P: (916) 653-8380
F: (916) 657-3903

COLORADO
Mr. Dean Winstanley
Director
Division of Parks & Outdoor Recreation
1313 Sherman Street, Suite 618
Denver, CO 80203
P: (303) 866-2884
F: (303) 866-3206

CONNECTICUT
Mr. Tom Tyler
Director
DEP, State Parks Division
79 Elm Street, 6th Floor
Hartford, CT 06106
P: (860) 424-3203
F: (860) 424-4070

DELAWARE
Mr. Charles A. Salkin
Director
Division of Parks & Recreation
89 Kings Highway
Dover, DE 19901
P: (302) 739-4401
F: (302) 739-3817
E: Charles.Salkin
@state.de.us

FLORIDA
Mr. Donald Forgione
Director
State Parks, Department of Environmental Protection
3900 Commonwealth Boulevard
Mail Station 500
Tallahassee, FL 32399
P: (850) 245-3029
F: (850) 245-3041

GEORGIA
Ms. Becky Kelley
Director
State Parks, Recreation & Historic Sites Division
2 Martin Luther King, Jr. Drive, SE
Suite 1352, East
Atlanta, GA 30334
P: (404) 656-9448
F: (404) 651-5871

HAWAII
Mr. Dan S. Quinn
Administrator
Division of State Parks
P.O. Box 621
Honolulu, HI 96809
P: (808) 587-0290
F: (808) 587-0311

IDAHO
Ms. Nancy Merrill
Director
Department of Parks & Recreation
P.O. Box 83720
5657 Warm Springs Avenue
Boise, ID 83720
P: (208) 334-4187
F: (208) 334-5232

ILLINOIS
Mr. Ron House
Director
DNR, Office of Land Management & Education
One Natural Resources Way
Springfield, IL 62702
P: (217) 782-1395
F: (217) 524-5612

INDIANA
Mr. Daniel W. Bortner
Director
Division of State Parks & Reservoirs
402 West Washington Street, Room W 298
Indianapolis, IN 46204
P: (317) 232-4124
F: (317) 232-4132
E: dbortner@dnr.IN.gov

IOWA
Mr. Kevin Szcodronski
Bureau Chief
State Parks
Department of Natural Resources
Wallace State Office Building
Des Moines, IA 50319
P: (515) 281-8674
F: (515) 281-6794

KANSAS
Ms. Linda Lanterman
Acting Director
Division of State Parks
512 Southeast 25th Avenue
Pratt, KS 67124
P: (620) 672-5911
F: (620) 672-2972

KENTUCKY
Mr. Gerry Van Der Meer
Commissioner
State Parks
500 Mero Street, 10th Floor
Frankfort, KY 40601
P: (502) 564-2172
F: (502) 564-9015

LOUISIANA
Mr. Stuart Johnson
Assistant Secretary
Office of State Parks
P.O. Box 44426
Baton Rouge, LA 70804
P: (225) 342-8111
F: (225) 342-8107

MAINE
Mr. Will Harris
Director
Bureau of Parks & Lands
22 State House Station
18 Elkins Lane (AMHI Campus)
Augusta, ME 04333
P: (207) 287-3821
F: (207) 287-8111

MARYLAND
Ms. Nita Settina
Superintendent
Park Service
580 Taylor Avenue
Tawes State Office Building E-3
Annapolis, MD 21401
P: (410) 260-8186
F: (410) 260-8191

MASSACHUSETTS
Ms. Priscilla H. Geigis
Director
Division of State Parks & Recreation
Department of Conservation & Recreation
251 Causeway Street, 9th Floor
Boston, MA 02114
P: (617) 626-4986
F: (617) 626-1351

MICHIGAN
Mr. Ronald Olson
Chief
Parks & Recreation Division
P.O. Box 30257
Lansing, MI 48909
P: (517) 335-4827
F: (517) 373-4625
E: OLSONR@michigan.gov

Parks and Recreation

MINNESOTA
Mr. Courtland Nelson
Director
Division of Parks & Recreation
500 Lafayette Road
St. Paul, MN 55155
P: (651) 296-2270
F: (651) 297-1157
E: courtland.nelson
@state.mn.us

MISSISSIPPI
Ramie Ford
Director
State Parks
P.O. Box 451
Jackson, MS 39205
P: (601) 432-2218
F: (601) 432-2236

MISSOURI
Mr. William Bryan
Director
Division of State Parks
P.O. Box 176
Jefferson City, MO 65102
P: (573) 751-9392
F: (573) 526-7716

MONTANA
Mr. Chas Van Genderen
Acting Administrator
Parks Division
1420 East Sixth
P.O. Box 200701
Helena, MT 59620
P: (406) 444-3750
F: (406) 444-4952

NEBRASKA
Mr. Roger L. Kuhn
Assistant Director
Parks Division
Game & Parks Commission
P.O. Box 30370
Lincoln, NE 68503
P: (402) 471-5512
F: (402) 471-5528

NEVADA
Mr. David K. Morrow
Administrator
Division of State Parks
1300 South Curry Street
Carson City, NV 89703
P: (775) 687-4384 Ext. 223
F: (775) 687-4117

NEW HAMPSHIRE
Ms. Gail Wolek
Acting Director
Division of Parks & Recreation
172 Pembroke Road
P.O. Box 1856
Concord, NH 03302
P: (603) 271-3556
F: (603) 271-3553

NEW JERSEY
Ms. Amy Cradic
Acting Director
Division of Parks & Forestry
P.O. Box 404
Trenton, NJ 08625
P: (609) 292-2733
F: (609) 984-0503

NEW MEXICO
Mr. Tommy Mutz
Director
State Park Division
P.O. Box 1147
Santa Fe, NM 87504
P: (505) 476-3357
F: (505) 476-3361

NEW YORK
Ms. Rose Harvey
Commissioner, SHPO, Vice
Chair, Advisory Council on
Historic Preservation
Office of Parks, Recreation &
Historic Preservation
Empire State Plaza
Agency Building No. 1
Albany, NY 12238
P: (518) 474-0443
F: (518) 474-1365

NORTH CAROLINA
Mr. Lewis Ledford
Director
Division of Parks & Recreation
1615 Mail Service Center
Raleigh, NC 27699
P: (919) 715-8710
F: (919) 715-3085

NORTH DAKOTA
Mr. Mark Zimmerman
Director
Parks & Recreation Department
1600 East Century Avenue,
Suite # 3
Bismarck, ND 58503
P: (701) 328-5361
F: (710) 328-5363

OHIO
Mr. David Payne
Chief
Division of Parks & Recreation
2045 Morse Road, Building C-3
Columbus, OH 43229
P: (614) 265-6511
F: (614) 261-8407

OKLAHOMA
Ms. Kris Marek
Director
State Parks, Resorts & Golf
P.O. Box 52002
Oklahoma City, OK 73152
P: (405) 521-3790
F: (405) 521-2428

OREGON
Mr. Tim Wood
Director
Parks & Recreation Department
725 Summer Street, Northeast
Salem, OR 97301
P: (503) 986-0718
F: (503) 986-0796
E: tim.wood@state.or.us

PENNSYLVANIA
Mr. John W. Norbeck
Director
Bureau of State Parks
P.O. Box 8551
Harrisburg, PA 17105
P: (717) 787-6640
F: (717) 787-8817

RHODE ISLAND
Mr. Robert Paquette
Chief
Division of Parks & Recreation
2321 Hartford Avenue
Johnson, RI 02919
P: (401) 222-2632
F: (401) 934-0610

SOUTH CAROLINA
Mr. Phil Gaines
Director
Division of Parks & Recreation
1205 Pendleton Street, Suite 251
Columbia, SC 29201
P: (803) 734-0159
F: (803) 734-1017
E: pgaines@scprt.com

SOUTH DAKOTA
Mr. Doug Hofer
Director
Division of Parks & Recreation
Foss Building
523 East Capitol
Pierre, SD 57501
P: (605) 773-3391
F: (605) 773-6245
E: doug.hofer@state.sd.us

TENNESSEE
Mr. Mike Carlton
Assistant Commissioner
State Parks & Conservation
401 Church Street
21st Floor, L & C Tower
Nashville, TN 37243
P: (615) 532-0025
F: (615) 741-8858

TEXAS
Mr. Brent Leisure
Director
State Parks
4200 Smith School Road
Austin, TX 78744
P: (512) 389-4966
F: (512) 389-4960

UTAH
Ms. Mary Tullius
Director
Division of State Parks &
Recreation
1594 West North Temple, Suite
116
P.O. Box 146001
Salt Lake City, UT 84114
P: (801) 538-7362
F: (801) 538-7378
E: marytullius@utah.gov

VERMONT
Mr. Craig Whipple
Director
Division of State Parks
103 South Main Street, 10 South
Waterbury, VT 05671
P: (802) 241-3664
F: (802) 244-1481
E: craig.whipple
@state.vt.us

VIRGINIA
Mr. Joe Elton
Director
Division of State Parks
203 Governor Street, Suite 306
Richmond, VA 23219
P: (804) 786-4375
F: (804) 786-9294
E: joe.elton
@dcr.virginia.gov

Parks and Recreation

WASHINGTON
Mr. Don Hoch
Director
State Parks & Recreation
Commission
P.O. Box 42650
Olympia, WA 98504
P: (360) 902-8501
F: (360) 902-8681

WEST VIRGINIA
Mr. Kenneth Caplinger
Chief
Parks & Recreation
Capitol Complex, Building 3,
Room 714
Charleston, WV 25305
P: (304) 558-2764
F: (304) 558-0077

WISCONSIN
Mr. Dan Schuller
Director
Bureau of Parks & Recreation
P.O. Box 7921
Madison, WI 53707
P: (608) 264-6035
F: (607) 267-7474

WYOMING
Mr. Domenic Bravo
Director
Division of State Parks &
Historic Sites
2301 Central Avenue
Barrett Building, 4th Floor
Cheyenne, WY 82002
P: (307) 777-6324
F: (307) 777-6005

Parole and Probation (Adult)

Determines whether paroles should be granted or revoked and supervises adult parolees and probationers.

For more information contact:

American Probation & Parole Association
Carl Wicklund
Executive Director
P.O. Box 11910
Lexington, KY 40578
P: (859) 244-8203
F: (859) 244-8001
cwicklund@csg.org
www.appa-net.org

ALABAMA
Ms. Cynthia S. Dillard
Executive Director
Board of Pardons & Paroles
301 South Ripley Street
P.O. Box 302405
Montgomery, AL 36130
P: (334) 353-3480
F: (334) 353-1157
E: cynthia.dillard
  @alabpp.gov

ALASKA
Mr. Ronald Taylor
Executive Director
Parole Board
Department of Corrections
550 West Seventh Avenue, Suite 601
Anchorage, AK 99501
P: (907) 770-3610
F: (907) 770-6308
E: ronald.taylor@alaska.gov

AMERICAN SAMOA
Mr. Tuaolo M. Fruean
Commissioner
Department of Public Safety
American Samoa Government
P.O. Box 3699
Pago Pago, AS 96799
P: (684) 633-1111
F: (684) 633-7296

ARIZONA
Mr. Duane Belcher Sr.
Chair & Executive Director
Board of Executive Clemency
1645 West Jefferson Street, Suite 101
Phoenix, AZ 85007
P: (602) 542-5656
F: (602) 542-5680

ARKANSAS
Mr. Dan Roberts
Deputy Director, Parole and Probation
Department of Community Correction
Two Union National Plaza
105 West Capitol
Little Rock, AR 72201
P: (501) 682-9510
F: (501) 682-9513
E: dan.roberts@arkansas.gov

COLORADO
Ms. Jeaneene Miller
Director
Divisions of Adult Parole, Community Corrections & YOS
12157 West Cedar Drive
Lakewood, CO 80228
P: (303) 763-2420
E: jeaneene.miller
  @doc.state.co.us

CONNECTICUT
Mr. John DeFeo
Acting Executive Director
Board of Pardons & Paroles
24 Wolcott Hill Road
Wethersfield, CT 06109
P: (203) 805-6605

DELAWARE
Mr. Dwight F. Holden
Chairperson
Board of Parole
820 North French Street, 5th Floor
Wilmington, DE 19801
P: (302) 577-5233
F: (302) 577-3501

DISTRICT OF COLUMBIA
Mr. Paul A. Quander Jr.
Director
Court Services & Offender Supervision Agency
633 Indiana Avenue, Northwest
Washington, DC 20004
P: (202) 220-5300

FLORIDA
Ms. Monica David
Commissioner
Parole Commission
2601 Blair Stone Road
Tallahassee, FL 32399
P: (850) 487-1978
F: (850) 487-1220

GEORGIA
Mr. James E. Donald
Chair
Board of Pardons & Paroles
2 Martin Luther King Jr. Drive Southeast
5th Floor, East
Atlanta, GA 30334
P: (404) 651-6597
F: (404) 651-8502

GUAM
Mr. Edward A. Alvarez
Chief Probation Officer
Probation Services Division
Superior Court of Guam
120 West O'Brien Drive
Hagatna, GU 96910
P: (671) 475-3448
F: (671) 477-4944

HAWAII
Mr. Bert Y. Matsuoka
Chair
Paroling Authority
1177 Alakea Street, Ground Floor
Honolulu, HI 96813
P: (808) 587-5604
F: (808) 587-1314

IDAHO
Ms. Olivia Craven
Executive Director
Commission of Pardons & Parole
P.O. Box 83720
Statehouse Mail
Boise, ID 83720
P: (208) 334-2520
F: (208) 334-3501

ILLINOIS
Mr. Jesse Montgomery
Chief of Parole
Parole Division
1301 Concordia Court
P.O. Box 19277
Springfield, IL 62794
P: (309) 755-4511

INDIANA
Mr. Gregory Server
Chair
Parole Board
402 West Washington Street, Room W466
Indianapolis, IN 46204
P: (317) 232-5737
F: (317) 232-5738
E: GServer@idoc.IN.gov

IOWA
Mr. Jerry Bartruff
Acting Deputy Director, Offender Services
Department of Corrections
Jessie Parker Building
510 East 12th Street
Des Moines, IA 50319
P: (319) 626-2391
E: jerry.bartruff@iowa.gov

KANSAS
Mr. Robert Sanders
Chair
Parole Board
Landon State Office Building
900 Southwest Jackson, Suite 452-S
Topeka, KS 66612
P: (785) 296-3469
F: (785) 296-7949

KENTUCKY
Mr. Verman Winburn
Chair
Parole Board
P.O. Box 2400
Frankfort, KY 40602
P: (502) 564-3620
F: (502) 564-8995

LOUISIANA
Ms. Eugenie C. Powers
Director
Division of Probation & Parole
504 Mayflower Street
P.O. Box 94304
Baton Rouge, LA 70804
P: (225) 342-6609
F: (225) 342-3087

MAINE
Mr. Harold Doughty Jr.
Associate Commissioner for Adult Services
Department of Corrections
State House Station 111
Augusta, ME 04333
P: (207) 287-4340

Parole and Probation (Adult)

MARYLAND
Mr. Patrick McGee
Director
Division of Parole & Probation
6776 Reisterstown Road, Suite 305
Baltimore, MD 21215
P: (410) 585-3525
F: (410) 764-4091
E: pmcgee@dpscs.state.md.us

MICHIGAN
Mr. Thomas Combs
Chair
Parole Board
P.O. Box 30003
Lansing, MI 48909
P: (517) 373-5314

MINNESOTA
Mr. Tom Roy
Commissioner
Department of Corrections
1450 Energy Park Drive, Suite 200
St. Paul, MN 55108
P: (651) 361-7226
F: (651) 642-0414
E: tom.roy@state.mn.us

MISSISSIPPI
Ms. Shannon Warnock
Chair
State Parole Board
201 West Capitol Street, Suite 800
Jackson, MS 39201
P: (601) 354-7716
F: (601) 354-7725
E: ghamilton
    @mdoc.state.ms.us

MISSOURI
Mr. Tom Hodges
Chief State Supervisor
Division of Parole & Probation
3400 Knipp Drive
Jefferson City, MO 65109
P: (573) 751-8488
F: (573) 751-8501

MONTANA
Mr. Craig Thomas
Executive Director
Board of Pardons & Parole
1002 Hollenbeck Road
Deer Lodge, MT 59722
P: (406) 846-1404
F: (406) 846-3512

NEBRASKA
Ms. Esther Casmer
Chair
Board of Parole
P.O. Box 94661
State House Station
Lincoln, NE 68509
P: (402) 471-2156
F: (402) 471-2453

NEVADA
Mr. Bernard W. Curtis
Division Administrator
Division of Parole & Probation
1445 Old Hot Springs Road, Suite 104
Carson City, NV 89706
P: (775) 684-2605
F: (775) 684-2693

NEW HAMPSHIRE
Mr. Michael McAlister
Director
Division of Field Services
Department of Corrections
P.O. Box 1806
Concord, NH 03302
P: (603) 271-5652

NEW JERSEY
Mr. David W. Thomas
Executive Director
State Parole Board
P.O. Box 862
Trenton, NJ 08625
P: (609) 292-4257
F: (609) 943-4769

NEW MEXICO
Mr. David Jablonski
Director
Probation & Parole Division
4337 State Road 14
P.O. Box 27116
Santa Fe, NM 87502
P: (505) 827-8830
F: (505) 827-8679

NEW YORK
Ms. Andrea W. Evans
Chair & CEO
Division of Parole
97 Central Avenue
Albany, NY 12206
P: (518) 473-9400
F: (212) 345-6670
E: nysparole
    @parole.state.ny.us

NORTH DAKOTA
Ms. Leann Bertsch
Commissioner
Department of Corrections & Rehabilitation
Field Services Division
P.O. Box 5521
Bismarck, ND 58506
P: (701) 328-6190
F: (701) 328-6186
E: lbertsch@asca.net

NORTHERN MARIANA ISLANDS
Ms. Ursula L. Aldan
Chief Probation Officer
Superior Court
P.O. Box 500137
Saipan, MP 96950
P: (670) 236-9865
F: (670) 236-9866
E: ualdan@hotmail.com

Mr. Eugene Villagomez
Chief Parole Officer
Board of Parole
P.O. Box 502641
Saipan, MP 95950
P: (670) 664-3300
F: (670) 664-3310
E: ualdan@hotmail.com

OKLAHOMA
Mr. Terry Jenks
Director
Pardon & Parole Board
First National Center
120 North Robinson Avenue, Suite 900W
Oklahoma City, OK 73102
P: (405) 602-5863
F: (405) 602-6437
E: terry.jenks
    @ppb.state.ok.us

OREGON
Mr. Jeremiah Stromberg
Executive Director
Board of Parole & Post-Prison Supervision
2575 Center Street, Northeast
Suite 100
Salem, OR 97301
P: (503) 945-0919
F: (503) 373-7558
E: jeremiah.p.stromberg
    @doc.state.or.us

PENNSYLVANIA
Ms. Catherine C. McVey
Chair
Board of Probation & Parole
1101 South Front Street, Suite 5600
Harrisburg, PA 17104
P: (717) 787-5699
F: (717) 772-4375

PUERTO RICO
Mr. Enrique Garcia-Garcia
President
Parole Board
Minillas Station
P.O. Box 40945
San Juan, PR 00940
P: (787) 754-8115 Ext. 241
F: (787) 754-8181

RHODE ISLAND
Mr. Kenneth R. Walker
Chair
Parole Board
Varley Building
40 Howard Avenue
Cranston, RI 02920
P: (401) 462-0900
F: (401) 462-0915
E: parolebd@doc.ri.gov

SOUTH CAROLINA
Ms. Kela E. Thomas
Director
Department of Probation, Parole & Pardon Services
2221 Devine Street, Suite 600
P.O. Box 50666
Columbia, SC 29250
P: (803) 734-9278
F: (803) 734-9440

SOUTH DAKOTA
Mr. Ed Ligtenberg
Executive Director
Department of Corrections
Board of Pardons & Paroles
1600 N. Drive, P.O. Box 5911
Sioux Falls, SD 57117
P: (605) 367-5040
F: (605) 367-5115

TENNESSEE
Mr. Charles M. Traughber
Chair
Board of Probation & Parole
404 James Robertson Parkway
Suite 1300
Nashville, TN 37243
P: (615) 741-1673
F: (615) 532-8581

TEXAS

Ms. Rissie L. Owens
Presiding Officer
Board of Pardons & Paroles
1300 11th Street, Suite 520
P.O. Box 599
Huntsville, TX 77342
P: (936) 291-2161
F: (936) 291-8367

U.S. VIRGIN ISLANDS

Hon. Verne A. Hodge
Presiding Judge
Territorial Court
P.O. Box 70
St. Thomas, VI 00804
P: (340) 774-6680
F: (340) 777-8187

Mr. Chesley Roebuck
Chair
Board of Parole
P.O. Box 2668
St. Thomas, VI 00802
P: (340) 778-2036
F: (340) 778-1637

UTAH

Mr. Brent Butcher
Director
Probation & Parole
Department of Corrections
14717 South Minuteman Drive
Draper, UT 84020
P: (801) 545-5901
F: (801) 545-5911
E: BRENTBUTCHER@utah.gov

VERMONT

Mr. Peter Danles
Director
Parole Board
Department of Corrections
103 South Main Street
Waterbury, VT 05671
P: (802) 241-2312
F: (802) 241-3969
E: pdanles@doc.state.vt.us

VIRGINIA

Ms. Helen H. Fahey
Chair
Parole Board
6900 Atmore Drive
Richmond, VA 23225
P: (804) 674-3081
F: (804) 674-3284
E: helen.fahey
    @vadoc.virginia.gov

WASHINGTON

Ms. Lynn DeLano
Chair
Indeterminate Sentence Review
Board
4317 6th Avenue, Southeast
P.O. Box 40907
Olympia, WA 98504
P: (360) 493-9266
F: (360) 493-9287

WEST VIRGINIA

Mr. Dennis W. Foreman
Chair
Parole Board
112 California Avenue
Room 307
Charleston, WV 25305
P: (304) 558-6366

WISCONSIN

Mr. Steve Landreman
Acting Chair
Earned Release Review
Commission
3099 East Washington Avenue
P.O. Box 7960
Madison, WI 53707
P: (608) 240-7280
F: (608) 240-7299

WYOMING

Mr. Patrick M. Anderson
Executive Director
Board of Parole
1934 Wyott Drive
Cheyenne, WY 82002
P: (307) 777-5444
E: pander@state.wy.us

Personnel

Formulates, implements, and enforces personnel management policies and procedures for the state.

Information provided by:

National Association of State Personnel Executives
Leslie Scott
Association Manager
P.O. Box 11910
Lexington, KY 40578
P: (859) 244-8182
F: (859) 244-8001
lscott@csg.org
www.naspe.net

ALABAMA
Jackie Graham
State Personnel Director
State Personnel Department
313 Folsom Administration Building
64 North Union Street, Suite 300
Montgomery, AL 36130
P: (334) 242-3711
F: (334) 353-3320
E: jgraham
@personnel.state.al.us

ALASKA
Ms. Nicki Neal
Director
Division of Personnel
Department of Administration
P.O. Box 110201
Juneau, AK 99811
P: (907) 465-4431
F: (907) 465-3415
E: nicki.neal@alaska.gov

AMERICAN SAMOA
Mr. Puni Penei H. Sewell
Director
Department of Human Resources
American Samoa Government
Pago Pago, AS 96799
P: (684) 633-4485
F: (684) 633-1139
E: sewells_1@hotmail.com

ARIZONA
Ms. Kathy Peckardt
Human Resources Director
Human Resource Division
Department of Administration
100 North 15th Avenue, Suite 261
Phoenix, AZ 85007
P: (602) 542-8378
F: (602) 542-2796
E: kathy.peckardt
@ad.state.az.us

ARKANSAS
Ms. Kay Barnhill Terry
State Personnel Administrator
Office of Personnel Management
Department of Finance & Administration
1509 West 7th Street
Little Rock, AR 72201
P: (501) 682-1753
F: (501) 682-5104
E: kay.terry
@dfa.state.ar.us

CALIFORNIA
Ms. Suzanne M. Ambrose
Executive Officer
State Personnel Board
801 Capitol Mall
Sacramento, CA 95814
P: (916) 653-1028
F: (916) 653-8147
E: sambrose@spb.ca.gov

Mr. Ronald Yank
Director
Department of Personnel Administration
1515 S Street, Suite 400
Sacramento, CA 96814
P: (916) 327-4024
F: (916) 322-3769
E: ron.yank@dpa.ca.gov

COLORADO
Mr. Guy Mellor
Director
Division of Human Resources
Dept. of Personnel and Administration
1313 Sherman Street, 1st Floor
Denver, CO 80203
P: (303) 866-2105
F: (303) 866-2021
E: guy.mellor@state.co.us

CONNECTICUT
Dr. Pamela L. Libby
Director
Human Resource Management
165 Capitol Avenue, Room 411
Hartford, CT 06106
P: (860) 713-5204
F: (860) 622-2965
E: pamela.libby
@po.state.ct.us

DELAWARE
Ms. Linda McCloskey
Director
Human Resource Management
Carvel Office Building
820 North French Street, 10th Floor
Wilmington, DE 19801
P: (302) 577-9877
F: (302) 577-3996
E: linda.mccloskey
@state.de.us

DISTRICT OF COLUMBIA
Ms. Judy D. Banks
Interim Director
Department of Human Resources
One Judiciary Square
441 4th Street Northwest, Suite 300S
Washington, DC 20001
P: (202) 671-1300
F: (202) 727-6827
E: judy.banks@dc.gov

FLORIDA
Ms. Sharon Larson
Director
Division of Human Resources
Department of Management Services
4050 Esplanade Way, Suite 235
Tallahassee, FL 32399
P: (850) 413-8725
F: (850) 922-6642
E: sharon.larson
@dms.myflorida.com

GEORGIA
Mr. Joseph B. Doyle
Commissioner
State Personnel Administration
2 Martin Luther King, Jr. Dr., Southwest
West Tower, Room 504
Atlanta, GA 30334
P: (404) 656-2705
F: (404) 656-5979
E: jdoyle@spa.ga.gov

GUAM
Mr. Michael Reidy
Director
Department of Administration
P.O. Box 884
Agana, GU 96932
P: (671) 475-1250
F: (671) 477-6788
E: mreidy@ns.gov.gu

HAWAII
Ms. Sunshine P.W. Topping
Director
Department of Human Resources
State Office Tower
235 South Beretania Street, 14th Floor
Honolulu, HI 96813
P: (808) 587-1100
F: (808) 587-1106
E: sunshine.p.w.topping
@hawaii.gov

IDAHO
Ms. Vicki Tokita
HR Program Manager
Division of Human Resources
700 West State Street
P.O. Box 83720
Boise, ID 83720
P: (208) 429-5529
F: (208) 334-3182
E: vicki.tokita
@dhr.idaho.gov

ILLINOIS
Ms. Christina Griffin
Human Resource Director
Bureau of Personnel
Central Management Services
503 William G. Stratton Building
Springfield, IL 62706
P: (217) 524-8773
F: (217) 558-4497
E: christina.griffin
@illinois.gov

INDIANA
Mr. Daniel Hackler
Director
State Personnel Department
402 West Washington Street, Room W161
Indianapolis, IN 46204
P: (317) 234-3830
F: (317) 233-1979
E: dhackler@spd.in.gov

IOWA
Mr. Jeff Panknen
Chief Operating Officer
Human Resources Enterprise
Grimes State Office Building
400 East 14th Street
Des Moines, IA 50319
P: (515) 281-5064
F: (515) 242-6450
E: jeff.panknen@iowa.gov

KENTUCKY
Mr. Timothy Longmeyer
Secretary
Personnel Cabinet
State Office Building
501 High Street, Third Floor
Frankfort, KY 40601
P: (502) 564-7430
F: (502) 564-7603
E: timothy.longmeyer@ky.gov

LOUISIANA
Shannon Templet
Director
Department of State Civil
Service
1201 North Third Street, Suite
3-280
P.O. Box 94111
Baton Rouge, LA 70804
P: (225) 342-8272
F: (225) 342-0966
E: shannon.templet@la.gov

MAINE
Ms. Joyce Oreskovich
Acting Director
Bureau of Human Resources
#4 State House Station
220 Capitol Street
Augusta, ME 04330
P: (207) 287-6780
E: joyce.a.oreskovich
    @maine.gov

MARYLAND
Ms. Cynthia Kollner
Executive Director
Office of Personnel Services &
Benefits
Department of Budget &
Management
301 West Preston Street, Room
609
Baltimore, MD 21201
P: (410) 767-4715
F: (410) 333-5262
E: ckollner@dbm.state.md.us

MASSACHUSETTS
Mr. Paul Dietl
Chief Human Resources Officer
Human Resource Division
1 Ashburton Palce, Room 301
Boston, MA 02108
P: (617) 878-9705
F: (617) 727-1175
E: paul.d.dietl@state.ma.us

MICHIGAN
Mr. Jeremy S. Stephens
Director
Civil Service Commission
400 South Pine Street
P.O. Box 30002
Lansing, MI 48909
P: (517) 373-3020
F: (517) 373-3103
E: StephensJ5@michigan.gov

MINNESOTA
Ms. Judy Plante
Assistant Commissioner
Department of Finance &
Employment Relations
658 Cedar Street
St. Paul, MN 55155
P: (651) 201-8008
F: (651) 296-1990
E: judy.plante@state.mn.us

MISSISSIPPI
Ms. Lynn Fitch
Executive Director
State Personnel Board
301 North Lamar Street
Jackson, MS 39201
P: (601) 359-2702
F: (601) 359-2729
E: lfitch@spb.state.ms.us

MISSOURI
Mr. Bill Miller
Director
Division of Personnel
Office of Administration, P.O.
Box 388
301 West High Street, Suite 430
Jefferson City, MO 65102
P: (573) 751-4514
F: (573) 751-8641
E: bill.miller@oa.mo.gov

MONTANA
Mr. Randy Morris
HRIS Bureau Chief
Human Resources Division
Department of Administration
P.O. Box 200127
Helena, MT 59620
P: (406) 444-3894
F: (406) 444-0703
E: ramorris@mt.gov

NEBRASKA
Mr. Mike McCrory
Director
State Personnel Division
Department of Administrative
Services
P.O. Box 94905
Lincoln, NE 68509
P: (409) 471-2833
F: (402) 471-3754
E: mike.mccrory
    @nebraska.gov

NEVADA
Ms. Teresa J. Thienhaus
Director
Department of Personnel
209 East Musser Street, Room
101
Carson City, NV 89701
P: (775) 684-0101
F: (775) 684-0124
E: thienhaus@dop.nv.gov

NEW HAMPSHIRE
Ms. Karen D. Hutchins
Director
Division of Personnel
Department of Administrative
Services
25 Capital Street
Concord, NH 03301
P: (603) 271-1420
F: (603) 271-1422
E: karen.hutchins@nh.gov

NEW JERSEY
Mr. Robert M. Czech
Chair/Chief Executive Officer
Civil Service Commission
P.O. Box 317
Trenton, NJ 08625
P: (606) 292-4125
E: robert.czech
    @csc.state.nj.us

NEW MEXICO
Mr. Gene Moser
Director
State Personnel Office
2600 Cerrillos Road
Santa Fc, NM 87505
P: (505) 476-7751
F: (505) 476-8705
E: eugene.moser@state.nm.us

NEW YORK
Ms. Patricia Hite
Acting Commissioner
Department of Civil Service
Alfred E. Smith State Office
Building
Albany, NY 12239
P: (518) 457-3701
F: (518) 473-5696
E: robin.farrell
    @cs.state.ny.us

NORTH CAROLINA
Ms. Linda Coleman
Director
Office of State Personnel
116 West Jones Street
1331 Mail Service Center
Raleigh, NC 27699
P: (919) 807-4908
E: linda.coleman@osp.nc.gov

NORTH DAKOTA
Ms. Laurie
    Sterioti-Hammeren
Director
Human Resource Management
Services
600 East Boulevard Avenue
Department 113
Bismarck, ND 58505
P: (701) 328-4735
F: (701) 328-1475
E: lhammeren@state.nd.us

**NORTHERN MARIANA
ISLANDS**
Mr. Norbert S. Sablan
Executive Assistant
Civil Services Commission
P.O. Box 5150, CHRB
Saipan, MP 96950
P: (670) 322-6954
F: (670) 322-3327
E: csc@saipan.com

OHIO
Ms. Brenda Gerhardstein
HRD Deputy Director
Human Resources Division
30 East Broad Street, 27th Floor
Columbus, OH 43215
P: (614) 466-3455
E: Brenda.Gerhardstein
    @das.state.oh.us

Personnel

OKLAHOMA
Mr. Oscar B. Jackson Jr.
Administrator & Cabinet
Secretary
Office of Personnel
Management
Human Resources &
Administration
2101 North Lincoln Boulevard,
Room G-80
Oklahoma City, OK 73105
P: (405) 521-6301
F: (405) 522-0694
E: oscar.jackson@opm.ok.gov

OREGON
Ms. Diana Foster
Administrator
Human Resource Services
Division
Department of Administrative
Services
155 Cottage Street, Northeast
Salem, OR 97310
P: (503) 378-3020
F: (503) 373-7684
E: diana.l.foster
   @state.or.us

PENNSYLVANIA
Mr. James A. Honchar
Deputy Secretary for Human
Resources & Management
Human Resources &
Management
517 Finance Building
Harrisburg, PA 17110
P: (717) 787-5545
F: (717) 783-4429
E: jhonchar@state.pa.us

PUERTO RICO
Ms. Marta Beltran
Administrator
Central Labor Advisory
P.O. Box 8476
Ponce De Leon Avenue, Suite
1507
San Juan, PR 00910
P: (787) 706-5967
F: (787) 706-5697

RHODE ISLAND
Mr. Stephen E. Johnston
Executive Director, Human
Resources
Office of Personnel
Administration
1 Capitol Hill
Providence, RI 02908
P: (401) 222-3252
F: (401) 222-2490
E: SJohnston
   @mail.state.ri.us

SOUTH CAROLINA
Mr. Samuel L. Wilkins
Director
Office of Human Resources
1201 Main Street, Suite 800
Columbia, SC 29229
P: (803) 896-5172
F: (803) 896-5050
E: swilkins@ohr.sc.gov

SOUTH DAKOTA
Ms. Sandra Jorgensen
Director
Bureau of Personnel
500 East Capitol Avenue
Pierre, SD 57501
P: (605) 773-4918
F: (605) 773-4344
E: sandy.jorgensen
   @state.sd.us

Ms. Sandy Zinter
Commissioner
Bureau of Personnel
500 East Capitol Avenue
Pierre, SD 57501
P: (605) 773-4918
F: (605) 773-4344
E: sandy.zinter@state.sd.us

TENNESSEE
Ms. Rebecca Hunter
Commissioner
Department of Human
Resources
James K. Polk Building, 1st
Floor
505 Deaderick Street
Nashville, TN 37243
P: (615) 741-2958
F: (615) 741-7880
E: rebecca.hunter@tn.gov

U.S. VIRGIN ISLANDS
Mr. Kenneth L. Hermon Jr.
Director
Division of Personnel
GERS Building, 3rd Floor
3438 Kronprindsens Gade
St. Thomas, VI 00802
P: (340) 774-8588
F: (340) 714-5040
E: kenne@viaccess.net

UTAH
Mr. Jeff Herring
Executive Director
Department of Human Resource
Management
2120 State Office Building
P.O. Box 141531
Salt Lake City, UT 84114
P: (801) 538-3403
F: (801) 538-3081
E: jherring@utah.gov

VERMONT
Ms. Kate Duffy
Commissioner
Department of Human
Resources
110 State Street
Montpelier, VT 05620
P: (802) 828-3491
E: kate.duffy@state.vt.us

VIRGINIA
Mrs. Sara Redding Wilson
Director
Department of Human Resource
Management
101 North 14th Street, 12th
Floor
Richmond, VA 23219
P: (804) 225-2237
F: (804) 371-7401
E: sara.wilson
   @dhrm.virginia.gov

WASHINGTON
Ms. Eva Santos
Director
Department of Personnel
P.O. Box 47500
Olympia, WA 98504
P: (360) 664-6350
F: (360) 753-1003
E: Eva.Santos@dop.wa.gov

WEST VIRGINIA
Ms. Sara Walker
Director
Division of Personnel
1900 Kanawha Boulevard, East
Charleston, WV 25305
P: (304) 558-3950
E: sara.p.walker@wv.gov

WISCONSIN
Mr. Gregory L. Gracz
Director
Office of State Employment
Relations
101 East Wilson Street
P.O. Box 7855
Madison, WI 53707
P: (608) 266-9820
F: (608) 267-1014
E: greg.gracz@wi.gov

WYOMING
Mr. Dean Fausset
Administrator
Human Resources Division
Administration & Information
Emerson Building, 2001 Capitol
Avenue
Cheyenne, WY 82002
P: (307) 777-6738
F: (307) 777-6562
E: dfauss@state.wy.us

Port Authority

Agency housed under the department of transportation that oversees coastal transportation, international transportation, shipping, and all other acts involving state ports.

ALABAMA
Mr. James K. Lyons
Director/CEO
Port Authority
250 North Water Street
P.O. Box 1588
Mobile, AL 36633
P: (251) 441-7200
E: jlyons@asdd.com

GEORGIA
Mr. Curtis Foltz
Executive Director
Ports Authority
P.O. Box 2406
Savannah, GA 31402
P: (912) 964-3874
F: (912) 966-3615

HAWAII
Mr. Randy Grune
Deputy Director
Harbors Division
79 South Nimitz Highway
Honolulu, HI 96813
P: (808) 587-3651
F: (808) 587-3652
E: Randy.Grune@hawaii.gov

INDIANA
Mr. Rich Cooper
Chief Executive Officer
Ports of Indiana
150 West Market Street, Suite 100
Indianapolis, IN 46204
P: (317) 232-9202
F: (317) 232-0137
E: rcooper
    @portsofindiana.com

KANSAS
Ms. Debra L. Miller
Secretary
Department of Transportation
Eisenhower State Office Building
700 Harrison
Topeka, KS 66603
P: (785) 296-3461
F: (785) 296-1095

MAINE
Mr. John H. Henshaw
Executive Director
Port Authority
16 State House Station
Augusta, ME 04333
P: (207) 624-3564
F: (207) 624-3251
E: john.h.henshaw@maine.gov

MARYLAND
Mr. James J. White
Executive Director
Port Administration
World Trade Center
401 Pratt Street
Baltimore, MD 21202
P: (410) 385-4401
E: jjwhite
    @marylandports.com

MASSACHUSETTS
Mr. Thomas J. Kinton Jr.
CEO and Executive Director
Port Authority
One Harborside Drive, Suite 200S
East Boston, MA 02128
P: (617) 568-5000

MINNESOTA
Mr. Thomas Sorel
Commissioner
Department of Transportation
Transportation Building
395 John Ireland Boulevard
St. Paul, MN 55155
P: (651) 366-4800
F: (651) 366-4795
E: thomas.sorel
    @dot.state.mn.us

MISSISSIPPI
Mr. Mark L. McAndrews
Port Director
Pascagoula Port Authority
P.O. Box 70
Pascagoula, MS 39568
P: (228) 762-4041
F: (228) 762-7476
E: mmcandrews
    @portofpascagoula.com

NEW HAMPSHIRE
Mr. Geno Marconi
Director
Division of Ports & Harbors
555 Market Street
Portsmouth, NH 03801
P: (603) 436-8500
F: (603) 436-2780
E: g.marconi@peasedev.org

NEW YORK
Mr. Christopher O. Ward
Executive Director
The Port Authority of New York & New Jersey
225 Park Avenue South
New York, NY 10003
P: (212) 435-7000

NORTH CAROLINA
Mr. Thomas Eagar
Executive Director
State Ports Authority
2202 Burnett Boulevard
P.O. Box 9002
Wilmington, NC 28402
P: (910) 763-1621
F: (910) 763-6440

NORTHERN MARIANA ISLANDS
Mr. Edward M.
    Deleon Guerrero
Secretary
Commonwealth Ports Authority
P.O. Box 501055
Saipan, MP 96950
F: (670) 234-5962

OHIO
Mr. Jerry Wray
Director
Department of Transportation
1980 West Broad Street
Columbus, OH 43223
P: (614) 466-2335
F: (614) 4664-8662

OKLAHOMA
Mr. Robert W. Portiss
Director
Tulsa Port of Catoosa
5350 Cimarron Road
Catoosa, OK 74015
P: (918) 266-2291
F: (918) 266-7678
E: bob@tulsaport.com

Mr. Scott Robinson
Director
The Port of Muskogee
P.O. Box 2819
Muskogee, OK 74402
P: (918) 682-7886
F: (918) 683-4811
E: Scott@muskogeeport.com

SOUTH CAROLINA
Mr. James I. Newsome III
President and CEO
State Ports Authority
176 Concord Street
P.O.Box 22287
Charleston, SC 29413
P: (843) 577-8600
E: scspainfo@scspa.com

U.S. VIRGIN ISLANDS
Mr. Kenn Hobson
Executive Director
Port Authority
P.O. Box 301707
St. Thomas, VI 00803
P: (340) 774-1629
F: (340) 774-0025

UTAH
Mr. Richard A. Clasby
Director
Motor Carriers Division
Department of Transportation
4501 South 2700 West, P.O. Box 148240
Salt Lake City, UT 84114
P: (801) 965-4156
F: (801) 965-4847
E: RCLASBY@utah.gov

VIRGINIA
Mr. Jerry A. Bridges
Executive Director
Port Authority
600 World Trade Center
Norfolk, VA 23510
P: (757) 683-2103
F: (757) 683-8500
E: jbridges
    @portofvirginia.com

WEST VIRGINIA
Mr. David E. Cramer
Acting Director
Public Port Authority
1900 Kanawha Boulevard, East
Building 5, Room 125-A
Charleston, WV 25305
P: (304) 558-0330
F: (304) 558-0333
E: David.E.Cramer@wv.gov

WISCONSIN
Mr. Ron Adams
Director
Railroads & Harbors Bureau
P.O. Box 7914
Madison, WI 53707
P: (608) 266-2941
F: (608) 267-3567
E: ron.adams@dot.wi.gov

Public Defender

Represents indigent criminal defendants who desire to appeal their convictions to the state's intermediate appellate court or court of last resort.

ALASKA
Mr. Quinlan Steiner
Director
Public Defender Agency
Department of Administration
900 West 5th Avenue, Suite 200
Anchorage, AK 99501
P: (907) 334-4400
F: (907) 269-5746
E: quinlan.steiner
    @alaska.gov

ARKANSAS
Ms. Didi Sallings
Director
Public Defender Commission
101 East Capitol, Suite 201
Little Rock, AR 72201
P: (501) 682-9070
F: (501) 682-9073

CALIFORNIA
Mr. Michael J. Hersek
State Public Defender
Office of the State Public
Defender
221 Main Street, 10th Floor
San Francisco, CA 94105
P: (415) 904-5600
F: (415) 904-5635

COLORADO
Mr. Douglas Wilson
State Public Defender
Office of the State Public
Defender
110 16th Street
Petroleum Building, Suite 800
Denver, CO 80202
P: (303) 620-4888
F: (303) 620-4931

CONNECTICUT
Ms. Susan O. Storey
Chief Public Defender
Division of Public Defender
Services
30 Trinity Street, 4th Floor
Hartford, CT 06106
P: (860) 509-6429
E: susan.storey@jud.ct.gov

DELAWARE
Mr. Brendan O'Neill
Public Defender
Office of the Public Defender
Carvel State Office Building
820 North French Street, 3rd
Floor
Wilmington, DE 19801
P: (302) 577-5200
F: (302) 577-3995

DISTRICT OF COLUMBIA
Ms. Avis Buchanan
Director
Public Defender Service
633 Indiana Avenue, Northwest
Washington, DC 20004
P: (202) 628-1200
F: (202) 824-2423
E: abuchanan@pdsdc.org

FLORIDA
Mr. Sheldon Gusky
Executive Director
Public Defender Association
103 North Gadsden Street
P.O. Box 11057
Tallahassee, FL 32302
P: (850) 488-6850
F: (850) 488-4720
E: sgusky@st.flpda.org

GEORGIA
Hon. Sam S. Olens (R)
Attorney General
Office of the Attorney General
40 Capitol Square, Southwest
Atlanta, GA 30334
P: (404) 656-3300
F: (404) 657-8733

GUAM
Mr. Mike Nisperos
Executive Director
Public Defender Service
Corporation
Judicial Center, 2nd Floor
110 West O'Brien Drive
Agana, GU 96910
P: (671) 475-3100
F: (671) 477-5844
E: mnisperos@guampdsc.net

HAWAII
Mr. John M. Tonaki
Public Defender
Office of the Public Defender
1130 North Nimitz Highway
Suite A-254
Honolulu, HI 96817
P: (808) 586-2200
F: (808) 586-2222

IDAHO
Ms. Molly J. Huskey
State Appellate Public Defender
Appellate Public Defender
3647 Lake Harbor Lane
Boise, ID 83703
P: (208) 334-2712
F: (208) 334-2985
E: mhusky@sapd.state.id.us

ILLINOIS
Mr. Michael J. Pelletier
State Appellate Defender
Office of the State Appellate
Defender
400 West Monroe, Suite 202
P.O. Box 5240
Springfield, IL 62704
P: (217) 782-7203
F: (217) 782-5385
E: Michael.Pelletier
    @osad.state.il.us

IOWA
Mr. Tomas Rodriguez
State Public Defender
State Public Defender Office
Lucas Building, 4th Floor
321 East 12th Street
Des Moines, IA 50319
P: (515) 242-6158
F: (515) 281-7289
E: tomas.rodriguez
    @spd.state.ia.us

KANSAS
Ms. Patricia A. Scalia
Executive Director
Board of Indigents' Defense
Services
714 Southwest Jackson, Suite
200
Topeka, KS 66603
P: (785) 296-4505
F: (785) 291-3082

KENTUCKY
Mr. Edward C. Monahan
Public Advocate
Department of Public Advocacy
100 Fair Oaks Lane, Suite 302
Frankfort, KY 40601
P: (502) 564-8006
F: (502) 564-7890

LOUISIANA
Ms. Jean M. Faria
State Public Defender
Public Defender Board
5000 Laurel Street, Suite 300
Baton Rouge, LA 70801
P: (225) 219-9305
F: (225) 219-9326
E: jfaria@lpdb.la.gov

MARYLAND
Mr. Paul B. DeWolfe Jr.
Public Defender
Public Defender System
William Donald Schefer Tower
6 St. Paul Street, Suite 1400
Baltimore, MD 21202
P: (410) 767-8479
F: (410) 333-8496
E: pdewolfe@opd.state.md.us

MASSACHUSETTS
Mr. Anthony Benedetti
Chief Counsel
Public Defender Division
Committee for Public Counsel
Services
44 Bromfield Street
Boston, MA 02108
P: (617) 988-8322
F: (617) 988-8495

MICHIGAN
Mr. James Neuhard
Director
State Appellate Defender Office
Suite 3300, Penobscot Building
645 Griswald
Detroit, MI 48226
P: (313) 256-9833

MINNESOTA
Mr. John Stuart
State Public Defender
Office of the State Public
Defender
331 Second Avenue South, Suite
900
Minneapolis, MN 55401
P: (612) 279-3512
E: John.Stuart@state.mn.us

MISSOURI
Ms. Cathy R. Kelly
State Public Defender
State Public Defender System
Woodrail Centre
1000 West Nifong, Building 7,
Suite 100
Columbia, MO 65203
P: (573) 882-9855
F: (573) 882-9740
E: public.defender
    @mspd.mo.gov

MONTANA
Ms. Randi M. Hood
Chief Public Defender
Office of the State Public
Defender
44 West Park Street
Butte, MT 59701
P: (406) 496-6082
F: (406) 496-6098

NEBRASKA
Mr. James Mowbray
Chief Counsel
Commission on Public
Advocacy
P.O. Box 98932
Lincoln, NE 68509
P: (402) 471-7774
E: jmowbray@ncpa.ne.gov

NEVADA
Mr. Steven G. McGuire
State Public Defender
Office of the Public Defender
Department of Health & Human
Services
511 East Robinson Street, #1
Carson City, NV 89701
P: (775) 687-4880
F: (775) 687-4993
E: smcguire
@govmail.state.nv.us

NEW HAMPSHIRE
Mr. Christopher Keating
Executive Director
Public Defender
10 Ferry Street, Suite 202
Concord, NH 03301
P: (603) 224-1236
F: (603) 227-9367
E: ckeating@nhpd.org

NEW JERSEY
Ms. Yvonne Smith Segars
Public Defender
Office of the Public Defender
25 Market Street, 1st Floor
N-Wing
P.O. Box 850
Trenton, NJ 08625
P: (609) 292-7087
F: (609) 777-1795
E: thedefenders
@opd.state.nj.us

NEW MEXICO
Mr. Hugh Dangler
Chief Public Defender
Public Defender Department
301 North Guadalupe Street,
Suite 101
Santa Fe, NM 87501
P: (505) 827-3931
F: (505) 827-3999

NORTH CAROLINA
Mr. Thomas Maher
Executive Director
Office of Indigent Defense
Services
123 W. Main Street
Suite 400
Durham, NC 27701
P: (919) 560-3380
F: (919) 560-3332
E: Thomas.K.Maher
@nccourts.org

NORTH DAKOTA
Hon. Wayne Stenehjem (R)
Attorney General
Office of the Attorney General
State Capitol, Department 125
600 East Boulevard Avenue
Bismarck, ND 58505
P: (701) 328-2210
F: (701) 328-2226
E: wstenehjem@nd.gov

**NORTHERN MARIANA
ISLANDS**
Ms. Adam Hardwicke
Public Defender
Office of the Public Defender
Caller Box 10007, Capitol Hill
Saipan, MP 96950
P: (670) 234-2421
F: (670) 234-1009

OHIO
Mr. Timothy Young
Director
Office of the Public Defender
250 East Broad Street, Suite
1400
Columbus, OH 43215
P: (614) 466-5394
F: (614) 644-9972

OKLAHOMA
Mr. Joe P. Robertson
Executive Director
Indigent Defense System
P.O. Box 926
Norman, OK 73070
P: (405) 801-2601

OREGON
Ms. Ingrid Swenson
Executive Director
Office of Public Defense
Services
1320 Capitol Street, Northeast
Suite 200
Salem, OR 97303
P: (503) 378-2515
F: (503) 378-4462
E: Ingrid.Swenson
@opds.state.or.us

RHODE ISLAND
Mr. John J. Hardiman
Public Defender
Office of the Public Defender
160 Pine Street
Providence, RI 02903
P: (401) 222-3492
E: Information@ripd.org

SOUTH DAKOTA
Hon. Marty J. Jackley (R)
Attorney General
Office of the Attorney General
1302 East Highway 14,
Suite 1
Pierre, SD 57501
P: (605) 773-3215
F: (605) 773-4106
E: atghelp@state.sd.us

U.S. VIRGIN ISLANDS
Mr. Thurston McKelvin
Federal Public Defender
Office of the Public Defender
P.O. Box 3450
Christiansted
St. Croix, VI 00820
P: (340) 773-3585
F: (340) 773-3742

VERMONT
Mr. Matthew F. Valerio
Defender General
Office of the Defender General
6 Baldwin Street, 4th Floor
Montpelier, VT 05633
P: (802) 828-3168
F: (802) 828-3163
E: matthew.valerio
@state.vt.us

VIRGINIA
Mr. David J. Johnson
Executive Director
Indigent Defense Commission
1604 Santa Rosa Road, Suite
109
Richmond, VA 23229
P: (804) 662-7249
F: (804) 662-7359
E: djohnson
@idc.virginia.gov

WASHINGTON
Ms. Joanne Moore
Director
State Office of Public Defense
711 Capitol Way South, Suite
106
Evergreen Plaza Building, P.O.
Box 40957
Olympia, WA 98504
P: (360) 586-3164, Ext. 112
F: (360) 586-8165
E: opd@opd.wa.gov

WEST VIRGINIA
Mr. Russ Cook
Acting Executive Director
Public Defender Services
One Players Club Drive, Suite
301
Charleston, WV 25311
P: (304) 558-3905
F: (304) 558-1098
E: Russell.S.Cook@wv.gov

WISCONSIN
Ms. Kelli Thompson
State Public Defender
Office of the State Public
Defender
315 North Henry, 2nd Floor
Madison, WI 53707
P: (608) 266-0087
F: (608) 267-0584

WYOMING
Ms. Diane Lozano
State Public Defender
State Public Defenders Office
2020 Carey Avenue, 3rd Floor
Cheyenne, WY 82002
P: (307) 777-7137
F: (307) 777-6253

Public Lands

Manages state-owned lands.

ALABAMA
Ms. Patti Powell
Director
State Lands Division
64 North Union Street
Montgomery, AL 36130
P: (334) 242-3484
F: (334) 242-0999
E: patti.powell
   @dcnr.alabama.gov

ALASKA
Mr. Wyn Menefee
Acting Director
Division of Mining, Land &
Water
Department of Natural
Resources
550 West Seventh Avenue, Suite
1070
Anchorage, AK 99501
P: (907) 269-8600
F: (907) 269-8904
E: wyn.menefee@alaska.gov

ARIZONA
Ms. Maria Baier
State Land Commissioner
State Land Department
1616 West Adams Street
Phoenix, AZ 85007
P: (602) 542-4621

ARKANSAS
Hon. John Thurston
Commissioner of State Lands
Commissioner of State Lands
State Capitol, Room 109
Little Rock, AR 72201
P: (501) 324-9222
F: (501) 324-9421

CALIFORNIA
Mr. Jim Abbott
Acting Director
Bureau of Land Management
2800 Cottage Way, Suite
W-1623
Sacramento, CA 95825
P: (916) 978-4600
F: (916) 978-4416
E: Jim_Abbott@blm.gov

COLORADO
Mr. Bill Ryan
Director
Board of Land Commissioners
Department of Natural
Resources
1127 Sherman Street, Suite 300
Denver, CO 80203
P: (303) 866-3454
F: (303) 866-3152
E: bill.ryan@state.co.us

CONNECTICUT
Mr. Daniel C. Esty
Commissioner
Department of Environmental
Protection
79 Elm Street
Hartford, CT 06106
P: (860) 424-3009
F: (860) 424-4054
E: daniel.esty@ct.gov

DELAWARE
Mr. Charles A. Salkin
Director
Division of Parks & Recreation
89 Kings Highway
Dover, DE 19901
P: (302) 739-4401
F: (302) 739-3817
E: Charles.Salkin
   @state.de.us

DISTRICT OF COLUMBIA
Mr. Jesus Aguirre
Interim Director
Department of Parks &
Recreation
3149 16th Street, Northwest
Washington, DC 20010
P: (202) 673-7647
F: (202) 673-2087
E: dpr@dc.gov

FLORIDA
Mr. Mike Long
Assistant Director of State Lands
Department of Environmental
Protection
State Lands
3900 Commonwealth Boulevard,
M.S. 100
Tallahassee, FL 32399
P: (850) 245-2555
F: (850) 245-2572
E: mike.long
   @dep.state.fl.us

GEORGIA
Mr. Mark Williams
Commissioner
Department of Natural
Resources
2 Martin Luther King Jr. Drive
Southeast
Floyd Towers, Suite 1252 East
Atlanta, GA 30334
P: (404) 656-3500
F: (404) 656-0770
E: mark@markwilliams.com

HAWAII
Mr. William J. Aila Jr.
Chairperson
Department of Land & Natural
Resources
1151 Punchbowl Street
P.O. Box 621
Kapolei, HI 96809
P: (808) 587-0400
F: (808) 587-0390
E: dlnr@hawaii.gov

IDAHO
Mr. George Bacon
Director
Department of Lands
300 North 6th Street, Suite 103
P.O. Box 83720
Boise, ID 83720
P: (208) 334-0242
F: (208) 334-2339
E: gbacon@idl.idaho.gov

ILLINOIS
Mr. Tony Mayville
Director
Office of Land Management &
Education
Department of Natural
Resources
One Natural Resources Way
Springfield, IL 62702
P: (217) 782-1395
F: (217) 524-5612

INDIANA
Mr. Robert E. Carter Jr.
Director
Department of Natural
Resources
402 West Washington Street,
Room W256
Indianapolis, IN 46204
P: (317) 232-4020
F: (317) 233-6811
E: rcarter@dnr.IN.gov

IOWA
Mr. Roger L. Lande
Director
Department of Natural
Resources
East Ninth & Grand Avenue
Des Moines, IA 50319
P: (515) 281-5385
F: (515) 281-6794
E: roger.lande@dnr.iowa.gov

KANSAS
Mr. Robin Jennison
Secretary
Department of Wildlife & Parks
1020 South Kansas Avenue,
Room 200
Topeka, KS 66612
P: (785) 296-2281
F: (785) 296-6953

KENTUCKY
Dr. Jonathan Gassett
Commissioner
Department of Fish & Wildlife
Resources
One Sportsman's Lane
Frankfort, KY 40601
P: (502) 564-7109 Ext. 4555
F: (502) 564-6508

LOUISIANA
Mr. Charles St. Romain
Director
State Land Office
Division of Administration
P.O. Box 44124
Baton Rouge, LA 70804
P: (225) 342-4575
F: (225) 342-5458
E: charles.stromain@la.gov

MAINE
Mr. Will Harris
Director
Bureau of Parks & Lands
22 State House Station
18 Elkins Lane (AMHI Campus)
Augusta, ME 04333
P: (207) 287-3821
F: (207) 287-8111

MARYLAND
Ms. Kristin Saunders
Assistant Secretary for Land
Resources
Department of Natural
Resources
Tawes State Office Building, C4
580 Taylor Avenue
Annapolis, MD 21401
P: (410) 260-8106
F: (410) 260-8111
E: ksaunders
   @dnr.state.md.us

MASSACHUSETTS
Mr. Edward M. Lambert Jr.
Commissioner
Department of Conservation &
Recreation
20 Somerset Street
Boston, MA 02108
P: (617) 722-5500
F: (617) 727-0891

MICHIGAN
Mr. Ronald Olson
Chief
Parks & Recreation Division
P.O. Box 30257
Lansing, MI 48909
P: (517) 335-4827
F: (517) 373-4625
E: OLSONR@michigan.gov

MINNESOTA
Mr. Tom Landwehr
Commissioner
Department of Natural
Resources
500 Lafayette Road
P.O. Box 37
St. Paul, MN 55155
P: (651) 259-5022
F: (651) 296-4799
E: Tom.Landwehr@state.mn.us

MISSISSIPPI
Mr. Gerald McWhorter
Assistant Secretary of State for
Public Lands
Public Lands Division
P.O. Box 136
Jackson, MS 39205
P: (601) 359-6373
F: (601) 359-1461
E: gmcwhorter
    @sos.state.ms.us

MISSOURI
Mr. Bill Bryan
Director
Division of State Parks
P.O. Box 176
Jefferson City, MO 65102
P: (573) 751-9392
F: (573) 526-7716
E: Bill.Bryan@dnr.mo.gov

MONTANA
Ms. Mary Sexton
Director
Department of Natural
Resources & Conservation
1625 11th Avenue
P.O. Box 201601
Helena, MT 59620
P: (406) 444-2074
F: (406) 444-2684
E: msexton@mt.gov

NEBRASKA
Mr. Roger L. Kuhn
Assistant Director
Parks Division
Game & Parks Commission
P.O. Box 30370
Lincoln, NE 68503
P: (402) 471-5512
F: (402) 471-5528

NEVADA
Mr. James R. Lawrence
Administrator
Department of Conservation &
Natural Resources
State Lands Division
901 South Stewart, Suite 5003
Carson City, NV 89701
P: (775) 684-2720
F: (775) 684-2721
E: lawrence@lands.nv.gov

NEW HAMPSHIRE
Mr. Brad Simpkins
Director/State Forester
Division of Forests & Lands
P.O. Box 1856
Concord, NH 03302
P: (603) 271-2214
F: (603) 271-6488
E: brad.simpkins
    @dred.state.nh.us

NEW JERSEY
Mr. Dave Chanda
Director
Division of Fish & Wildlife
P.O. Box 400
Trenton, NJ 08625
P: (609) 292-9410
F: (609) 292-8207

NEW MEXICO
Mr. Ray Powell
Commissioner of Public Lands
State Land Office
310 Old Santa Fe Trail
P.O. Box 1148
Santa Fe, NM 87504
P: (505) 87-5760
F: (505) 827-5766

NEW YORK
Mr. Joe Martens
Commissioner
Department of Environmental
Conservation
625 Broadway, 14th Floor
Albany, NY 12233
P: (518) 402-8540
F: (518) 402-8541
E: joemartens
    @gw.dec.state.ny.us

**NORTHERN MARIANA
ISLANDS**
Rep. Oscar M. Babauta (C)
Secretary
Department of Public Lands
Caller Box 10007, Capital Hill
Saipan, MP 96950
P: (670) 234-3751
F: (670) 234-3755

OHIO
Mr. David Mustine
Director
Department of Natural
Resources
2045 Morse Road
Columbus, OH 43229
P: (614) 265-6565
F: (614) 261-9601

OKLAHOMA
Mr. Scott Thompson
Director
Land Protection Division
Department of Environmental
Quality
P.O. Box 1677
Oklahoma City, OK 73101
P: (405) 702-5100
F: (405) 702-5101
E: scott.thompson
    @deq.state.ok.us

OREGON
Ms. Louise Solliday
Director
Department of State Lands
775 Summer Street, Northeast
Suite 100
Salem, OR 97301
P: (503) 378-3805
F: (503) 378-4844
E: louise.c.solliday
    @state.or.us

PENNSYLVANIA
Mr. John W. Norbeck
Director
Bureau of State Parks
P.O. Box 8551
Harrisburg, PA 17105
P: (717) 787-6640
F: (717) 787-8817

RHODE ISLAND
Ms. Janet Coit
Director
Department of Environmental
Management
235 Promenade Street, 4th Floor
Providence, RI 02908
P: (401) 222-2771
F: (401) 222-6802
E: janet.coit@dem.ri.gov

SOUTH DAKOTA
Hon. Jarrod Johnson (R)
Commissioner
School & Public Lands
500 East Capital Avenue
Pierre, SD 57501
P: (605) 773-3303
F: (605) 773-5520

TENNESSEE
Mr. Julius Johnson
Commissioner
Department of Agriculture
Melrose Station
P.O. Box 40627
Nashville, TN 37204
P: (615) 837-5100
F: (615) 837-5333

TEXAS
Mr. Carter P. Smith
Executive Director
Parks & Wildlife Department
4200 Smith School Road
Austin, TX 78744
P: (512) 389-4802
F: (512) 389-4814

U.S. VIRGIN ISLANDS
Ms. Kim Aska
Manager
Property & Procurement
Division
5400 Veteran's Drive
St. Thomas, VI 00802
P: (340) 774-6680
F: (340) 776-9889

Mr. Kenn Hobson
Executive Director
Port Authority
P.O. Box 301707
St. Thomas, VI 00803
P: (340) 774-1629
F: (340) 774-0025

Mr. Robert Mathes
State Historic Preservation
Officer
Department of Planning &
Natural Resources
Cyril E. King Airport
Terminal Building - 2nd Floor
St. Thomas, VI 00802
P: (340) 776-8605
F: (340) 776-7236

Public Lands

UTAH
Mr. Richard J. Buehler
State Forester/Director
Division of Forestry, Fire &
State Lands
1594 West North Temple, Suite
3520
P.O. Box 145703
Salt Lake City, UT 84114
P: (801) 538-5389
F: (801) 533-4111
E: DICKBUEHLER@utah.gov

VERMONT
Ms. Deborah L. Markowitz
Secretary
Agency of Natural Resources
103 South Main Street
Center Building
Waterbury, VT 05671
P: (802) 241-3600
F: (802) 244-1102
E: deb.markowitz
  @state.vt.us

VIRGINIA
Mr. Richard F. Sliwoski
Director
Department of General Services
1100 Bank Street, Suite 420
Richmond, VA 23219
P: 804-786-3311
F: 804-371-8305
E: richard.sliwoski
  @dgs.virginia.gov

WASHINGTON
Hon. Peter J. Goldmark (D)
Commissioner of Public Lands
Department of Natural
Resources
1111 Washington Street,
Southeast
P.O. Box 47000
Olympia, WA 98504
P: (360) 902-1004
F: (360) 902-1775
E: cpl@dnr.wa.gov

WEST VIRGINIA
Mr. Joe T. Scarberry
Supervisor
Office of Land & Streams
Building 74, Room 200
324 Fourth Avenue
South Charleston, WV 25303
P: (304) 558-3225
F: (304) 558-6048
E: Joe.T.Scarberry@wv.gov

WISCONSIN
Ms. Tia Nelson
Executive Secretary
Board of Commissioners of
Public Lands
P.O. Box 8943
Madison, WI 53708
P: (608) 266-8369
F: (608) 267-2787
E: Tia.Nelson@wisconsin.gov

WYOMING
Mr. Ryan Lance
Director
Office of State Lands &
Investments
122 West 25th Street, 3rd Floor
West
Cheyenne, WY 82002
P: (307) 777-6629
F: (307) 777-5400
E: slfmail@wyo.gov

Public Safety

Provides information and services to insure the protection and safety of citizens and property.

ALABAMA
Colonel Hugh B. McCall
Director
Department of Public Safety
301 South Ripley Street
P.O. Box 1511
Montgomery, AL 36102
P: (334) 242-4394
F: (334) 242-0512
E: director@alalinc.net

ALASKA
Mr. Joseph A. Masters
Commissioner
Department of Public Safety
5700 East Tudor Road
P.O. Box 111200
Anchorage, AK 99811
P: (907) 269-5086
F: (907) 269-4543
E: joseph.masters
    @alaska.gov

AMERICAN SAMOA
Mr. Tuaolo M. Fruean
Commissioner
Department of Public Safety
American Samoa Government
P.O. Box 3699
Pago Pago, AS 96799
P: (684) 633-1111
F: (684) 633-7296

ARIZONA
Mr. Robert Halliday
Director
Department of Public Safety
2102 West Encanto Boulevard
P.O. Box 6638
Phoenix, AZ 85005
P: (602) 223-2000
F: (602) 223-2917

ARKANSAS
Col. Winford E. Phillips
Director
State Police
1 State Police Plaza Drive
Little Rock, AR 72209
P: (501) 618-8299
F: (501) 618-8222
E: winford.phillips
    @asp.arkansas.gov

CALIFORNIA
Ms. Peggy Okabayashi
Assistant Secretary
Emergency Management
Agency
3650 Schriever Avenue
Mather, CA 95655
P: (916) 845-8321
F: (916) 845-8394

COLORADO
Mr. James H. Davis
Executive Director
Department of Public Safety
700 Kipling Street, Suite 3000
Lakewood, CO 80215
P: (303) 239-4400
F: (303) 239-4670
E: Public.Safety
    @cdps.state.co.us

CONNECTICUT
Mr. Reuben Bradford
Commissioner
Department of Public Safety
1111 Country Club Road
Middletown, CT 06457
P: (860) 685-8000
F: (860) 685-8354
E: reuben.bradford@ct.gov

DELAWARE
Mr. Lewis D. Schiliro
Cabinet Secretary
Department of Safety &
Homeland Security
303 Transportation Circle
P.O. Box 818
Dover, DE 19903
P: (302) 744-2680
F: (302) 739-4874

DISTRICT OF COLUMBIA
Ms. Cathy L. Lanier
Chief of Police
Metropolitan Police Department
300 Indiana Avenue, Northwest
Washington, DC 20001
P: (202) 727-4218
F: (202) 727-9524
E: cathy.lanier@dc.gov

FLORIDA
Mr. Gerald M. Bailey
Commissioner
Department of Law
Enforcement
2331 Phillips Road
P.O. Box 1489
Tallahassee, FL 32302
P: (850) 410-7001
E: GeraldBailey
    @fdle.state.fl.us

GEORGIA
Col. Bill Hitchens
Commissioner
Department of Public Safety
959 East Confederate Avenue,
Southeast
P.O. Box 1456
Atlanta, GA 30371
P: (404) 624-7477
F: (404) 624-7788

GUAM
Mr. Paul Suba
Commander
Police Department
233 Central Avenue
Tiyan, GU 96913
P: (671) 475-8512
F: (671) 472-2825

HAWAII
Ms. Jodie F. Maesaka-Hirata
Director
Department of Public Safety
919 Ala Moana Boulevard,
Room 400
Honolulu, HI 96814
P: (808) 587-1288
F: (808) 587-1282

IDAHO
Col. Jerry Russell
Director
State Police
P.O. Box 700
Meridian, ID 83680
P: (208) 884-7003
F: (208) 884-7090
E: jerry.russell
    @isp.idaho.gov

ILLINOIS
Mr. Michael J. McCotter
Chief Public Safety Officer
Department of Corrections
P.O. Box 19277
Springfield, IL 62794
P: (217) 558-2200

INDIANA
Dr. Paul Whitesell
Superintendent
State Police
100 North Senate Avenue, Room
IGCN N340
Indianapolis, IN 46204
P: (317) 232-8241
E: pwhitesell@isp.in.gov

IOWA
Mr. Larry L. Noble
Commissioner
Department of Public Safety
215 East 7th Street
Des Moines, IA 50319
P: (515) 725-6182
E: noble@dps.state.ia.us

KANSAS
Maj. Gen. Lee E.
    Tafanelli (R)
Adjutant General
Adjutant General's Department
2800 South Topeka Boulevard
Topeka, KS 66611
P: (785) 274-1001
F: (913) 274-1682

KENTUCKY
Mr. J. Michael Brown
Secretary
Justice & Public Safety Cabinet
125 Holmes Street
Frankfort, KY 40601
P: (502) 564-7554
F: (502) 564-4840

LOUISIANA
Col. Michael D. Edmonson
Superintendent of State Police
Public Safety Services
7919 Independence Boulevard
Baton Rouge, LA 70806
P: (225) 925-6118
F: (225) 925-6006

Mr. James M. LeBlanc
Secretary
Department of Public Safety &
Corrections
504 Mayflower Street
P.O. Box 94304
Baton Rouge, LA 70804
P: (225) 342-6740
F: (225) 342-3095
E: jleblanc@asca.net

MAINE
Mr. John E. Morris
Commissioner
Department of Public Safety
45 Commerce Drive, Suite 1
104 State House Station
Augusta, ME 04333
P: (207) 626-3800
F: (207) 287-3042
E: john.e.morris@maine.gov

Public Safety

MARYLAND
Mr. Gary D. Maynard
Secretary
Department of Public Safety &
Correctional Services
300 East Joppa Road, Suite 1000
Towson, MD 21286
P: (410) 339-5005
F: (410) 339-4243
E: gmaynard
@dpscs.state.md.us

MASSACHUSETTS
Mr. Thomas G. Gatzunis
Commissioner
Department of Public Safety
One Ashburton Place, Suite
2133
Boston, MA 02108
P: (617) 727-7775
F: (617) 727-4764
E: thomas.gatzunis
@state.ma.us

MICHIGAN
Colonel Kriste Kibbey Etue
Director
State Police
714 South Harrison Road
East Lansing, MI 48823
P: (517) 336-6157
F: (517) 336-6551

MINNESOTA
Ms. Ramona Dohman
Commissioner
Department of Public Safety
Bremer Tower, Suite 1000
445 Minnesota Street
St. Paul, MN 55101
P: (651) 201-7160
F: (651) 297-5728
E: Mona.Dohman@state.mn.us

MISSISSIPPI
Mr. Albert Santa Cruz
Commissioner
Department of Public Safety
P.O. Box 958
Jackson, MS 39205
P: (601) 987-1212
F: (601) 987-1488
E: commissioner
@mdps.state.ms.us

MISSOURI
Mr. John M. Britt
Director
Department of Public Safety
P.O. Box 749
Jefferson City, MO 65102
P: (573) 751-4905
F: (573) 751-5399

MONTANA
Mr. Ed Tinsley
State Director
Disaster & Emergency Services,
Department of Military Affairs
1956 Mt. Majo Street
P.O. Box 4789
Fort Harrison, MT 59636
P: (406) 324-4777
F: (406) 841-3965
E: edtinsley@mt.gov

NEBRASKA
Colonel David Sankey
Superintendent of Law
Enforcement & Public Safety
State Police
P.O. Box 94907
Lincoln, NE 68509
P: (402) 471-4545
F: (402) 479-4002

NEVADA
Col. Chris Perry
Acting Director
Department of Public Safety
555 Wright Way
Carson City, NV 89711
P: (775) 684-4808
F: (775) 684-4809
E: cperry@dps.state.nv.us

NEW HAMPSHIRE
Mr. John J. Barthelmes
Commissioner
Department of Safety
James H. Hayes Safety Building
33 Hazen Drive
Concord, NH 03305
P: (603) 271-2791
F: (603) 271-3903
E: john.barthelmes
@dos.nh.gov

NEW JERSEY
Col. Rick Fuentes
Superintendent
State Police
P.O. Box 7068
West Trenton, NJ 08628
P: (609) 882-2000
F: (609) 530-4383

NEW MEXICO
Mr. Gorden E. Eden Jr.
Secretary
Department of Public Safety
4491 Cerrillos Road
P.O. Box 1628
Santa Fe, NM 87504
P: (505) 827-3370

NEW YORK
Mr. Sean M. Byrne
Acting Commissioner
Division of Criminal Justice
Services
4 Tower Place, 10th Floor
Albany, NY 12203
P: (518) 457-5837
F: (518) 473-1271

NORTH CAROLINA
Mr. Reuben Young
Secretary
Department of Crime Control &
Public Safety
4701 Mail Service Center
Raleigh, NC 27699
P: (919) 733-2126
F: (919) 715-8477
E: reuben.young@ncmail.net

NORTH DAKOTA
Colonel James Prochniak
Superintendent
Highway Patrol
600 East Boulevard Avenue
Department 504
Bismarck, ND 58505
P: (701) 328-2455
F: (701) 328-1717
E: jprochni@nd.gov

**NORTHERN MARIANA
ISLANDS**
Mr. Ramon Mafnas
Commissioner
Department of Public Safety
Caller Box 10007, Capitol Hill
Caller Box 10007, Capitol Hill
Saipan, MP 96950
P: (670) 664-9022
F: (670) 664-9027

OHIO
Mr. Thomas P. Charles
Director
Department of Public Safety
1970 West Broad Street
P.O. Box 182081
Columbus, OH 43223
P: (614) 466-3383
F: (614) 466-0433

OKLAHOMA
Mr. Michael C. Thompson
Secretary of Safety & Security
Department of Public Safety
P.O. Box 11415
Oklahoma City, OK 73136
P: (405) 425-2424

OREGON
Mr. Eriks Gabliks
Director
Department of Public Safety
Standards & Training
4190 Aumsville Highway,
Southeast
Salem, OR 97317
P: (503) 378-2332
F: (503) 378-2043
E: eriks.gabliks
@state.or.us

PENNSYLVANIA
Mr. Frank Noonan
Commissioner
State Police
3rd Floor, Department
Headquarters
1800 Elmerton Avenue
Harrisburg, PA 17110
P: (717) 783-5558
F: (717) 787-2948

PUERTO RICO
Mr. Jose Figueroa Sancha
Superintendent
Puerto Rico Police
P.O. Box 70166
San Juan, PR 00936
P: (787) 793-1234
F: (787) 781-0080

RHODE ISLAND
Colonel Steven G. O'Donnell
Superintendent
State Police
311 Danielson Pike
North Scituate, RI 02857
P: (401) 444-1000
F: (401) 444-1105
E: sodonnell
@risp.state.ri.us

SOUTH CAROLINA
Mr. Mark A. Keel
Director
Department of Public Safety
P.O. Box 1993
10311 Wilson Boulevard
Blythewood, SC 29016
P: (803) 896-7979
F: (803) 896-7881

SOUTH DAKOTA
Mr. Trevor Jones
Secretary
Department of Public Safety
118 West Capitol Avenue
Pierre, SD 57501
P: (605) 773-3178
F: (605) 773-3018
E: DPSInfo@state.sd.us

TENNESSEE
Mr. Bill Gibbons
Commissioner
Department of Safety &
Homeland Security
1150 Foster Avenue
P.O. Box 945
Nashville, TN 37202
P: (615) 251-5166
E: email.safety@tn.gov

TEXAS
Capt. Laurencio Saenz
Captain
Patrol & Security Operations
Department of Public Safety
5805 North Lamar
Austin, TX 78752
P: (512) 475-4821
F: (512) 305-9136

U.S. VIRGIN ISLANDS
Mr. Novelle E. Francis Jr.
Commissioner
Police Department
Alexander Farrelly Criminal
Justice Ctr.
Charlotte Amalie
St. Thomas, VI 00802
P: (340) 774-2211
F: (340) 715-5517

UTAH
Mr. D. Lance Davenport
Commissioner
Department of Public Safety
4501 South 2700 West
P.O. Box 141775
Salt Lake City, UT 84114
P: (801) 965-4464
F: (801) 965-4608
E: LDAVENPORT@utah.gov

VIRGINIA
Ms. Marla Graff Decker
Secretary of Public Safety
Office of the Secretary of Public
Safety
1111 East Broad Street
Patrick Henry Building
Richmond, VA 23219
P: (804) 786-5351
F: (804) 371-6381
E: marla.decker
@governor.virginia.gov

WASHINGTON
Mr. John R. Batiste
Chief
State Patrol
General Administration Building
P.O. Box 42600
Olympia, WA 98504
P: (360) 596-4101

WEST VIRGINIA
Mr. Joe Thornton
Cabinet Secretary
Department of Military Affairs
& Public Safety
Building 1, Room W-400
1900 Kanawha Boulevard, East
Charleston, WV 25305
P: (304) 558-2930
F: (304) 558-6221
E: joseph.c.thornton@wv.gov

WISCONSIN
Mr. Edward F. Wall
Administrator
Division of Criminal
Investigation
17 West Main Street
P.O. Box 7865
Madison, WI 53707
P: (608) 266-1221
F: (608) 267-2779
E: edward.wall
@wisconsin.gov

WYOMING
Lt. Col. Jess Oyler
Administrator
Highway Patrol
5300 Bishop Boulevard
Cheyenne, WY 82009
P: (307) 777-4301

Public Utility Regulation

Supervises and regulates the electric, gas, telephone and water utilities in the state.

Information provided by:

National Association of Regulatory Utility Commissioners
Charles D. Gray
Executive Director
1101 Vermont Avenue NW, Suite 200
Washington, DC 20005
P: (202) 898-2208
F: (202) 898-2213
cgray@naruc.org
www.naruc.org

ALABAMA
Ms. Lucy Baxley
President
Public Service Commission
100 North Union Street, Suite 850
Montgomery, AL 36104
P: (334) 242-5207
F: (334) 353-9246
E: lucy.baxley
@psc.alabama.gov

ALASKA
Mr. Robert Pickett
Chairman
Regulatory Commission of Alaska
701 West 8th Avenue, Suite 300
Anchorage, AK 99501
P: (907) 276-6222
F: (907) 276-0160
E: bob.pickett@alaska.gov

ARIZONA
Hon. Gary Pierce (R)
Chair
Corporation Commission
1200 West Washington Street
Phoenix, AZ 85007
P: (602) 542-3933
F: (602) 542-5560
E: gpierce@azcc.gov

ARKANSAS
Ms. Colette D. Honorable
Chair
Public Service Commission
P.O. Box 400
Little Rock, AR 72203
P: (501) 682-1455
F: (501) 683-3670
E: chonorable
@psc.state.ar.us

CALIFORNIA
Mr. Michael R. Peevey
President
Public Utilities Commission
California State Building
505 Van Ness Avenue
San Francisco, CA 94102
P: (415) 703-3703
F: (415) 703-5091
E: mp1@cpuc.ca.gov

COLORADO
Mr. Matt Baker
Commissioner
Public Utilities Commission
1560 Broadway, Suite 250
Denver, CO 80202
P: (303) 894-2007
F: (303) 894-2065
E: matt.baker
@dora.state.co.us

Mr. James K. Tarpey
Commissioner
Public Utilities Commission
1560 Broadway, Suite 250
Denver, CO 80202
P: (303) 894-2007
F: (303) 894-2065
E: james.tarpey
@dora.state.co.us

CONNECTICUT
Mr. Kevin DelGobbo
Chair
Department of Public Utility Control
10 Franklin Square
New Britain, CT 06051
P: (860) 827-2809
F: (334) 242-0921
E: kevin.delgobbo
@po.state.ct.us

DELAWARE
Ms. Arnetta McRae
Chair
Public Service Commission
861 Silver Lake Boulevard
Cannon Building, Suite 100
Dover, DE 19904
P: (302) 736-7535
F: (302) 739-4849
E: arnetta.mcrae
@state.de.us

DISTRICT OF COLUMBIA
Ms. Betty Ann Kane
Chair
Public Service Commission
1333 H Street Northwest
2nd Floor West Tower
Washington, DC 20005
P: (202) 626-5125
F: (202) 626-9212
E: bakane@psc.dc.gov

FLORIDA
Mr. Art Graham
Chair
Public Service Commission
2540 Shumard Oak Boulevard
Gerald Gunter Building
Tallahassee, FL 32399
P: (850) 413-6040
F: (850) 413-6025
E: art.graham
@psc.state.fl.us

GEORGIA
Mr. Stan Wise
Chair
Public Service Commission
244 Washington Street
Atlanta, GA 30334
P: (404) 657-4574
F: (404) 657-4576
E: stanwise@psc.state.ga.us

GUAM
Mr. Jeffrey C. Johnson
Chair
Public Utilities Commission
414 West Soledad Avenue, Suite 207
GCIC Building, P.O. Box 862
Hagatna, GU 96910
P: (334) 242-5207
F: (334) 242-0921
E: jjohnson@guampuc.com

HAWAII
Ms. Hermina M. Morita
Chair
Public Utilities Commission
465 South King Street
Kekuanao'a Building
Honolulu, HI 96813
P: (808) 586-2020
F: (808) 586-2066
E: hermina.m.morita
@hawaii.gov

IDAHO
Mr. Paul Kjellander
President
Public Utilities Commission
472 West Washington Street
P.O. Box 83720
Boise, ID 83720
P: (208) 334-0300
F: (208) 334-3762
E: paul.kjellander
@puc.idaho.gov

ILLINOIS
Mr. Douglas P. Scott
Director
Commerce Commission
160 North LaSalle Street, Suite C-800
Chicago, IL 60601
P: (312) 814-2850
F: (312) 814-1818
E: dscott@icc.illinois.gov

INDIANA
Mr. James D. Atterholt
Chair
Utility Regulatory Commission
PNC Center, Suite 1500 East
101 West Washington Street
Indianapolis, IN 46204
P: (317) 232-2704
F: (317) 232-6758
E: jatterholt@urc.in.gov

IOWA
Mr. Rob Berntsen
Chair
Utilities Board
1375 East Court Avenue, Room 69
Des Moines, IA 50319
P: (515) 281-5167
F: (515) 281-8821
E: rob.berntsen
@iub.iowa.gov

KANSAS
Mr. Thomas E. Wright
Chair
Corporation Commission
1500 Southwest Arrowhead Road
Topeka, KS 66604
P: (785) 271-3166
F: (785) 271-3354
E: t.wright@kcc.ks.gov

KENTUCKY
Mr. David Armstrong
Chair
Public Service Commission
211 Sower Boulevard
Frankfort, KY 40601
P: (502) 564-3940
F: (502) 564-8992
E: david.armstrong@ky.gov

LOUISIANA
Mr. James M. Field
Chair
Public Service Commission
P.O. Box 91154
602 North Fifth Street
Baton Rouge, LA 70821
P: (225) 342-6900
F: 225-342-6912
E: jimmyfield@cox.net

MAINE
Mr. Jack Cashman
Chairman
Public Utilities Commission
18 State House Station
Augusta, ME 04333
P: (207) 287-3831
F: (207) 287-1039
E: jamie.a.waterbury
@maine.gov

MARYLAND
Mr. Douglas R.M. Nazarian
Chair
Public Service Commission
16th Floor
6 St. Paul Street
Baltimore, MD 21202
P: (410) 767-8073
F: (410) 333-6495
E: dnazarian
@psc.state.md.us

MASSACHUSETTS
Ms. Ann Berwick
Chair
Department of Public Utilities
One South Station
Boston, MA 02110
P: (617) 305-3653
F: (617) 345-9102
E: ann.berwick@state.ma.us

Mr. Geoffrey G. Why
Commissioner
Department of
Telecommunications & Cable
1000 Washington Street, Suite
820
Boston, MA 02118
P: (617) 368-1109
F: (617) 988-8286
E: geoffrey.g.why
@state.ma.us

MICHIGAN
Mr. Orjiakor N. Isiogu
Chair
Public Service Commission
6545 Mercantile Way
Lansing, MI 48911
P: (517) 241-6190
F: (517) 241-6189
E: isioguo@michigan.gov

MINNESOTA
Ms. Ellen Anderson
Chair
Public Utilities Commission
121 Seventh Place East, Suite
350
St. Paul, MN 55101
P: (651) 201-2250
F: (651) 297-7073
E: ellen.anderson
@state.mn.us

MISSISSIPPI
Mr. Lynn Posey
Chair
Public Service Commission
501 North West Street
Woolfolk State Office Building
Jackson, MS 39201
P: (800) 356-6430
F: (601) 961-5824
E: lynn.posey
@psc.state.ms.us

MISSOURI
Mr. Kevin D. Gunn
Chair
Public Service Commission
200 Madison Street
Governor Office Building
Jefferson City, MO 65101
P: (573) 751-0946
F: (573) 526-7341
E: kevin.gunn@psc.mo.gov

MONTANA
Mr. Bill Gallagher
Chair
Public Service Commission
1701 Prospect Avenue
P.O. Box 202601
Helena, MT 59620
P: (406) 444-6169
F: (406) 444-7618
E: bgallagher@mt.gov

NEBRASKA
Mr. Gerald L. Vap
Chair
Public Service Commission
PO Box 94927
Lincoln, NE 68509
P: (402) 471-0216
F: (402) 471-0233
E: jerry.vap@nebraska.gov

NEVADA
Ms. Alaina C. Burtenshaw
Chair
Public Utilities Commission
1150 East William Street, Suite
250
Carson City, NV 89701
P: (702) 486-7234
F: (702) 486-7206
E: aburtens@puc.nv.gov

NEW HAMPSHIRE
Mr. Thomas B. Getz
Chair
Public Utilities Commission
21 South Fruit Street, Suite 10
Concord, NH 03301
P: (603) 271-2442
F: (334) 242-0921
E: tom.getz@puc.nh.gov

NEW JERSEY
Ms. Jeanne M. Fox
Commissioner
Board of Public Utilities
Two Gateway Center, 8th Floor
Newark, NJ 07102
P: (973) 648-2013
F: (973) 468-8514
E: jeanne.fox
@bpu.state.nj.us

Mr. Lee A. Solomon
President
Board of Public Utilities
Two Gateway Center, 8th Floor
Newark, NJ 07102
P: (973) 648-2026
E: lee.solomon
@bpu.state.nj.us

NEW MEXICO
Mr. Patrick H. Lyons
Chairman
Public Regulation Commission
1120 Paseo De Peralta
PERA Building
Santa Fe, NM 87501
P: (505) 827-4531
F: (505) 827-6522
E: patrick.lyons
@state.nm.us

NEW YORK
Mr. Garry A. Brown
Chair
Public Service Commission
Three Empire State Plaza
Albany, NY 12223
P: (518) 474-2523
F: (518) 486-1947
E: gary_brown
@dps.state.ny.us

NORTH CAROLINA
Mr. Edward S. Finley Jr.
Chair
Utilities Commission
4325 Mail Service Center
Raleigh, NC 27699
P: (919) 733-6067
F: (919) 733-7300
E: finley@ncuc.net

NORTH DAKOTA
Hon. Tony Clark (R)
Chairman
Public Service Commission
600 East Boulevard Avenue
Department 408
Bismarck, ND 58505
P: (701) 328-2400
F: (701) 328-2410
E: tclark@nd.gov

OHIO
Mr. Todd Snitchler
Chairman
Public Utilities Commission
180 East Broad Street
Columbus, OH 43215
P: (614) 466-3016
F: (614) 466-7366
E: todd.snitchler
@puc.state.oh.us

OKLAHOMA
Hon. Dana Murphy (R)
Chair
Corporation Commission
Jim Thorpe Office Building
2101 North Lincoln Boulevard
Oklahoma City, OK 73105
P: (405) 521-2267
F: (405) 522-1623
E: d.murphy@occemail.com

Public Utility Regulation

OREGON

Ms. Susan K. Ackerman
Commissioner
Public Utility Commission
550 Capitol Street, Northeast,
Suite 215
P.O. Box 2148
Salem, OR 97308
P: (503) 378-6611
F: (503) 378-5505
E: susan.ackerman
   @state.or.us

Mr. John Savage
Commissioner
Public Utility Commission
550 Capitol Street, Northeast,
Suite 215
P.O. Box 2148
Salem, OR 97308
P: (503) 378-6611
F: (503) 378-5505
E: John.F.Savage
   @State.Or.Us

PENNSYLVANIA

Mr. Robert F. Powelson
Chair
Public Utility Commission
400 North Street
Commonwealth Keystone
Building
Harrisburg, PA 17120
P: (717) 787-4301
F: (717) 783-8698
E: rfp@state.pa.us

PUERTO RICO

Mr. Jose H.
   Banuchi-Hernandez
Chair
Public Service Commission
P.O. Box 190870
San Juan, PR 00919
E: jbanuchi@csp.gobierno.pr

Ms. Sandra E. Torres-Lopez
President
Telecommunications Regulatory
Board
500 Avenue Roberto H. Todd
(Pda. 18-Santurce)
San Juan, PR 00907
P: (787) 756-0804
F: (787) 756-0814
E: sandra.torre
   @jrtpr.gobierno.pr

RHODE ISLAND

Mr. Elia Germani
Chair
Public Utilities Commission
89 Jefferson Boulevard
Warwick, RI 02888
P: (401) 941-4500
F: (401) 941-1691
E: egermani@puc.state.ri.us

SOUTH DAKOTA

Hon. Steve Kolbeck (D)
Chair
Public Utilities Commission
State Capitol
500 East Capitol Avenue
Pierre, SD 57501
P: (605) 773-3201
F: (866) 757-6031
E: steve.kolbeck
   @state.sd.us

Hon. Chris Nelson (R)
Commissioner
Public Utilities Commission
State Capitol
500 East Capitol Avenue
Pierre, SD 57501
P: (605) 773-3201
F: (866) 757-6031
E: Chris.Nelson@state.sd.us

TENNESSEE

Ms. Mary Freeman
Chair
Regulatory Authority
460 James Robertson Parkway
Nashville, TN 37243
P: (615) 741-3668
F: (615) 532-4698
E: mary.w.freeman@tn.gov

TEXAS

Mr. Barry T. Smitherman
Chair
Public Utility Commission
P.O. Box 13326
Austin, TX 78711
P: (512) 936-7025
F: (512) 936-7028
E: barry.smitherman
   @puc.state.tx.us

U.S. VIRGIN ISLANDS

Mr. Donald G. Cole
Chairman
Public Service Commission
P.O. Box 40
Charlotte Amalie
St. Thomas, VI 00804
P: (340) 774-4603
F: (340) 774-4971
E: duxcole@gmail.com

UTAH

Mr. Ted Boyer
Chair
Public Service Commission
160 East 300 South, 4th Floor
Salt Lake City, UT 84111
P: (801) 530-6716
F: (801) 530-6796
E: tboyer@utah.gov

VERMONT

Ms. Elizabeth H. Miller
Commissioner
Department of Public Service
112 State Street
Montpelier, VT 05620
P: (802) 828-4071
F: (802) 828-2342
E: elizabeth.miller
   @state.vt.us

Mr. James Volz
Chair
Public Service Board
112 State Street, 4th Floor
Montpelier, VT 05620
P: (802) 828-2358
F: (802) 828-3351
E: james.volz@state.vt.us

VIRGINIA

Ms. Judith W. Jagdmann
Chairman
State Corporation Commission
P.O. Box 1197
Richmond, VA 23218
P: (804) 371-9608
F: (804) 371-9376
E: commissioners
   @scc.virginia.gov

WASHINGTON

Mr. Jeffrey D. Goltz
Chair
Utilities & Transportation
Commission
1300 South Evergreen Park
Drive
P.O. Box 47250
Olympia, WA 98504
P: (360) 664-1173
F: (360) 586-1150
E: jgoltz@utc.wa.gov

WEST VIRGINIA

Mr. Michael A. Albert
Chair
Public Service Commission
201 Brooks Street
Charleston, WV 25301
P: (304) 340-0306
F: (304) 340-3758
E: malbert@psc.state.wv.us

WISCONSIN

Mr. Phil Montgomery
Chair
Public Service Commission
P.O. Box 7854
Madison, WI 53707
P: (608) 266-5481
F: (608) 266-1401
E: phil.montgomery
   @wisconsin.gov

WYOMING

Mr. Alan B. Minier
Chair
Public Service Commission
2515 Warren Avenue, Suite 300
Cheyenne, WY 82002
P: (307) 777-5725
F: (307) 777-5700
E: aminie@state.wy.us

Purchasing

Central screening and acquisition point for supplies, equipment, and/or services for state agencies.

ALABAMA
Mr. Michael Jones
State Purchasing Director
Department of Finance
Division of Purchasing
100 North Union Street, Suite 192
Montgomery, AL 36104
P: (334) 242-7250
F: (334) 242-4419
E: michael.jones
   @purchasing.alabama.gov

ALASKA
Mr. Vern Jones
Chief Procurement Officer
Division of General Services
Department of Administration
P.O. Box 110210
Juneau, AK 99801
P: (907) 465-5684
F: (907) 465-2189
E: vern.jones@alaska.gov

ARIZONA
Ms. Jean Clark
State Procurement Administrator
State Procurement Office
Department of Administration
100 North 15th Avenue, Suite 201
Phoenix, AZ 85007
P: (602) 542-9136
F: (602) 542-5508
E: jean.clark@azdoa.gov

ARKANSAS
Ms. Jane Benton
Director
Office of State Procurement
Department of Finance & Administration
1509 West 7th Street
Little Rock, AR 72201
P: (501) 324-9312
F: (501) 324-9311
E: jane.benton
   @dfa.arkansas.gov

CALIFORNIA
Mr. Jim Butler
Chief Procurement Officer
Department of General Services
Procurement Division
707 Third Street, Floor 2
West Sacramento, CA 95605
P: (916) 375-4417
F: (916) 375-4421
E: jim.butler@dgs.ca.gov

COLORADO
Mr. John Utterback
Purchasing Director
Division of Finance & Procurement
Department of Personnel & Administration
633 17th Street, Suite 1520
Denver, CO 80202
P: (303) 866-6181
F: (303) 866-6016
E: john.utterback
   @state.co.us

CONNECTICUT
Ms. Carol Wilson
Director of Procurement Programs & Services
Department of Administrative Services
Procurement Services
165 Capitol Avenue, Floor 5 South
Hartford, CT 06106
P: (860) 713-5093
F: (860) 622-2904
E: carol.wilson@ct.gov

DELAWARE
Mr. Dean W. Stotler
Director
Government Support Services
Office of Management & Budget
100 Enterprise Place, Suite 4
Dover, DE 19904
P: (302) 857-4501
F: (302) 739-2564
E: dean.stotler@state.de.us

DISTRICT OF COLUMBIA
Mr. James Staton
Director
Office of Contracting & Procurement
441 4th Street, Northwest
Suite 700S
Washington, DC 20001
P: (202) 724-4242
E: james.staton@dc.gov

FLORIDA
Ms. Ellen Potts
Bureau Chief
Transportation, Facilities & Supplies
Department of Management Services
4050 Esplanade Way, Suite 360
Tallahassee, FL 32399
P: (850) 488-2773
F: (850) 414-6122
E: ellen.potts
   @dms.myflorida.com

GEORGIA
Mr. Timothy Gibney
Assistant Commissioner
State Purchasing Division
Department of Administrative Services
200 Piedmont Avenue, Southeast, 1308
Atlanta, GA 30334
P: (404) 656-0934
F: (770) 344-4903
E: tim.gibney@doas.ga.gov

HAWAII
Mr. Aaron Fujioka
Administrator
Department of Accounting & General Services
State Procurement Office
1151 Punchbowl Street, Room 230A
Honolulu, HI 96813
P: (808) 587-4700
F: (808) 587-4703
E: aaron.fujioka@hawaii.gov

IDAHO
Mr. Bill Burns
Administrator
Department of Administration
Division of Purchasing
P.O. Box 83720
Boise, ID 83720
P: (208) 332-1610
F: (208) 327-7320
E: bill.burns@adm.idaho.gov

ILLINOIS
Mr. Matt Brown
Chief Procurement Officer
Executive Ethics Commission
401 South Spring Street
William G. Stratton Building, Room 301
Springfield, IL 62706
P: (217) 558-5373
E: matt.brown@illinois.gov

INDIANA
Ms. Jessica Robertson
Deputy Commissioner
Division of Procurement
Department of Administration
402 West Washington Street, Room W468
Indianapolis, IN 46204
P: (317) 234-5906
F: (317) 232-7312
E: jrobertson@idoa.in.gov

IOWA
Ms. Debbie O'Leary
Division Administrator
DAS Procurement Services
1305 East Walnut, Level A
Des Moines, IA 50319
P: (515) 281-8384
F: (515) 242-5974
E: debbie.oleary@iowa.gov

KANSAS
Mr. Chris Howe
Director of Purchases
Department of Administration
Division of Purchases
900 Southwest Jackson, Room 102N
Topeka, KS 66612
P: (785) 296-2374
F: (785) 296-7240
E: chris.howe@da.ks.gov

KENTUCKY
Mr. Donald Speer
Executive Director
Office of Procurement Services
Finance & Administration Cabinet
702 Capitol Annex, Room 096
Frankfort, KY 40601
P: (502) 564-4510
E: don.speer@ky.gov

LOUISIANA
Ms. Denise Lea
Director
Office of State Purchasing & Travel
1201 North 3rd Street, Suite 2-160
Baton Rouge, LA 70802
P: (225) 342-8057
F: (225) 342-8688
E: denise.lea@la.gov

Purchasing

MAINE
Ms. Betty Lamoreau
Acting Director
Division of Purchases
77 State House Station
Augusta, ME 04333
P: (207) 624-7314
F: (207) 624-5086
E: Betty.M.Lamoreau
@maine.gov

MARYLAND
Mr. Michael Haifley
Director of Procurement
Department of General Services
301 West Preston Street
State Office Building, Room
M-10
Baltimore, MD 21201
P: (410) 767-4429
F: (410) 333-5164
E: michael.haifley
@dgs.state.md.us

MASSACHUSETTS
Mr. Gary Lambert
Assistant Secretary for
Operational Services
Executive Office for
Administration & Finance
Operational Services Division
One Ashburton Place, Room
1017
Boston, MA 02108
P: (617) 720-3330
F: (617) 727-4527
E: gary.lambert@state.ma.us

MICHIGAN
Mr. Anthony Des Chenes
Director, Commodities Division
Department of Management &
Budget
Purchasing Operations
530 West Allegan Street
Lansing, MI 48909
P: (517) 373-9417
F: (517) 335-0046
E: deschenesa1@michigan.gov

MINNESOTA
Mr. Kent Allin
Chief Procurement Officer
Materials Management Division
Department of Administration
50 Sherburne Avenue, Suite 112
St. Paul, MN 55155
P: (651) 201-2400
F: (651) 297-3996
E: kent.allin@state.mn.us

MISSISSIPPI
Mr. Milo Crabtree
Director of Purchasing, Travel &
Fleet Management
Office of Purchasing & Travel
701 Woolfolk Building, Suite A
501 North West Street
Jackson, MS 39201
P: (601) 359-2007
F: (601) 359-3910
E: crabtrm@dfa.state.ms.us

MISSOURI
Mr. Jim Miluski
Director
Division of Purchasing &
Materials Management
Department of Administration
P.O. Box 809
Jefferson City, MO 65102
P: (573) 751-3273
F: (573) 526-9815
E: jim.miluski@oa.mo.gov

MONTANA
Mr. Marvin Eicholtz
Administrator
General Services Division
Department of Administration
P.O. Box 200110
Helena, MT 59620
P: (406) 444-3119
F: (406) 444-3039
E: meicholtz@mt.gov

NEBRASKA
Ms. Brenda Pape
Procurement Manager
State Purchasing Bureau
301 Centennial Mall South,
Floor 1
P.O. Box 94847
Lincoln, NE 68509
P: (402) 471-0970
F: (402) 471-2089
E: Brenda.Pape@Nebraska.gov

NEVADA
Mr. Greg Smith
Administrator
Purchasing Division
Department of Administration
515 East Musser Street, Suite
300
Carson City, NV 89701
P: (775) 684-0170
F: (775) 684-0188
E: gmsmith
@purchasing.state.nv.us

NEW HAMPSHIRE
Mr. Robert Stowell
Administrator
Bureau of Purchase & Property
State House Annex, Room 102
25 Capitol Street
Concord, NH 03301
P: (603) 271-3606
F: (603) 271-2700
E: robert.stowell@nh.gov

NEW JERSEY
Jignasa Desai-McCleary
Acting Director
Division of Purchase & Property
P.O. Box 039
Trenton, NJ 08625
P: (609) 292-4886
F: (609) 984-2575
E: robert.beauregard
@treas.state.nj.us

NEW MEXICO
Mr. Michael Vinyard
State Purchasing Agent
Purchasing Division
General Services Department
1100 St. Francis Drive, Room
2016
Santa Fe, NM 87505
P: (505) 827-0472
F: (505) 827-2484
E: michael.vinyard
@state.nm.us

NEW YORK
Mr. Don Greene
Acting Director
Procurement Services Group
Corning Tower Floor 38
Empire State Plaza
Albany, NY 12242
P: (518) 474-3695
F: (518) 486-6099
E: don.greene
@ogs.state.ny.us

NORTH CAROLINA
Mr. Sam Byassee
Director of Purchase &
Contracts
Division of Purchase & Contract
1305 Mail Service Center
Raleigh, NC 27699
P: (919) 275-0440
E: sam.byassee@nc.gov

NORTH DAKOTA
Ms. Sherry Neas
State Procurement Officer
Central Services Division
Capitol Tower, Floor 14
600 East Boulevard Avenue
Bismarck, ND 58505
P: (701) 328-1726
F: (701) 328-1615
E: sneas@nd.gov

OHIO
Mr. Jeffrey Westhoven
Administrator, State Purchasing
Department of Administrative
Services
Office of Procurement Services
4200 Surface Road
Columbus, OH 43228
P: (614) 995-3258
F: (614) 466-1040
E: jeff.westhoven
@das.state.oh.us

OKLAHOMA
Mr. Scott Schlotthauer
State Purchasing Director
Central Purchasing Division
Will Rogers Office Building
2401 North Lincoln Street, Suite
116
Oklahoma City, OK 73152
P: (405) 521-2115
F: (405) 521-4475
E: scott_schlotthauer
@dcs.state.ok.us

OREGON
Ms. Dianne Lancaster
Chief Procurement Officer
Division of Purchasing
Department of Administrative
Services
1225 Ferry Street, Southeast,
U140
Salem, OR 97301
P: (503) 378-3529
F: (503) 373-1626
E: dianne.lancaster
@das.state.or.us

PENNSYLVANIA
Mr. Michael Richart
Chief Procurement Officer
Department of General Services
Bureau of Procurement
555 Walnut Street, Floor 6
Harrisburg, PA 17101
P: (717) 787-5862
F: (717) 214-9505
E: mirichart@state.pa.us

RHODE ISLAND
Ms. Lorraine A. Hynes
Acting Director
Division of Purchases
Department of Administration
One Capitol Hill
Providence, RI 02908
P: (401) 574-8100
E: LHynes
@purchasing.state.ri.us

SOUTH CAROLINA
Mr. Voight Shealy
Materials Management Officer
Materials Management Office
Budget & Control Board
1201 Main Street, Suite 600
Columbia, SC 29201
P: (803) 737-0635
F: (803) 737-0639
E: vshealy@mmo.sc.gov

SOUTH DAKOTA
Mr. Jeff T. Holden
Procurement Director
Office of Procurement
Management
523 East Capitol Avenue, PMB
01231
Pierre, SD 57501
P: (605) 773-4280
F: (605) 773-4840
E: jeff.holden@state.sd.us

TENNESSEE
Mr. John Bissell
Director of Purchasing
Purchasing Division
Department of General Services
665 Mainstream Drive
Nashville, TN 37243
P: (615) 741-4302
F: (615) 532-8795
E: john.bissell@tn.gov

TEXAS
Mr. Ron Pigott
Director
Procurement & Support
Services
Comptroller of Public Accounts
P.O. Box 13186
Austin, TX 78711
P: (512) 463-5038
F: (512) 475-0851
E: ron.pigott
@cpa.state.tx.us

UTAH
Mr. Kent Beers
Director of Purchasing
Department of Administrative
Services
3140 State Office Building,
Capitol Hill
P.O. Box 141061
Salt Lake City, UT 84114
P: (801) 538-3143
F: (801) 538-3882
E: kbeers@utah.gov

VERMONT
Ms. Deb Damore
Chief Procurement Officer
Office of Purchasing &
Contracting
10 Baldwin Street
Montpelier, VT 05633
P: (802) 828-5784
F: (802) 828-2222
E: deborah.damore
@state.vt.us

VIRGINIA
Mr. Ron Bell
Director
Division of Purchases & Supply
1111 East Broad Street
Patrick Henry Building, Floor 6
Richmond, VA 23218
P: (804) 786-3846
F: (804) 371-7877
E: ron.bell
@dgs.virginia.gov

WASHINGTON
Ms. Christine Warnock
Chief Procurement Officer
Office of State Procurement
Department of General
Administration
210 11th Avenue, Southwest,
Room 201
Olympia, WA 98504
P: (360) 902-7417
F: (360) 586-2426
E: cwarnoc@ga.wa.gov

WEST VIRGINIA
Mr. David R. Tincher
Director
Purchasing Division
Department of Administration
2019 Washington Street, East
Charleston, WV 25305
P: (304) 558-2538
F: (304) 558-0006
E: david.tincher@wv.gov

WISCONSIN
Ms. Helen McCain
Administrator
Department of Administration
Division of Enterprise
Operations
101 East Wilson Street, Floor 6
Madison, WI 53703
P: (608) 267-9634
F: (608) 267-0600
E: helen.mccain
@wisconsin.gov

WYOMING
Ms. Lori Galles
Interim Procurment Manager
Procurement Division
Herschler Building, Floor 2,
East
Cheyenne, WY 82002
P: (307) 777-6707
F: (307) 777-5852
E: lgalle@wyo.gov

Recycling

Responsible for promoting and implementing state oversight of municipal solid waste recycling, source reduction and recycling within state government and industry.

ALABAMA
Mr. Lance LeFleur
Director
Department of Environmental Management
1400 Coliseum Boulevard
P.O. Box 301463
Montgomery, AL 36130
P: (334) 271-7710
F: (334) 271-7950

ARIZONA
Ms. Amanda Stone
Waste Programs Division Director
Department of Environmental Quality
ADEQ Central Office
1110 West Washington Street
Phoenix, AZ 85007
P: (602) 771-4567
F: (602) 771-2302
E: stone.amanda@azdeq.gov

ARKANSAS
Mr. Roger Lawrence
Chief
Solid Waste Division
P.O. Box 8913
Little Rock, AR 72209
P: (501) 682-0600
F: (501) 682-0611
E: lawrence
    @adeq.state.ar.us

CALIFORNIA
Ms. Margo Reid Brown
Acting Director
Department of Resources Recycling & Recovery
801 K Street, MS 19-01
Sacramento, CA 95814
P: (916) 322-4032
F: (916) 327-2144
E: Margo.Reid.Brown
    @CalRecycle.ca.gov

Mr. Mark Leary
Acting Director
Department of Resources, Recycling & Recovery
1001 I Street
P.O. Box 4025
Sacramento, CA 95812
P: (916) 341-6544
F: (916) 319-7319
E: Mark.Leary
    @CalRecycle.ca.gov

COLORADO
Mr. Gary Baughman
Director
Hazardous Materials & Waste Management Division
Dept. of Public Health & Environment
Denver, CO 80246
P: (303) 692-3320
F: (303) 759-5355
E: comments.hmwnd
    @state.co.us

CONNECTICUT
Mr. Richard J. Barlow
Bureau Chief
Waste Bureau
Department of Environmental Protection
79 Elm Street
Hartford, CT 06106
P: (860) 424-3021
F: (860) 424-4060

DELAWARE
Mr. Pasquale S. Canzano
Chief Executive Officer
Solid Waste Authority
1128 South Bradford Street
P.O. Box 455
Dover, DE 19903
P: (302) 739-5361
F: (302) 739–4287
E: info@dswa.com

DISTRICT OF COLUMBIA
Mr. William O. Howland Jr.
Director
Department of Public Works
2000 14th Street, Northwest, 6th Floor
Washington, DC 20009
P: (202) 673-6833
F: (202) 671-0642
E: dpw@dc.gov

FLORIDA
Mr. Jorge Caspary
Director
Division of Waste Management
Department of Environmental Protection
2600 Blairstone Road, MS 4500
Tallahassee, FL 32399
P: (850) 245-8693
E: jorge.caspary
    @dep.state.fl.us

GEORGIA
Mr. Kevin Clark
Executive Director
Environmental Finance Authority
233 Peachtree Street, Northwest
Peachtree Center, Harris Tower
Suite 900
Atlanta, GA 30303
P: (404) 584-1000
F: (404) 584-1069

GUAM
Ms. Joanne Brown
Director
Department of Public Works
542 North Marine Drive
Tamuning, GU 96913
P: (671) 646-3131
F: (671) 649-6178
E: joanne.brown
    @dpw.guam.gov

HAWAII
Mr. Gary Gill
Deputy Director for Environmental Health
Department of Health
1250 Punchbowl Street, 3rd Floor
Honolulu, HI 96801
P: (808) 586-4424
F: (808) 586-4368
E: gary.gill@doh.hawaii.gov

IDAHO
Ms. Toni Hardesty
Director
Department of Environmental Quality
1410 North Hilton
Boise, ID 83706
P: (208) 373-0240
F: (208) 373-0417
E: toni.hardesty
    @deq.idaho.gov

ILLINOIS
Mr. Warren Ribley
Director
Department of Commerce & Economic Opportunity
James R. Thompson Center
100 West Randolph
Chicago, IL 60601
P: (312) 814-7179

INDIANA
Ms. Monica Hartke-Tarr
Director
Office of Compliance Support/Planning & Assessment
Department of Environmental Management
100 North Senate Avenue, Room IGCN 1301
Indianapolis, IN 46204
P: (317) 233-5431
E: mhartke@idem.in.gov

KANSAS
Mr. William L. Bider
Director
Bureau of Waste Management
1000 Southwest Jackson Street
Suite 320
Topeka, KS 66612
P: (785) 296-1600
F: (785) 296-8909

KENTUCKY
Mr. Anthony Hatton
Division Director
Division of Waste Management
Department for Environmental Protection
200 Fair Oaks Lane
Frankfort, KY 40601
P: (502) 564-6716
F: (502) 564-4049
E: tony.hatton@ky.gov

LOUISIANA
Mr. Lourdes Iturralde
Administrator
Public Participation & Permits Support Services
Department of Environmental Quality
P.O. Box 4313
Baton Rouge, LA 70821
P: (225) 219-3180
F: (225) 219-3309

MAINE
Mr. Sam Morris
Senior Planner
Waste Management &
Recycling Program
State Planning Office
38 State House Station
Augusta, ME 04333
P: (207) 287-8054
F: (207) 287-6489
E: sam.morris@maine.gov

MARYLAND
Ms. Hilary Miller
Program Administrator
Technical Services & Operating
Program
Department of the Environment
1800 Washington Boulevard
Baltimore, MD 21230
P: (410) 537-3314
F: (410) 537-3321
E: hmiller@mde.state.md.us

MASSACHUSETTS
Mr. Rick Sullivan
Commissioner
Executive Office of Energy &
Environmental Affairs
100 Cambridge Street, Suite 900
Boston, MA 02114
P: (614) 626-1000
F: (614) 626-1181

MICHIGAN
Ms. Amy A. Butler
Chief
Environmental Science &
Services Division
525 West Allegan Street
P.O. Box 30473
Lansing, MI 48909
P: (517) 241-0490
E: BUTLERA1@michigan.gov

MINNESOTA
Mr. Spencer Cronk
Commissioner
Department of Administration
50 Sherburne Avenue
200 Administration Building
St. Paul, MN 55155
P: (651) 201-2555
F: (651) 297-7909
E: Spencer.Cronk
@state.mn.us

MISSISSIPPI
Mr. John D. Burns
Management
Recycling & Solid Waste
Reduction Program
P.O. Box 10385
Jackson, MS 39289
P: (601) 961-5005
F: (601) 961-5703
E: John_D_Burns
@deg.state.ms.us

MISSOURI
Mr. Chris Nagel
Program Director
Solid Waste Management
Program
P.O. Box 176
Jefferson City, MO 65102
P: (573) 526-3900
F: (573) 526-3902
E: swmp@dnr.mo.gov

MONTANA
Hon. Janet Kelly
Director
Department of Administration
125 North Roberts Street
Room 155, Mitchell Building
Helena, MT 59620
P: (406) 444-3033
F: (406) 444-6194
E: jakelly@mt.gov

NEBRASKA
Mr. Michael J. Linder
Director
Department of Environmental
Quality
1200 N Street, Suite 400
P.O. Box 98922
Lincoln, NE 68509
P: (402) 471-3585
F: (402) 471-2909
E: mike.linder@nebraska.gov

NEVADA
Mr. Eric Noack
Bureau Chief
Bureau of Waste Management
Division of Environmental
Protection
901 South Stewart Street, Suite
4001
Carson City, NV 89701
P: (775) 687-9366
F: (775) 687-6396
E: enoack@ndep.nv.gov

NEW HAMPSHIRE
Mr. Thomas S. Burack
Commissioner
Department of Environmental
Services
29 Hazen Drive
P.O. Box 95
Concord, NH 03302
P: (603) 271-2958
F: (603) 271-2867
E: thomas.burack@des.nh.gov

NEW JERSEY
Mr. Guy Watson
Bureau Chief
Bureau of Recycling & Planning
Departmant of Environmental
Protection
P.O. Box 402
Trenton, NJ 08625
P: (609) 984-3438
F: (609) 633-1112
E: Guy.Watson
@dep.state.nj.us

NEW MEXICO
Ms. Auralie Ashley-Marx
Bureau Chief
Solid Waste Bureau
P.O. Box 26110
1190 St. Francis Drive, Room
S2050
Santa Fe, NM 87502
P: (505) 827-0197
F: (505) 827-2902
E: auralie.ashley-marx
@state.nm.us

NEW YORK
Mr. Salvatore Ervolina
Director
Division of Materials
Management
625 Broadway
Albany, NY 12233
P: (518) 402-8651
F: (518) 402-9024
E: dshm@gw.dec.state.ny.us

NORTH CAROLINA
Ms. Patricia Scurlock
Recycling Coordinator
Department of Administration
Facility Management Division
1313 Mail Service Center
Raleigh, NC 27699
P: (919) 733-3855
F: (919) 733-1430
E: patricia.scurlock
@doa.nc.gov

NORTH DAKOTA
Mr. Scott Radig
Director
Division of Waste Management
Department of Health
918 East Divide Avenue, 3rd
Floor
Bismark, ND 58501
P: (701) 328-5166
F: (701) 328-5200
E: sradig@nd.gov

**NORTHERN MARIANA
ISLANDS**
Mr. Martin C. Sablan
Department of Public Works
Caller Box 10007, Capitol Hill
Saipan, MP
P: (670) 235-5827
F: (670) 235-6346

OHIO
Mr. David Mustine
Director
Department of Natural
Resources
2045 Morse Road
Columbus, OH 43229
P: (614) 265-6565
F: (614) 261-9601

OKLAHOMA
Mr. Scott Thompson
Director
Land Protection Division
Department of Environmental
Quality
P.O. Box 1677
Oklahoma City, OK 73101
P: (405) 702-5100
F: (405) 702-5101
E: scott.thompson
@deq.state.ok.us

OREGON
Ms. Robin Kirkpatrick
Statewide
Sustainability/Resource
Coordinator
Department of Administration
1225 Ferry Street, Southeast
U100
Salem, OR 97301
P: (503) 373-7112
F: (503) 373-7210
E: robin.kirkpatrick
@state.or.us

Recycling

PENNSYLVANIA
Mr. Todd M. Wallace
Acting Bureau Director
Bureau of Waste Management
P.O. Box 8471
Harrisburg, PA 17105
P: (717) 783-2388
F: (717) 787-1904
E: ra-epwaste@state.pa.us

PUERTO RICO
Mr. Luis Bernal-Jimenez
Executive Director
Energy Affairs Administration
P.O. Box 41314
San Juan, PR 00940
P: (787) 999-2200 x2886
F: (787) 999-2246
E: lbernal@aae.gobierno.pr

Mr. Javier Quintana Mendez
Director
Solid Waste Management
Authority
P.O. Box 40285
San Juan, PR 00918
P: (787) 765-7575
F: (787) 753-2220

RHODE ISLAND
Mr. Michael O'Connell
Executive Director
Resource Recovery Corporation
65 Shun Pike
Johnston, RI 02919
P: (401) 942-1430
F: (401) 942-3280
E: moconnell@rirrc.org

SOUTH CAROLINA
Ms. Daphne G. Neel
Bureau Chief
Bureau of Land & Waste
Management
Dept. of Health &
Environmental Control
2600 Bull Street
Columbia, SC 29201
P: (803) 896-4007
F: (803) 896-4001

SOUTH DAKOTA
Mr. Andrew McCloud
Environmental Project Scientist
DENR - Waste Management
Program
Joe Foss Building
523 East Capitol Avenue
Pierre, SD 57501
P: (605) 773-4985
F: (605) 773-5286

TENNESSEE
Mr. Robert J. Martineau Jr.
Commissioner
Department of Environment and
Conservation
401 Church Street
1st Floor, L&C Annex
Nashville, TN 37243

TEXAS
Mr. Gregg Werkenthin
Deputy Executive Director
Space Management & State
Leasing Services
Facilities Commission
P.O. Box 13047
Austin, TX 78711
P: (512) 463-0909
F: (512) 239-5533

U.S. VIRGIN ISLANDS
Mr. Darryl Smalls
Commissioner
Department of Public Works
6002 Estate Anna's Hope
Christiansted, VI 00820
P: (340) 773-1789
F: (340) 773-0670

UTAH
Ms. Renette Anderson
Director
Office of Planning/Public
Affairs
195 North 1950 West
P.O. Box 144810
Salt Lake City, UT 84114
P: (801) 536-4478
F: (801) 536-4480
E: RENETTEANDERSON@utah

VERMONT
Mr. Marc Roy
Section Chief
Technical Services/Underground
Storage Tanks
Waste Management Division
103 South Main St., West Office
Building
Waterbury, VT 05671
P: (802) 241-3874
F: (802) 241-3296
E: marc.roy@state.vt.us

VIRGINIA
Mr. David K. Paylor
Director
Department of Environmental
Quality
629 East Main Street
P.O. Box 1105
Richmond, VA 23218
P: (804) 698-4390
F: (804) 698-4019
E: dkpaylor
@deq.virginia.gov

WASHINGTON
Ms. Laurie G. Davies
Program Manager
Solid Waste and Financial
Assistance
Department of Ecology
P.O. Box 47600
Olympia, WA 98504
P: (360) 407-6103
F: (360) 407-6102
E: ldav461@ecy.wa.gov

WEST VIRGINIA
Mr. Richard P. Cooke
Director
Solid Waste Management Board
601 57th Street, Southeast
Charleston, WV 25304
P: (304) 926-0499 Ext. 1680
F: (304) 926-0472
E: Richard.P.Cooke@wv.gov

WISCONSIN
Ms. Catherine Cooper
Coordinator
Waste Management Program
101 South Webster, 3rd Floor
P.O. Box 7921
Madison, WI 53707
P: (608) 267-3133
F: (608) 267-2768
E: catherinee.cooper
@wisconsin.gov

WYOMING
Mr. John V. Corra
Director
Department of Environmental
Quality
Herschler Building
122 West 25th Street, 4th Floor,
West
Cheyenne, WY 82002
P: (307) 777-7937
F: (307) 777-7682
E: jcorra@wyo.gov

Revenue

Administers state tax laws and the collection and processing of state taxes.

ALABAMA
Ms. Julie P. McGee
Commissioner
Department of Revenue
50 North Ripley Street
Montgomery, AL 36132
P: (334) 242-1170
F: (334) 242-0550

ALASKA
Mr. Bryan Butcher
Commissioner
Department of Revenue
550 West 7th Avenue, Suite 1820
Juneau, AK 99501
P: (907) 465-2301
F: (907) 465-2389
E: bryan.butcher@alaska.gov

AMERICAN SAMOA
Hon. Magalei Logovi'i
Treasurer
Department of the Treasury
American Samoa Government
Pago Pago, AS 96799
P: (684) 633-4155
F: (684) 633-4100

ARIZONA
Mr. Gale Garriott
Director
Department of Revenue
1600 West Monroe
Phoenix, AZ 85007
P: (602) 716-6090
F: (602) 542-2072
E: ggarriott@azdor.gov

ARKANSAS
Mr. John H. Theis
Assistant Commissioner of Revenue
Department of Finance & Administration
P.O. Box 1272
Little Rock, AR 72203
P: (501) 682-7000
F: (501) 682-1161
E: john.theis
    @rev.state.ar.us

CALIFORNIA
Mr. Selvi Stanislaus
Executive Officer
Franchise Tax Board
P.O. Box 1468
Sacramento, CA 95812
P: (916) 845-4543
F: (916) 845-3191

COLORADO
Ms. Roxy Huber
Executive Director
Department of Revenue
1375 Sherman Street
Denver, CO 80261
P: (303) 866-5610
F: (303) 866-2400

CONNECTICUT
Mr. Kevin B. Sullivan
Commissioner
Department of Revenue
25 Sigourney Street, Suite 2
Hartford, CT 06106
P: (860) 297-5612
F: (860) 297-5698

DELAWARE
Mr. Patrick T. Carter
Director
Division of Revenue
820 North French Street, 8th Floor
Wilmington, DE 19801
P: (302) 577-8686
F: (302) 577-8656
E: patrick.carter
    @state.de.us

DISTRICT OF COLUMBIA
Mr. Stephen M. Cordi
Deputy Chief Financial Officer
Office of Tax & Revenue
1101 4th Street, Southwest, Suite W270
Suite 203
Washington, DC 20024
P: (202) 727-4829
F: (202) 727-1643
E: stephen.cordi@dc.gov

FLORIDA
Ms. Lisa Vickers
Executive Director
Department of Revenue
5050 West Tennessee Street
Tallahassee, FL 32399
P: (850) 617-8600
E: vickersl@dor.state.fl.us

GEORGIA
Mr. Doug MacGinnitie
Commissioner
Department of Revenue
1800 Century Center Boulevard
Suite 15300
Atlanta, GA 30345
P: (404) 417-2100
F: (404) 417-2101

GUAM
Mr. Artemio B. Ilagan
Director
Department of Revenue & Taxation
P.O. Box 23607
GMF, GU 96921
P: (671) 635-1835
F: (671) 633-2643
E: ilagan@revtax.gov.gu

HAWAII
Mr. Frederick D. Pablo
Director
Department of Taxation
Princess Ruth Keelikolani Building
830 Punchbowl Street
Honolulu, HI 96813
P: (808) 587-1510
F: (808) 587-1560
E: Tax.Directors.Office
    @hawaii.gov

IDAHO
Mr. Robert L. Geddes
Chair
Tax Commission
P.O. Box 36
Boise, ID 83722
P: (208) 334-7660
E: robert.geddes
    @tax.idaho.gov

ILLINOIS
Mr. Brian A. Hamer
Director of Revenue
Department of Revenue
Willard Ice Building
101 West Jefferson Street
Springfield, IL 62794
P: (217) 785-7570
F: (217) 782-6337

INDIANA
Mr. John Eckart
Commissioner
Department of Revenue
100 North Senate Avenue, Room N248
Indianapolis, IN 46204
P: (317) 232-8039
F: (317) 232-2103
E: jeckart@dor.in.gov

IOWA
Ms. Courtney M. Kay-Decker
Director
Department of Revenue
Hoover State Office Building
1305 East Walnut Street
Des Moines, IA 50319
P: (515) 281-3204
E: courtney.decker@iowa.gov

KANSAS
Mr. Nick Jordan
Secretary
Department of Revenue
Docking State Office Building, Room 230
915 Southwest Harrison Street
Topeka, KS 66612
P: (785) 296-3909
F: (785) 296-7928

KENTUCKY
Mr. Thomas B. Miller
Commissioner
Department of Revenue
501 High Street
Frankfort, KY 40620
P: (502) 564-3226
F: (502) 564-3875

LOUISIANA
Ms. Cynthia Bridges
Secretary
Department of Revenue
1702 North 3rd Street
P.O. Box 94214
Baton Rouge, LA 70804
P: (225) 219-2700
F: (225) 219-2708

MAINE
Mr. Jerome D. Gerard
Acting Executive Director
Revenue Services
24 State House Station
26 Edison Drive
Augusta, ME 04333
P: (207) 626-8475
E: Jerome.D.Gerard
    @maine.gov

MARYLAND
Mr. James M. Arnie
Director
Revenue Administration Division
Comptroller of Maryland
110 Carroll Street, Room 105
Annapolis, MD 21411
P: (410) 260-7445
F: (410) 974-3456
E: jarnie@comp.state.md.us

MASSACHUSETTS
Ms. Navjeet Bal
Commissioner
Department of Revenue
100 Cambridge Street, 8th Floor
Boston, MA 02114
P: (617) 626-2201
F: (617) 626-2299

Revenue

MICHIGAN
Mr. Jeff Guilfoyle
Administrator
Office of Revenue & Tax
Analysis
Richard H. Austin Building
430 West Allegan Street
Lansing, MI 48922
P: (517) 373-2158
F: (517) 335-3298

MINNESOTA
Mr. Myron Frans
Commissioner
Department of Revenue
600 North Robert Street, 4th
Floor
St. Paul, MN 55146
P: (651) 556-6003
F: (651) 556-3133
E: myron.frans@state.mn.us

MISSISSIPPI
Mr. Ed Morgan
Commissioner
Department of Revenue
P.O. Box 1033
Jackson, MS 39215
P: (601) 923-7000
F: (601) 923-7423

MISSOURI
Ms. Alana M. Barragan-Scot
Director
Department of Revenue
301 West High Street
P.O. Box 311
Jefferson City, MO 65105
P: (573) 751-4450
F: (573) 751-7150
E: dormail@dor.mo.gov

MONTANA
Mr. Dan Bucks
Director
Department of Revenue
P.O. Box 5805
Helena, MT 59604
P: (406) 444-0761
F: (406) 444-1505
E: dbucks@mt.gov

NEBRASKA
Mr. Doug Ewald
Tax Commissioner
Department of Revenue
P.O. Box 94818
Lincoln, NE 68509
P: (402) 471-5605
F: (402) 471-5608
E: doug.ewald@nebraska.gov

NEVADA
Mr. Christopher Nielsen
Interim Executive Director
Department of Taxation
1550 College Parkway, Suite
115
Carson City, NV 89706
P: (775) 684-2070
F: (775) 684-2020
E: cnielsen@tax.state.nv.us

NEW HAMPSHIRE
Mr. Kevin A. Clougherty
Commissioner
Department of Revenue
Administration
109 Pleasant Street
P.O. Box 457
Concord, NH 03302
P: (603) 271-2318
F: (603) 271-6121
E: kevin.clougherty
@rev.state.nh.us

Ms. Margaret Fulton
Assistant Commissioner
Department of Revenue
Administration
109 Pleasant Street
P.O. Box 457
Concord, NH 03302
P: (603) 271-2318
F: (603) 271-6121
E: MFulton@rev.state.nh.us

NEW JERSEY
Mr. Michael J. Bryan
Acting Director
Division of Taxation
P.O. Box 281
Trenton, NJ 08695
P: (609) 292-5185

NEW MEXICO
Ms. Demesia Padilla
Secretary
Taxation & Revenue
Department
1100 South St. Francis Drive
Santa Fe, NM 87504
P: (505) 827-0700
F: (505) 827-1759

NEW YORK
Mr. Thomas H. Mattox
Commissioner
Department of Taxation &
Finance
W.A. Harriman Campus,
Building 9
Albany, NY 12227

NORTH CAROLINA
Mr. David Hoyle
Secretary
Department of Revenue
P.O. Box 25000
Raleigh, NC 27640
P: (919) 733-7211
F: (919) 733-0023

NORTH DAKOTA
Hon. Cory Fong (R)
Commissioner
Office of State Tax
Commissioner
600 East Boulevard Avenue
Department 127
Bismarck, ND 58505
P: (701) 328-7088
F: (701) 328-3700
E: cfong@nd.gov

**NORTHERN MARIANA
ISLANDS**
Ms. Estrellita S. Ada
Director of Revenue & Tax
Division of Revenue & Taxation
Caller Box 10007, Capitol Hill
Saipan, MP 96950
P: (670) 664-1000
F: (670) 664-1015
E: revtax@gtepacifica.net

OHIO
Mr. Joseph W. Testa
Tax Commissioner
Department of Taxation
30 East Broad Street, 22nd Floor
P.O. Box 530
Columbus, OH 43216
P: (614) 466-2166
F: (614) 466-6401

OKLAHOMA
Mr. Thomas Kemp Jr.
Chair
Tax Commission
2501 North Lincoln Boulevard
Oklahoma City, OK 73194
P: (405) 521-3160
F: (405) 522-0074

OREGON
Ms. Karen S. Gregory
Acting Director
Department of Revenue
Room 457, Revenue Building
Salem, OR 97301
P: (503) 945-8214
F: (503) 945-8290
E: karen.s.gregory
@state.or.us

PENNSYLVANIA
Mr. Dan Meuser
Secretary
Department of Revenue
11th Floor, Stawberry Square
Harrisburg, PA 17128
P: (717) 783-3680
F: (717) 787-3990

RHODE ISLAND
Ms. Rosemary Booth Gallogly
State Budget Officer
Department of Revenue
One Capitol Hill
Providence, RI 02908
P: (401) 574-8999
F: (401) 574-8997

SOUTH CAROLINA
Mr. James F. Etter
Director
Department of Revenue
P.O. Box 125
Columbia, SC 29214
P: (803) 898-5040
E: Director@sctax.org

SOUTH DAKOTA
Mr. Andy Gerlach
Secretary of Revenue &
Regulation
Department of Revenue &
Regulation
445 East Capital Avenue
Pierre, SD 57501
P: (605) 773-3311
F: (605) 773-5129

Mr. David Wiest
Interim Secretary of Revenue &
Regulation
Department of Revenue &
Regulation
445 East Capital Avenue
Pierre, SD 57501
P: (605) 773-3311
F: (605) 773-5129

TENNESSEE
Mr. Richard H. Roberts
Commissioner
Department of Revenue
500 Deaderick Street
Andrew Jackson Building
Nashville, TN 37242
P: (615) 741-2461
F: (615) 741-2883

TEXAS
Ms. Susan Combs
Comptroller of Public Accounts
Office of the Comptroller of
Public Accounts
111 East 17th
P.O.Box 13528
Austin, TX 78711
P: (512) 463-4444
F: (512) 463-4965
E: susan.combs
@cpa.state.tx.us

U.S. VIRGIN ISLANDS
Ms. Claudette J.
Watson-Anderson
Director
Internal Revenue Bureau
9601 Estate Thomas
St. Thomas, VI 00802
P: (340) 774-5865
F: (340) 714-9345

UTAH
Mr. Barry C. Conover
Executive Director
State Tax Commission
210 North 1950 West
Salt Lake City, UT 84134
P: (801) 297-3820
F: (801) 297-6358
E: bconover@utah.gov

VERMONT
Mr. James B. Reardon
Commissioner
Department of Finance &
Management
109 State Street
Montpelier, VT 05602
P: (802) 828-2376
F: (802) 828-2428
E: jim.reardon@state.vt.us

VIRGINIA
Mr. Craig M. Burns
Tax Commissioner
Department of Taxation
Main Street Centre
600 East Main Street, 23rd Floor
Richmond, VA 23219
P: (804) 786-3301
F: (804) 786-4208
E: craig.burns
@tax.virginia.gov

WEST VIRGINIA
Mr. Charles O. Lorensen
Cabinet Secretary
Department of Revenue
Building 1, W-300
P.O. Box 963
Charleston, WV 25324
P: (304) 558-0211
F: (304) 558-2324
E: Charles.O.Lorensen
@wv.gov

WISCONSIN
Mr. Richard Chandler
Secretary
Department of Revenue
P.O. Box 8933
Mail Stop #624-A
Madison, WI 53708
P: (608) 266-6466
F: (608) 266-5718
E: dorsecretary
@revenue.wi.gov

WYOMING
Mr. Edmund J. Schmidt
Director
Department of Revenue
Herschler Building
122 West 25th Street, 2nd West
Cheyenne, WY 82002
P: (307) 777-5287
F: (307) 777-7722
E: Ed.Schmidt@wyo.gov

Savings and Loan

Administers laws regulating the operation of savings and loan associations in the state.

ALABAMA
Mr. John D. Harrison
Superintendent
Banking Department
P.O. Box 4600
Montgomery, AL 36130
P: (334) 242-3452
F: (334) 242-3500
E: john.harrison
    @banking.alabama.gov

ALASKA
Ms. Lori L. Hovanec
Director
Department of Commerce,
Community & Economic
Development
Division of Banking &
Securities
P.O. Box 110807
Juneau, AK 99811
P: (907) 465-2521
F: (907) 465-2549
E: lori.hovanec@alaska.gov

ARIZONA
Mr. Lauren W. Kingry
Superintendent
Department of Financial
Institutions
2910 North 44th Street, Suite
310
Phoenix, AZ 85018
P: (602) 771-2800
F: (602) 381-1225

ARKANSAS
Mr. A. Heath Abshure
Securities Commissioner
Securities Department
Heritage West Building
201 East Markham, Room 300
Little Rock, AR 72201
P: (501) 324-9260
F: (501) 324-9268
E: aabshure
    @securities.arkansas.gov

CALIFORNIA
Mr. William S. Haraf
Commissioner
Department of Financial
Institutions
45 Fremont Street, Suite 1700
San Francisco, CA 94105
P: (415) 263-8507
F: (415) 288-8830
E: wharaf@dfi.ca.gov

COLORADO
Mr. Chris Myklebust
Commissioner
Division of Financial Services
Department of Regulatory
Agencies
1560 Broadway, Room 1520
Denver, CO 80202
P: (303) 894-7741
F: (303) 894-7886

CONNECTICUT
Mr. Howard F. Pitkin
Commissioner
Department of Banking
260 Constitution Plaza
Hartford, CT 06103
P: (860) 240-8100
F: (860) 240-8178
E: howard.pitkin@ct.gov

DELAWARE
Mr. Robert A. Glen
Commissioner
Office of State Bank
Commissioner
555 East Lockerman Street,
Suite 210
Dover, DE 19901
P: (302) 739-4235
F: (302) 739-3609

DISTRICT OF COLUMBIA
Mr. William P. White
Commissioner
Department of Insurance,
Securities & Banking
810 First Street, Northeast, Suite
70
Washington, DC 20002
P: (202) 727-8000
F: (202) 535-1196

GEORGIA
Mr. Rob Braswell
Commissioner
Department of Banking &
Finance
2990 Brandywine Road, Suite
200
Atlanta, GA 30341
P: (770) 986-1628
F: (770) 986-1654
E: robertb@dbf.state.ga.us

HAWAII
Ms. Iris Ikeda Catalani
Commissioner
Division of Financial
Institutions
King Kalakaua Building
335 Merchant Street, Room 221
Honolulu, HI 96813
P: (808) 586-2820
F: (808) 586-2818

IDAHO
Mr. Gavin M. Gee
Director
Department of Finance
800 Park Boulevard, Suite 200
Boise, ID 83712
P: (208) 332-8010
F: (208) 332-8097
E: ggee@finance.idaho.gov

ILLINOIS
Mr. Manuel Flores
Director
Division of Banking
122 South Michigan Avenue,
Suite 1900
Chicago, IL 60603
P: (312) 793-3000
F: (312) 793-0756

INDIANA
Mr. David Mills
Director
Department of Financial
Institutions
30 South Meridian Street, Suite
300
Indianapolis, IN 46204
P: (317) 233-9460
F: (317) 232-7655
E: DaMills@dfi.IN.gov

IOWA
Mr. James M. Schipper
Superintendent
Division of Banking
200 East Grand Avenue, Suite
300
Des Moines, IA 50309
P: (515) 281-4014
F: (515) 281-4862
E: jschipper
    @idob.state.ia.us

KANSAS
Mr. Ed Splichal
Commissioner
Office of the State Banking
Commissioner
700 Jackson, Suite 300
Topeka, KS 66603
P: (785) 296-2266
F: (785) 296-0168

KENTUCKY
Mr. Charles A. Vice
Commissioner
Department of Financial
Institutions
1025 Capital Center Drive, Suite
200
Frankfort, KY 40601
P: (502) 573-3390
F: (502) 573-0086
E: charles.vice@ky.gov

LOUISIANA
Mr. Sidney E. Seymour
Chief Examiner
Office of Financial Institutions
8660 United Plaza Boulevard,
2nd Floor
P.O. Box 94095
Baton Rouge, LA 70804
P: (225) 925-4660
F: (225) 925-4548
E: sseymour@ofi.la.gov

MAINE
Mr. Lloyd P. LaFountain III
Superintendent
Bureau of Financial Institutions
Bureau of Financial Institutions
36 State House Station
Augusta, ME 04333
P: (207) 624-8570
F: (207) 624-8590
E: lloyd.p.lafountain.III
    @maine.gov

MARYLAND
Mr. Mark Kaufman
Commissioner of Financial
Regulation
Department of Labor, Licensing
& Regulation
500 North Calvert Street, Room
402
Baltimore, MD 21202
P: (410) 230-6100
F: (410) 333-0475
E: mkaufman
    @dllr.state.md.us

MASSACHUSETTS
Mr. David Cotney
Commissioner
Division of Banks
1000 Washington Street,
10th Floor
Boston, MA 02118
P: (617) 956-1500
F: (617) 956-1599

MICHIGAN
Mr. R. Kevin Clinton
Commissioner
Office of Financial & Insurance
Regulation
P.O. Box 30220
Lansing, MI 48909
P: (517) 373-0220
F: (517) 373-4978

MINNESOTA
Mr. Mike Rothman
Commissioner of Commerce
Department of Commerce
85 7th Place East, Suite 500
St. Paul, MN 55101
P: (651) 296-6025
F: (651) 297-1959
E: commerce.commissioner
@state.mn.us

MISSISSIPPI
Mr. John S. Allison
Commissioner
Department of Banking &
Consumer Finance
501 North West Street
901 Woolfolk Building, Suite A
Jackson, MS 39202
P: (601) 359-1031
F: (601) 359-3557
E: john.allison@dbcf.ms.gov

MISSOURI
Mr. Richard J. Weaver
Commissioner
Division of Finance
Truman State Office Building,
Room 630
P.O. Box 716
Jefferson City, MO 65102
P: (573) 751-3242
F: (573) 751-9192
E: finance@dof.mo.gov

MONTANA
Ms. Melanie Griggs
Commissioner
Division of Banking &
Financial Institutions
301 South Park, Suite 316
P.O. Box 200546
Helena, MT 59620
P: (406) 841-2920
F: (406) 841-2930
E: mgriggs@mt.gov

NEBRASKA
Mr. John Munn
Director
Department of Banking &
Finance
P.O. Box 95006
Lincoln, NE 68509
P: (402) 471-2171
E: john.munn@nebraska.gov

NEVADA
Mr. Steven W. Kondrup
Administrator
Financial Institutions Division
Department of Business &
Industry
2785 East Desert Inn Road, Suite
180
Las Vegas, NV 89121
P: (702) 486-4120
F: (702) 486-4563
E: skondrup@fid.state.nv.us

NEW HAMPSHIRE
Mr. Ronald A. Wilbur
Commissioner
Banking Department
53 Regional Drive, Suite 200
Concord, NH 03301
P: (603) 271-3561
F: (603) 271-1090
E: Commissioner
@banking.state.nh.us

NEW JERSEY
Mr. Thomas B. Considine
Commissioner
Department of Banking &
Insurance
20 West State Street
P.O. Box 325
Trenton, NJ 08625
P: (609) 292-7272
F: (609) 663-3601
E: commissioner
@dobi.state.nj.us

NORTH CAROLINA
Mr. Joseph A. Smith Jr.
Commissioner of Banks
Banking Commission
316 West Edenton Street
4309 Mail Service Center
Raleigh, NC 27699
P: (919) 733-3016
F: (919) 733-6918
E: jsmith@nccob.org

NORTH DAKOTA
Mr. Robert J. Entringer
Commissioner
Department of Financial
Institutions
2000 Schafer Street, Suite G
Bismarck, ND 58501
P: (701) 328-9933
F: (701) 328-0290
E: rentring@nd.gov

**NORTHERN MARIANA
ISLANDS**
Mr. Sixto Igisomar
Acting Secretary
Department of Commerce
Caller Box 10007
Saipan, MP 96950
P: (670) 664-3064
F: (670) 664-3067

OHIO
Mr. Charles J. Dolezal
Superintendent
Division of Financial
Institutions
Department of Commerce
77 South High Street
Columbus, OH 43215
P: (614) 728-8400
F: (614) 728-0380

OKLAHOMA
Mr. Mick Thompson
Commissioner
State Banking Department
2900 North Lincoln Boulevard
Oklahoma City, OK 73105
P: (405) 521-2782
F: (405) 522-2993
E: rmt1@onenet.net

OREGON
Mr. David C. Tatman
Division Administrator
Division of Finance &
Corporate Securities
350 Winter Street, Northeast,
Room 410
Salem, OR 97301
P: (503) 378-4140
F: (503) 947-7862
E: dcbs.dfcsmail
@state.or.us

PENNSYLVANIA
Mr. Glenn E. Moyer
Secretary of Banking
Department of Banking
17 North 2nd Street, Suite 1300
Harrisburg, PA 17101
P: (717) 787-2665
F: (717) 787-8773
E: ra-pabanking@state.pa.us

SOUTH DAKOTA
Mr. Bret Afdahl
Director
Division of Banking
Department of Revenue &
Regulation
217 1/2 West Missouri Avenue
Pierre, SD 57501
P: (605) 773-3421
F: (866) 326-7504
E: drr.banking.info
@state.sd.us

TENNESSEE
Mr. Greg Gonzales
Commissioner
Department of Financial
Institutions
414 Union Street, Suite 1000
Nashville, TN 37219
P: (615) 741-2236
F: (615) 253-6306
E: Greg.Gonzales@tn.gov

TEXAS
Mr. Doug Foster
Commisssioner
Department of Savings &
Mortgage Lending
2601 North Lamar Boulevard,
Suite 201
Austin, TX 78705
P: (512) 475-1353
F: (512) 475-1360

U.S. VIRGIN ISLANDS
Mr. John McDonald
Director
Division of Banking &
Insurance
#18 Kongens Gade
St. Thomas, VI 00802
P: (340) 774-7166
F: (340) 774-9458

UTAH
Mr. G. Edward Leary
Commissioner
Department of Financial
Institutions
324 South State Street, Suite
201
P.O. Box 146800
Salt Lake City, UT 84114
P: (801) 538-8761
F: (801) 538-8894
E: ELEARY@utah.gov

Savings and Loan

VERMONT
Mr. Steve Kimbell
Commissioner
Department of Banking,
Insurance, Securities & Health
Care Administration
89 Main Street
Montpelier, VT 05620
P: (802) 828-3301
F: (802) 828-3306
E: steve.kimbell
@state.vt.us

VIRGINIA
Mr. E. Joseph Face Jr.
Director
Bureau of Financial Institutions
1300 East Main Street, Suite
800
P.O. Box 640
Richmond, VA 23218
P: (804) 371-9657
F: (804) 371-9416
E: joe.face
@scc.virginia.gov

WASHINGTON
Ms. Gloria McVey
Acting Director of Banks
Division of Banks
Department of Financial
Institutions
P.O. Box 41200
Olympia, WA 98504
P: (360) 902-8704
F: (360) 753-6070
E: banks@dfi.wa.gov

WEST VIRGINIA
Ms. Sara M. Cline
Commissioner
Division of Banking
One Players Club Drive, Suite
300
Charleston, WV 25311
P: (304) 558-2294
F: (304) 558-0442
E: scline@wvdob.org

WISCONSIN
Mr. Michael Mach
Administrator
Division of Banking
345 West Washington Avenue
P.O. Box 7876
Madison, WI 53707
P: (608) 261-7578
F: (608) 267-6889
E: Mike.Mach
@dfi.wisconsin.gov

WYOMING
Mr. Jeffrey C. Vogel
Commissioner
Division of Banking
Herschler Building, 3rd Floor,
East
122 West 25th Street
Cheyenne, WY 82002
P: (307) 777-7797
F: (307) 777-5341
E: jvogel
@wyaudit.state.wy.us

Secretary of State

Statewide official who oversees a variety of electoral, registration, publication, and legislative duties for the state.

Information provided by:

National Association of Secretaries of State
Leslie Reynolds
Executive Director
444 North Capitol Street, NW
Suite 401
Washington, DC 20001
P: (202) 624-3525
F: (202) 624-3527
reynolds@sso.org
www.nass.org

ALABAMA
Hon. Beth Chapman (R)
Secretary of State
Office of the Secretary of State
P.O. Box 5616
Montgomery, AL 36103
P: (334) 242-7200
F: (334) 242-4993
E: Beth.Chapman
@sos.alabama.gov

ARIZONA
Hon. Ken Bennett (R)
Secretary of State
Office of the Secretary of State
Capitol Executive Tower, 7th Floor
1700 West Washington Street
Phoenix, AZ 85007
P: (602) 542-4285
F: (602) 542-1575
E: sosadmin@azsos.gov

ARKANSAS
Hon. Mark Martin (R)
Secretary of State
Office of the Secretary of State
256 State Capitol Building
Little Rock, AR 72201
P: (501) 682-1010
F: (501) 682-3510
E: sos@sos.arkansas.gov

CALIFORNIA
Hon. Debra Bowen (D)
Secretary of State
Office of the Secretary of State
1500 11th Street
Sacramento, CA 95814
P: (916) 653-7244
F: (916) 653-4795
E: secretarybowen
@sos.ca.gov

COLORADO
Hon. Scott Gessler (R)
Secretary of State
Office of the Secretary of State
1700 Broadway, Suite 250
Denver, CO 80290
P: (303) 894-2200
F: (303) 869-4860
E: secretary
@sos.state.co.us

CONNECTICUT
Hon. Denise W. Merrill (D)
Secretary of State
Office of the Secretary of State
State Capitol, Room 104
Hartford, CT 06105
P: (860) 509-6200
F: (860) 509-6209
E: denise.merrill@ct.gov

DELAWARE
Hon. Jeffrey Bullock (D)
Secretary of State
Office of the Secretary of State
Townsend Building
401 Federal Street, Suite 3
Dover, DE 19901
P: (302) 739-4111
F: (302) 739-3811
E: Monique.hampton
@state.de.us

DISTRICT OF COLUMBIA
Hon. Cynthia Brock-Smith
(appointed)
Secretary of the District
Office of the Secretary
1350 Pennsylvania Avenue, Northwest
Suite 419
Washington, DC 20004
P: (202) 727-6306
F: (202) 727-3582
E: secretary@dc.gov

FLORIDA
Hon. Kurt S. Browning (R)
(appointed)
Secretary of State
Office of the Secretary of State
500 South Bronough, Suite 100
Tallahassee, FL 32399
P: (850) 245-6500
F: (850) 245-6125
E: secretaryofstate
@dos.state.fl.us

GEORGIA
Hon. Brian Kemp (R)
Secretary of State
Office of the Secretary of State
214 State Capitol
Atlanta, GA 30334
P: (404) 656-2881
F: (404) 656-0513
E: sos@sos.ga.gov

IDAHO
Hon. Ben T. Ysursa (R)
Secretary of State
Office of the Secretary of State
P.O. Box 83720
Boise, ID 83720
P: (208) 334-2300
F: (208) 334-2282
E: secstate@sos.idaho.gov

ILLINOIS
Hon. Jesse White (D)
Secretary of State
Office of the Secretary of State
213 State Capitol
Springfield, IL 62756
P: (217) 782-2201
F: (217) 785-0358
E: jessewhite@ilsos.net

INDIANA
Hon. Charlie White (R)
Secretary of State
Office of the Secretary of State
201 State House
Indianapolis, IN 46204
P: (317) 232-6532
F: (317) 233-3283
E: sos@sos.in.gov

IOWA
Hon. Matt Schultz (R)
Secretary of State
Office of the Secretary of State
State Capitol, Room 105
1007 East Grand Avenue
Des Moines, IA 50319
P: (515) 281-8993
F: (515) 242-5952
E: sos@sos.state.ia.us

KANSAS
Hon. Kris Kobach (R)
Secretary of State
Office of the Secretary of State
120 Southwest 10th Avenue
Memorial Hall, 1st Floor
Topeka, KS 66612
P: (785) 296-4575
F: (785) 368-8033
E: sos@sos.ks.gov

KENTUCKY
Hon. Elaine Walker (D)
Secretary of State
Office of the Secretary of State
700 Capital Avenue, Suite 152
Frankfort, KY 40601
P: (502) 564-3490
F: (502) 564-5687
E: sos.secretary@ky.gov

LOUISIANA
Hon. Tom Schedler (R)
Secretary of State
Office of the Secretary of State
P.O. Box 94125
Baton Rouge, LA 70804
P: (225) 342-4479
F: (225) 342-5577

MAINE
Hon. Charlie Summers (R)
Secretary of State
Office of the Secretary of State
148 State House Station
Augusta, ME 04333
P: (207) 626-8400
F: (207) 287-8598
E: sos.office@maine.gov

MARYLAND
Hon. John P. McDonough (D)
(appointed)
Secretary of State
Office of the Secretary of State
16 Francis Street
Annapolis, MD 21401
P: (410) 974-5521
F: (410) 974-5527
E: swiedemer
@sos.state.md.us

MASSACHUSETTS
Hon. William Francis
Galvin (D)
Secretary of the Commonwealth
Office of the Secretary of the Commonwealth
State House, Room 337
Boston, MA 02133
P: (617) 727-9180
F: (617) 742-4722
E: cis@sec.state.ma.us

Secretary of State

MICHIGAN
Hon. Ruth Johnson (R)
Secretary of State
Office of the Secretary of State
430 West Allegan Street
Lansing, MI 48918
P: (517) 373-2510
F: (517) 373-0727
E: secretary@michigan.gov

MINNESOTA
Hon. Mark Ritchie (DFL)
Secretary of State
Office of the Secretary of State
180 State Office Building
100 Martin Luther King Jr.
Boulevard
St. Paul, MN 55155
P: (651) 201-1328
F: (651) 215-0682
E: secretary.state
    @state.mn.us

MISSISSIPPI
Hon. C. Delbert
    Hosemann Jr. (R)
Secretary of State
Office of the Secretary of State
P.O. Box 136
Jackson, MS 39205
P: (601) 359-1350
F: (601) 359-6700
E: delbert.hosemann
    @sos.ms.gov

MISSOURI
Hon. Robin Carnahan (D)
Secretary of State
Office of the Secretary of State
State Capitol, Room 208
Jefferson City, MO 65101
P: (573) 751-4936
F: (573) 552-3082
E: SOSMain@sos.mo.gov

MONTANA
Hon. Linda McCulloch (D)
Secretary of State
Office of the Secretary of State
P.O. Box 202801
Helena, MT 59620
P: (406) 444-2034
F: (406) 444-4249
E: sos@mt.gov

NEBRASKA
Hon. John A. Gale (R)
Secretary of State
Office of the Secretary of State
P.O. Box 94608
Lincoln, NE 68509
P: (402) 471-2554
F: (402) 471-3237
E: secretaryofstate
    @nebraska.gov

NEVADA
Hon. Ross Miller (D)
Secretary of State
Office of the Secretary of State
101 North Carson Street, Suite 3
Carson City, NV 89701
P: (775) 684-5708
F: (775) 684-5724
E: sosmail@sos.nv.gov

NEW HAMPSHIRE
Hon. William M. Gardner (D)
    (elected by the Legislature)
Secretary of State
Office of the Secretary of State
State House, Room 204
Concord, NH 03301
P: (603) 271-3242
F: (603) 271-6316
E: kladd@sos.state.nh.us

NEW JERSEY
Hon. Kim Guadagno (R)
    (appointed)
Lieutenant Governor/Secretary
of State
Office of the Lieutenant
Governor
125 West 8th Street
P.O. Box 300
Trenton, NJ 08625
P: (609) 292-6000
F: (609) 292-3454

NEW MEXICO
Hon. Dianna J. Duran (R)
Secretary of State
Office of the Secretary of State
325 Don Gaspar, Suite 300
Capitol Annex
Santa Fe, NM 87503
P: (505) 827-3600
F: (505) 827-3634
E: diannaj.duran
    @state.nm.us

NEW YORK
Hon. Cesar A. Perales
    (appointed)
Acting Secretary of State
Office of the Secretary of State
One Commerce Plaza
99 Washington Avenue, Suite
1100
Albany, NY 12231
P: (518) 486-9844
F: (518) 474-4765
E: malli@dos.state.ny.us

NORTH CAROLINA
Hon. Elaine F. Marshall (D)
Secretary of State
Office of the Secretary of State
P.O. Box 29622
Raleigh, NC 27626
P: (919) 807-2005
F: (919) 807-2010
E: emarshal@sosnc.com

NORTH DAKOTA
Hon. Alvin A. Jaeger (R)
Secretary of State
Office of the Secretary of State
600 East Boulevard
Department 108
Bismarck, ND 58505
P: (701) 328-2900
F: (701) 328-2992
E: sos@nd.gov

OHIO
Hon. Jon Husted (R)
Secretary of State
Office of the Secretary of State
180 East Broad Street
Columbus, OH 43215
P: (614) 466-2655
F: (614) 644-0649
E: jhusted@sos.state.oh.us

OKLAHOMA
Hon. Glenn Coffee (R)
    (appointed)
Secretary of State
Office of the Secretary of State
2300 North Lincoln Boulevard,
Suite 101
Oklahoma City, OK 73105
P: (405) 521-3912
F: (405) 521-3771
E: michelle.waddell
    @sos.ok.gov

OREGON
Hon. Kate Brown (D)
Secretary of State
Office of the Secretary of State
136 State Capitol
Salem, OR 97301
P: (503) 986-1523
F: (503) 986-1616
E: oregon.sos@sos.or.us

PENNSYLVANIA
Hon. Carol Aichele (R)
    (appointed)
Acting Secretary of the
Commonwealth
Office of the Secretary of State
302 North Office Building
Harrisburg, PA 17120
P: (717) 787-8727
F: (717) 787-1734
E: ST-PRESS@state.pa.us

PUERTO RICO
Hon. Kenneth D.
    McClintock (NPP)
    (appointed)
Secretary of State
Department of State
P.O. Box 9023271
San Juan, PR 00902
P: (787) 722-4010
F: (787) 722-2684
E: kenneth.mcclintock
    @yahoo.com

RHODE ISLAND
Hon. A. Ralph Mollis (D)
    (elected by the Legislature)
Secretary of State
Office of the Secretary of State
82 Smith Street
217 State House
Providence, RI 02903
P: (401) 222-1035
F: (401) 222-1356
E: armollis@sos.ri.gov

SOUTH CAROLINA
Hon. Mark Hammond (R)
Secretary of State
Office of the Secretary of State
P.O. Box 11350
Columbia, SC 29211
P: (803) 734-2170
F: (803) 734-1661
E: rdaggerhart@sos.sc.gov

SOUTH DAKOTA
Hon. Jason M. Gant (R)
Secretary of State
Office of the Secretary of State
500 East Capitol Avenue, Suite 204
Pierre, SD 57501
P: (605) 773-3537
F: (605) 773-6580
E: sdsos@state.sd.us

TENNESSEE
Hon. Tre Hargett (R)
    (elected by the Legislature)
Secretary of State
Office of the Secretary of State
First Floor, State Capitol
Nashville, TN 37243
P: (615) 741-2819
F: (615) 741-5962
E: tre.hargett@tn.gov

TEXAS
Hon. Esperanza Andrade
    (appointed)
Secretary of State
Office of the Secretary of State
P.O. Box 12887
Austin, TX 78711
P: (512) 463-5770
F: (512) 475-2761
E: secretary
    @sos.state.tx.us

VERMONT
Hon. Jim Condos (D)
Secretary of State
Office of the Secretary of State
26 Terrace Street
Montpelier, VT 05609
P: (802) 828-2148
F: (802) 828-2496
E: jim.condos
    @sec.state.vt.us

VIRGINIA
Hon. Janet Polarek
    (appointed)
Secretary of the Commonwealth
Office of the Secretary of the Commonwealth
P.O. Box 2454
Richmond, VA 23218
P: (804) 786-2441
F: (804) 371-0017
E: socmail
    @governor.virginia.gov

WASHINGTON
Hon. Sam Reed (R)
Secretary of State
Office of the Secretary of State
P.O. Box 40220
Olympia, WA 98504
P: (360) 902-4151
F: (360) 586-5629
E: sam.reed@sos.wa.gov

WEST VIRGINIA
Hon. Natalie Tennant (D)
Secretary of State
Office of the Secretary of State
Building 1, Suite-157K
1900 Kanawha Boulevard, East
Charleston, WV 25305
P: (304) 558-6000
F: (304) 558-0900
E: wvsos@wvsos.com

WISCONSIN
Hon. Douglas J.
    La Follette (D)
Secretary of State
Office of the Secretary of State
P.O. Box 7848
Madison, WI 53707
P: (608) 266-8888
F: (608) 266-3159
E: doug.lafollette
    @sos.state.wi.us

WYOMING
Hon. Max Maxfield (R)
Secretary of State
Office of the Secretary of State
State Capitol Building
200 West 24th
Cheyenne, WY 82002
P: (307) 777-7378
F: (307) 777-6217
E: Secofstate@state.wy.us

Securities

Regulates the sale of securities and registers securities prior to public sale.

ALABAMA
Mr. Joseph P. Borg
Director
Securities Commission
401 Adams Avenue, Suite 280
P.O. Box 304700
Montgomery, AL 36130
P: (334) 242-2386
F: (334) 242-0240
E: Joseph.Borg
@asc.alabama.gov

ALASKA
Ms. Lori L. Hovanec
Director
Department of Commerce,
Community & Economic
Development
Division of Banking &
Securities
P.O. Box 110807
Juneau, AK 99811
P: (907) 465-2521
F: (907) 465-2549
E: lori.hovanec@alaska.gov

ARIZONA
Mr. Matthew J. Neubert
Director
Securities Division
Corporation Commission
1300 West Washington, 3rd
Floor
Phoenix, AZ 85007
P: (602) 542-4242
F: (602) 594-7470
E: securitiesdiv@azcc.gov

ARKANSAS
Mr. A. Heath Abshure
Securities Commissioner
Securities Department
Heritage West Building
201 East Markham, Room 300
Little Rock, AR 72201
P: (501) 324-9260
F: (501) 324-9268
E: aabshure
@securities.arkansas.gov

CALIFORNIA
Mr. Robert
Van Der Volgen Jr.
Deputy Commissioner
Division of Securities
Regulation
Department of Corporations
1515 K Street, Suite 200
Sacramento, CA 95814
P: (916) 324-9011
F: (916) 445-7975

COLORADO
Mr. Fred J. Joseph
Securities Commissioner
Division of Securities
1580 Lincoln Street, Suite 420
Denver, CO 80203
P: (303) 894-2320
F: (303) 861-2126

CONNECTICUT
Mr. Eric J. Wilder
Assistant Division Director
Securities & Business
Investments Division
Department of Banking
260 Constitution Plaza
Hartford, CT 06103
P: (860) 240-8230
F: (860) 240-8295
E: eric.wilder@ct.gov

DELAWARE
Mr. Peter O. Jamison III
Securities Commissioner
Division of Securities
Carvel State Office Building
820 North French Street, 5th
Floor
Wilmington, DE 19801
P: (302) 577-8424
F: (302) 577-6987
E: Peter.Jamison
@state.de.us

DISTRICT OF COLUMBIA
Mr. William P. White
Commissioner
Department of Insurance,
Securities & Banking
810 First Street, Northeast, Suite
70
Washington, DC 20002
P: (202) 727-8000
F: (202) 535-1196

FLORIDA
Mr. J. Thomas Cardwell
Commissioner
Office of Financial Regulation
200 East Gaines Street
Tallahassee, FL 32399
P: (850) 410-9601
F: (850) 410-9663
E: OFR@flofr.com

GEORGIA
Mr. Robert Terry
Director of Securities
Securities & Business
Regulation Division
2 Martin Luther King Jr. Drive
Southeast
Suite 802, West Tower
Atlanta, GA 30334
P: (404) 656-9721
F: (404) 657-8410

HAWAII
Ms. Tung Chan
Commissioner
Business Registration Division
Business Registration Division
P.O. Box 40
Honolulu, HI 96810
P: (808) 586-2744
F: (808) 586-2733
E: breg@dcca.hawaii.gov

IDAHO
Ms. Marilyn T. Chastain
Securities Bureau Chief
Department of Finance
800 Park Boulevard, Suite 200
P.O. Box 83720
Boise, ID 83720
P: (208) 332-8004
F: (208) 332-8099
E: marilync
@finance.idaho.gov

ILLINOIS
Ms. Tanya Solov
Director of Securities
Securities Department
69 West Washington Street,
Suite 1220
Chicago, IL 60602
P: (312) 793-3384
F: (312) 793-1202

INDIANA
Mr. Jeff Bush
Chief Deputy Commissioner
Securities Division
Secretary of State
302 West Washington Street,
Room E-111
Indianapolis, IN 46204
P: (317) 234-2741
F: (317) 233-3675
E: jabush@sos.in.gov

IOWA
Mr. Craig A. Goettsch
Superintendent of Securities
Securities & Regulated
Industries Bureau
310-350 Maple Street
Des Moines, IA 50319
P: (515) 281-5705
F: (515) 281-3059
E: craig.goettsch
@iid.iowa.gov

KANSAS
Mr. Aaron Jack
Securities Commissioner
Office of the Securities
Commissioner
109 Southwest 9th Street, Suite
600
Topeka, KS 66612
P: (785) 296-3307
F: (785) 296-6872
E: ksc@ksc.ks.gov

LOUISIANA
Ms. Rhonda Reeves
Deputy Securities Commissioner
Office of Financial Institutions
8660 United Plaza Boulevard,
2nd Floor
P.O. Box 94095
Baton Rouge, LA 70804
P: (225) 925-4660
F: (225) 925-4548
E: rreeves@ofi.la.gov

MAINE
Ms. Judith M. Shaw
Securities Administrator
Department of Professional &
Financial Regulation
Office of Securities
121 State House Station
Augusta, ME 04333
P: (207) 624-8551
F: (207) 624-8590
E: judith.m.shaw@maine.gov

MARYLAND
Ms. Melanie Senter Lubin
Commissioner
Securities Division
Office of the Attorney General
200 Saint Paul Place
Baltimore, MD 21202
P: (410) 576-6365
F: (410) 576-6532
E: mlubin@oag.state.md.us

MASSACHUSETTS
Mr. Bryan Lantagne
Director
Securities Division
One Ashburton Place, Room 1701
Boston, MA 02108
P: (617) 727-3548
F: (617) 248-0177

MICHIGAN
Mr. R. Kevin Clinton
Commissioner
Office of Financial & Insurance Regulation
P.O. Box 30220
Lansing, MI 48909
P: (517) 373-0220
F: (517) 373-4978

MINNESOTA
Mr. Manny Munson-Regala
Deputy Commissioner, Market Assurance
Department of Commerce
85 East 7th Place, Suite 500
St. Paul, MN 55101
P: (651) 296-6025
F: (651) 282-2568
E: manny.munson-regala
    @state.mn.us

MISSISSIPPI
Mr. David Scott
Assistant Secretary of State
Business Regulation & Enforcement Division
700 North Street
Jackson, MS 39202
P: (601) 359-6371
F: (601) 359-2663

MISSOURI
Mr. Matthew Kitzi
Securities Commissioner
Securities Division
600 West Main Street
P.O. Box 1276
Jefferson City, MO 65102
P: (573) 751-4136
F: (573) 526-3124
E: securities@sos.mo.gov

MONTANA
Hon. Monica J. Lindeen (D)
State Auditor
Office of the Auditor
840 Helena Avenue
Helena, MT 59601
P: (406) 444-2006
F: (406) 444-3497
E: monica@lindeen.net

NEBRASKA
Mr. Jack E. Herstein
Assistant Director, Bureau of Securities
Department of Banking & Finance
1230 "O" Street, Suite 400
P.O. Box 95006
Lincoln, NE 68509
P: (402) 471-3445

NEVADA
Ms. Carolyn Ellsworth
Securities Administrator
Securities Division
Office of the Secretary of State
555 East Washington Avenue, Suite 5200
Las Vegas, NV 89101
P: (702) 486-2475
F: (702) 486-2452

NEW HAMPSHIRE
Mr. Joseph C. Long
Director of Securities Regulation
Bureau of Securities Regulation
Department of State
107 North Main Street, Room 204
Concord, NH 03301
P: (603) 271-1463
F: (603) 271-7933

NEW JERSEY
Ms. Amy Kopleton
Acting Bureau Chief
Bureau of Securities
153 Halsey Street, 6th Floor
P.O. Box 47029
Newark, NJ 07101
P: (973) 504-3600
F: (973) 504-3601

NEW MEXICO
Mr. Daniel S. Tanaka
Director
Securities Division
Regulation & Licensing Department
2550 Cerrillos Road
Santa Fe, NM 87505
P: (505) 476-4580
F: (505) 984-0617
E: daniel.tanaka
    @state.nm.us

NEW YORK
Mr. David Markowitz
Bureau Chief
Division of Economic Justice - Investor Protection Bureau
120 Broadway, 23rd Floor
New York, NY 10271
P: (212) 416-8222
F: (212) 416-8816

NORTH CAROLINA
Mr. David S. Massey
Deputy Securities Administrator
Department of the Secretary of State
Securities Division
P.O. Box 29622
Raleigh, NC 27626
P: (919) 733-3924
F: (919) 821-0818

NORTH DAKOTA
Ms. Karen Tyler
Commissioner
Securities Department
600 East Boulevard Avenue
State Capitol, 5th Floor
Bismarck, ND 58505
P: (701) 328-2910
F: (701) 328-2946
E: ktyler@nd.gov

OHIO
Ms. Andrea L. Seidt
Commissioner
Division of Securities
Department of Commerce
77 South High Street, 22nd Floor
Columbus, OH 43215
P: (614) 644-7381
E: securitiesgeneral.
    questions@com.state.oh.us

OKLAHOMA
Mr. Irving L. Faught
Administrator
Department of Securities
1st National Center, Suite 860
120 North Robinson
Oklahoma City, OK 73102
P: (405) 280-7700
F: (405) 280-7742

OREGON
Mr. David C. Tatman
Division Administrator
Division of Finance & Corporate Securities
350 Winter Street, Northeast, Room 410
Salem, OR 97301
P: (503) 378-4140
F: (503) 947-7862
E: dcbs.dfcsmail
    @state.or.us

PENNSYLVANIA
Mr. Robert M. Lam
Acting Chair
Securities Commission
Eastgate Office Building, 2nd Floor
1010 North 7th Street
Harrisburg, PA 17102
P: (717) 787-8061
F: (717) 783-5122

PUERTO RICO
Mr. Felipe B. Cruz
Assistant Commissioner
Commission of Financial Institutions
1492 Ponce De Leon Avenue
Suite 600
San Juan, PR 00907
P: (787) 723-3131 Ext. 2222

RHODE ISLAND
Ms. Maria D'Alessandro
Deputy Director & Superintendent
Commercial Licensing & Racing & Athletics
Department of Business Regulation
1511 Pontiac Avenue
Cranston, RI 02920
P: (401) 462-9506
F: (401) 462-9645

SOUTH CAROLINA
Mr. Stephen Lynch
Deputy Securities Commissioner
Securities Division
Office of the Attorney General
P.O. Box 11549
Columbia, SC 29211
P: (803) 734-3718
F: (803) 734-0032

SOUTH DAKOTA
Mr. Michael J. Youngberg
Director
Division of Securities
Department of Labor & Regulation
445 East Capitol Avenue
Pierre, SD 57501
P: (605) 773-4823
F: (605) 773-5953
E: drr.securities
    @state.sd.us

Securities

TENNESSEE
Ms. Daphne D. Smith
Assistant Commissioner for
Securities
Securities Division
Department of Commerce and
Insurance
500 James Robertson Parkway
Nashville, TN 37243
P: (615) 741-2947
F: (615) 532-8375

TEXAS
Ms. Benette Zivley
Commissioner
State Securities Board
208 East 10th Street, 5th Floor
P.O. Box 13167
Austin, TX 78711
P: (512) 305-8300
F: (512) 305-8310

UTAH
Mr. Keith Woodwell
Director
Division of Securities
Department of Commerce
P.O. Box 146760
Salt Lake City, UT 84114
P: (801) 530-6606
F: (801) 530-6980
E: kwoodwell@utah.gov

VERMONT
Mr. Thomas J. Candon
Deputy Commissioner,
Securities Division
Department of Banking,
Insurance, Securities & Health
Care Administration
89 Main Street
Montpelier, VT 05620
P: (802) 828-4874
F: (802) 828-2896
E: tom.candon@state.vt.us

VIRGINIA
Mr. Ronald W. Thomas
Director
Division of Securities & Retail
Franchising
1300 East Main Street
9th Floor
Richmond, VA 23219
P: (804) 371-9051
F: (804) 371-9911
E: ron.thomas
    @scc.virginia.gov

WASHINGTON
Mr. Scott Jarvis
Director
Department of Financial
Institutions
P.O. Box 41200
Olympia, WA 98504
P: (360) 902-8700
F: (360) 586-5068
E: confsec@dfi.wa.gov

WEST VIRGINIA
Ms. Lisa Hopkins
Senior Deputy Commissioner of
Securities
Securities Division
Office of the State Auditor
State Capitol Building 1, Room
W-100
Charleston, WV 25305
P: (304) 558-2261
F: (304) 558-5200
E: lisa.hopkins@wvsao.gov

WISCONSIN
Ms. Patricia D. Struck
Administrator
Division of Securities
345 West Washington Avenue
P.O. Box 1768
Madison, WI 53701
P: (608) 266-1064
F: (608) 264-7979
E: patricia.struck
    @dfi.wisconsin.gov

WYOMING
Mr. Thomas Cowan
Division Director
Securities Division
State Capitol, Room 109
200 West 24th Street
Cheyenne, WY 82002
P: (307) 777-7370
F: (307) 777-5339

Small and Minority Business Assistance

Provides assistance and information on financing and government procurement opportunities to small and minority business ventures.

ALABAMA

Mr. Seth Hammett
Director
Development Office
401 Adams Avenue, 6th Floor
Montgomery, AL 36130
P: (334) 242-0400
F: (334) 242-5669
E: seth.hammett
@ado.alabama.gov

ALASKA

Mr. Michael Hanzuk
Development Specialist
Department of Commerce,
Community & Economic
Development
Office of Economic
Development
550 West Seventh Avenue, Suite
1770
Anchorage, AK 99501
P: (907) 269-8104
F: (907) 269-8125
E: michael.hanzuk
@alaska.gov

AMERICAN SAMOA

Mr. Faleseu Eliu Paopao
Director
Department of Commerce
American Samoa Government
Executive Office Building,
Utulei
Pago Pago, AS 96799
P: (684) 633-5155
F: (684) 633-4195

ARIZONA

Mr. Donald E. Cardon
President & CEO
Commerce Authority
1110 West Washington Street,
Suite 600
Phoenix, AZ 85007
P: (602) 771-1160
F: (602) 771-1200
E: commerce@azcommerce.com

ARKANSAS

Ms. Patricia Nunn Brown
Director of Small & Minority
Business
Economic Development
Commission
900 West Capital Avenue
Little Rock, AR 72201
P: (501) 682-2559
E: pbrown@arkansasedc.com

CALIFORNIA

Ms. Karen Mills
Administrator
Office of Small Business
Advocate
P.O. Box 3044
Sacramento, CA 95812
P: (916) 445-9874
F: (916) 445-6305

COLORADO

Ms. Kelly Manning
Director
Small Business Development
Center
1625 Broadway, Suite 1710
Denver, CO 80202
P: (303) 892-3840
F: (303) 892-3848
E: kelly.manning
@state.co.us

Mr. LeRoy Romero
Division Director
Minority & Women's Business
Office
1625 Broadway, Suite 1700
Denver, CO 80202
P: (303) 892-3840
F: (303) 892-3848
E: l.romero@state.co.us

DISTRICT OF COLUMBIA

Mr. Gustavo F. Velasquez
Director
Office of Human Rights
441 4th Street, Northwest
Suite 570 North
Washington, DC 20001
P: (202) 727-4559
F: (202) 727-9589
E: ohr@dc.gov

FLORIDA

Mr. Jack Miles
Secretary
Department of Management
Services
4050 Esplande Way, Suite 280
Tallahassee, FL 32399
P: (850) 488-2786
F: (850) 922-6149

GEORGIA

Mr. Chris Cummiskey
Commissioner
Department of Economic
Development
75 Fifth Street, Northwest
Suite 1200
Atlanta, GA 30308
P: (404) 962-4003
F: (404) 962-4009
E: ccummiskey@geogia.org

HAWAII

Mr. Richard C. Lim
Director
Department of Business,
Economic Development &
Tourism
P.O. Box 2359
Honolulu, HI 96804
P: (808) 586-2355
F: (808) 586-2377
E: director
@dbedt.hawaii.gov

IDAHO

Mr. Donald A. Dietrich
Director
Department of Commerce
700 West State Street
P.O. Box 83720
Boise, ID 83720
P: (208) 334-2470
F: (208) 334-2631
E: don.dietrich
@commerce.idaho.gov

ILLINOIS

Mr. Warren Ribley
Director
Department of Commerce &
Economic Opportunity
James R. Thompson Center
100 West Randolph
Chicago, IL 60601
P: (312) 814-7179

INDIANA

Ms. Felecia Roseburgh
Deputy Commissioner
Minority & Women's Business
Enterprises
Department of Administration
402 West Washington Street,
Room W-469
Indianapolis, IN 46204
P: (317) 232-3061
F: (317) 233-6921
E: froseburgh@idoa.in.gov

IOWA

Ms. Debi Durham
Director
Department of Economic
Development
200 East Grand Avenue
Des Moines, IA 50309
P: (515) 725-3022
F: (515) 725-3010
E: debi.durham@iowa.gov

KANSAS

Ms. Rhonda F. Harris
Director
Office of Minority & Women
Business Development
Suite 100, Curtis State Office
Building
1000 Southwest Jackson Street
Topeka, KS 66612
P: (785) 296-3425
F: (785) 296-3487
E: rharris
@kansascommerce.com

KENTUCKY

Mr. Mark Johnson
Branch Manager
Small & Minority Business
Branch
Old Capitol Annex
300 West Broadway
Frankfort, KY 40601
P: (502) 564-7140
F: (502) 564-3256
E: markl.johnson@ky.gov

LOUISIANA

Mr. Stephen Moret
Secretary
Economic Development
1051 North Third Street
Baton Rouge, LA 70802
P: (225) 342-5388
F: (225) 342-9095
E: Allison.Gilmore@la.gov

MAINE

Mr. George Gervais
Acting Commissioner
Department of Economic &
Community Development
59 State House Station
Augusta, ME 04330
P: (207) 624-9800

MARYLAND

Mr. James J. King
Small Business Advisor
Department of Business &
Economic Development
401 East Pratt Street
Baltimore, MD 21202
P: (410) 767-6799
E: JKing@choosemaryland.org

Small and Minority Business Assistance

MASSACHUSETTS
Ms. Sandra E. Borders
Director
Office of Diversity & Equal
Opportunity
One Ashburton Place, Room 213
Boston, MA 02108
P: (617) 727-7441
F: (617) 727-0568

MICHIGAN
Mr. Michael A. Finney
President & CEO
Economic Development
Corporation
300 North Washington Square
Lansing, MI 48913
P: (517) 241-1400
F: (517) 241-3683

MINNESOTA
Mr. Spencer Cronk
Commissioner
Department of Administration
50 Sherburne Avenue
200 Administration Building
St. Paul, MN 55155
P: (651) 201-2555
F: (651) 297-7909
E: Spencer.Cronk
    @state.mn.us

MISSISSIPPI
Mr. Leland R. Speed
Executive Director
Development Authority
501 North West Street
P.O. Box 849
Jackson, MS 39205
P: (601) 359-3449
F: (601) 359-3613
E: lspeed@mississippi.org

MISSOURI
Mr. Alan Green
Director
Office of Supplier & Workforce
Diversity
Harry S. Truman Building
301 West High Street, Room 630
Jefferson City, MO 65101
P: (573) 751-8130
F: (573) 522-8078
E: alan.green@oa.mo.gov

MONTANA
Mr. Dore Schwinden
Director
Department of Commerce
301 South Park
P.O. Box 200501
Helena, MT 59620
P: (406) 841-2704
F: (406) 841-2701
E: dschwinden@mt.gov

NEBRASKA
Mr. Richard Baier
Director
Department of Economic
Development
P.O. Box 94666
Lincoln, NE 68509
P: (402) 471-3111
F: (402) 471-3778
E: richard.baier
    @nebraska.gov

NEVADA
Mr. Rico White
Chair
Commission on Minority Affairs
Department of Business &
Industry
555 East Washington Avenue,
Suite 4900
Las Vegas, NV 89101
P: (775) 486-9752
E: info
    @minorityaffairs.nv.gov

NEW HAMPSHIRE
Mr. Jack Donovan
Executive Director
Business Finance Authority
2 Pillsbury Street, Suite 201
Concord, NH 03301
P: (603) 415-0191
F: (603) 415-0194
E: JackD@nhbfa.com

NEW JERSEY
Ms. Caren S. Franzini
Chief Executive Officer
Economic Development
Authority
36 West State Street
P.O. Box 990
Trenton, NJ 08625
P: (609) 292-1800
F: (609) 292-0885
E: njeda@njeda.com

NEW MEXICO
Ms. Nancy Baker
Regional Representative
Economic Development
Department
1100 South Saint Francis Drive
Suite 1060
Santa Fe, NM 87505
P: (505) 827-0228
F: (505) 827-0328
E: Nancy.Baker@state.nm.us

NEW YORK
Mr. Kenneth Adams
President & CEO
Empire State Development
Corporation
633 Third Avenue
New York, NY 10017
P: (212) 803-3700
F: (212) 803-3715

NORTH CAROLINA
Mr. Scott Daugherty
Executive Director
Small Business & Technology
Development Center
5 West Hargett Street, Suite 600
Raleigh, NC 27601
P: (919) 715-7272
F: (919) 715-7777

NORTH DAKOTA
Mr. Al Anderson
Commissioner
Department of Commerce
1600 East Century Avenue,
Suite 2
P.O. Box 2057
Bismarck, ND 58503
P: (701) 328-7284
F: (701) 328-5320
E: alrandeson@nd.gov

**NORTHERN MARIANA
ISLANDS**
Mr. Manuel Sablan
Director
Commonwealth Development
Authority
P.O. Box 502149
Saipan, MP 96950
P: (670) 234-6245
F: (670) 234-7144

OKLAHOMA
Ms. Vikki Dearing
Director, Business Solutions
Department of Commerce
900 North Stiles Avenue
Oklahoma City, OK 73104
P: (405) 815-5114
F: (405) 605-2811

PENNSYLVANIA
Mr. C. Alan Walker
Acting Secretary
Department of Community &
Economic Development
Commonwealth Keystone
Building
400 North Street, 4th Floor
Harrisburg, PA 17120
P: (866) 466-3972
F: (717) 787-6866

RHODE ISLAND
Mr. Charles C. Newton
Administrator
Department of Administration
Minority Business Enterprise
One Capitol Hill, 2nd Floor
Providence, RI 02908
P: (401) 574-8670
F: (401) 574-8387
E: CNewton
    @gw.doa.state.ri.us

SOUTH CAROLINA
Ms. Andrena Washington
Interim Director
Office of Small & Minority
Business Assistance
1205 Pendleton Street, Suite
440-A
Columbia, SC 29201
P: (803) 734-0507
F: (803) 734-2498
E: anwashington@oepp.sc.gov

SOUTH DAKOTA
Mr. Pat Costello
Commissioner
Governor's Office of Economic
Development
711 East Wells Avenue
Pierre, SD 57501
P: (605) 773-3301
F: (605) 773-3256
E: goedinfo@state.sd.us

TENNESSEE
Ms. Lorie Shauntee
Diversity Business Liaison
Department of Economic &
Community Development
Business Development
312 Rosa L. Parks Avenue,
Eleventh Floor
Nashville, TN 37243
P: (615) 532-3915
F: (615) 741-5829
E: Lorie.Shauntee@tn.gov

TEXAS
Mr. Terry Keel
Executive Director
Facilities Commission
1711 San Jacinto
Austin, TX 78701
P: (512) 463-3446
E: terry.keel
    @tfc.state.tx.us

U.S. VIRGIN ISLANDS
Mr. Percival Clouden
Chief Executive Officer
Economic Development
Authority
1050 Norre Gade
P.O. Box 305038
St. Thomas, VI 00803
P: (340) 714-1700

UTAH
Mr. Spencer Peterson Eccles
Executive Director
Governor's Office of Economic
Development
324 South State Street, Suite
500
Salt Lake City, UT 84111
P: (801) 538-8700
F: (801) 538-8888
E: speccles@utah.gov

VIRGINIA
Ms. Ida McPherson
Director
Department of Minority
Business Enterprise
1100 East Main Street, Suite 300
Richmond, VA 23219
P: (804) 371-6228
F: (804) 371-7359
E: ida.mcpherson
    @dmbe.virginia.gov

WASHINGTON
Mr. Rogers Weed
Director
Department of Commerce
128 10th Avenue, Southwest
P.O. Box 42525
Olympia, WA 98504
P: (360) 725-4000
F: (360) 586-8440
E: rogersw@cted.wa.gov

WEST VIRGINIA
Mr. J. Keith Burdette
Secretary of Commerce
Department of Commerce
Capitol Complex Building 6,
Room 525
1900 Kanawha Boulevard East
Charleston, WV 25305
P: (304) 558-2234
F: (304) 558-1189
E: J.Keith.Burdette@wv.gov

WISCONSIN
Mr. Jim O'Keefe
Administrator
Business Development Division
201 West Washington Avenue,
5th Floor
Madison, WI 53703
P: (608) 267-9384
E: jim.okeefe@wisconsin.gov

WYOMING
Mr. Bob Jensen
Chief Executive Officer
Business Council
214 West 15th Street
Cheyenne, WY 82002
P: (307) 777-2800
F: (307) 777-2837
E: bob.jensen
    @wybusiness.org

Social Services

Responsible for the delivery of services to children, disabled, and elderly.

ALABAMA
Ms. Nancy T. Buckner
Commissioner
Department of Human Resources
50 North Ripley Street
Montgomery, AL 36130
P: (334) 242-1160
F: (334) 242-0198
E: Nancy.Buckner
@dhr.alabama.gov

ALASKA
Mr. William Streur
Commissioner
Department of Health and Social Services
3601 C Street
Suite 902
Anchorage, AK 99503
P: (907) 465-3030
F: (907) 465-3068
E: william.streur
@alaska.gov

AMERICAN SAMOA
Ms. Leilua Stevenson
Director
Department of Human & Social Services
American Samoa Government
P.O. Box 997534
Pago Pago, AS
P: (684) 633-7506
F: (684) 633-7449

ARIZONA
Mr. Clarence H. Carter
Director
Department of Economic Security
1717 West Jefferson Street
Phoenix, AZ 85007
P: (602) 542-4791

ARKANSAS
Ms. Joni Jones
Director
Division of County Operations
P.O. Box 1437, Slot S301
Little Rock, AR 72203
P: (501) 682-8375
F: (501) 682-8367
E: joni.jones@arkansas.gov

CALIFORNIA
Mr. Will Lightbourne
Director
Department of Social Services
744 P Street
Sacramento, CA 95814
P: (916) 657-2598
F: (916) 651-6569

COLORADO
Mr. Reginald L. Bicha
Executive Director
Department of Human Services
1575 Sherman Street
Denver, CO 80203
P: (303) 866-5700
F: (303) 866-4740

CONNECTICUT
Mr. Roderick L. Bremby
Commissioner
Department of Social Services
25 Sigourney Street
Hartford, CT 06106
P: (860) 424-5053
E: roderick.bremby@ct.gov

DELAWARE
Ms. Rita Landgraf
Secretary
Department of Health & Social Services
Main Building
1901 North DuPont Highway
New Castle, DE 19720
P: (302) 255-9040
F: (302) 255-4429

DISTRICT OF COLUMBIA
Mr. David A. Berns
Director
Department of Human Services
64 New York Avenue, Northeast
6th Floor
Washington, DC 20002
P: (202) 671-4200
E: dhs@dc.gov

FLORIDA
Mr. David Wilkins
Secretary
Department of Children & Families
1317 Winewood Boulevard
Building 1, Room 202
Tallahassee, FL 32399
P: (850) 487-1111
F: (850) 922-2993
E: david_wilkins
@dcf.state.fl.us

GEORGIA
Mr. Clyde Reese
Commissioner
Department of Human Services
2 Peachtree Street, Northwest
Room 29-250
Atlanta, GA 30303
P: (404) 463-3390
F: (404) 651-8669

HAWAII
Ms. Patricia McManaman
Director
Department of Human Services
1390 Miller Street, Room 209
Honolulu, HI 96813
P: (808) 586-4997
F: (808) 586-4890
E: dhs@dhs.hawaii.gov

IDAHO
Mr. Ron Luce
Administrator
Division of Family & Community Services
450 West State Street
5th Floor, Pete T. Cenarrusa Building
Boise, ID 83720
P: (208) 334-5680
F: (208) 332-7331
E: lucer@dhw.idaho.gov

ILLINOIS
Mr. Erwin McEwen
Director
Department of Children & Family Services
406 East Monroe Street
Springfield, IL 62701
P: (217) 785-2509
F: (217) 785-1052

INDIANA
Mr. Mike Carr
Director, Division of Family Resources
Family & Social Services Administration
402 West Washington Street, Room W392
P.O. Box 7083
Indianapolis, IN 46207
P: (317) 233-4450
E: michael.carr@fssa.in.gov

IOWA
Ms. Sally Titus
Deputy Director
Department of Human Services
Hoover Building
1305 East Walnut
Des Moines, IA 50319
P: (515) 281-6360
F: (515) 281-4597
E: stitus@dhs.state.ia.us

KANSAS
Mr. Robert Siedlecki
Secretary
Department of Social & Rehabilitation Services
915 Southwest Harrison Street, 6th Floor
Topeka, KS 66612
P: (785) 296-3271
F: (785) 296-2173

KENTUCKY
Ms. Janie Miller
Secretary
Cabinet for Health & Family Services
275 East Main Street
Mailstop 5W-A
Frankfort, KY 40621
P: (502) 564-7042
F: (502) 564-7091

LOUISIANA
Ms. Ruth Johnson
Secretary
Department of Children & Family Services
627 North 4th Street
P.O. Box 3776
Baton Rouge, LA 70821
P: (225) 342-0286
F: (225) 342-8636

MAINE
Ms. Mary Mayhew
Commissioner
Department of Health & Human Services
221 State Street
Augusta, ME 04333
P: (207) 287-3707
F: (207) 287-3005
E: mary.mayhew@maine.gov

MARYLAND
Mr. Theodore Dallas
Interim Secretary
Department of Human Resources
311 West Saratoga Street
Baltimore, MD 21201
P: (410) 767-7109

MASSACHUSETTS
Mr. Angelo McClain
Commissioner
Department of Children & Families
24 Farnsworth Street
Boston, MA 02210
P: (617) 748-2000

MICHIGAN
Ms. Maura D. Corrigan
Director
Department of Human Services
235 South Grand Avenue
P.O. Box 30037
Lansing, MI 48909
P: (517) 373-2035
F: (517) 335-6101
E: dhsweb@michigan.gov

MISSISSIPPI
Mr. Derra Dukes
Director
Office of Social Services Block
Grant
Department of Human Services
750 North State Street
Jackson, MS 39202
P: (601) 359-4500

MISSOURI
Mr. Ronald J. Levy
Director
Department of Social Services
221 West High Street
P.O. Box 1527
Jefferson City, MO 65102
P: (573) 751-4815
F: (573) 751-3203

MONTANA
Ms. Anna Whiting Sorrell
Director
Department of Public Health &
Human Services
111 North Sanders, Room 301
P.O. Box 4210
Helena, MT 59604
P: (406) 444-5622
F: (406) 444-1970

NEBRASKA
Mr. Todd Reckling
Director
Division of Children & Family
Services
Department of Health & Human
Services
P.O. Box 95026
Lincoln, NE 60509
P: (402) 471-1878

NEVADA
Mr. Michael J. Willden
Director
Department of Health & Human
Services
4126 Technology Way, Room
100
Carson City, NV 89706
P: (775) 684-4000
F: (775) 684-4010
E: mwillden@dhhs.nv.gov

NEW HAMPSHIRE
Mr. Nicholas A. Toumpas
Commissioner
Department of Health & Human
Services
129 Pleasant Street
Concord, NH 03301
P: (603) 271-4331
F: (603) 271-4912
E: ntoumpas
   @dhhs.state.nh.us

NEW JERSEY
Ms. Jennifer Velez
Commissioner
Department of Human Services
222 South Warren Street
P.O. Box 700
Trenton, NJ 08625
P: (609) 292-3717

NEW MEXICO
Ms. Veronica Gonzales
Secretary
Department of Cultural Affairs
407 Galisteo, Suite 260
Santa Fe, NM 87501
P: (505) 827-6364

Ms. Sidonie Squier
Secretary
Human Services Department
P.O. Box 2348
Santa Fe, NM 87504
P: (505) 827-7750
F: (505) 827-3185

NEW YORK
Ms. Elizabeth R. Berlin
Executive Deputy Secretary
Office of Temporary &
Disability Assistance
40 North Pearl Street
Albany, NY 12243
P: (518) 474-4152
F: (518) 486-9179

NORTH CAROLINA
Ms. Sherry S. Bradsher
Director
Division of Social Services
325 North Salisbury Street
2401 Mail Service Center
Raleigh, NC 27699
P: (919) 733-3055
F: (919) 733-9386
E: sherry.bradsher
   @dhhs.nc.gov

NORTH DAKOTA
Ms. Carol K. Olson
Executive Director
Department of Human Services
State Capitol, Judicial Wing
600 East Boulevard Avenue,
Dept. 325
Bismarck, ND 58505
P: (701) 328-2538
F: (701) 328-1545
E: colson@nd.gov

**NORTHERN MARIANA
ISLANDS**
Mr. Joseph P. Villagomez
Secretary of Public Health
Department of Public Health
P.O. Box 500409
Saipan, MP 96950
P: (670) 236-8201
F: (670) 234-8930
E: jkvsaipan@aol.com

OHIO
Mr. Michael B. Colbert
Director
Department of Job & Family
Services
30 East Broad Street, 32nd Floor
Columbus, OH 43215
P: (614) 466-6283
F: (614) 466-2815

OKLAHOMA
Mr. Howard H. Hendrick
Secretary
Department of Human Services
2400 North Lincoln Boulevard
P.O. Box 25352
Oklahoma City, OK 73125
P: (405) 521-3646

OREGON
Ms. Erinn L. Kelley-Siel
Acting Director
Department of Human Services
500 Summer Street, Northeast,
E-62
Salem, OR 97301
P: (503) 945-5944
F: (503) 378-2897
E: erinn.kelley-siel
   @state.or.us

PENNSYLVANIA
Mr. Gary D. Alexander
Acting Secretary
Department of Public Welfare
P.O. Box 2675
Harrisburg, PA 17105
P: (717) 787-2600
F: (717) 772-2062

PUERTO RICO
Ms. Yanitsia Irizarry
   Mendez
Secretary
Department of the Family
P.O. Box 11398
San Juan, PR 00910
P: (787) 294-4900
F: (787) 294-0732

RHODE ISLAND
Ms. Sandra M. Powell
Director
Department of Human Services
Louis Pasteur Building
600 New London Avenue
Cranston, RI 02920
P: (401) 462-2121
F: (401) 462-3677
E: Director@dhs.ri.gov

SOUTH CAROLINA
Ms. Lillian B. Koller
Director
Department of Social Services
1535 Confederate Avenue
Extension
P.O. Box 1520
Columbia, SC 29202
P: (803) 898-7360
F: (803) 898-7277

SOUTH DAKOTA
Ms. Kim Malsam-Rysdon
Secretary
Department of Social Services
700 Governors Drive
Pierre, SD 57501
P: (605) 773-3165
F: (605) 773-4855
E: DSSInfo@state.sd.us

TENNESSEE
Dr. Raquel Hatter
Commissioner
Department of Human Services
400 Deaderick Street, 15th Floor
Nashville, TN 37243
P: (615) 313-4700
F: (615) 741-4165

TEXAS
Mr. Lawrence Parker
Deputy Executive Commissioner
for Social Services
Health & Human Services
Commission
4900 North Lamar
P.O. Box 13247
Austin, TX 78711
P: (512) 424-3427
F: (512) 424-6587

Social Services

U.S. VIRGIN ISLANDS
Mr. Christopher Finch
Commissioner
Department of Human Services
Knud Hansen Complex,
Building A
1303 Hospital Grounds
St. Thomas, VI 00802
P: (340) 774-0930
F: (340) 774-3466

UTAH
Mr. Palmer DePaulis
Executive Director
Department of Human Services
195 North 1950 West
Salt Lake City, UT 84116
P: (801) 538-4171
F: (801) 538-4016
E: palmer@utah.gov

VIRGINIA
Mr. Martin D. Brown
Commissioner
Department of Social Services
801 East Main Street
Richmond, VA 23219
P: (804) 726-7000
E: martin.brown
    @dss.virginia.gov

WASHINGTON
Ms. Susan N. Dreyfus
Secretary
Department of Social & Health
Services
P.O. Box 45130
Olympia, WA 98504
P: (360) 902-7800

WEST VIRGINIA
Mr. Michael J. Lewis
Cabinet Secretary
Department of Health & Human
Resources
One Davis Square, Suite 100
East
Charleston, WV 25301
P: (304) 558-0684
F: (304) 558-1130
E: DHHRSecretary@wv.gov

WISCONSIN
Mr. Dennis G. Smith
Secretary
Department of Health & Family
Services
1 West Wilson Street, Room 650
Madison, WI 53702
P: (608) 266-1865
E: dennis.smith
    @dhs.wisconsin.gov

WYOMING
Mr. Steve Corsi
Director of Family Services
Department of Family Services
Hathaway Building, 3rd Floor
2300 Capitol Avenue
Cheyenne, WY 82002
P: (307) 777-7564
F: (307) 777-7747

State Data Center

Center that acts as an information clearinghouse for the Census Bureau and other data sources within the state.

ALABAMA
Ms. Annette Watters
Director
State Data Center
University of Alabama
P.O. Box 870221
Tuscaloosa, AL 35487
P: (205) 348-6191
F: (205) 348-2951
E: awatters@cba.ua.edu

ALASKA
Mr. Click Bishop
Commissioner
Department of Labor &
Workforce Development
P.O. Box 21149
Juneau, AK 99802
P: (907) 465-2700
F: (907) 465-2784
E: commissioner.labor
    @ak.gov

AMERICAN SAMOA
Mr. Vai Filiga
Statistician
Department of Commerce
American Samoa Government
Pago Pago, AS 96799
P: (684) 633-5155
F: (684) 633-4195
E: JRScanlan@samoatelco.com

ARIZONA
Mr. Allen L. Barnes
State Data Center Lead
Population Statistics Unit
Commerce Authority
1700 West Washington Street,
Suite 600
Phoenix, AZ 85007
P: (602) 542-5746
F: (602) 771-1207
E: AllenB@azcommerce.com

ARKANSAS
Ms. Phyllis Poche
Director
Census State Data Center
2801 South University
Little Rock, AR 72204
P: (501) 569-8530
F: (501) 569-8538
E: pnpoche@ualr.edu

CALIFORNIA
Mr. John Malson
Acting Chief
Demographic Research Unit
915 L Street
Sacramento, CA 95814
P: (916) 323-4086
F: (916) 327-0222
E: john.malson@dof.ca.gov

COLORADO
Ms. Elizabeth Garner
State Demographer
Demography Office
Department of Local Affairs
1313 Sherman Street, Room 521
Denver, CO 80203
P: (303) 866-3096
F: (303) 866-2660
E: elizabeth.garner
    @state.co.us

CONNECTICUT
Mr. Orlando Rodriguez
Manager and Demographer
State Data Center
University of Connecticut
341 Mansfield Road, Room 401
Storrs, CT 06269
P: (860) 486-9269
E: Orlando.Rodriguez
    @uconn.edu

DELAWARE
Mr. Michael B. Mahaffie
GIS/Spatial Data
Coordinator/Webmaster
Office of State Planning
Coordination
122 William Penn Street, Suite
302
Haslet Building, Third Floor
Dover, DE 19901
P: (302) 739-3090
F: (302) 739-6958
E: mike.mahaffie
    @state.de.us

DISTRICT OF COLUMBIA
Ms. Joy E. Phillips
Associate Director
State Data Center
801 North Capitol Street,
Northeast
Suite 4000
Washington, DC 20002
P: (202) 442-7600
F: (202) 442-7637

FLORIDA
Mr. David W. Taylor
Executive Director & Chief
Information Officer
Agency for Enterprise
Information Technology
4030 Esplanade Way, Suite 135
Tallahassee, FL 32399
P: (850) 922-7502
F: (850) 487-9937
E: David.Taylor
    @aeit.myflorida.com

GEORGIA
Mr. Robert Giacomini
Director of Research
Office of Planning & Budget
270 Washington Street,
Southwest
8th Floor
Atlanta, GA 30334
P: (404) 653-4445
F: (404) 656-3828
E: robert.giacomini
    @opb.state.ga.us

GUAM
Mr. Alberto C. Lamorena V
Acting Director
Bureau of Statistics & Plans
P.O. Box 2950
Hagatna, GU 96932
P: (671) 472-4201
F: (671) 477-1812

HAWAII
Ms. Jan Nakamoto
Research & Economic Analysis
Division
State Data Center
P.O. Box 2359
Honolulu, HI 96804
P: (808) 586-2493
F: (808) 586-8449
E: jnakamot
    @dbedt.hawaii.gov

IDAHO
Mr. Donald A. Dietrich
Director
Department of Commerce
700 West State Street
P.O. Box 83720
Boise, ID 83720
P: (208) 334-2470
F: (208) 334-2631
E: don.dietrich
    @commerce.idaho.gov

ILLINOIS
Ms. Suzanne Ebetsch
Coordinator
Information Management
Commerce & Economic
Opportunity
620 East Adams
Springfield, IL 62701
P: (217) 524-0187
F: (217) 524-4876

INDIANA
Ms. Roberta L. Brooker
State Librarian
State Library
315 West Ohio Street, Room
407
Indianapolis, IN 46202
P: (317) 232-3692
E: rbrooker@library.in.gov

IOWA
Mr. Gary Krob
Data Warehouse Analyst
State Data Center
Ola Babcock Miller Building
1112 East Grand Avenue
Des Moines, IA 50319
P: (515) 281-6618
F: (515) 242-6543
E: gary.krob
    @lib.state.ia.us

KENTUCKY
Mr. Michael Price
Interim Director
State Data Center
University of Louisville
426 West Bloom Street
Louisville, KY 40208
P: (502) 852-7990
F: (502) 852-7386

LOUISIANA
Mr. Neal Underwood
Program Management Director
Office of Information
Technology
Division of Administration
P.O. Box 94095
Baton Rouge, LA 70804
P: (225) 219-9470
F: (225) 219-9465
E: neal.underwood@la.gov

MAINE
Mr. Michael LeVert
State Economist
State Planning Office
38 State House Station
Augusta, ME 04333
P: (207) 287-1479
F: (207) 287-6489
E: michael.levert@maine.gov

State Data Center

MARYLAND
Ms. Jane Traynham
Manager
Research & State Data Center
Department of Planning
301 West Preston Street
Baltimore, MD 21201
P: (410) 767-4450
F: (410) 767-4480
E: jtraynham
　@mdp.state.md.us

MASSACHUSETTS
Mr. John Gaviglio
Data Manager
State Data Center
UMASS Donahue Institute
100 Venture Way, Suite 9
Hadley, MA 02035
P: (413) 545-0176
F: (413) 545-3420
E: jgaviglio
　@donahue.umassp.edu

MICHIGAN
Mr. David Behen
Director & CIO
Department of Technology,
Management & Budget
320 South Walnut Street, 2nd
Floor
Lansing, MI 48933
P: (517) 373-1006
F: (517) 373-8213

MINNESOTA
Mr. Spencer Cronk
Commissioner
Department of Administration
50 Sherburne Avenue
200 Administration Building
St. Paul, MN 55155
P: (651) 201-2555
F: (651) 297-7909
E: Spencer.Cronk
　@state.mn.us

MISSISSIPPI
Mr. Cliff Holley
Director
Center for Population Studies
Leavel Hall, Room 101
University, MS 38677
P: (662) 232-7288
F: (662) 915-7736
E: saholley@olemiss.edu

MISSOURI
Ms. Katina Jones
Statistical Research Analyst
Census Data Center
State Library
P.O. Box 387
Jefferson City, MO 65101
P: (573) 526-1087
E: katina.jones@sos.mo.gov

MONTANA
Mr. Richard Clark
Chief Information Officer
Information Technology
Services Division
Department of Administration
P.O. Box 200113
Helena, MT 59620
P: (406) 444-2700
F: (406) 444-2701
E: dclark@mt.gov

NEBRASKA
Mr. Jerome Deichart
Director
Center for Public Affairs
Research
University of Nebraska Omaha
Omaha, NE 68182
P: (402) 554-2134
F: (402) 554-4946
E: jdeicher@unomaha.edu

NEVADA
Mr. William D. Anderson
Chief Economist
Department of Employment,
Training & Rehabilitation
Research & Analysis Bureau
500 East Third Street
Carson City, NV 89713
P: (775) 684-0387
F: (775) 684-3850
E: wdanderson@nvdetr.org

NEW HAMPSHIRE
Ms. Joanne L. Cassulo
Senior Planner
State Data Center
Office of Energy & Planning
4 Chenell Drive
Concord, NH 03301
P: (603) 271-1755
F: (603) 271-2615
E: joanne.cassulo@nh.gov

NEW JERSEY
Mr. Len Preston
Director
State Data Center
P.O. Box 388
Trenton, NJ 08625
P: (609) 984-2595
F: (609) 984-6833
E: lpreston@dol.state.nj.us

NEW MEXICO
Ms. Elizabeth Davis
Research Program Officer
Economic Development
Department
1100 St. Francis Drive
P.O. Box 20003
Santa Fe, NM 87504
P: (505) 827-0264
F: (505) 827-0211
E: Elizabeth.Davis
　@state.nm.us

NEW YORK
Mr. Robert Scardamalia
Chief Demographer
State Data Center
30 South Pearl Street
Albany, NY 12207
P: (518) 292-5300
E: rscardamalia
　@empire.state.ny.us

NORTH CAROLINA
Ms. Francine Stephenson
Manager
Office of State Budget &
Management
State Data Center
116 West Jones Street
Raleigh, NC 27603
P: (919) 807-4700
E: francine.stephenson
　@osbm.nc.gov

NORTH DAKOTA
Dr. Lisa Feldner
Chief Information Officer
Information Technology
Department
600 East Boulevard Avenue
Department 112
Bismarck, ND 58505
P: (701) 328-1000
F: (701) 328-3000
E: lfeldner@nd.gov

**NORTHERN MARIANA
ISLANDS**
Mr. Sixto Igisomar
Acting Secretary
Department of Commerce
Caller Box 10007
Saipan, MP 96950
P: (670) 664-3064
F: (670) 664-3067

OHIO
Mr. James A. Leftwich
Director
Department of Development
77 South High Street
P.O. Box 1001
Columbus, OH 43216
P: (614) 466-3379
F: (614) 644-0745
E: jim.leftwich
　@development.oh.gov

OKLAHOMA
Ms. Deidre Myers
Division Director
Policy, Research & Economic
Analysis
900 North Stiles Avenue
Oklahoma City, OK 73104
P: (405) 815-5383
F: (405) 605-2807
E: deidre_myers
　@okcommerce.gov

OREGON
Ms. Julie Bozzi
Administrator
State Data Center
530 Airport Road
Salem, OR 97301
P: (503) 378-4578
E: julie.bozzi@state.or.us

PENNSYLVANIA
Ms. Sue Copella
Director
State Data Center
777 West Harrisburg Pike
Middletown, PA 17057
P: (717) 948-6427
F: (717) 948-6754
E: sdc3@psu.edu

PUERTO RICO
Mr. Juan C. Pavia
Director
Office of Budget &
Management
P.O. Box 9023228
San Juan, PR 00902
P: (787) 725-9420
F: (787) 721-8329

RHODE ISLAND
Mr. Mark Brown
Principal Planner
Division of Planning,
Geographic & Demographic
Data Center
Department of Administration
One Capitol Hill
Providence, RI 02908
P: (401) 222-6183
F: (401) 222-2083
E: mbrown@doa.ri.gov

SOUTH CAROLINA
Mr. Bobby M. Bowers
Office Director
Office of Research & Statistics,
Budget & Control Board
1201 Main Street, Suite 715
P.O. Box 27
Columbia, SC 29201
P: (803) 734-3798
E: bobby@drss.state.sc.us

SOUTH DAKOTA
Ms. Nancy Nelson
Director
State Data Center
University of South Dakota
132 Patterson Hall, 414 East
Clark
Vermillion, SD 57069
P: (605) 677-5287
F: (605) 677-5427
E: nnelson@usd.edu

TENNESSEE
Mr. Mark Bengel
Chief Information Officer
Office for Information
Resources
312 Rosa L. Parks Avenue
16th Floor, Tennessee Tower
Nashville, TN 37343
P: (615) 741-7951
F: (615) 532-0471

TEXAS
Ms. Karen W. Robinson
Chief Technology Officer
Department of Information
Resources
300 West 15th Street, Suite 1300
P.O. Box 13564
Austin, TX 78711
P: (512) 475-4720
F: (512) 475-4759

U.S. VIRGIN ISLANDS
Mr. Dayle Barry
Coordinator
Conservation Data Center
Eastern Caribbean Center, UVI
#2 John Brewer Bay
St. Thomas, VI 00802
P: (340) 693-1030
F: (340) 693-1025

UTAH
Mr. Ron Bigelow
Executive Director
Governor's Office of Planning &
Budget
State Capitol, Suite 150
P.O. Box 132210
Salt Lake City, UT 84114
P: (801) 538-1555
F: (801) 538-1547
E: ronbigelow@utah.gov

VERMONT
Mr. Will Sawyer
Program Manager & State Data
Center Manager
State Data Center
Center for Rural Studies
207 Morrill Hall, University of
Vermont
Burlington, VT 05405
P: (802) 656-0892
E: william.sawyer@uvm.edu

VIRGINIA
Mr. John R. Broadway
Commissioner
Employment Commission
703 East Main Street
Richmond, VA 23219
P: (804) 786-1485
E: john.broadway
   @vec.virginia.gov

WEST VIRGINIA
Mr. J. Keith Burdette
Secretary of Commerce
Department of Commerce
Capitol Complex Building 6,
Room 525
1900 Kanawha Boulevard East
Charleston, WV 25305
P: (304) 558-2234
F: (304) 558-1189
E: J.Keith.Burdette@wv.gov

WISCONSIN
Mr. Phil Wells
Census Data Consultant
Demographic Services Center
101 East Wilson, 9th Floor
Madison, WI 53703
P: (608) 266-1927
F: (608) 267-6931
E: philip.wells
   @wisconsin.gov

WYOMING
Mr. Buck McVeigh
Administrator
Economic Analysis Division
Dept. of Administration &
Information
1807 Capitol Avenue, Suite 206
Cheyenne, WY 82002
P: (307) 777-7504
F: (307) 632-1819
E: bmcvei@wyo.gov

State and Public Libraries

Serves the information and research needs of state executive and legislative branch officials. Also oversees the development of public libraries in the state and federal programs related to such libraries.

ALABAMA
Ms. Rebecca Mitchell
Director
Public Library Service
6030 Monticello Drive
Montgomery, AL 36130
P: (334) 213-3901
F: (334) 213-3993
E: Rebecca.Mitchell
  @apls.alabama.gov

ALASKA
Ms. Linda Thibodeau
Director
Division of Libraries, Archives
& Museums
Department of Education
P.O. Box 110571
Juneau, AK 99811
P: (907) 465-2912
F: (907) 465-2151
E: linda.thibodeau
  @alaska.gov

AMERICAN SAMOA
Ms. Cheryl Morales
  Polataivao
Territorial Librarian
Feleti Barstow Public Library
P.O. Box 997687
Pago Pago, AS 96799
P: (684) 633-5816
F: (684) 633-5816
E: feletibarstow@yahoo.com

ARIZONA
Ms. Janet Fisher
Acting Director
State Library, Archives &
Public Records
1700 West Washington Street,
Suite 200
Phoenix, AZ 85007
P: (602) 926-4035
F: (602) 256-7983

ARKANSAS
Ms. Carolyn Ashcraft
State Librarian
State Library
900 West Capital Avenue
Suite 100
Little Rock, AR 72201
P: (501) 682-2848
F: (501) 682-1899
E: cashcraf@asl.lib.ar.us

CALIFORNIA
Ms. Stacey Aldrich
State Librarian
State Library
P.O. Box 942837
Sacramento, CA 94237
P: (916) 654-0188
E: saldrich@library.ca.gov

COLORADO
Mr. Gene Hainer
State Librarian & Assistant
Commissioner
State Library
201 East Colfax Avenue, Room
309
Denver, CO 80203
P: (303) 866-6730
F: (303) 866-6940
E: hainer_g@cde.state.co.us

CONNECTICUT
Mr. Kendall F. Wiggin
State Librarian
State Library
231 Capitol Avenue
Hartford, CT 06106
P: (860) 757-6500
F: (860) 757-6503
E: kwiggin@cslib.org

DELAWARE
Ms. Annie E.C. Norman
Director
Division of Libraries
43 South DuPont Highway
Dover, DE 19901
P: (302) 739-4748 Ext. 126
F: (302) 739-6787
E: annie.norman@state.de.us

DISTRICT OF COLUMBIA
Ms. Ginnie Cooper
Chief Librarian
Public Libraries
901 G Street, Northwest
Washington, DC 20001
P: (202) 727-0321

FLORIDA
Ms. Judith Ring
Director
State Library & Archives
Department of State, R.A. Gray
Building
500 South Bronough Street
Tallahassee, FL 32399
P: (850) 245-6600
F: (850) 488-4894
E: jring@dos.state.fl.us

GEORGIA
Dr. Lamar Veatch
State Librarian
Public Library Service
1800 Century Place, Suite 150
Atlanta, GA 30345
P: (404) 235-7200
F: (404) 235-7201
E: lveatch
  @georgialibraries.org

GUAM
Ms. Teresita L.G. Kennimer
Acting Territorial Librarian &
Director
Public Library System
254 Martyr Street
Hagatna, GU 96910
P: (671) 475-4754
F: (671) 477-9777

HAWAII
Mr. Richard P. Burns
State Librarian
State Public Library System
478 South King Street
Honolulu, HI 96813
P: (808) 586-3704
F: (808) 586-3715

IDAHO
Ms. Ann Joslin
State Librarian
Commission for Libraries
702 West Idaho
P.O. Box 83720
Boise, ID 83702
P: (208) 334-2150
F: (208) 334-4016
E: ann.joslin
  @libraries.idaho.gov

ILLINOIS
Ms. Anne Craig
Director
State Library
300 South Second Street
Gwendolyn Brooks Building
Springfield, IL 62701
P: (217) 785-5600
E: acraig@ilsos.net

INDIANA
Ms. Roberta L. Brooker
State Librarian
State Library
315 West Ohio Street, Room
407
Indianapolis, IN 46202
P: (317) 232-3692
E: rbrooker@library.in.gov

IOWA
Ms. Mary Wegner
State Librarian
State Library
Ola Babcock Miller Building
1112 East Grand Avenue
Des Moines, IA 50319
P: (515) 281-4105
F: (515) 281-6191
E: mary.wegner
  @lib.state.ia.us

KANSAS
Ms. Joanne Budler
State Librarian
State Library
Capitol Building, Room 169-W
300 Southwest 10th Avenue
Topeka, KS 66612
P: (785) 296-5466
F: (785) 368-7291
E: jobudler@kslib.info

KENTUCKY
Mr. Wayne Onkst
State Librarian & Commissioner
Department for Libraries &
Archives
300 Coffee Tree Road
P.O. Box 537
Frankfort, KY 40602
P: (502) 564-8300, Ext. 312
F: (502) 564-5773
E: wayne.onkst@ky.gov

LOUISIANA
Ms. Rebecca Hamilton
State Librarian
State Library
701 North 4th Street
P.O. Box 131
Baton Rouge, LA 70821
P: (225) 342-4923
F: (225) 219-4804
E: rhamilton
  @crt.state.la.us

MAINE
Ms. Linda H. Lord
State Librarian
State Library
64 State House Station
230 State Street
Augusta, ME 04333
P: (207) 287-5600
F: (207) 287-5624

MARYLAND
Ms. Irene M. Padilla
Assistant Superintendent,
Library Development and
Services
Department of Education
State Education Building
200 West Baltimore Street
Baltimore, MD 21201
P: (410) 767-0434
F: (410) 333-2507
E: ipadilla
@msde.state.md.us

MASSACHUSETTS
Ms. Elvernoy Johnson
State Librarian
State Library
State House, Room 341
24 Beacon Street
Boston, MA 02133
P: (617) 727-2592
F: (617) 727-9730
E: elvernoy.johnson
@state.ma.us

Mr. Robert C. Maier
Director
Board of Library
Commissioners
98 North Washington Street,
Suite 401
Boston, MA 02114
P: (617) 725-1860
F: (617) 725-0140
E: robert.maier@state.ma.us

MICHIGAN
Ms. Nancy Robertson
State Librarian
State Library
P.O. Box 30007
Lansing, MI 48909
P: (517) 373-5504
F: (517) 373-4480
E: nrobertson@michigan.gov

MINNESOTA
Ms. Nancy Walton
Acting Director
State Library Services
1500 Highway 36 West
Roseville, MN 55113
P: (651) 582-8881
F: (651) 582-8752
E: mde.lst@state.mn.us

MISSISSIPPI
Ms. Sharman B. Smith
Executive Director
Library Commission
3881 Eastwood Drive
Jackson, MS 39211
P: (601) 432-4039
F: (601) 432-4480
E: sharman@mlc.lib.ms.us

MISSOURI
Ms. Margaret M. Conroy
State Librarian
State Library
600 West Main Street
P.O. Box 387
Jefferson City, MO 65101
P: (573) 526-4783
F: (573) 751-3612
E: margaret.conroy
@sos.mo.gov

MONTANA
Ms. Darlene Staffeldt
State Librarian
State Library
P.O. Box 201800
1515 East 6th Avenue
Helena, MT 59620
P: (406) 444-3116
F: (406) 444-0266
E: dstaffeldt@mt.gov

NEBRASKA
Mr. Rod Wagner
Director
Library Commission
The Atrium
1200 North Street, Suite 120
Lincoln, NE 68508
P: (402) 471-4001
F: (402) 471-2083
E: rod.wagner@nebraska.gov

NEVADA
Ms. Daphne DeLeon
Division Administrator
State Library & Archives
100 North Stewart Street
Carson City, NV 89701
P: (775) 684-3315
F: (775) 684-3330
E: ddeleon
@nevadaculture.org

NEW HAMPSHIRE
Mr. Michael York
State Librarian
State Library
20 Park Street
Concord, NH 03301
P: (603) 271-2397
F: (603) 271-6826
E: myork
@library.state.nh.us

NEW JERSEY
Ms. Norma E. Blake
State Librarian
State Library
185 West State Street
P.O. Box 520
Trenton, NJ 08625
P: (609) 278-2640 Ext. 101
F: (609) 292-2746
E: nblake@njstatelib.org

NEW MEXICO
Mr. Benjamin T. Wakashige
Interim State Librarian
State Library
1209 Camino Carlos Rey
Santa Fe, NM 87505
P: (505) 476-9762
F: (505) 476-9701
E: ben.wakashige
@state.nm.us

NEW YORK
Mr. Bernard A. Margolis
State Librarian & Assistant
Commissioner for Libraries
State Library
Cultural Education Center
222 Madison Avenue
Albany, NY 12230
P: (518) 474-5930
F: (518) 486-6880

NORTH CAROLINA
Ms. Mary Boone
State Librarian
State Library
4640 Mail Service Center
Raleigh, NC 27699
P: (919) 807-7410
E: mary.boone@ncdcr.gov

NORTH DAKOTA
Hulen Bivins
State Librarian
State Library
604 East Boulevard Avenue
Department 250
Bismarck, ND 58505
P: (701) 328-4622
F: (701) 328-2040
E: hbivins@nd.gov

OHIO
Ms. Beverly Cain
State Librarian
State Library
274 East 1st Avenue
Columbus, OH 43201
P: (614) 466-3584

OKLAHOMA
Ms. Susan C. McVey
Director
Department of Libraries
200 Northeast 18th Street
Oklahoma City, OK 73105
P: (405) 521-2502
F: (405) 525-7804

OREGON
Mr. Jim Scheppke
State Librarian
State Library
250 Winter Street, Northeast
Salem, OR 97301
P: (503) 378-4367
F: (503) 585-8059
E: jim.b.scheppke
@state.or.us

PENNSYLVANIA
Ms. Mary Clare Zales
State Librarian
Office of Commonwealth
Libraries
333 Market Street
Harrisburg, PA 17126
P: (717) 787-2646
F: (717) 772-3265
E: mzales@state.pa.us

RHODE ISLAND
Mr. Thomas Evans
State Librarian
Secretary of State
State House, Room 208
Smith Street
Providence, RI 02903
P: (401) 222-2473
F: (401) 222-3034
E: statelibrary
@sec.state.ri.us

SOUTH CAROLINA
Mr. David S. Goble
Director & State Librarian
State Library
P.O. Box 11469
Columbia, SC 29211
P: (803) 734-8656
F: (803) 734-8676

State and Public Libraries

SOUTH DAKOTA
Mr. Daniel Siebersma
State Librarian
State Library
800 Governors Drive
Mercedes MacKay Building
Pierre, SD 57501
P: (605) 773-3131
F: (605) 773-4950
E: dan.siebersma
   @state.sd.us

TENNESSEE
Mr. Charles A. Sherrill
State Librarian & Archivist
State Library & Archives
403 7th Avenue, North
Nashville, TN 37243
P: (615) 741-7996
F: (615) 532-9293
E: Chuck.Sherrill@tn.gov

TEXAS
Ms. Peggy D. Rudd
Director & Librarian
Library & Archives
Commission
1201 Brazos Street
P.O. Box 12927
Austin, TX 78711
P: (512) 463-5460
F: (512) 463-5436
E: prudd@tsl.state.tx.us

U.S. VIRGIN ISLANDS
Ms. Susan Laura Lugo
Territorial Librarian for the
Archives
Division of Libraries, Archives
& Museums
1122 King Street
St. Croix, VI 00820
P: (304) 773-5715
F: (304) 773-5327

UTAH
Ms. Donna Jones Morris
Director
State Library Division
Department of Community &
Culture
250 North 1950 West, Suite A
Salt Lake City, UT 84116
P: (801) 715-6770
F: (801) 715-6767
E: dmorris@utah.gov

VERMONT
Ms. Martha Reid
State Librarian
Department of Libraries
Agency of Adminstration
109 State Street
Montpelier, VT 05609
P: (802) 828-3265
F: (802) 828-2199
E: martha.reid@state.vt.us

VIRGINIA
Ms. Sandra Treadway
State Librarian
The Library of Virginia
800 East Broad Street
Richmond, VA 23219
P: (804) 692-3535
F: (804) 692-3594
E: Sandra.Treadway
   @lva.virginia.gov

WASHINGTON
Mr. Rand Simmons
Acting State Librarian
State Library
P.O. Box 42460
Olympia, WA 98504
P: (360) 704-5200
F: (360) 586-7575
E: rand.simmons@sos.wa.gov

WEST VIRGINIA
Ms. Karen E. Goff
State Librarian
Library Commission
1900 Kanawha Boulevard, East
Building 9, Cultural Center
Charleston, WV 25305
P: (304) 558-3978
F: (304) 558-2044
E: karen.e.goff@wv.gov

WISCONSIN
Mr. Kurt Kiefer
Assistant State Superintendent
Division for Libraries,
Technology & Community
Learning
125 South Webster Street
Madison, WI 53707
P: (608) 266-2205
F: (608) 267-1052
E: Kurt.Kiefer@dpi.wi.gov

WYOMING
Ms. Lesley D. Boughton
State Librarian
State Library, Department of
Administration & Information
2301 Capitol Avenue
Cheyenne, WY 82002
P: (307) 777-5911
F: (307) 777-6289
E: lesley.boughton@wyo.gov

State Police

Patrols the state's highways and enforces the motor vehicle laws of the state.

ALABAMA
Colonel Hugh B. McCall
Director
Department of Public Safety
301 South Ripley Street
P.O. Box 1511
Montgomery, AL 36102
P: (334) 242-4394
F: (334) 242-0512
E: director@alalinc.net

ALASKA
Mr. Joseph A. Masters
Commissioner
Department of Public Safety
5700 East Tudor Road
P.O. Box 111200
Anchorage, AK 99811
P: (907) 269-5086
F: (907) 269-4543
E: joseph.masters
    @alaska.gov

AMERICAN SAMOA
Mr. Tuaolo M. Fruean
Commissioner
Department of Public Safety
American Samoa Government
P.O. Box 3699
Pago Pago, AS 96799
P: (684) 633-1111
F: (684) 633-7296

ARIZONA
Mr. Robert Halliday
Director
Department of Public Safety
2102 West Encanto Boulevard
P.O. Box 6638
Phoenix, AZ 85005
P: (602) 223-2000
F: (602) 223-2917

ARKANSAS
Col. Winford E. Phillips
Director
State Police
1 State Police Plaza Drive
Little Rock, AR 72209
P: (501) 618-8299
F: (501) 618-8222
E: winford.phillips
    @asp.arkansas.gov

CALIFORNIA
Mr. J.A. Farrow
Commissioner
Highway Patrol
601 North 7th Street
P.O. Box 942898
Sacramento, CA 94298
P: (916) 843-3001
F: (916) 843-3264

COLORADO
Mr. James Wolfinbarger
Chief
State Police
Department of Public Safety
700 Kipling Street, Suite 3000
Lakewood, CO 80215
P: (303) 239-4403
F: (303) 239-4481

CONNECTICUT
Mr. Reuben Bradford
Commissioner
Department of Public Safety
1111 Country Club Road
Middletown, CT 06457
P: (860) 685-8000
F: (860) 685-8354
E: reuben.bradford@ct.gov

DELAWARE
Colonel Robert M. Coupe
Superintendent
State Police
1441 North DuPont Highway
Dover, DE 19901
P: (302) 739-5960
F: (302) 739-5966

DISTRICT OF COLUMBIA
Ms. Cathy L. Lanier
Chief of Police
Metropolitan Police Department
300 Indiana Avenue, Northwest
Washington, DC 20001
P: (202) 727-4218
F: (202) 727-9524
E: cathy.lanier@dc.gov

FLORIDA
Mr. Gerald M. Bailey
Commissioner
Department of Law
Enforcement
2331 Phillips Road
P.O. Box 1489
Tallahassee, FL 32302
P: (850) 410-7001
E: GeraldBailey
    @fdle.state.fl.us

GEORGIA
Col. Bill Hitchens
Commissioner
Department of Public Safety
959 East Confederate Avenue,
Southeast
P.O. Box 1456
Atlanta, GA 30371
P: (404) 624-7477
F: (404) 624-7788

IDAHO
Col. Jerry Russell
Director
State Police
P.O. Box 700
Meridian, ID 83680
P: (208) 884-7003
F: (208) 884-7090
E: jerry.russell
    @isp.idaho.gov

ILLINOIS
Mr. Hiram Grau
State Director
State Police
2200 South Dirksen Parkway
Springfield, IL 62703
P: (217) 782-7263
E: hiram.grau@illinois.gov

INDIANA
Dr. Paul Whitesell
Superintendent
State Police
100 North Senate Avenue, Room
IGCN N340
Indianapolis, IN 46204
P: (317) 232-8241
E: pwhitesell@isp.in.gov

IOWA
Col. Patrick J. Hoye
Colonel
State Patrol Division
Department of Public Safety
215 East 7th Street
Des Moines, IA 50319
P: (515) 725-6090
E: hoye@dps.state.ia.us

KANSAS
Colonel Ernest E. Garcia
Superintendent
Highway Patrol
122 Southwest 7th Street
Topeka, KS 66603
P: (785) 296-6800
F: (785) 296-3049

KENTUCKY
Mr. Rodney Brewer
Commissioner
State Police
919 Versailles Road
Frankfort, KY 40601
P: (502) 695-6300
F: (502) 573-1479

LOUISIANA
Col. Michael D. Edmonson
Superintendent of State Police
Public Safety Services
7919 Independence Boulevard
Baton Rouge, LA 70806
P: (225) 925-6118
F: (225) 925-6006

MAINE
Col. Patrick J. Fleming
Chief
State Police
42 State House Station
45 Commerce Drive
Augusta, ME 04333
P: (207) 624-7200
E: patrick.j.fleming
    @maine.gov

MARYLAND
Colonel Terrence Sheridan
Superintendent
Department of State Police
1201 Reisterstown Road
Pikesville, MD 21208
P: (410) 653-4219
F: (410) 653-4269
E: superintendent@mdsp.org

MASSACHUSETTS
Colonel Marian McGovern
Superintendent
State Police
470 Worcester Road
Framingham, MA 01702
P: (508) 820-2300
F: (617) 727-6874

MICHIGAN
Colonel Kriste Kibbey Etue
Director
State Police
714 South Harrison Road
East Lansing, MI 48823
P: (517) 336-6157
F: (517) 336-6551

MINNESOTA
Col. Mark A. Dunaski
Chief
State Patrol
444 Cedar Street
Suite 130, Town Square
St. Paul, MN 55101
P: (651) 201-7100
E: mark.dunaski@state.mn.us

State Police

MISSISSIPPI
Lt. Col. Stanley Sisk
Director
Bureau of Investigation
P.O. Box 958
Jackson, MS 39205
P: (601) 987-1212
F: (601) 987-1488
E: ssisk@mdps.state.ms.us

MISSOURI
Colonel Ronald K. Replogle
Superintendent
State Highway Patrol
1510 East Elm Street
Jefferson City, MO 65102
P: (573) 751-3313
F: (573) 526-1111

MONTANA
Hon. Steve Bullock (D)
Attorney General
Department of Justice
215 North Sanders, Third Floor
Helena, MT 59620
P: (406) 444-2026
F: (404) 444-3549
E: contactdoj@mt.gov

NEBRASKA
Colonel David Sankey
Superintendent of Law
Enforcement & Public Safety
State Police
P.O. Box 94907
Lincoln, NE 68509
P: (402) 471-4545
F: (402) 479-4002

NEVADA
Mr. Tony Alvarez
Chief
Highway Patrol
Department of Public Safety
555 Wright Way
Carson City, NV 89711
P: (775) 684-4867
E: talmaraz@dps.state.nv.us

NEW HAMPSHIRE
Colonel Robert L. Quinn
Director
Division of State Police
Department of Safety
33 Hazen Drive
Concord, NH 03305
P: (603) 271-2450
F: (603) 271-1153
E: robert.quinn@dos.nh.gov

NEW JERSEY
Col. Rick Fuentes
Superintendent
State Police
P.O. Box 7068
West Trenton, NJ 08628
P: (609) 882-2000
F: (609) 530-4383

NEW MEXICO
Mr. Robert Shilling
State Police Chief
Department of Public Safety
4491 Cerrillos Road
P.O. Box 1628
Santa Fe, NM 87504
P: (505) 827-9219
F: (505) 827-3395
E: robert.shilling
@state.nm.us

NEW YORK
Mr. Joseph D'Amico
Superintendent
State Police
1220 Washington Avenue,
Building 22
Albany, NY 12226
P: 518) 457-6721

NORTH CAROLINA
Colonel Michael Gilchrist
Commander
State Highway Patrol
4702 Mail Service Center
Raleigh, NC 27699
P: (919) 733-7952
F: (919) 733-1189

NORTH DAKOTA
Colonel James Prochniak
Superintendent
Highway Patrol
600 East Boulevard Avenue
Department 504
Bismarck, ND 58505
P: (701) 328-2455
F: (701) 328-1717
E: jprochni@nd.gov

**NORTHERN MARIANA
ISLANDS**
Mr. Ramon Mafnas
Commissioner
Department of Public Safety
Caller Box 10007, Capitol Hill
Caller Box 10007, Capitol Hill
Saipan, MP 96950
P: (670) 664-9022
F: (670) 664-9027

OHIO
Colonel John Born
Superintendent
State Highway Patrol
1970 West Broad Street
P.O. Box 182074
Columbus, OH 43218
P: (614) 644-5837

OKLAHOMA
Mr. Michael C. Thompson
Secretary of Safety & Security
Department of Public Safety
P.O. Box 11415
Oklahoma City, OK 73136
P: (405) 425-2424

PENNSYLVANIA
Mr. Frank Noonan
Commissioner
State Police
3rd Floor, Department
Headquarters
1800 Elmerton Avenue
Harrisburg, PA 17110
P: (717) 783-5558
F: (717) 787-2948

PUERTO RICO
Mr. Jose Figueroa Sancha
Superintendent
Puerto Rico Police
P.O. Box 70166
San Juan, PR 00936
P: (787) 793-1234
F: (787) 781-0080

RHODE ISLAND
Colonel Steven G. O'Donnell
Superintendent
State Police
311 Danielson Pike
North Scituate, RI 02857
P: (401) 444-1000
F: (401) 444-1105
E: sodonnell
@risp.state.ri.us

Lt. Col. Raymond S. White
Acting Superintendent & Interim
Commissioner
Department of Public Safety
Headquarters
311 Danielson Pike
Scituate, RI 02857
P: (401) 444-1010
F: (401) 444-1105
E: rwhite@risp.dps.ri.gov

SOUTH CAROLINA
Colonel F. K. Lancaster Jr.
Commander
Highway Patrol
10311 Wilson Boulevard
P.O. Box 1993
Blythewood, SC 29016
P: (803) 896-7920
F: (803) 896-7922

SOUTH DAKOTA
Colonel Craig Price
Superintendent
Highway Patrol
Department of Public Safety
118 West Capitol Avenue
Pierre, SD 57501
P: (605) 773-3105
F: (605) 773-6046

TENNESSEE
Mr. Bill Gibbons
Commissioner
Department of Safety &
Homeland Security
1150 Foster Avenue
P.O. Box 945
Nashville, TN 37202
P: (615) 251-5166
E: email.safety@tn.gov

TEXAS
Mr. Steve McCraw
Director
Department of Public Safety
5805 North Lamar Boulevard
P.O. Box 4087
Austin, TX 78773
P: (512) 424-2000
F: (512) 475-0876

U.S. VIRGIN ISLANDS
Mr. Novelle E. Francis Jr.
Commissioner
Police Department
Alexander Farrelly Criminal
Justice Ctr.
Charlotte Amalie
St. Thomas, VI 00802
P: (340) 774-2211
F: (340) 715-5517

UTAH
Col. Daniel Fuhr
Superintendent
Department of Public Safety
Utah Highway Patrol
4501 South 2700 West, P.O. Box
141775
Salt Lake City, UT 84114
P: (801) 965-4379
F: (801) 965-4716
E: dfuhr@utah.gov

VERMONT
Mr. Thomas L'Esperance
Director
State Police
103 South Main Street
Waterbury, VT 05671
P: (802) 244-7345

VIRGINIA
Col. W. Steven Flaherty
Superintendent
Department of State Police
7700 Midlothian Turnpike
P.O. Box 27472
Richmond, VA 23235
P: (804) 674-2087
F: (804) 674-2132
E: steve.flaherty
    @vsp.virginia.gov

WASHINGTON
Mr. John R. Batiste
Chief
State Patrol
General Administration Building
P.O. Box 42600
Olympia, WA 98504
P: (360) 596-4101

WEST VIRGINIA
Colonel Timothy S. Pack
Superintendent
State Police
725 Jefferson Road
South Charleston, WV 25309
P: (304) 746-2111
F: (304) 746-2230
E: tspack@wvsp.state.wv.us

WISCONSIN
Mr. David L. Collins
Superintendent
Division of State Patrol
4802 Sheboygan Avenue, Room 551
P.O. Box 7912
Madison, WI 53707
P: (608) 266-0454
F: (608) 267-4495
E: david.collins
    @dot.state.wi.us

WYOMING
Lt. Col. Jess Oyler
Administrator
Highway Patrol
5300 Bishop Boulevard
Cheyenne, WY 82009
P: (307) 777-4301

State Security

Develops and oversees operations to insure the safety of state citizens from threats of violence and terrorism.

ALABAMA
Mr. Art Faulkner
State Director
Emergency Management
Agency
5898 County Road 41
P.O. Drawer 2160
Clanton, AL 35046
P: (205) 280-2201
F: (205) 280-2410
E: art.faulkner
   @ema.alabama.gov

ALASKA
Brigadier Thomas H. Katkus
Acting Adjutant General
Department of Military &
Veterans Affairs
P.O. Box 5800
Camp Denali
Fort Richardson, AK 99505
P: (907) 428-6003
F: (907) 428-6019

AMERICAN SAMOA
Mr. Tuaolo M. Fruean
Commissioner
Department of Public Safety
American Samoa Government
P.O. Box 3699
Pago Pago, AS 96799
P: (684) 633-1111
F: (684) 633-7296

ARIZONA
Mr. Robert Halliday
Director
Department of Public Safety
2102 West Encanto Boulevard
P.O. Box 6638
Phoenix, AZ 85005
P: (602) 223-2000
F: (602) 223-2917

ARKANSAS
Mr. David Maxwell
State Director
Department of Emergency
Management
Building 9501
Camp Joseph T. Robinson
North Little Rock, AR 72199
P: (501) 683-7834
F: (501) 683-7890
E: david.maxwell
   @adem.arkansas.gov

CALIFORNIA
Mr. Mike Dayton
State Director
Emergency Management
Agency
3650 Schriever Avenue
Mather, CA 95655
P: (916) 845-8506
F: (916) 845-8511
E: mike.dayton
   @calema.ca.gov

Mr. J.A. Farrow
Commissioner
Highway Patrol
601 North 7th Street
P.O. Box 942898
Sacramento, CA 94298
P: (916) 843-3001
F: (916) 843-3264

COLORADO
Mr. Larry E. Trujillo Sr.
Director
Governor's Office of Homeland
Security
9195 East Mineral Avenue, Suite
200
Centennial, CO 80112
P: (720) 852-6602
F: (720) 852-6750
E: larry.d.trujillo
   @state.co.us

CONNECTICUT
Mr. Peter J. Boynton
Commissioner
Department of Emergency
Management & Homeland
Security
25 Sigourney Street, 6th Floor
Hartford, CT 06106
P: (860) 256-0800
F: (860) 256-0815
E: comm.demhs@ct.gov

DELAWARE
Mr. Lewis D. Schiliro
Cabinet Secretary
Department of Safety &
Homeland Security
303 Transportation Circle
P.O. Box 818
Dover, DE 19903
P: (302) 744-2680
F: (302) 739-4874

DISTRICT OF COLUMBIA
Ms. Cathy L. Lanier
Chief of Police
Metropolitan Police Department
300 Indiana Avenue, Northwest
Washington, DC 20001
P: (202) 727-4218
F: (202) 727-9524
E: cathy.lanier@dc.gov

FLORIDA
Mr. Gerald M. Bailey
Commissioner
Department of Law
Enforcement
2331 Phillips Road
P.O. Box 1489
Tallahassee, FL 32302
P: (850) 410-7001
E: GeraldBailey
   @fdle.state.fl.us

GEORGIA
Col. Bill Hitchens
Commissioner
Department of Public Safety
959 East Confederate Avenue,
Southeast
P.O. Box 1456
Atlanta, GA 30371
P: (404) 624-7477
F: (404) 624-7788

GUAM
Maj. Gen. Benny M. Paulino
Adjutant General
National Guard
430 Army Drive
Building 300
Barrigada, GU 96913
P: (671) 735-0400
E: benny.paulino
   @gu.ngb.army.mil

HAWAII
Maj. Gen. Darryl D.M. Wong
Adjutant General
Department of Defense
3949 Diamond Head Road
Honolulu, HI 96816
P: (808) 733-4246
F: (808) 733-4499

IDAHO
Maj. Gen. Gary L. Sayler
Adjutant General
Military Division
4040 West Guard Building 600
Boise, ID 83705
P: (208) 422-5242
F: (208) 422-6179

ILLINOIS
Mr. Hiram Grau
State Director
State Police
2200 South Dirksen Parkway
Springfield, IL 62703
P: (217) 782-7263
E: hiram.grau@illinois.gov

Mr. Jonathon E. Monken
State Director
Emergency Management
Agency
2200 South Dirksen Parkway
Springfield, IL 62703
P: (217) 557-6225
F: (217) 524-7967
E: jonathon.monken
   @illinois.gov

Mr. Andrew Velasquez III
Director/State Homeland
Security Advisor
Emergency Management
Agency
2200 South Dirksen Parkway
Springfield, IL 62703
P: (217) 557-6225
F: (217) 524-7967
E: andrew.velasquez
   @illinois.gov

INDIANA
Dr. Paul Whitesell
Superintendent
State Police
100 North Senate Avenue, Room
IGCN N340
Indianapolis, IN 46204
P: (317) 232-8241
E: pwhitesell@isp.in.gov

IOWA
Brigadier Derek Hill
State Director
Homeland Security &
Emergency Management
Division
7105 Northwest 70th Avenue
Camp Dodge, W4
Johnston, IA 50131
P: (515) 725-3230
F: (515) 725-3290
E: derek.hill@Iowa.gov

KANSAS
Maj. Gen. Lee E.
   Tafanelli (R)
Adjutant General
Adjutant General's Department
2800 South Topeka Boulevard
Topeka, KS 66611
P: (785) 274-1001
F: (913) 274-1682

KENTUCKY
Maj. Gen. Edward W. Tonini
Adjutant General
Department of Military Affairs
100 Minuteman Parkway
Frankfort, KY 40601
P: (502) 607-1240
F: (502) 607-1558

LOUISIANA

Mr. Mark Cooper
State Director
Governor's Office of Homeland
Security & Emergency
Preparedness
7667 Independence Boulevard
Baton Rouge, LA 70806
P: (225) 925-7345
F: (225) 925-7348
E: mark.a.cooper@la.gov

MAINE

Mr. Robert McAleer
State Director
State Emergency Management
Agency
45 Commercial Drive, Suite #2,
#72 SHS
Augusta, ME 04333
P: (207) 624-4402
F: (207) 287-3180
E: robert.mcaleer@maine.gov

MARYLAND

Mr. Andrew Lauland
Homeland Security Advisor
Governor's Office of Homeland
Security
6 St. Paul Street
24th Floor, Schaefer Tower
Annapolis, MD 21201
P: (410) 767-4511
E: alauland@gov.state.md.us

MASSACHUSETTS

Ms. Mary Elizabeth
    Heffernan
Secretary
Executive Office of Public
Safety
One Ashburton Place, Suite
2133
Boston, MA 02108
P: (617) 727-7775
F: (617) 727-4764

MICHIGAN

Colonel Kriste Kibbey Etue
Director
State Police
714 South Harrison Road
East Lansing, MI 48823
P: (517) 336-6157
F: (517) 336-6551

Capt. Eddie L.
    Washington Jr.
Division Commander
State Emergency Management
& Homeland Security Division
4000 Collins Road
P.O. Box 30636
Lansing, MI 48909
P: (517) 333-5042
F: (517) 333-4987
E: WashinE@michigan.gov

MINNESOTA

Ms. Ramona Dohman
Commissioner
Department of Public Safety
Bremer Tower, Suite 1000
445 Minnesota Street
St. Paul, MN 55101
P: (651) 201-7160
F: (651) 297-5728
E: Mona.Dohman@state.mn.us

MISSISSIPPI

Mr. Mike Womack
State Director
Emergency Management
Agency
#1 MEMA Drive
P.O. Box 5644
Pearl, MS 39288
P: (601) 933-6882
F: (601) 933-6810
E: mwomack@mema.ms.gov

MISSOURI

Mr. John M. Britt
Director
Department of Public Safety
P.O. Box 749
Jefferson City, MO 65102
P: (573) 751-4905
F: (573) 751-5399

MONTANA

Mr. Ed Tinsley
State Director
Disaster & Emergency Services,
Department of Military Affairs
1956 Mt. Majo Street
P.O. Box 4789
Fort Harrison, MT 59636
P: (406) 324-4777
F: (406) 841-3965
E: edtinsley@mt.gov

NEBRASKA

Hon. Rick Sheehy (R)
Lieutenant Governor
Office of the Lieutenant
Governor
State Capitol, Room 2315
P.O. Box 94863
Lincoln, NE 68509
P: (402) 471-2256
F: (402) 471-6031

NEVADA

Mr. James Wright
State Director
Division of Emergency
Management
2478 Fairview Drive
Carson City, NV 89701
P: (775) 687-0300
F: (775) 687-0322
E: jwright@dps.state.nv.us

NEW HAMPSHIRE

Colonel Robert L. Quinn
Director
Division of State Police
Department of Safety
33 Hazen Drive
Concord, NH 03305
P: (603) 271-2450
F: (603) 271-1153
E: robert.quinn@dos.nh.gov

NEW JERSEY

Mr. Charles B. McKenna
Director
Office fo Homeland Security &
Preparedness
P.O. Box 091
Trenton, NJ 08625
P: (609) 584-4000
F: (609) 631-4916

NEW MEXICO

Mr. Michael Duvall
State Director
Department of Homeland
Security & Emergency
Management
130 South Capitol
P.O. Box 27111
Santa Fe, NM 87502
P: (505) 476-9606
F: (505) 476-1057
E: michael.duvall
    @state.nm.us

NEW YORK

Mr. James M. Sherry
Acting Commissioner
Division of Homeland Security
& Emergency Services
633 Third Avenue, 32nd Floor
New York, NY 10017
P: (212) 867-7060

NORTH CAROLINA

Mr. Reuben Young
Secretary
Department of Crime Control &
Public Safety
4701 Mail Service Center
Raleigh, NC 27699
P: (919) 733-2126
F: (919) 715-8477
E: reuben.young@ncmail.net

NORTH DAKOTA

Ms. Debbie LaCombe
State Director
Homeland Security Division
Fraine Barracks Lane, Building
35
P.O. Box 5511
Bismarck, ND 58504
P: (701) 328-8100
F: (701) 328-8181
E: dlacombe@nd.gov

Colonel James Prochniak
Superintendent
Highway Patrol
600 East Boulevard Avenue
Department 504
Bismarck, ND 58505
P: (701) 328-2455
F: (701) 328-1717
E: jprochni@nd.gov

NORTHERN MARIANA ISLANDS

Mr. Marvin P. Seman
Acting Special Assistant
Office of Homeland Security
Caller Box 10007, Capitol Hill
Saipan, MP 96950
P: (670) 664-2208
F: (670) 664-2211

OHIO

Mr. Thomas P. Charles
Director
Department of Public Safety
1970 West Broad Street
P.O. Box 182081
Columbus, OH 43223
P: (614) 466-3383
F: (614) 466-0433

OKLAHOMA

Mr. Michael C. Thompson
Secretary of Safety & Security
Department of Public Safety
P.O. Box 11415
Oklahoma City, OK 73136
P: (405) 425-2424

State Security

PENNSYLVANIA
Mr. Glenn Cannon
State Director
Office of Homeland Security
2605 Interstate Drive
Harrisburg, PA 17110
P: (717) 651-2224
F: (717) 651-2040
E: glcannon@state.pa.us

PUERTO RICO
Mr. Jose Figueroa Sancha
Superintendent
Puerto Rico Police
P.O. Box 70166
San Juan, PR 00936
P: (787) 793-1234
F: (787) 781-0080

RHODE ISLAND
Maj. Gen. Robert T. Bray
Adjutant General
National Guard
Joint Force Headquarters
645 New London Avenue
Cranston, RI 02920
P: (401) 275-4102
F: (401) 275-4338

SOUTH CAROLINA
Mr. Reginald I. Lloyd
Director
State Law Enforcement Division
4400 Broad River Road
P.O. Box 21398
Columbia, SC 29221
P: (803) 737-9000
F: (803) 896-7041

SOUTH DAKOTA
Mr. James Carpenter
Director
Office of Homeland Security
118 West Capitol Avenue
Pierre, SD 57501
P: (605) 773-3450
F: (605) 773-3018
E: James.Carpenter
    @state.sd.us

Mr. Trevor Jones
Secretary
Department of Public Safety
118 West Capitol Avenue
Pierre, SD 57501
P: (605) 773-3178
F: (605) 773-3018
E: DPSInfo@state.sd.us

TENNESSEE
Mr. Bill Gibbons
Commissioner
Department of Safety &
Homeland Security
1150 Foster Avenue
P.O. Box 945
Nashville, TN 37202
P: (615) 251-5166
E: email.safety@tn.gov

TEXAS
Mr. Steve McCraw
Director
Department of Public Safety
5805 North Lamar Boulevard
P.O. Box 4087
Austin, TX 78773
P: (512) 424-2000
F: (512) 475-0876

U.S. VIRGIN ISLANDS
Mr. Renaldo Rivera
Adjutant General
National Guard
4031 LaGrande Princess, Lot 1B
Christiansted, VI 00820
P: (340) 712-7710
F: (340) 712-7711
E: renaldo.rivera
    @vi.ngb.army.mil

UTAH
Col. Keith D. Squires
State Director
Division of Emergency
Management
4501 South 2700 West
P.O. Box 141775
Salt Lake City, UT 84114
P: (801) 965-4498
F: (801) 965-4608
E: ksquires@utah.gov

WASHINGTON
Maj. Gen. Timothy J.
    Lowenberg
Adjutant General
Military Department
Camp Murray, Building 1
Tacoma, WA 98327
P: (253) 512-8000
F: (253) 512-8497

WEST VIRGINIA
Mr. Joe Thornton
Cabinet Secretary
Department of Military Affairs
& Public Safety
Building 1, Room W-400
1900 Kanawha Boulevard, East
Charleston, WV 25305
P: (304) 558-2930
F: (304) 558-6221
E: joseph.c.thornton@wv.gov

WISCONSIN
Mr. Michael Hinman
State Director
Division of Emergency
Management
2400 Wright Street
P.O. Box 7865
Madison, WI 53707
P: (608) 242-3210
F: (608) 242-3247
E: mike.hinman
    @wisconsin.gov

WYOMING
Mr. Guy Cameron
Director
Office of Homeland Security
Herschler Building, 1E
122 West 25th Street
Cheyenne, WY 82002
P: (307) 777-4663
F: (307) 777-8515

Telecom- munications

Responsible for communications planning and organizing a statewide plan for total communications, especially with local government emergency matters.

ALABAMA
Mr. Andy Cannon
Assistant Director, Office of Operations
Information Services Division
Department of Finance
64 North Union Street, Suite 200
Montgomery, AL 36130
P: (334) 242-3045
F: (334) 242-7002
E: andy.cannon
@isd.alabama.gov

ALASKA
Mr. Pat Shier
Director
Division of Enterprise
Technology Services
333 Willoughby Avenue
State Office Building, 5th Floor
Juneau, AK 99801
P: (907) 382-3512
F: (907) 465-3450
E: pat.shier@alaska.gov

ARIZONA
Ms. Lori Boak
Interim Assistant Director & CIO
Information Services Division
Department of Administration
100 North 15th Avenue
Phoenix, AZ 85007
P: (602) 542-2250
F: (602) 542-4272
E: lori.boak@azdoa.gov

ARKANSAS
Mr. Don McDaniel
Administrator, Enterprise
Network Services
Department of Information
Services
P.O. Box 3155
Little Rock, AR 72203
P: (501) 682-5027
F: (501) 682-4316
E: don.mcdaniel
@arkansas.gov

CALIFORNIA
Mr. Steve Rushing
Deputy Director
Statewide Telecommunications & Network Division
P.O. Box 1810
Rancho Cordova, CA 95741
P: (916) 657-9150
E: steve.rushing@dts.ca.gov

COLORADO
Ms. Kelley Eich
Director of Service Operations
Office of Information
Technology
601 East 18th Avenue, Suite 250
Denver, CO 80203
P: (303) 764-7700
F: (303) 764-7725
E: kelley.eich@state.co.us

CONNECTICUT
Mr. Bernard O'Donnell
Director
Communication Services
Department of Information
Technology
101 East River Drive
East Hartford, CT 06108
P: (860) 622-2444
F: (860) 622-4900
E: bernard.odonnell@ct.gov

DELAWARE
Ms. Kay Buck
Lead Telecommunications
Specialist
Department of Technology & Information
William Penn Building
801 Silver Lake Boulevard
Dover, DE 19904
P: (302) 739-9649
F: (302) 677-7002
E: kay.buck@state.de.us

FLORIDA
Mr. Jack Miles
Secretary
Department of Management
Services
4050 Esplande Way, Suite 280
Tallahassee, FL 32399
P: (850) 488-2786
F: (850) 922-6149

GEORGIA
Mr. Charlie Sasser
Interim Director
Enterprise Governance & Planning
Georgia Technology Authority
47 Trinity Avenue, Southwest
Atlanta, GA 30334
P: (404) 463-2300
F: (404) 463-2380
E: csasser@gta.ga.gov

HAWAII
Ms. Debra A. Gagne
Administrator
INformation & Communications
Services Division
1151 Punchbowl Street
Honolulu, HI 96813
P: (808) 586-1920
F: (808) 586-1922

ILLINOIS
Mr. Rich Fetter
Chief of Staff
Bureau of Communications & Computer Services
120 West Jefferson Street, 2nd Floor
Springfield, IL 62702
P: (217) 785-1943
E: rich_fetter
@cms.state.il.us

INDIANA
Mr. William Pierce
Systems Consultant
Office of Technology
100 North Senate Avenue, Room N-551
Indianapolis, IN 46204
P: (317) 233-2009
F: (317) 232-0748
E: bpierce@iot.in.gov

IOWA
Mr. Joseph Cassis
Deputy Director
Communications Network
400 East 14th Street
Des Moines, IA 50131
P: (515) 725-4600
F: (515) 725-4765
E: joseph.cassis@iowa.gov

KANSAS
Mr. Jay Coverdale
Deputy Director
Bureau of Telecommunications
Department of Administration
900 Southwest Jackson, Room 751-S
Topeka, KS 66612
P: (785) 296-3937

KENTUCKY
Mr. Brett McDonald
Director of Communications
Commonwealth Office of
Technology
101 Cold Harbor Drive
Frankfort, KY 40601
P: (502) 564-8747
E: brett.mcdonald@ky.gov

LOUISIANA
Mr. F. Derald Kirkland Jr.
Director
Office of Telecommunications
Management
Division of Administration
P.O. Box 94280
Baton Rouge, LA 70804
P: (225) 342-7701
F: (225) 342-6867
E: otm@la.gov

MAINE
Ms. Ellen Lee
Director, Performance
Management & Administration
Department of Administrative & Financial Services
Office of Information
Technology
26 Edison Drive, 145 State
House Station
Augusta, ME 04333
P: (207) 624-8866
F: (207) 287-4563
E: ellen.lee@maine.gov

MASSACHUSETTS
Ms. April May
Telecommunications Manager
Information Technology
Division
One Ashburton Place, Room 801
Boston, MA 02108
P: (617) 626-4645
F: (617) 626-4685
E: april.may@state.ma.us

MICHIGAN
Mr. Jack Harris
Director
Telecommunications & Network
Management
Department of Information
Technology
608 West Allegan Street, 1st
Floor
Lansing, MI 48913
P: (517) 241-7567
F: (517) 241-1633
E: harrisjl@michigan.gov

MINNESOTA
Mr. Dan Oehmke
Systems Supervisor
Office of Enterprise Technology
658 Cedar Street, Room 510
St. Paul, MN 55155
P: (651) 201-1037
F: (651) 297-5368
E: Dan.Oehmke@state.mn.us

Telecommunications

MISSISSIPPI
Mr. Roger Graves
Telecom Services Director
Information Technology
Services
301 North Lamar Street
Suite 508
Jackson, MS 39201
P: (601) 359-2892
F: (601) 354-6016
E: roger.graves@its.ms.gov

MISSOURI
Mr. Pete Wieberg
Director of Networks &
Telecommunications
Information Technology
Services Division
301 West High Street, Room
280
P.O. Box 809
Jefferson City, MO 65102
P: (573) 526-2603
F: (573) 751-3299
E: pete.wieberg@oa.mo.gov

MONTANA
Mr. Steve Noland
Chief, Network Technology
Services Bureau
Department of Administration
125 N. Roberts, Room 229
P.O. Box 200113
Helena, MT 59620
P: (406) 444-3344

NEBRASKA
Ms. Jayne Scofield
IT Administrator
Network Services
Office of the CIO
501 South 14th Street
Lincoln, NE 68509
P: (402) 471-2761
F: (402) 471-3339
E: jayne.scofield
    @cio.ne.gov

NEVADA
Mr. Mark Blomstrom
Director, Telecommunications
Department of Information
Technology
505 East King Street, Room 403
Carson City, NV 89701
P: (775) 684-5807
F: (775) 684-7345

NEW JERSEY
Mr. Adel W. Ebeid
Chief Technology Officer
Office of Information
Technology
200/300 Riverview Plaza
P.O. Box 212
Trenton, NJ 08625
P: (609) 984-4082
F: (609) 633-9100
E: abel.ebeid
    @oit.state.nj.us

NEW MEXICO
Ms. Jacqueline Miller
Deputy Director
Communications Division
Department of General Services
715 Alta Vista, P.O. Box 26110
Santa Fe, NM 87505
P: (505) 476-1849
F: (505) 827-2998
E: jacque.miller
    @state.nm.us

NEW YORK
Mr. Peter J. Arment
First Deputy Director
Division of Telecommunications
Empire State Building
Corning Tower Building, 27th
Floor
Albany, NY 12242
P: (518) 402-2324
F: (518) 473-7145
E: peter.arment
    @oft.state.ny.us

NORTH CAROLINA
Mr. Steve Stoneman
Executive Director
Telecommunications Services
4110 Mail Service Center
P.O. Box 17209
Raleigh, NC 26719
P: (919) 981-5261
F: (919) 850-2827
E: steve.stoneman
    @ncmail.net

NORTH DAKOTA
Mr. Mike J. Ressler
Deputy Chief Information
Officer & Director of ITD
Information Technology
Department
600 East Boulevard Avenue
Department 112
Bismarck, ND 58505
P: (701) 328-3190
F: (701) 328-1075
E: mressler@state.nd.us

OHIO
Mr. Dan Orr
Interim Chief Operating
Officer/Deputy Director
Infrastructure Services Division
Office of Information
Technology
1320 Arthur E. Adams Drive
Columbus, OH 43221
P: (614) 752-7320
F: (614) 466-7345
E: dan.orr@oit.ohio.gov

OKLAHOMA
Mr. Alex Pettit
Chief Information Officer
Office of State Finance
3115 North Lincoln Boulevard
Oklahoma City, OK 73105
P: (405) 522-4667
E: alex.pettit@osf.ok.gov

OREGON
Mr. Al Grapoli
Voice Services Manager
State Data Center
Department of Administrative
Services
955 Center Street, Northeast
U510
Salem, OR 97383
P: (503) 378-3338
F: (503) 378-8333
E: al.grapoli@state.or.us

PENNSYLVANIA
Mr. George White
Chief Information Officer
Office for Information
Technology
209 Finance Building
Harrisburg, PA 17120
P: (717) 787-5440
F: (717) 787-4523

RHODE ISLAND
Mr. Clarence Bussius
Enterprise Telecommunications
Manager
Division of Information
Technology
6 Harrington Road
Cranston, RI 02920
P: (401) 462-1432
E: clarence.bussius
    @doit.ri.gov

SOUTH CAROLINA
Mr. Tom Fletcher
Deputy CIO, Operations
State Budget & Control Board
Office of Chief Information
Officer
4430 Broad River Road
Columbia, SC 29210
P: (803) 896-0404
F: (803) 896-0099
E: fletcher@cio.sc.gov

SOUTH DAKOTA
Mr. Dennis Nincehelser
Director
Division of Telecommunications
Sammons Building
910 East Sioux
Pierre, SD 57501
P: (605) 773-4264
F: (605) 773-3741
E: dennis.nincehelser
    @state.sd.us

TENNESSEE
Mr. Jack McFadden
Planning Consultant
Office of Information Resources
Department of Finance &
Administration
312 8th Avenue, North, 17th
Floor
Nashville, TN 37243
P: (615) 741-5080
E: jack.mcfadden
    @state.tn.us

TEXAS
Mr. Brian Kelly
Director
Telecommunications Division
Department of Information
Resources
300 West 15th Street, Suite 1300
Austin, TX 78701
P: (512) 463-9672
F: (512) 463-3304
E: brian.kelly
    @dir.state.tx.us

UTAH
Mr. Scott Peterson
Network Planning Group
Manager
Department of Technology
Services
6000 State Office Building
Salt Lake City, UT 84114
P: (801) 538-3149
F: (801) 538-3622
E: speterso@utah.gov

VERMONT
Ms. Ruthann Sullivan
Interim Commissioner & Chief
Information Officer
Department of Information &
Innovation
Agency of Administration
133 State Street
Montpelier, VT 05633
P: (802) 828-4141
F: (802) 828-3398
E: ruthann.sullivan
  @state.vt.us

VIRGINIA
Ms. Marcella K. Williamson
Executive Director ITSB, Public
Information & Communications
Information Technologies
Agency
110 South 7th Street
Richmond, VA 23219
P: (804) 416-6002
E: marcella.williamson
  @vita.virginia.gov

WASHINGTON
Mr. Michael Martel
Assistant Director
Telecommunication Services
Division
512 12th Street, Southeast
P.O. Box 42445
Olympia, WA 98504
P: (360) 902-3333
F: (360) 902-3453
E: michael.martel
  @dis.wa.gov

WEST VIRGINIA
Mr. John Dunlap
Director of Telecommunications
Office of Technology
1900 Kanawha Boulevard, East
Capitol Complex, Building 5,
10th Floor
Charleston, WV 25305
P: (304) 957-6864
E: John.D.Dunlap@wv.gov

WISCONSIN
Mr. Tim Herbert
Assistant Bureau Director
Bureau of Infrastructure Support
101 East Wilson Street
Madison, WI 53707
P: (608) 261-8550
E: tim.herbert
  @wisconsin.gov

WYOMING
Mr. John Hartwig
Administrator
Information Technology
Division
Dept. of Administration &
Information
2001 Capitol Avenue
Cheyenne, WY 82002
P: (307) 777-5600
F: (307) 777-6725

Tourism

Coordinates promotional and advertising programs for the tourism industry in the state.

ALABAMA
Mr. Lee Sentell
Director
Tourism Department
401 Adams Avenue, Suite 126
P.O. Box 4927
Montgomery, AL 36103
P: (334) 242-4169
F: (334) 242-1478
E: Lee.Sentell
@tourism.alabama.gov

ALASKA
Ms. Caryl McConkie
Tourism Program Manager
Department of Commerce,
Community & Economic
Development
Office of Economic
Development
P.O. Box 110804
Juneau, AK 99811
P: (907) 465-5478
F: (907) 465-3767
E: caryl.mcconkie
@alaska.gov

AMERICAN SAMOA
Ms. Virginia Samuelu
Deputy Director
Office of Tourism, Department
of Commerce
American Samoa Government
PO Box 1147
Pago Pago, AS 96799
P: (684) 699-9411
F: (684) 699-9414
E: amsamoa
@amerikasamoa.info

ARIZONA
Ms. Sherry Henry
Executive Director
Office of Tourism
1110 West Washington Street,
Suite 155
Phoenix, AZ 85007
P: (602) 364-3717
F: (602) 364-3701
E: shenry@azot.gov

ARKANSAS
Mr. Richard Davies
Director
Parks & Tourism
#1 Capitol Mall
Little Rock, AR 72201
P: (501) 682-7777
F: (501) 682-1364
E: richard.davies
@mail.state.ar.us

CALIFORNIA
Ms. Caroline Beteta
Executive Director
Travel & Tourism
980 9th Street, Suite 480
Sacramento, CA 95814
P: (916) 322-5587
F: (916) 322-3402
E: cbeteta@commerce.ca.gov

COLORADO
Mr. Al White
Director
Tourism Office
1625 Broadway, Suite 1700
Denver, CO 80202
P: (303) 892-3885
F: (303) 892-3848
E: Al.White@state.co.us

CONNECTICUT
Ms. Karen J. Senich
State Historic Preservation
Officer
Commission on Culture &
Tourism
One Constitution Plaza
Hartford, CT 06103
P: (860) 256-2753
F: (860) 256-2811
E: karen.senich@ct.gov

FLORIDA
Chris Hart
Director
Office of Tourism, Trade &
Economic Development
Office of the Governor
The Capitol, Suite 2001
Tallahassee, FL 32399
P: (850) 487-2568
F: (850) 487-3014
E: chris.hart
@eog.myflorida.com

GEORGIA
Mr. Kevin Langston
Deputy Commissioner of
Tourism
Department of Economic
Development
75 Fifth Street, Northwest
Suite 1200
Atlanta, GA 30308
P: (404) 962-4082
F: (404) 962-4093
E: klangston@georgia.org

GUAM
Mr. Gerald Perez
General Manager
Visitor's Bureau
401 Pale San Vitores Road
Tumon, GU 96913
P: (671) 646-5278
F: (671) 646-8861

HAWAII
Mr. Mike McCartney
President & CEO
Tourism Authority
1801 Kalakaua Avenue, 1st
Floor
Honolulu, HI 96815
P: (808) 973-2255
F: (808) 973-2253

IDAHO
Ms. Karen Ballard
Administrator, Tourism
Development
Department of Commerce
700 West State Street
P.O. Box 83720
Boise, ID 83720
P: (208) 334-2650
F: (208) 334-2631
E: karen.ballard
@tourism.idaho.gov

ILLINOIS
Mr. Jan Kostner
Deputy Director of Tourism
Tourism Bureau
James R. Thompson Center,
Suite 3-400
100 West Randolph
Chicago, IL 60601
P: (312) 814-4735

INDIANA
Hon. Becky Skillman (R)
Lieutenant Governor
Office of Tourism Development
State Capitol, Room 333
Indianapolis, IN 46204
P: (317) 232-4545
F: (317) 232-4788

IOWA
Ms. Shawna Lode
Manager
Tourism Office
200 East Grand Avenue
Des Moines, IA 50309
P: (515) 725-3090
F: (515) 242-4718
E: shawna.lode@iowa.gov

KANSAS
Ms. Becky Blake
Director
Travel & Tourism
1000 Southwest Jackson Street,
Suite 100
Topeka, KS 66612
P: (785) 296-8478
F: (785) 296-6988
E: bblake
@kansascommerce.com

KENTUCKY
Mr. Mike Cooper
Commissioner
Department of Tourism
500 Mero Street, 22nd Floor
Frankfort, KY 40601
P: (502) 564-4930
F: (502) 564-5695

LOUISIANA
Ms. Pam Breaux
Secretary
Department of Culture,
Recreation & Tourism
P.O. Box 94361
Baton Rouge, LA 70804
P: (225) 342-8115
F: (225) 342-3207
E: pbreaux@crt.state.la.us

MAINE
Ms. Carolann Ouellette
Director
Office of Tourism
#59 State House Station
Augusta, ME 04333
P: (207) 624-7483
F: (207) 287-8070
E: Carolann.Ouellette
@maine.gov

MARYLAND
Ms. Hannah Byron
Assistant Secretary
Department of Business &
Economic Development
Division of Tourism, Film &
The Arts
401 East Pratt Street
Baltimore, MD 21202
P: (410) 767-6266
F: (410) 333-2065
E: HByron
@choosemaryland.org

MASSACHUSETTS
Ms. Betsy Wall
Executive Director
Office of Travel & Tourism
10 Park Plaza, Suite 4510
Boston, MA 02116
P: (617) 973-8500
F: (617) 973-8525

MICHIGAN
Mr. George Zimmerman
Vice President
Travel Michigan
300 North Washington Square
Lansing, MI 48913
P: (517) 335-1862
E: zimmermanng@michigan.gov

MINNESOTA
Mr. John Edman
Director
Explore Minnesota Tourism
121 7th Place East, #100
St. Paul, MN 55101
P: (651) 296-4783
F: (651) 296-7095
E: john.edman@state.mn.us

MISSISSIPPI
Mr. Craig Ray
Director
Division of Tourism
P.O. Box 849
Jackson, MS 39205
P: (601) 359-3297
F: (601) 359-5757
E: cray@mississippi.org

MONTANA
Mr. Dore Schwinden
Director
Department of Commerce
301 South Park
P.O. Box 200501
Helena, MT 59620
P: (406) 841-2704
F: (406) 841-2701
E: dschwinden@mt.gov

NEBRASKA
Mr. Richard Baier
Director
Department of Economic
Development
P.O. Box 94666
Lincoln, NE 68509
P: (402) 471-3111
F: (402) 471-3778
E: richard.baier
    @nebraska.gov

NEVADA
Mr. Larry Friedman
Interim Director
Commission on Tourism
401 North Carson Street
Carson City, NV 89701
P: (775) 687-4322
F: (775) 687-6779
E: lfriedman
    @travelnevada.com

NEW HAMPSHIRE
Ms. Alice L. DeSouza
Director
Department of Resources &
Economic Development
Division of Travel & Tourism
P.O. Box 1856
Concord, NH 03302
P: (603) 271-2665
F: (603) 271-6870
E: adesouza
    @dred.state.nh.us

NEW MEXICO
Ms. Monique Jacobson
Secretary
Tourism Department
491 Old Santa Fe Trail
Santa Fe, NM 87502
P: (505) 827-7400
F: (505) 827-7402
E: monique.jacobson
    @state.nm.us

NEW YORK
Mr. Kenneth Adams
President & CEO
Empire State Development
Corporation
633 Third Avenue
New York, NY 10017
P: (212) 803-3700
F: (212) 803-3715

NORTH CAROLINA
Ms. Lynn Minges
Assistant Secretary
Division of Tourism, Marketing
& Global Branding
Department of Commerce
4324 Mail Service Center
Raleigh, NC 27699
P: (919) 733-4171
F: (919) 733-8582
E: lminges@nccommerce.com

NORTH DAKOTA
Ms. Sarah Otte-Coleman
Director
Tourism Division
Department of Commerce
1600 East Century Avenue, Suite
2
Bismarck, ND 58503
P: (701) 328-2525
F: (701) 328-4878
E: socoleman@nd.gov

NORTHERN MARIANA
ISLANDS
Mr. Perry J.P. Tenorio
Managing Director
Visitor's Authority
P.O. Box 500861
Saipan, MP 96950
P: (670) 664-3200
F: (670) 664-3237
E: gov.wia1@gtepacifica.net

OHIO
Mr. Amir Eylon
Director
Division of Travel & Tourism
Department of Development
77 South High Street, 29th Floor
Columbus, OH 43215
P: (614) 466-8844
F: (614) 466-6744

OKLAHOMA
Mr. Deby Snodgrass
Executive Director
Tourism & Recreation
Department
120 North Robinson, 6th Floor
Oklahoma City, OK 73102
P: (405) 230-8301

OREGON
Mr. Todd Davidson
Executive Director
Tourism Commission
670 Hawthorne Avenue,
Southeast
Suite 240
Salem, OR 97301
P: (503) 378-8847
F: (503) 378-4574
E: Todd@TravelOregon.com

PENNSYLVANIA
Ms. Rose Mape
Deputy Secretary for Tourism &
Film
Tourism Office
Commonwealth Keystone
Building
4th Floor
Harrisburg, PA 17120
P: (717) 705-6759
F: (717) 787-0687

PUERTO RICO
Ms. Terestela
    Gonzalez-Denton
Director
Puerto Rico Tourism Company
P.O. Box 9023960
San Juan, PR 00901
P: (787) 721-2400
F: (787) 722-6238

RHODE ISLAND
Mr. Mark Brodeur
Director of Tourism
Economic Development
Corporation
315 Iron Horse Way, Suite 101
Providence, RI 02908
P: (401) 278-9100 Ext. 102
F: (401) 273-8270
E: mbrodeur@riedc.com

SOUTH CAROLINA
Mr. Duane Parrish
Director
Department of Parks, Recreation
& Tourism
1205 Pendleton Street
Columbia, SC 29201
P: (803) 734-0166
F: (803) 734-1409
E: dparrish@scprt.com

SOUTH DAKOTA
Mr. James D. Hagen
Secretary of Tourism
Office of Tourism
711 East Wells Avenue
Pierre, SD 57501
P: (605) 773-3301
F: (605) 773-5977
E: sdinfo@state.sd.us

TENNESSEE
Ms. Susan Whitaker
Commissioner
Department of Tourist
Development
William Snodgrass/Tennessee
Tower
312 Rosa L. Parks Avenue, 25th
Floor
Nashville, TN 37243
P: (615) 741-9001
F: (615) 532-0477
E: Susan.Whitaker@tn.gov

TEXAS
Ms. Julie Chase
Director
Texas Tourism
Office of the Governor
P.O. Box 12428
Austin, TX 78711
P: (512) 936-0101
F: (512) 936-0303

Tourism

U.S. VIRGIN ISLANDS
Ms. Beverly Nicholson Doty
Commissioner
Department of Tourism
Elainco Building
78 Contant 1-2-3
St. Thomas, VI 00802
P: (340) 774-8784
F: (340) 774-4390

UTAH
Ms. Leigh Von Der Esch
Managing Director
Governor's Office of Economic
Development
Office of Tourism
Council Hall, 300 North State
Street
Salt Lake City, UT 84040
P: (801) 538-1370
F: (801) 538-1399
E: lvondere@utah.gov

VERMONT
Ms. Megan M. Smith
Commissioner
Agency of Commerce &
Community Development
Department of Tourism &
Marketing
National Life Building, 6th Floor
Montpelier, VT 05620
P: (802) 828-3649
F: (802) 828-3366
E: megan.smith@state.vt.us

VIRGINIA
Ms. Alisa L. Bailey
President & CEO
Tourism Authority
901 East Byrd Street
19th Floor
Richmond, VA 23219
P: (804) 371-8174
F: (804) 786-1919
E: abailey@virginia.org

WASHINGTON
Ms. Patti Brooke
Assistant Director
Business Services Division
P.O. Box 42525
Olympia, WA 98504
P: (360) 725-4035
E: patti.brooke
    @commerce.wa.gov

WEST VIRGINIA
Ms. Betty Carver
Commissioner
Tourism Division
90 MacCorkle Avenue,
Southwest
South Charleston, WV 25303
P: (304) 957-9345
F: (304) 558-2956
E: Betty.B.Carver@wv.gov

WISCONSIN
Ms. Stephanie Klett
Secretary
Department of Tourism
P.O. Box 8690
Madison, WI 53707
P: (608) 266-2345
F: (608) 266-3403
E: sklett
    @travelwisconsin.com

WYOMING
Ms. Diane Shober
Director of Travel & Tourism
Business Council
214 West 15th Street
Cheyenne, WY 82002
P: (307) 777-2800
F: (307) 777-2837
E: Diane.Shober
    @Visitwyo.Gov

Training and Development

Responsible for the training and development of state employees.

ALABAMA
Ms. Norma L. Taylor
Manager of Training
State Personnel Department
300 Folsom Administration
Building
64 North Union Street
Montgomery, AL 36130
P: (334) 242-3494
F: (334) 242-1110

ALASKA
Ms. Nicki Neal
Director
Division of Personnel
Department of Administration
P.O. Box 110201
Juneau, AK 99811
P: (907) 465-4431
F: (907) 465-3415
E: nicki.neal@alaska.gov

AMERICAN SAMOA
Lt. Col. Evelyn Vaiautolu
    Langford
Director
Department of Human
Resources
American Samoa Government
Pago Pago, AS 96799
P: (684) 644-4485
F: (684) 633-1139

CALIFORNIA
Mr. Brian McMahon
Executive Director
Employment Training Panel
1100 J Street, Suite 400
Sacramento, CA 95814
P: (916) 327-5640
F: (916) 445-5972

COLORADO
Mr. Tom LeBlanc
Director
Division of Human Resources
Department of Personnel &
Administration
1313 Sherman Street, Room 122
Denver, CO 80203
P: (303) 866-2105
F: (303) 866-2021
E: tom.leblanc@state.co.us

CONNECTICUT
Mr. Martin W. Anderson
Commissioner
Department of Administrative
Services
165 Capitol Avenue
Room 491
Hartford, CT 06106
P: (860) 713-5100
F: (860) 713-7481
E: martin.anderson@ct.gov

DELAWARE
Ms. Lori Reeder
Director
Department of Labor
Division of Employment &
Training
4425 North Market Street
Wilmington, DE 19802
P: (302) 761-8110
E: lori.reeder@state.de.us

DISTRICT OF COLUMBIA
Ms. Brender L. Gregory
Director
Department of Human
Resources
441 4th Street, Northwest, Suite
300S
Washington, DC 20001
P: (202) 442-9600
F: (202) 727-6827
E: dchr@dc.gov

FLORIDA
Ms. Cynthia R. Lorenzo
Director
Agency for Workforce
Innovation
107 East Madison Street
MSC 110, Caldwell Building
Tallahassee, FL 32399
P: (850) 245-7298
F: (850) 921-3223
E: cynthia.lorenzo
    @flaawi.com

GEORGIA
Mr. James Anderson
Program Manager
Leadership Institute
Suite 504, West Tower
2 Martin Luther King Jr. Drive
Southeast
Atlanta, GA 30334
P: (404) 651-8717
F: (770) 357-9019
E: james.anderson
    @spa.ga.gov

GUAM
Ms. Lourdes M. Perez
Director
Department of Administration
P.O. Box 884
Hagatna, GU 96932
P: (671) 475-1122
F: (671) 475-1243
E: lou.perez@doa.guam.gov

HAWAII
Ms. Sunshine P.W. Topping
Director
Department of Human
Resources Development
State Office Tower
235 South Beretania Street, 14th
Floor
Honolulu, HI 96813
P: (808) 587-1100
F: (808) 587-1106
E: sunshine.p.w.topping
    @hawaii.gov

IDAHO
Mr. Jay E. Engstrom
Assistant Deputy Director
Workforce Development
Division
317 West Main Street
Boise, ID 83735
P: (208) 332-3570 Ext. 2121
F: (208) 334-6430
E: jay.engstrom
    @labor.idaho.gov

ILLINOIS
Ms. Roneta Taylor
Division Manager
Technical Services & Agency
Training Division
Stratton Office Building, Room
504
401 South Spring
Springfield, IL 62706
P: (217) 557-0225

INDIANA
Ms. Lisa Tabor
Training Director
Division of Training &
Development
State Personnel Department
402 West Washington Street,
Room W161
Indianapolis, IN 46204
P: (317) 234-3111
F: (317) 232-3089
E: ltabor@spd.in.gov

KANSAS
Mr. Pat George
Secretary
Department of Commerce
1000 Southwest Jackson Street,
Suite 100
Topeka, KS 66612
P: (785) 296-3481
F: (785) 296-5055
E: pgeorge
    @kansascommerce.com

KENTUCKY
Mr. Timothy Longmeyer
Secretary
Personnel Cabinet
State Office Building
501 High Street, Third Floor
Frankfort, KY 40601
P: (502) 564-7430
F: (502) 564-7603
E: timothy.longmeyer@ky.gov

LOUISIANA
Ms. Karen Puckett
Chief of Operations
Comprehensive Public Training
Program
Division of Administration
P.O. Box 94111
Baton Rouge, LA 70804
P: (225) 342-8545
F: (225) 342-2386
E: Karen.Puckett@la.gov

MAINE
Mr. Denis Normandin
Director
Office of State Training &
Organizational Development
Bureau of Human Resources
#4 State House Station
Augusta, ME 04333
P: (207) 624-7764
F: (207) 287-2896
E: denis.g.normandin
    @maine.gov

MARYLAND
Ms. Cynthia Kollner
Executive Director
Office of Personnel Services &
Benefits
Department of Budget &
Management
301 West Preston Street, Room
609
Baltimore, MD 21201
P: (410) 767-4715
F: (410) 333-5262
E: ckollner@dbm.state.md.us

Training and Development

MASSACHUSETTS
Mr. Paul Dietl
Chief Human Resources Officer
Human Resources Division
1 Ashburton Palce, Room 301
Boston, MA 02108
P: (617) 878-9705
F: (617) 727-1175
E: paul.d.dietl@state.ma.us

MICHIGAN
Mr. Jeremy S. Stephens
Director
Civil Service Commission
400 South Pine Street
P.O. Box 30002
Lansing, MI 48909
P: (517) 373-3020
F: (517) 373-3103
E: StephensJ5@michigan.gov

MINNESOTA
Mr. Jim Schowalter
Commissioner
Management & Budget
658 Cedar Street, Suite 400
St. Paul, MN 55155
P: (651) 201-8010
F: (651) 296-7714
E: James.Schowalter
    @state.mn.us

MISSISSIPPI
Ms. Lynn Fitch
Executive Director
State Personnel Board
301 North Lamar Street
Jackson, MS 39201
P: (601) 359-2702
F: (601) 359-2729
E: lfitch@spb.state.ms.us

MISSOURI
Mr. Bill Miller
Director
Division of Personnel
Office of Administration, P.O.
Box 388
301 West High Street, Suite 430
Jefferson City, MO 65102
P: (573) 751-4514
F: (573) 751-8641
E: bill.miller@oa.mo.gov

MONTANA
Hon. Janet Kelly
Director
Department of Administration
125 North Roberts Street
Room 155, Mitchell Building
Helena, MT 59620
P: (406) 444-3033
F: (406) 444-6194
E: jakelly@mt.gov

NEBRASKA
Mr. Mike McCrory
Director
State Personnel Division
Department of Administrative
Services
P.O. Box 94905
Lincoln, NE 68509
P: (409) 471-2833
F: (402) 471-3754
E: mike.mccrory
    @nebraska.gov

NEVADA
Ms. Patricia L. Hoppe
Employee Development
Manager & Program
Administrator
Department of Personnel
555 East Washington Avenue,
Suite 1400
Las Vegas, NV 89101
P: (702) 486-2928
F: (702) 486-2661
E: phoppe@dop.nv.gov

NEW HAMPSHIRE
Ms. Karen D. Hutchins
Director
Division of Personnel
Department of Administrative
Services
25 Capital Street
Concord, NH 03301
P: (603) 271-1420
F: (603) 271-1422
E: karen.hutchins@nh.gov

NEW JERSEY
Mr. Dennis M. Bone
Chair
State Employment & Training
Commission
P.O. Box 940
Trenton, NJ 08625
P: (609) 633-0605
F: (609) 633-1359

NEW MEXICO
Mr. Gene Moser
Director
State Personnel Office
2600 Cerrillos Road
Santa Fe, NM 87505
P: (505) 476-7751
F: (505) 476-8705
E: eugene.moser@state.nm.us

NEW YORK
Ms. Nancy G. Groenwegen
Commissioner
Department of Civil Service
Alfred E. Smith State Office
Building
Albany, NY 12239
P: (518) 457-2487
F: (518) 473-5696
E: robin.farrell
    @cs.state.ny.us

NORTH CAROLINA
Ms. Paula Kukulinski
Director
Human Resources Development
Office of State Personnel
1333 Mail Service Center
Raleigh, NC 27699
P: (919) 733-2474
E: paula.kukulinski
    @osp.nc.gov

NORTH DAKOTA
Ms. Linda Jensen
Manager
Training & Development
600 East Boulevard Avenue
Department 113
Bismarck, ND 58505
P: (701) 328-3299
F: (701) 328-1475
E: lijensen@nd.gov

**NORTHERN MARIANA
ISLANDS**
Ms. Edith DeLeon Guerrero
Director
Workforce Investment Agency
Caller Box 10007, Capitol Hill
Saipan, MP 96950
P: (670) 664-1700
F: (670) 322-7333
E: gov.wia1@gtepacifica.net

OHIO
Mr. Bob Blair
Director
Department of Administrative
Services
30 East Broad Street, Suite 4040
Columbus, OH 43215
P: (614) 466-6511
F: (614) 644-8151
E: robert.blair
    @das.state.oh.us

OKLAHOMA
Ms. Lisa Fortier
Director
Human Resource Development
Services Division
Office of Personnel
Management
2101 North Lincoln Boulevard
Oklahoma City, OK 73105
P: (405) 521-2177
F: (405) 524-6942
E: lisa.fortier@opm.ok.gov

OREGON
Mr. Twyla Lawson
Senior Recruitment Consultant
HR Management &
Consultation
Human Resource Services
Division
155 Cottage Street, Northeast,
U-30
Salem, OR 97301
P: (503) 373-7677
F: (503) 373-7684
E: Twyla.lawson@state.or.us

PENNSYLVANIA
Mr. James A. Honchar
Deputy Secretary for Human
Resources & Management
Governor's Office of
Administration
517 Finance Building
Harrisburg, PA 17110
P: (717) 787-5545
F: (717) 783-4429
E: jhonchar@state.pa.us

PUERTO RICO
Ms. Marta Beltran
Administrator
Central Labor Advisory &
Human Resources
Administrative Office
P.O. Box 8476
Ponce De Leon Avenue, Suite
1507
San Juan, PR 00910
P: (787) 706-5967
F: (787) 706-5697

Mr. Miguel Romero
Director
Department of Labor & Human
Resources
P.O. Box 191020
San Juan, PR 00919
P: (787) 754-5353
F: (787) 756-1149

RHODE ISLAND
Ms. Melissa Day
Assistant Administrative Officer
Department of Administration
Office of Training &
Development
One Capitol Hill
Providence, RI 02908
P: (401) 222-2178
F: (401) 222-6378
E: mday@gw.doa.state.ri.us

SOUTH CAROLINA
Mr. Samuel L. Wilkins
Director
Office of Human Resources
1201 Main Street, Suite 800
Columbia, SC 29229
P: (803) 896-5172
F: (803) 896-5050
E: swilkins@ohr.sc.gov

SOUTH DAKOTA
Ms. Ellen Zeller
Director of Training
Bureau of Personnel - Training
Joe Foss Building
523 East Capitol Avenue
Pierre, SD 57501
P: (605) 773-3461
F: (605) 773-5389
E: ctr@state.sd.us

TENNESSEE
Ms. Trish Pulley
Assistant Director
Division of Employee Learning
& Development
505 Deaderick Street
James K. Polk Building
Nashville, TN 37243
P: (615) 741-4126
F: (615) 532-0728

U.S. VIRGIN ISLANDS
Mr. Kenneth L. Hermon Jr.
Director
Division of Personnel
GERS Building, 3rd Floor
3438 Kronprindsens Gade
St. Thomas, VI 00802
P: (340) 774-8588
F: (340) 714-5040
E: kenne@viaccess.net

UTAH
Mr. J.J. Acker
Administrative Director
Department of Human Resource
Management
State Office Building, Room
2120
Salt Lake City, UT 84114
P: (801) 538-4297
F: (801) 538-3081
E: JACKER@utah.gov

VERMONT
Ms. Rose Gowdey
Director
Workforce Development,
Wellness & Recruitment
Division
Department of Human
Resources
103 South Main Street, Osgood
Building
Waterbury, VT 05671
P: (802) 241-1115
F: (802) 241-1119
E: rose.gowdey@state.vt.us

VIRGINIA
Mrs. Sara Redding Wilson
Director
Department of Human Resource
Management
101 North 14th Street, 12th
Floor
Richmond, VA 23219
P: (804) 225-2237
F: (804) 371-7401
E: sara.wilson
   @dhrm.virginia.gov

WASHINGTON
Ms. Eva Santos
Director
Department of Personnel
P.O. Box 47500
Olympia, WA 98504
P: (360) 664-6350
F: (360) 753-1003
E: Eva.Santos@dop.wa.gov

WISCONSIN
Mr. Robert Toomey
Administrator
Office of State Employment
Relations
345 West Washington, 2nd Floor
Madison, WI 53702
P: (608) 266-0664
F: (608) 267-1020
E: robert.toomey
   @wisconsin.gov

WYOMING
Ms. Joan Evans
Director
Department of Workforce
Services
122 West 25th Street
Herschler Building, 2 East
Cheyenne, WY 82002
P: (307) 777-8650
E: jevans1@state.wy.us

Transportation and Highways

Umbrella agency responsible for planning, designing, constructing and maintaining public transportation services, highways and facilities throughout the state.

ALABAMA
Mr. John R. Cooper
Transportation Director
Department of Transportation
1409 Coliseum Boulevard
P.O. Box 303050
Montgomery, AL 36130
P: (334) 242-6311
F: (334) 262-8041

Mr. Donald W. Vaughn
Chief Engineer/Deputy Director
Department of Transportation
1409 Coliseum Boulevard
P.O. Box 303050
Montgomery, AL 36130
P: (334) 242-6319
F: (334) 262-8041

ALASKA
Mr. Patrick J. Kemp
Deputy Commissioner,
Highways & Public Facilities
Department of Transportation &
Public Facilities
3132 Channel Drive
P.O. Box 112500
Juneau, AK 99811
P: (907) 465-3906
F: (907) 586-8365

Mr. Marc Luiken
Commissioner
Department of Transportation &
Public Facilities
3132 Channel Drive
P.O. Box 112500
Juneau, AK 99811
P: (907) 465-3901
F: (907) 586-8365

ARIZONA
Mr. John Halikowski
Director
Department of Transportation
206 South 17th Avenue
Phoenix, AZ 85007
P: (602) 712-7011
F: (602) 712-6941

ARKANSAS
Mr. Dan Flowers
Director of Highways &
Transportation
State Highway & Transportation
Department
10324 Interstate 30
P.O. Box 2261
Little Rock, AR 72203
P: (501) 569-2211
F: (501) 569-2400

Mr. Frank Vozel
Deputy Director & Chief
Engineer
State Highway & Transportation
Department
10324 Interstate 30
P.O. Box 2261
Little Rock, AR 72203
P: (501) 569-2214
F: (501) 569-2400

CALIFORNIA
Mr. Cindy McKim
Chief Deputy Director
Department of Transportation
1120 N Street
P.O. Box 942873
Sacramento, CA 94273
P: (916) 654-5267
F: (916) 654-6608

COLORADO
Ms. Margaret A. Catlin
Deputy Executive Director
Department of Transportation
4201 East Arkansas Avenue
Denver, CO 80222
P: (303) 757-9208
F: (303) 757-9656

Mr. Don Hunt
Executive Director
Department of Transportation
4201 East Arkansas Avenue
Denver, CO 80222
P: (303) 757-9201
F: (303) 757-9656

CONNECTICUT
Mr. James Redeker
Acting Commissioner
Department of Transportation
2800 Berlin Turnpike
P.O. Box 317546
Newington, CT 06131
P: (860) 594-3000
F: (860) 594-3008

DELAWARE
Mr. Cleon Cauley Sr.
Acting Secretary
Department of Transportation
800 Bay Road, Route 113
P.O. Box 778
Dover, DE 19903
P: (302) 760-2303
F: (302) 739-2895

Ms. Keesha Wilson
Executive Assistant To the
Secretary
Department of Transportation
800 Bay Road, Route 113
P.O. Box 778
Dover, DE 19903
P: (302) 760-2202
F: (302) 739-2895

DISTRICT OF COLUMBIA
Terry Bellamy
Interim Director
Department of Transportation
Franklin D. Reeves Center,
Sixth Floor
2000 14th Street, Northwest
Washington, DC 20009
P: (202) 673-6813
F: (202) 671-0642

Mr. Renaldo Nicholson
Chief Engineer/Associate
Director
Infrastructure Project
Management Administration
Franklin D. Reeves Center,
Sixth Floor
2000 14th Street, Northwest
Washington, DC 20009
P: (202) 671-4691
F: (202) 671-0642

FLORIDA
Francis Gibbs
Acting Secretary
Department of Transportation
605 Suwannee Street
Tallahassee, FL 32399
P: (850) 414-5200
F: (850) 414-5201

GEORGIA
Mr. Todd I. Long
Director of Planing &
Transportation Data
Department of Transportation
600 West Peachtree, Northwest
Atlanta, GA 30308
P: (404) 631-1021
F: (404) 631-1022

Mr. Gerald Ross
Deputy Commissioner & Chief
Engineer
Department of Transportation
600 West Peachtree, Northwest
Atlanta, GA 30308
P: (404) 631-1000
F: (404) 631-1022

Mr. Vance Smith Jr.
Commissioner
Department of Transportation
One Georgia Center
600 West Peachtree Street,
Northwest
Atlanta, GA 30308
P: (404) 631-1000
F: (404) 631 1846

HAWAII
Jamie Ho
Interim Highways Administrator
Department of Transportation
869 Punchbowl Street
Honolulu, HI 96813
P: (808) 587-2220
F: (808) 587-2167

Dr. Glenn M. Okimoto
Director
Department of Transportation
869 Punchbowl Street
Honolulu, HI 96813
P: (808) 587-2150
F: (808) 587-2167

IDAHO
Mr. Brian W. Ness
Director
Transportation Department
3311 West State Street
P.O. Box 7129
Boise, ID 83707
P: (208) 334-8807
F: (208) 334-3858

Mr. Scott L. Stokes
Deputy Director
Transportation Department
3311 West State Street
P.O. Box 7129
Boise, ID 83707
P: (208) 334-8827
F: (208) 334-3858

ILLINOIS
Mr. Gary Hannig
Secretary
Department of Transportation
2300 South Dirksen Parkway
Springfield, IL 62764
P: (217) 782-5597
F: (217) 782-6828

INDIANA
Mr. Michael B. Cline
Commissioner
Department of Transportation
Indiana Government Center
North
100 North Senate Avenue, Room
N 758
Indianapolis, IN 46204
P: (317) 232-5525
F: (317) 232-0238

IOWA
Mr. Daniel R. Franklin
Director, Office of Policy &
Legislative Services
Department of Transportation
800 Lincoln Way
Ames, IA 50010
P: (515) 239-1131
F: (515) 817-6508

Ms. Nancy J. Richardson
Director
Department of Transportation
800 Lincoln Way
Ames, IA 50010
P: (515) 239-1111
F: (515) 817-6508

KANSAS
Mr. Chris J. Herrick
Director of Planning &
Development
Department of Transportation
Eisenhower State Office
Building
700 Harrison
Topeka, KS 66603
P: (785) 296-2252
F: (785) 296-1095

Ms. Debra L. Miller
Secretary
Department of Transportation
Eisenhower State Office
Building
700 Harrison
Topeka, KS 66603
P: (785) 296-3461
F: (785) 296-1095

Mr. Jerome T. Younger
Deputy Secretary for
Engineering & Design/State
Transportation Engineer
Department of Transportation
Eisenhower State Office
Building
700 Harrison
Topeka, KS 66603
P: (785) 296-3285
F: (785) 296-1095

KENTUCKY
Mr. Mike Hancock
Secretary
Transportation Cabinet
200 Mero Street
Frankfort, KY 40622
P: (502) 564-4890
F: (502) 564-4809

LOUISIANA
Mr. Eric I. Kalivoda
Acting Deputy Secretary
Department of Transportation &
Development
1201 Capitol Access Road
P.O. Box 94245
Baton Rouge, LA 70804
P: (225) 379-1200
F: (225) 379-1851

Ms. Sherri LeBas
Secretary
Department of Transportation &
Development
1201 Capitol Access Road
P.O. Box 94245
Baton Rouge, LA 70804
P: (225) 379-1200
F: (225) 379-1851

Mr. Richard L. Savoie
Chief Engineer
Department of Transportation &
Development
1201 Capitol Access Road
P.O. Box 94245
Baton Rouge, LA 70804
P: (225) 379-1234
F: (225) 379-1851

MAINE
Mr. David Bernhardt
Acting Commissioner
Department of Transportation
Child Street
16 State House Station
Augusta, ME 04333
P: (207) 624-3000
F: (207) 624-3001

Mr. Bruce A. Van Note
Deputy Commissioner
Department of Transportation
Child Street
16 State House Station
Augusta, ME 04333
P: (207) 624-3002
F: (207) 624-3001

MARYLAND
Mr. Harold M. Bartlett
Deputy Secretary
Department of Transportation
Office of the Secretary, P.O.
Box 548
7201 Corporate Center Drive
Hanover, MD 21076
P: (410) 865-1002
F: (410) 865-1334

Ms. Beverley Swaim-Staley
Secretary
Department of Transportation
Office of the Secretary, P.O.
Box 548
7201 Corporate Center Drive
Hanover, MD 21076
P: (888) 713-1414
F: (410) 865-1334

MASSACHUSETTS
Mr. Jeffrey B. Mullan
Secretary of Transportation &
Public Works
Department of Transportation
10 Park Plaza, Suite 3170
Boston, MA 02116
P: (617) 973-7000
F: (617) 973-8031

MICHIGAN
Mr. Kirk T. Steudle
Director
Department of Transportation
Murray D. Van Wagoner
Building
425 West Ottawa Street, P.O.
Box 30050
Lansing, MI 48933
P: (517) 373-2114
F: (517) 373-8841
E: mdotdirector
    @michigan.gov

MINNESOTA
Khani Sahebjam
Department of Transportation
Transportation Building
395 John Ireland Boulevard
St. Paul, MN 55155
P: (651) 366-4800
F: (651) 366-4795

Mr. Thomas Sorel
Commissioner
Department of Transportation
Transportation Building
395 John Ireland Boulevard
St. Paul, MN 55155
P: (651) 366-4800
F: (651) 366-4795
E: thomas.sorel
    @dot.state.mn.us

MISSISSIPPI
Ms. Melinda McGrath
Interim Executive Director,
Chief Administrative Officer
Department of Transportation
Administrative Office Building
401 North West Street, P.O. Box
1850
Jackson, MS 39215
P: (601) 359-7001
F: (601) 359-7050

MISSOURI
Mr. Kevin Keith
Chief Engineer
Department of Transportation
105 West Capitol Avenue
P.O. Box 270
Jefferson City, MO 65102
P: (573) 751-3692
F: (573) 751-6555

MONTANA
Mr. Dwane Kailey
Chief Operations Officer/Chief
Engineer
Department of Transportation
2701 Prospect Avenue
P.O. Box 201001
Helena, MT 59620
P: (406) 444-6414
F: (406) 444-7643

Mr. Jim Lynch
Director
Department of Transportation
2701 Prospect Avenue
P.O. Box 201001
Helena, MT 59620
P: (406) 444-6201
F: (406) 444-7643
E: jilynch@mt.gov

Lynn Zanto
Administrator, Rail, Transit, and
Planning Division
Department of Transportation
2701 Prospect Avenue
P.O. Box 201001
Helena, MT 59620
P: (406) 444-3445
F: (406) 444-7643

NEBRASKA
Mr. Monty W. Fredrickson
Director-State Engineer
Department of Roads
1500 Highway 2
P.O. Box 94759
Lincoln, NE 68509
P: (402) 479-4615
F: (402) 479-4325

Transportation and Highways

Mr. John R. Jacobson
Deputy
Director-Operations/Chief
Engineer
Department of Roads
1500 Highway 2
P.O. Box 94759
Lincoln, NE 68509
P: (402) 479-4671
F: (402) 479-4325

NEVADA
Ms. Susan Martinovich
Director
Department of Transportation
1263 South Stewart Street
Carson City, NV 89712
P: (775) 888-7440
F: (775) 888-7201
E: info@dot.state.nv.us

NEW HAMPSHIRE
Mr. George N. Campbell
Commissioner
Department of Transportation
John O. Morton Building
7 Hazen Drive, P.O. Box 483
Concord, NH 03302
P: (603) 271-3734
F: (603) 271-3914
E: gcampbell
    @dot.state.nh.us

NEW JERSEY
Mr. Joseph W. Mrozek
Deputy Commissioner
Department of Transportation
1035 Parkway Avenue
P.O. Box 600
Trenton, NJ 08625
P: (609) 530-4314
F: (609) 530-3894

Mr. James S. Simpson
Commissioner
Department of Transportation
1035 Parkway Avenue
P.O. Box 600
Trenton, NJ 08625
P: (609) 530-3536
F: (609) 530-3894

NEW MEXICO
Mr. Alvin Dominguez
Secretary
Department of Transportation
Joe M. Anaya Building
1120 Cerrilos Road, P.O. Box
1149
Santa Fe, NM 87504
P: (505) 827-5110
F: (505) 827-5469

NEW YORK
Ms. Diane Lombardi
Director, Office of External
Relations
Department of Transportation
50 Wolf Road
Albany, NY 12232
P: (518) 457-2345
F: (518) 457-4190

Ms. Joan McDonald
Commissioner
Department of Transportation
50 Wolf Road
Albany, NY 12232
P: (518) 457-4422
F: (518) 457-4190

NORTH CAROLINA
Mr. Gene Conti
Secretary
Department of Transportation
1507 Mail Service Center
1 South Wilmington Street
Raleigh, NC 27699
P: (919) 733-2520
F: (919) 733-9150

Terry R. Gibson
State Highway Administrator
Department of Transportation
1507 Mail Service Center
1 South Wilmington Street
Raleigh, NC 27699
P: (919) 733-7384
F: (919) 733-9150

NORTH DAKOTA
Mr. Grant Levi
Deputy Director for Engineering
Department of Transportation
608 East Boulevard Avenue
Bismarck, ND 58505
P: (701) 328-2584
F: (701) 328-0310

Mr. Francis G. Ziegler
Director
Department of Transportation
608 East Boulevard Avenue
Bismarck, ND 58505
P: (701) 328-2500
F: (701) 328-0310
E: fziegler@nd.gov

OHIO
Mr. Jerry Wray
Director
Department of Transportation
1980 West Broad Street
Columbus, OH 43223
P: (614) 466-2335
F: (614) 4664-8662

OKLAHOMA
Mr. Gary Evans
Chief Engineer
Department of Transportation
200 Northeast 21st Street
Oklahoma City, OK 73105
P: (405) 521-2688
F: (405) 522-1805

Mr. John M. Fuller
Deputy Director
Department of Transportation
200 Northeast 21st Street
Oklahoma City, OK 73105
P: (405) 521-2688
F: (405) 522-1805

Mr. Gary Ridley
Director & Secretary of
Transportation
Department of Transportation
200 Northeast 21st Street
Oklahoma City, OK 73105
P: (405) 522-1800
F: (405) 522-1805

OREGON
Mr. Matthew Garrett
Director
Department of Transportation
1158 Chemeketa Street,
Northeast
Salem, OR 97301
P: (503) 986-3289
F: (503) 986-3432
E: Matthew.l.garrett
    @odot.state.or.us

Mr. Doug Tindall
Deputy Director, Highway
Division
Department of Transportation
1158 Chemeketa Street,
Northeast
Salem, OR 97301
P: (503) 986-3435
F: (503) 986-3432

PENNSYLVANIA
Mr. James D. Ritzman
Deputy Secretary for
Transportation Planning
Department of Transportation
Keystone Building
400 North Street
Harrisburg, PA 17120
P: (717) 787-3154
F: (717) 787-5491

Mr. Barry J. Schoch
Secretary
Department of Transportation
Keystone Building
400 North Street
Harrisburg, PA 17120
P: (717) 787-3154
F: (717) 787-5491

PUERTO RICO
Mr. Ruben A.
    Hernandez Gregorat
Secretary of Transportation and
Public Works
Department of Transportation &
Public Works
Office of the Secretary
P.O. Box 41269, Minillas Station
San Juan, PR 00940
P: (787) 722-2929
F: (787) 728-1620

Mr. Fernando I. Pont
Deputy Secretary of
Transportation
Department of Transportation &
Public Works
Office of the Secretary
P.O. Box 41269, Minillas Station
San Juan, PR 00940
P: (787) 723-1780
F: (787) 728-1620

RHODE ISLAND
Kazem Farhoumand
Chief Engineer
Department of Transportation
State Office Building
2 Capitol Hill
Providence, RI 02903
P: (401) 222-2492
F: (401) 222-2086

Mr. Michael P. Lewis
Director
Department of Transportation
State Office Building
2 Capitol Hill
Providence, RI 02903
P: (401) 222-2481
F: (401) 222-2086

Mr. Robert Rocchio
Managing Engineer, Traffic
Design
Department of Transportation
State Office Building
2 Capitol Hill
Providence, RI 02903
P: (401) 222-2694
F: (401) 222-2086

SOUTH CAROLINA
Mr. Tony L. Chapman
Deputy Secretary for
Engineering
Department of Transportation
Silas N. Pearman Building
955 Park Street
Columbia, SC 29201
P: (803) 737-7900
F: (803) 737-2038

Mr. Robert J. St. Onge Jr.
Secretary of Transportation
Department of Transportation
Silas N. Pearman Building
955 Park Street
Columbia, SC 29201
P: (803) 737-2314
F: (803) 737-2038

SOUTH DAKOTA
Mr. Darin Bergquist
Secretary
Department of Transportation
700 East Broadway Avenue
Pierre, SD 57501
P: (605) 773-3265
F: (605) 773-3921

Mr. Kevin Tveidt
Deputy Secretary
Department of Transportation
700 East Broadway Avenue
Pierre, SD 57501
P: (605) 773-3265
F: (605) 773-3921

TENNESSEE
Mr. Ed Cole
Chief of Environment and
Planning
Department of Transportation
700 James K. Polk Building
505 Deaderick Street
Nashville, TN 37243
P: (615) 741-2848
F: (615) 741-2508

Mr. Paul Degges
Chief Engineer
Department of Transportation
700 James K. Polk Building
505 Deaderick Street
Nashville, TN 37243
P: (615) 741-0791
F: (615) 741-2508

Mr. Randy Lovett
Chief of Administration
Department of Transportation
700 James K. Polk Building
505 Deaderick Street
Nashville, TN 37243
P: (615) 741-5374
F: (615) 741-2508

Mr. John Schroer
Commissioner
Department of Transportation
700 James K. Polk Building
505 Deaderick Street
Nashville, TN 37243
P: (615) 741-2848
F: (615) 741-2508

TEXAS
Mr. Amadeo Saenz
Executive Director
Department of Transportation
Dewitt C. Greer Highway
Building
125 East 11th Street
Austin, TX 78701
P: (512) 305-9501
F: (512) 305-9567

Mr. Steven E. Simmons
Deputy Executive Director
Department of Transportation
Dewitt C. Greer Highway
Building
125 East 11th Street
Austin, TX 78701
P: (512) 305-9502
F: (512) 305-9567

UTAH
Mr. Carlos Braceras
Deputy Director
Department of Transportation
P.O. Box 141265
Salt Lake City, UT 84114
P: (801) 965-4030
F: (801) 965-4338

Mr. John R. Njord
Executive Director
Department of Transportation
P.O. Box 141265
Salt Lake City, UT 84114
P: (801) 965-4000
F: (801) 965-4338
E: jnjord@utah.gov

VIRGINIA
Mr. Sean T. Connaughton
Secretary of Transportation
Department of Transportation
1401 East Broad Street
Richmond, VA 23219
P: (804) 786-2801
F: (804) 786-2940

Mr. Matt Strader
Assistant Secretary
Department of Transportation
1401 East Broad Street
Richmond, VA 23219
P: (804) 786-8032
F: (804) 786-2940

Mr. David Tyeryar
Deputy Secretary
Department of Transportation
1401 East Broad Street
Richmond, VA 23219
P: (804) 786-8032
F: (804) 786-2940

Mr. Gregory A. Whirley Sr.
Commissioner
Department of Transportation
1401 East Broad Street
Richmond, VA 23219
P: (804) 786-2801
F: (804) 786-2940
E: Greg.Whirley
    @VDOT.Virginia.gov

WASHINGTON
Mr. Dillon Auyoung
Director of Government
Relations
Department of Transportation
310 Maple Park Avenue,
Southeast
P.O. Box 47315
Olympia, WA 98504
P: (360) 705-7024
F: (360) 705-6888

Ms. Paula J. Hammond
Secretary of Transportation
Department of Transportation
310 Maple Park Avenue,
Southeast
P.O. Box 47315
Olympia, WA 98504
P: (360) 705-7054
F: (360) 705-6888
E: HAMMONP@wsdot.wa.gov

WEST VIRGINIA
Mr. Paul A. Mattox
Secretary of
Transportation/Commissioner of
Highways
Department of Transportation
1900 Kanawha Boulevard, East
Building 5, Room 110
Charleston, WV 25305
P: (304) 558-0444
F: (304) 558-1004
E: Paul.A.Mattox@wv.gov

WISCONSIN
Mr. Mark Gottlieb
Secretary
Department of Transportation
4802 Sheboygan Avenue
P.O. Box 7910
Madison, WI 53707
P: (608) 266-1114
F: (608) 266-9912

WYOMING
Mr. John F. Cox
Director
Department of Transportation
5300 Bishop Boulevard
Cheyenne, WY 82009
P: (307) 777-4484
F: (307) 777-4163

Treasurer

The custodian of all state funds and securities belonging to and held in trust by the state.

Information provided by:

National Association of State Treasurers
Jon Lawniczak
Director
P.O. Box 11910
Lexington, KY 40578
P: (859) 244-8175
F: (859) 244-8053
jlawniczak@csg.org
www.nast.org

ALABAMA
Hon. Young Boozer (R)
State Treasurer
Office of the State Treasurer
600 Dexter Avenue, S-106
Montgomery, AL 36104
P: (334) 242-7500
F: (334) 242-7592
E: alatreas
@treasury.alabama.gov

ALASKA
Hon. Jerry Burnett
(appointed)
Deputy Commissioner of Revenue
Department of Revenue
Treasury Division
P.O. Box 110405
Juneau, AK 99811
P: (907) 465-2312
F: (907) 465-2389
E: jerry.burnett@alaska.gov

AMERICAN SAMOA
Hon. Magalei Logovi'i
Treasurer
Department of the Treasury
American Samoa Government
Pago Pago, AS 96799
P: (684) 633-4155
F: (684) 633-4100

ARIZONA
Hon. Doug Ducey (R)
State Treasurer
Office of the State Treasurer
1700 West Washington Street
Phoenix, AZ 85007
P: (602) 604-7800
F: (602) 542-7176

ARKANSAS
Hon. Martha A. Shoffner (D)
State Treasurer
State Treasury
220 State Capitol
Little Rock, AR 72201
P: (501) 682-5888
F: (501) 682-3820

CALIFORNIA
Hon. Bill Lockyer (D)
State Treasurer
Office of the State Treasurer
P.O. Box 942809
915 Capitol Mall, C-15
Sacramento, CA 94209
P: (916) 653-2995
F: (916) 653-3125

COLORADO
Hon. Walker Stapleton (R)
State Treasurer
Office of the State Treasurer
140 State Capitol
Denver, CO 80203
P: (303) 866-2441
F: (303) 866-2123

CONNECTICUT
Hon. Denise L. Nappier (D)
State Treasurer
Office of State Treasurer
55 Elm Street
Hartford, CT 06106
P: (860) 702-3010
F: (860) 702-3043
E: denise.nappier@ct.gov

DELAWARE
Hon. Chip Flowers Jr. (D)
State Treasurer
Office of the State Treasurer
820 Silver Lake Boulevard,
Suite 100
Dover, DE 19904
P: (302) 672-6700
F: (302) 739-5635

DISTRICT OF COLUMBIA
Dr. Natwar M. Gandhi
(appointed)
Chief Financial Officer
Office of the Chief Financial
Officer
1350 Pennsylvania Avenue,
Northwest
Room 203
Washington, DC 20004
P: (202) 727-2476
F: (202) 727-1643
E: ocfo@dc.gov

FLORIDA
Hon. Jeffrey H. Atwater (R)
Chief Financial Officer
Department of Financial
Services
PL-11, The Capitol
Tallahassee, FL 32399
P: (850) 413-2907
F: (850) 413-2950
E: allison@jeffatwater.com

GEORGIA
Hon. Tommy D. Hills (R)
(appointed)
Treasurer and Director
Office of Treasury & Fiscal
Services
200 Piedmont Avenue
Suite 1202, West Tower
Atlanta, GA 30334
P: (404) 656-2168
F: (404) 656-9048
E: OTFSweb@otfs.ga.gov

GUAM
Hon. Rose T. Fejeran
Treasurer
Office of the Treasurer
P.O. Box 884
Hagatna, GU 96932
P: (671) 475-1161
E: rtfejeran@doa.guam.gov

HAWAII
Hon. Kalbert K. Young
(appointed)
Director of Finance
Department of Budget &
Finance
P.O. Box 150
Honolulu, HI 96810
P: (808) 586-1518
F: (808) 586-1976
E: HI.BudgetandFinance
@hawaii.gov

IDAHO
Hon. Ron G. Crane (R)
State Treasurer
State Treasurer's Office
P.O. Box 83720
Boise, ID 83720
P: (208) 334-3200
F: (208) 332-2960
E: ron.crane@sto.idaho.gov

ILLINOIS
Hon. Dan Rutherford (R)
State Treasurer
Office of the State Treasurer
Capitol Building
219 Statehouse
Springfield, IL 62704
P: (217) 782-2211
F: (217) 785-2777

INDIANA
Hon. Richard E.
Mourdock (R)
State Treasurer
Office of the State Treasurer
242 State House
Indianapolis, IN 46204
P: (217) 232-6386
F: (317) 232-5656

IOWA
Hon. Michael L.
Fitzgerald (D)
State Treasurer
State Treasurer's Office
Room 114, Capitol Building
Des Moines, IA 50319
P: (515) 281-5368
F: (515) 281-7562
E: mike.fitzgerald@iowa.gov

KANSAS
Hon. Ron Estes (R)
State Treasurer
Office of the State Treasurer
900 Southwest Jackson Street,
Suite 201
Topeka, KS 66612
P: (785) 296-3171
F: (785) 296-7950

KENTUCKY
Hon. Todd Hollenbach (D)
State Treasurer
State Treasury
1050 U.S. Highway 127 South
Frankfort, KY 40601
P: (502) 564-4722
F: (502) 564-6545
E: todd.hollenbach@ky.gov

LOUISIANA
Hon. John Neely Kennedy (R)
State Treasurer
Department of the Treasury
P.O. Box 44154
Baton Rouge, LA 70804
P: (225) 342-0010
F: (225) 342-0046
E: jkennedy
@treasury.state.la.us

MAINE
Hon. Bruce Poliquin (R)
State Treasurer
Office of the State Treasurer
39 State House Station
Augusta, ME 04333
P: (207) 624-7477
F: (207) 287-2367

MARYLAND
Hon. Nancy K. Kopp (D)
(elected by the Legislature)
State Treasurer
State Treasurer's Office
Goldstein Treasury Building
80 Calvert Street
Annapolis, MD 21401
P: (410) 260-7533
F: (410) 974-3530
E: nkopp
@treasurer.state.md.us

MASSACHUSETTS
Hon. Steven Grossman (D)
State Treasurer
Office of the State Treasurer
State House, Room 227
Boston, MA 02133
P: (617) 367-6900
F: (617) 248-0372

MICHIGAN
Hon. Andy Dillon (D)
(appointed)
State Treasurer
Office of the State Treasurer
P.O. Box 15128
Lansing, MI 48901
P: (517) 373-3223
F: (517) 335-1785

MINNESOTA
Mr. Jim Schowalter
Commissioner
Management & Budget
658 Cedar Street, Suite 400
St. Paul, MN 55155
P: (651) 201-8010
F: (651) 296-7714
E: James.Schowalter
@state.mn.us

MISSISSIPPI
Hon. Tate Reeves (R)
State Treasurer
Office of the State Treasurer
P.O. Box 138
Jackson, MS 39205
P: (601) 359-3600
F: (601) 576-4495
E: treeves
@treasury.state.ms.us

MISSOURI
Hon. Clint Zweifel (D)
State Treasurer
Office of the State Treasurer
P.O. Box 210
Jefferson City, MO 65102
P: (573) 751-4123
F: (573) 751-9443
E: clint.zweifel
@treasurer.mo.gov

MONTANA
Hon. Janet Kelly
(appointed)
Director
Department of Administration
125 North Roberts Street
Room 155, Mitchell Building
Helena, MT 59620
P: (406) 444-3033
F: (406) 444-6194
E: jakelly@mt.gov

NEBRASKA
Hon. Don B. Stenberg (R)
State Treasurer
Office of the State Treasruer
2005 State Capitol
Lincoln, NE 68509
P: (402) 471-2455
F: (402) 471-4390
E: Don.Stenberg
@nebraska.gov

NEVADA
Hon. Kate Marshall (D)
State Treasurer
Office of the State Treasurer
101 North Carson Street, #4
Carson City, NV 89701
P: (775) 684-5600
F: (775) 684-5623
E: katemarshall
@NevadaTreasurer.gov

NEW HAMPSHIRE
Hon. Catherine Provencher
(elected by the Legislature)
State Treasurer
State Treasury
25 Capitol Street, Room 121
Concord, NH 03301
P: (603) 271-2621
F: (603) 271-3922
E: cprovencher
@treasury.state.nh.us

NEW JERSEY
Hon. Andrew P.
Sidamon-Eristoff
(appointed)
State Treasurer
Office of the Treasurer
State House
P.O. Box 002
Trenton, NJ 08625
P: (608) 292-6748
F: (609) 984-3888

NEW MEXICO
Hon. James B. Lewis (D)
State Treasurer
Office of the State Treasurer
2019 Galisteo Street, Building K
P.O. Box 608
Santa Fe, NM 87504
P: (505) 955-1120
F: (505) 955-1195

NEW YORK
Hon. Aida M. Brewer
(appointed)
Deputy Commissioner and
Treasurer
Department of Taxation &
Finance
P.O. Box 7002
Albany, NY 12225
P: (518) 474-4250
F: (518) 402-4118
E: aida_brewer
@tax.state.ny.us

NORTH CAROLINA
Hon. Janet Cowell (D)
State Treasurer
Department of State Treasurer
325 North Salisbury Street,
Room 100
Raleigh, NC 27603
P: (919) 508-5176
F: (919) 508-5167
E: janet.cowell
@nctreasurer.com

NORTH DAKOTA
Hon. Kelly L. Schmidt (R)
State Treasurer
Office of State Treasurer
State Capitol, 3rd Floor
600 East Boulevard Avenue,
Dept. 120
Bismarck, ND 58505
P: (701) 328-2643
F: (701) 328-3002
E: treasurer@nd.gov

NORTHERN MARIANA ISLANDS
Hon. Antoinette S. Calvo
CMNI Treasurer
Department of Finance
P.O. Box 5234, CHRB
Saipan, MP 96950
P: (670) 664-1300
F: (670) 322-4643

OHIO
Hon. Josh Mandel (R)
Treasurer of State
Office of the State Treasurer
30 East Broad Street
9th Floor
Columbus, OH 43215
P: (614) 466-3639
F: (614) 644-7313

OKLAHOMA
Hon. Ken Miller (R)
State Treasurer
Office of the State Treasurer
Room 217, State Capitol
Building
2300 North Lincoln Boulevard
Oklahoma City, OK 73105
P: (405) 521-3191
F: (405) 521-4994

OREGON
Hon. Ted Wheeler
State Treasurer
Office of the State Treasurer
350 Winter Street, Northeast
Suite 100
Salem, OR 97301
P: (503) 378-4329
E: Oregon.Treasurer
@state.or.us

PENNSYLVANIA
Hon. Rob McCord (D)
State Treasurer
Treasury Department
Room 129, Finance Building
Harrisburg, PA 17120
P: (717) 787-2465
F: (717) 783-9760
E: rmm@patreasury.org

RHODE ISLAND
Hon. Gina M. Raimondo (D)
General Treasurer
Office of the State Treasurer
State House, Room 102
Providence, RI 02903
P: (401) 222-2397
F: (401) 222-6140
E: generaltreasurer
@treasury.ri.gov

SOUTH CAROLINA
Hon. Curtis Loftis (R)
State Treasurer
Office of the State Treasurer
P.O. Box 11778
Columbia, SC 29211
P: (803) 734-2101
F: (803) 734-2690
E: Linda.Champion-Gamble
@sto.sc.gov

Treasurer

SOUTH DAKOTA
Hon. Rich L. Sattgast (R)
State Treasurer
Office of the State Treasurer
State Capitol Building, Suite 212
500 East Capitol Avenue
Pierre, SD 57501
P: (605) 773-3378
F: (605) 773-3115
E: rich.sattgast
@state.sd.us

TENNESSEE
Hon. David H. Lillard Jr.
(elected by the Legislature)
State Treasurer
Department of Treasury
State Capitol, First Floor
Nashville, TN 37243
P: (615) 741-2956
F: (615) 253-1591
E: david.lillard
@state.tn.us

TEXAS
Ms. Susan Combs
Comptroller of Public Accounts
Office of the Comptroller of
Public Accounts
111 East 17th
P.O.Box 13528
Austin, TX 78711
P: (512) 463-4444
F: (512) 463-4965
E: susan.combs
@cpa.state.tx.us

U.S. VIRGIN ISLANDS
Hon. Laurel Payne
(appointed)
Director of Treasury
Office of the Treasury
2314 Kronprindsens Gade
Charlotte Amalie, VI 00802
P: (340) 774-4750
F: (340) 776-4028

UTAH
Hon. Richard K. Ellis (R)
State Treasurer
State Treasurer's Office
P.O. Box 142315
Salt Lake City, UT 84114
P: (801) 538-1042
F: (801) 538-1465
E: rellis@utah.gov

VERMONT
Hon. Elizabeth Pearce
State Treasurer
Office of the State Treasurer
109 State Street, 4th Floor
Montpelier, VT 05609
P: (802) 828-1452
F: (802) 828-2772
E: Beth.Pearce@state.vt.us

VIRGINIA
Hon. Manju Ganeriwala
(appointed)
State Treasurer
Department of the Treasury
101 North 14th Street, 3rd Floor
James Monroe Building, P.O.
Box 1879
Richmond, VA 23218
P: (804) 371-6011
F: (804) 786-0833
E: Manju.Ganeriwala
@trs.virginia.gov

WASHINGTON
Hon. James L. McIntire (D)
State Treasurer
Office of the State Treasurer
Legislative Building
P.O. Box 40200
Olympia, WA 98504
P: (360) 902-9001
F: (360) 902-9044
E: watreas@tre.wa.gov

WEST VIRGINIA
Hon. John D. Perdue (D)
State Treasurer
State Treasurer's Office
Building 1, State Capitol
Complex
1900 Kanawha Boulevard, Suite
E-145
Charleston, WV 25305
P: (304) 558-5000
F: (304) 558-4097
E: john.perdue@wvsto.com

WISCONSIN
Hon. Kurt W. Schuller (R)
State Treasurer
Office of the State Treasurer
P.O. Box 7871
Madison, WI 53707
P: (608) 266-1714
F: (608) 266-2647
E: Kurt.Schuller
@wisconsin.gov

WYOMING
Hon. Joe B. Meyer (R)
State Treasurer
Office of the State Treasurer
200 West 24th Street, Suite 122
Cheyenne, WY 82002
P: (307) 777-7408
F: (307) 777-5411
E: jmeyer3@state.wy.us

Tribal Affairs

Acts as a liaison between state and tribal officials and advances the concerns of Native Americans.

ALABAMA
Ms. Eloise P. Josey
Executive Director
Indian Affairs Commission
771 South Lawrence Street,
Suite 106
Montgomery, AL 36130
P: (334) 242-2831
F: (334) 240-3408
E: aiac@mindspring.com

ARIZONA
Ms. Kristine M. FireThunder
Director
Commission of Indian Affairs
State Capitol Building,
Executive Tower
1700 West Washington Street,
Suite 156
Phoenix, AZ 85007
P: (602) 542-4421
F: (602) 542-3712
E: iainfo@az.gov

CALIFORNIA
Mr. Larry Myers
Executive Secretary
Native American Heritage
Commission
915 Capitol Mall, Room 364
Sacramento, CA 95814
P: (916) 653-4082
F: (916) 657-5390

COLORADO
Ms. Carol Harvey
Executive Secretary
Commission on Indian Affairs
130 State Capitol
Denver, CO 80203
P: (303) 866-3027
F: (303) 866-5469
E: carol.harvey@state.co.us

CONNECTICUT
Mr. Ed W. Sarabia Jr.
Indian Affairs Coordinator
Indian Affairs Council
Department of Environmental
Protection
79 Elm Street
Hartford, CT 06106
P: (860) 424-3066
F: (860) 424-4070
E: edward.sarabia@ct.gov

FLORIDA
Mr. Joe Quetone
Executive Director
Governor's Council on Indian
Affairs
1341 Cross Creek Circle
Tallahassee, FL 32301
P: (850) 488-0730
E: quetonej@fgcia.com

GEORGIA
Dr. David Crass
Div. Director, Deputy State
Historic Preservation Officer &
State Archaeologist
Historical Preservation Division
254 Washington Street,
Southwest
Ground Level
Atlanta, GA 30334
P: (404) 651-5061
F: (404) 657-1046
E: david.crass
    @dnr.state.ga.us

HAWAII
Mr. Clyde W. Namu'o
Administrator
Office of Hawaiian Affairs
711 Kapi'olani Boulevard, Suite
500
Honolulu, HI 96813
P: (808) 594-1892
F: (808) 594-1865
E: info@oha.org

IOWA
Ms. Jill Avery
Board Administrator
Commission on Native
American Affairs
Lucas State Office Building
321 East 12th Street
Des Moines, IA 50319
P: (515) 242-6334
E: jill.avery@iowa.gov

KENTUCKY
Ms. Tressa Brown
Native American Heritage
Coordinator
State Heritage Council
State Historic Preservation
Office
300 Washington Street
Frankfort, KY 40601
P: (502) 564-7005 Ext. 125
F: (502) 564-5820

LOUISIANA
Mr. Mark Ford
Director
Governor's Office of Indian
Affairs
150 North Third Street, Suite
713
P.O. Box 94004
Baton Rouge, LA 70804
P: (225) 219-8715
F: (225) 219-7551
E: Mark.ford@la.gov

MAINE
Mr. John
    Dieffenbacher-Krall
Director
Indian Tribal-State Commission
P.O. Box 241
Stillwater, ME 04489
P: (207) 817-3799
F: (207) 394-9230
E: mitsced@roadrunner.com

MARYLAND
Mr. E. Keith Colston
Executive Director
Governor's Commission on
Indian Affairs
301 West Preston Street, Suite
1500
Baltimore, MD 21201
P: (410) 767-7631
F: (410) 333-7542
E: KColston
    @goci.state.md.us

MICHIGAN
Ms. Donna Budnick
American Indian Specialist
Department of Civil Rights
110 West Michigan Avenue
Suite 800
Lansing, MI 48933
P: (517) 241-7748
F: (517) 241-7520

Mr. Daniel Krichbaum
Director
Department of Civil Rights
Capitol Tower Building
110 West Michigan Avenue,
Suite 900
Lansing, MI 48933
P: (517) 335-3164
F: (517) 335-6513
E: krichbaumd@michigan.gov

MINNESOTA
Ms. Anna Marie
    Hill-Kleinhans
Executive Director
Indian Affairs Council
161 St. Anthony Avenue, Suite
924
St. Paul, MN 55103
P: (651) 296-0041
F: (651) 296-0309
E: annamarie.hill
    @state.mn.us

MONTANA
Ms. Lesa Evers
Acting Director
Office of Indian Affairs
Office of the Governor
P.O. Box 200801
Helena, MT 59620
P: (406) 444-3702
F: (406) 444-1350

NEBRASKA
Hon. Rick Sheehy (R)
Lieutenant Governor
Office of the Lieutenant
Governor
State Capitol, Room 2315
P.O. Box 94863
Lincoln, NE 68509
P: (402) 471-2256
F: (402) 471-6031

NEVADA
Ms. Sherry L. Rupert
Executive Director
Indian Commission
5366 Snyder Avenue
Carson City, NV 89701
P: (775) 687-8333
F: (775) 687-8330
E: srupert
    @govmail.state.nv.us

NEW JERSEY
Ms. Rowena Madden
Director
Commission on American
Indian Affairs
Office of the Secretary of State
P.O. Box 300
Trenton, NJ 08625
P: (609) 341-2740
F: (609) 777-1764
E: AmericanIndian
    @sos.state.nj.us

Tribal Affairs

NEW MEXICO
Mr. Arthur Allison
Secretary
Indian Affairs Department
Wendell Chino Building, 2nd
Floor
1220 South St. Francies Drive
Santa Fe, NM 87505
P: (505) 476-1600
F: (505) 476-1601
E: arthur.allison
   @state.nm.us

NEW YORK
Mr. David Rose
Assistant Counsel
Office of Counsel the Governor
State Capitol
Albany, NY 12224
P: (518) 474-2266

NORTH CAROLINA
Mr. Gregory A. Richardson
Director
Department of Administration
Commission of Indian Affairs
1317 Mail Service Center
Raleigh, NC 27699
P: (919) 789-5900
F: (919) 420-1373
E: greg.richardson
   @doa.nc.gov

NORTH DAKOTA
Mr. Scott J. Davis
Executive Director
Indian Affairs Commission
600 East Boulevard Avenue, 1st
Floor
Judicial Wing, Room #117
Bismarck, ND 58505
P: (701) 328-2432
F: (701) 328-1537
E: sjdavis@nd.gov

OKLAHOMA
Ms. Barbara A. Warner
Executive Director
Indian Affairs Commission
4545 North Lincoln Boulevard,
Suite 282
Oklahoma City, OK 73105
P: (405) 521-3828
F: (405) 522-4427

OREGON
Ms. Karen Quigley
Executive Director
Legislative Commission on
Indian Services
167 State Capitol
Salem, OR 97310
P: (503) 986-1067
F: (503) 986-1071
E: karen.m.quigley
   @state.or.us

SOUTH CAROLINA
Mr. Jesse Washington Jr.
Commissioner
Human Affairs Commission
P.O. Box 4490
2611 Forest Drive, Suite 200
Columbia, SC 29204
P: (803) 737-7800
E: jesse@schac.state.sc.us

SOUTH DAKOTA
Mr. Leroy LaPlante
Secretary of Tribal Relations
Department of Tribal
Governmental Relations
Capitol Lake Plaza
711 East Wells Avenue
Pierre, SD 57501
P: (605) 773-3415
F: (605) 773-6592

UTAH
Mr. Forrest Cuch
Director
Division of Indian Affairs
Department of Community &
Culture
324 South State Street, Suite 500
Salt Lake City, UT 84114
P: (801) 538-8757
F: (801) 538-8803
E: fscuch@utah.gov

VIRGINIA
Mr. Frank Adams
Chair
Council on Indians
P.O. Box 1475
Richmond, VA 23218
P: (703) 225-2084
F: (703) 225-2585
E: vci
   @governor.virginia.gov

WASHINGTON
Mr. Craig A. Bill
Executive Director
Governor's Office of Indian
Affairs
210 - 11th Avenue, Southwest,
Suite 415
P.O. Box 40909
Olympia, WA 98504
P: (360) 902-8827
F: (360) 902-8829
E: cbill@goia.wa.gov

WISCONSIN
Mr. Jason Culotta
Administrator
State Tribal Relations Initiative
Division of Intergovernmental
Relations
P.O. Box 8944
Madison, WI 53708
P: (608) 267-1824
F: (608) 267-6917
E: jason.culotta
   @wisconsin.gov

Unclaimed Property

Responsible for the marshaling, administration and disposition of unclaimed or abandoned property.

Information provided by:

National Association of Unclaimed Property Administrators
David D. Milby
Association Manager
P.O. Box 11910
Lexington, KY 40578
P: (859) 244-8150
F: (859) 244-8053
naupa@csg.org
www.unclaimed.org

ALABAMA
Hon. Young Boozer (R)
State Treasurer
Office of the State Treasurer
600 Dexter Avenue, S-106
Montgomery, AL 36104
P: (334) 242-7500
F: (334) 242-7592
E: alatreas
@treasury.alabama.gov

Ms. Daria Story
Assistant Treasurer/Chief Operating Officer
State Treasury
600 Dexter Avenue, S-100
Montgomery, AL 36130
P: (334) 242-7500
F: (334) 353-4080
E: daria.story
@treasury.alabama.gov

ALASKA
Hon. Jerry Burnett
Deputy Commissioner of Revenue
Department of Revenue
Treasury Division
P.O. Box 110405
Juneau, AK 99811
P: (907) 465-2312
F: (907) 465-2389
E: jerry.burnett@alaska.gov

Ms. Rachel Lewis
Unclaimed Property Manager
Unclaimed Property Section
P.O. Box 110420
Juneau, AK 99811
P: (907) 465-5885
F: (907) 465-2394
E: rachel.lewis@alaska.gov

ARIZONA
Mr. Gale Garriott
Director
Department of Revenue
1600 West Monroe
Phoenix, AZ 85007
P: (602) 716-6090
F: (602) 542-2072
E: ggarriott@azdor.gov

Mr. Joshua Joyce
Administrator
Unclaimed Property
Department of Revenue
1600 West Monroe
Phoenix, AZ 85007
P: (602) 716-6033
F: (602) 716-7997
E: JJoyce@azdor.gov

ARKANSAS
Hon. Charlie Daniels (D)
Auditor of State
State Auditor's Office
P.O. Box 251906
Little Rock, AR 72201
P: (501) 371-2124
F: (501) 682-6005
E: lisar@arauditor.com

Mr. Robert Scott
Unclaimed Property Division Manager
State Auditor's Office
P.O. Box 251906
Little Rock, AR 72225
P: (501) 371-2124
F: (501) 683-4285
E: RobS@auditor.ar.gov

CALIFORNIA
Hon. John Chiang (D)
State Controller
Office of the State Controller
300 Capitol Mall, Suite 1850
Sacramento, CA 94250
P: (916) 445-2636
F: (916) 445-6379
E: john@sco.ca.gov

Mr. Stephen Edwards
Chief
Unclaimed Property Division
State Controller's Office
10600 White Rock Road,
Building A
Rancho Cordova, CA 95670
P: (916) 445-8318
F: (916) 464-6222
E: sedwards@sco.ca.gov

COLORADO
Hon. Walker Stapleton (R)
State Treasurer
Office of the State Treasurer
140 State Capitol
Denver, CO 80203
P: (303) 866-2441
F: (303) 866-2123

Ms. Patty White
Program Director
Unclaimed Property Division
1580 Logan Street, Suite 500
Denver, CO 80203
P: (303) 866-6070
F: (303) 866-6154
E: patty.white@state.co.us

CONNECTICUT
Ms. Maria M. Greenslade
Assistant Deputy Treasurer
Unclaimed Property
55 Elm Street
Hartford, CT 06106
P: (860) 702-3125
E: maria.greenslade
@po.state.ct.us

Hon. Denise L. Nappier (D)
State Treasurer
Office of State Treasurer
55 Elm Street
Hartford, CT 06106
P: (860) 702-3010
F: (860) 702-3043
E: denise.nappier@ct.gov

DELAWARE
Mr. Patrick T. Carter
Director
Division of Revenue
820 North French Street, 8th Floor
Wilmington, DE 19801
P: (302) 577-8686
F: (302) 577-8656
E: patrick.carter
@state.de.us

Mr. Mark Udinski
Director
Division of Revenue
820 North French Street, 9th Floor
Wilmington, DE 19801
P: (302) 577-8260
F: (302) 577-1195
E: mark.udinski@state.de.us

DISTRICT OF COLUMBIA
Hon. Lasana K. Mack
Treasurer & Deputy CFO
Office of Finance & Treasury
1275 K Street, Northwest, Suite 600
Washington, DC 20005
P: (202) 727-6055
F: (202) 727-6049
E: lasana.mack@dc.gov

Mr. Gracie B. Musher
Manager, Unclaimed Property
Office of Finance & Treasury
1101 4th Street, Southwest
Suite W 800-B
Washington, DC 20024
P: (202) 442-8195
F: (202) 442-8180
E: gracie.musher@dc.gov

FLORIDA
Hon. Jeffrey H. Atwater (R)
Chief Financial Officer
Department of Financial Services
PL-11, The Capitol
Tallahassee, FL 32399
P: (850) 413-2907
F: (850) 413-2950
E: allison@jeffatwater.com

Mr. Walter Graham
Chief of Unclaimed Property
Department of Financial Services
200 East Gaines Street
353 Fletcher Building
Tallahassee, FL 32399
P: (850) 413-5522
F: (850) 413-3017
E: Walter.Graham
@myfloridacfo.com

GEORGIA
Mr. Doug MacGinnitie
Revenue Commissioner
Department of Revenue
1800 Century Center Boulevard,
Northeast
Atlanta, GA 30345
P: (404) 417-2100

Ms. Kelli Miller
Manager
Local Government Services Division
Unclaimed Property
4245 International Parkway,
Suite A
Hapeville, GA 30354
P: (404) 968-0754
F: (404) 968-0772
E: Kelli.Miller@dor.ga.gov

Unclaimed Property

HAWAII

Mr. Scott Kami
Administrator
Financial Administration
Division
Department of Budget &
Finance
P.O. Box 150
Honolulu, HI 96810
P: (808) 586-1612
F: (808) 586-1644
E: scott.a.kami@hawaii.gov

Hon. Kalbert K. Young
Director of Finance
Department of Budget &
Finance
P.O. Box 150
Honolulu, HI 96810
P: (808) 586-1518
F: (808) 586-1976
E: HI.BudgetandFinance
@hawaii.gov

IDAHO

Hon. Ron G. Crane (R)
State Treasurer
Office of the State Treasurer
P.O. Box 83720
Boise, ID 83720
P: (208) 334-3200
F: (208) 332-2960
E: ron.crane@sto.idaho.gov

Ms. Cozette Walters-Swanson
Administrator
Unclaimed Property
P.O. Box 83720
Boise, ID 83720
P: (208) 332-2979
F: (208) 332-2970
E: cozette.walters-swanson
@sto.idaho.gov

ILLINOIS

Hon. Dan Rutherford (R)
State Treasurer
Office of the State Treasurer
Capitol Building
219 Statehouse
Springfield, IL 62704
P: (217) 782-2211
F: (217) 785-2777

INDIANA

Ms. Becky Yuan
Director
Unclaimed Property Division
P.O. Box 2504
Greenwood, IN 46142
P: (317) 883-4537
F: (317) 883-4520
E: byuan@atg.in.gov

Hon. Greg Zoeller (R)
Attorney General
Office of the Attorney General
Indiana Government Center
South
302 West Washington Street
Indianapolis, IN 46204
P: (317) 232-6201
F: (317) 232-7979
E: Constituent@atg.in.gov

IOWA

Ms. Karen Austin
Deputy Treasurer
Office of the State Treasurer
Lucas State Office Building
321 East 12th Street
Des Moines, IA 50319
P: (515) 281-7677
F: (515) 281-6962
E: karen.austin@iowa.gov

Hon. Michael L.
Fitzgerald (D)
State Treasurer
State Treasurer's Office
Room 114, Capitol Building
Des Moines, IA 50319
P: (515) 281-5368
F: (515) 281-7562
E: mike.fitzgerald@iowa.gov

KANSAS

Ms. Rita Mohr
Director of Unclaimed Property
State Treasury
900 Southwest Jackson, Suite
201
Topeka, KS 66612
P: (785) 291-3171
F: (785) 296-7950
E: rita@treasurer.ks.gov

KENTUCKY

Hon. Todd Hollenbach (D)
State Treasurer
State Treasury
1050 U.S. Highway 127 South
Frankfort, KY 40601
P: (502) 564-4722
F: (502) 564-6545
E: todd.hollenbach@ky.gov

Ms. Brenda L. Sweatt
Director
Unclaimed Property Division
1050 U.S. Highway 127 South,
Suite 100
Frankfort, KY 40601
P: (502) 564-4722
F: (502) 564-4200
E: brenda.sweatt@ky.gov

LOUISIANA

Mr. Ron J. Henson
First Assistant State Treasurer
State Treasury
P.O. Box 44154
Baton Rouge, LA 70804
P: (225) 342-0055
F: (225) 219-7765
E: rhenson
@treasury.state.la.us

Hon. John Neely Kennedy (R)
State Treasurer
Department of the Treasury
P.O. Box 44154
Baton Rouge, LA 70804
P: (225) 342-0010
F: (225) 342-0046
E: jkennedy
@treasury.state.la.us

MAINE

Hon. Bruce Poliquin (R)
State Treasurer
Office of the State Treasurer
39 State House Station
Augusta, ME 04333
P: (207) 624-7477
F: (207) 287-2367

Ms. Barbara Raths
Deputy Treasurer
State Treasury
39 State House Station
Augusta, ME 04333
P: (207) 624-7477
F: (207) 287-2367
E: barbara.raths@maine.gov

MARYLAND

Ms. Tamarra Eaton
Manager
Unclaimed Property
Comptroller's Office
301 West Preston Street, Room
310
Baltimore, MD 21201
P: (410) 767-1705
E: teaton@comp.state.md.us

Hon. Peter Franchot (D)
Comptroller
Office of the Comptroller
L.L. Goldstein Treasury
Building
P.O. Box 466
Annapolis, MD 21404
P: (410) 260-7801
F: (410) 974-3808
E: pfrachot
@comp.state.md.us

MASSACHUSETTS

Mr. Mark W. Bracken
Director of Abandoned Property
State Treasury
One Ashburton Place, 12th Floor
Boston, MA 02108
P: (617) 367-0400
F: (617) 367-3645
E: mwbracken
@tre.state.ma.us

Hon. Steven Grossman (D)
State Treasurer
Office of the State Treasurer
State House, Room 227
Boston, MA 02133
P: (617) 367-6900
F: (617) 248-0372

MICHIGAN

Hon. Andy Dillon (D)
State Treasurer
Office of the State Treasurer
P.O. Box 15128
Lansing, MI 48901
P: (517) 373-3223
F: (517) 335-1785

Mr. Gonzalo G. Llano
Administrator
Unclaimed Property Division
P.O. Box 30756
Lansing, MI 48909
P: (517) 636-5307
F: (517) 322-5986
E: llanog@michigan.gov

MINNESOTA

Mr. Mike Rothman
Commissioner of Commerce
Department of Commerce
85 7th Place East, Suite 500
St. Paul, MN 55101
P: (651) 296-6025
F: (651) 297-1959
E: commerce.commissioner
@state.mn.us

Ms. Amy Trumper
Administrator
Department of Commerce
85 7th Place East, Suite 500
St. Paul, MN 55101
P: (651) 282-5087
F: (651) 296-4328
E: Amy.Trumper@state.mn.us

MISSISSIPPI

Hon. Tate Reeves (R)
State Treasurer
Office of the State Treasurer
P.O. Box 138
Jackson, MS 39205
P: (601) 359-3600
F: (601) 576-4495
E: treeves
@treasury.state.ms.us

Mr. John Younger
Assistant State Treasurer
Unclaimed Property Division
P.O. Box 138
Jackson, MS 39205
P: (601) 359-5223
F: (601) 359-4495
E: jyounger
@treasury.state.ms.us

MISSOURI

Mr. Scott Harper
Director of Unclaimed Property
& General Services
Division of Unclaimed Property
P.O. Box 1272
Jefferson City, MO 65102
P: (573) 751-2082
F: (573) 526-6027
E: scott.harper
@treasurer.mo.gov

Hon. Clint Zweifel (D)
State Treasurer
Office of the State Treasurer
P.O. Box 210
Jefferson City, MO 65102
P: (573) 751-4123
F: (573) 751-9443
E: clint.zweifel
@treasurer.mo.gov

MONTANA

Mr. Dan Bucks
Director
Department of Revenue
P.O. Box 5805
Helena, MT 59604
P: (406) 444-0761
F: (406) 444-1505
E: dbucks@mt.gov

Mr. Jim McKeon
Unit Manager
Department of Revenue
P.O. Box 5805
Helena, MT 59604
P: (406) 444-1940
F: (406) 444-4091
E: jmckeon@mt.gov

NEBRASKA

Ms. Meaghan Aguirre
Unclaimed Property Coordinator
State Treasury
809 P Street
Lincoln, NE 68509
P: (402) 471-1089
F: (402) 471-1167
E: meaghan.aguirre
@nebraska.gov

Hon. Don B. Stenberg (R)
State Treasurer
Office of the State Treasurer
2005 State Capitol
Lincoln, NE 68509
P: (402) 471-2455
F: (402) 471-4390
E: Don.Stenberg
@nebraska.gov

NEVADA

Hon. Kate Marshall (D)
State Treasurer
Office of the State Treasurer
101 North Carson Street, #4
Carson City, NV 89701
P: (775) 684-5600
F: (775) 684-5623
E: katemarshall
@NevadaTreasurer.gov

Ms. Mary McElhone
Deputy Treasurer, Unclaimed
Property
State Treasury
555 East Washington Avenue,
#4200
Las Vegas, NV 89101
P: (702) 486-3907
F: (702) 486-4177
E: mcmcelhone
@nevadatreasurer.gov

NEW HAMPSHIRE

Hon. Catherine Provencher
State Treasurer
Treasury Department
25 Capitol Street, Room 121
Concord, NH 03301
P: (603) 271-2621
F: (603) 271-3922
E: cprovencher
@treasury.state.nh.us

Mr. Brian Regan
Director
Abandoned Property Division
State Treasury
25 Capitol Street, Room 205
Concord, NH 03301
P: (603) 271-1499
F: (603) 271-2730
E: bregan
@treasury.state.nh.us

NEW JERSEY

Mr. Steven Harris
Chief of Unclaimed Property
Operations
Division of Taxation
P.O. Box 214
50 Barrack Street, 6th Floor
Trenton, NJ 08695
P: (609) 777-4655
F: (609) 984-0595
E: steven.harris
@treas.state.nj.us

Hon. Andrew P.
Sidamon-Eristoff
State Treasurer
Department of Treasury
State House
P.O. Box 002
Trenton, NJ 08625
P: (608) 292-6748
F: (609) 984-3888

NEW MEXICO

Ms. Stephanie Dennis
Tax Compliance Specialist
Supervisor
Taxation & Revenue
Department
P.O. Box 25123
Santa Fe, NM 87504
P: (505) 827-0762
F: (505) 827-1759
E: stephanie.dennis
@state.nm.us

Mr. Rick Homans
Secretary
Taxation & Revenue
Department
1100 South St. Francis Drive
Santa Fe, NM 87504
P: (505) 827-0700
F: (505) 827-1759

NEW YORK

Hon. Thomas P. DiNapoli (D)
Comptroller
Office of the State Comptroller
633 3rd Avenue, 21st Floor
New York, NY 10017
P: (518) 474-4040
F: (518) 474-3004
E: tdinapoli
@osc.state.ny.us

Mr. Lawrence Schantz
Director
Office of Unclaimed Funds
State Comptroller's Office
110 State Street, 8th Floor
Albany, NY 12236
P: (518) 473-6318
F: (518) 474-7016
E: lschantz@osc.state.ny.us

NORTH CAROLINA

Hon. Janet Cowell (D)
State Treasurer
Department of State Treasurer
325 North Salisbury Street,
Room 100
Raleigh, NC 27603
P: (919) 508-5176
F: (919) 508-5167
E: janet.cowell
@nctreasurer.com

Ms. Shirley Fowler
Administrator
Unclaimed Property Division
325 North Salisbury Street
Raleigh, NC 27603
P: (919) 508-5929
F: (919) 508-5181
E: shirley.fowler
@nctreasurer.com

NORTH DAKOTA

Ms. Linda Fisher
Administrator
State Land Department
P.O. Box 5523
Bismarck, ND 58506
P: (701) 328-2800
F: (701) 328-3650
E: llfisher@nd.gov

Mr. Lance Gaebe
Land Commissioner
State Land Department
P.O. Box 5523
Bismarck, ND 58506
P: (701) 328-2800
F: (701) 328-3650
E: lancegaebe@nd.gov

Unclaimed Property

OHIO

Mr. David Goodman
Director
Department of Commerce
77 South High Street, 23rd Floor
Columbus, OH 43266
P: (614) 466-3636
F: (614) 752-5078
E: Directorsoffice
    @com.state.oh.us

Mr. Yaw Obeng
Superintendent
Division of Unclaimed Funds
Department of Commerce
77 South High Street, 20th Floor
Columbus, OH 43266
P: (614) 644-6094
F: (614) 752-5078
E: Yaw.O'Beng
    @com.state.oh.us

OKLAHOMA

Ms. Kathy Janes
Director of Unclaimed Property
State Treasurer's Office
4545 North Lincoln Boulevard,
Suite 106
Oklahoma City, OK 73105
P: (405) 522-6743
F: (405) 521-2677
E: Kathy.Janes
    @treasurer.ok.gov

Hon. Ken Miller (R)
State Treasurer
Office of the State Treasurer
Room 217, State Capitol
Building
2300 North Lincoln Boulevard
Oklahoma City, OK 73105
P: (405) 521-3191
F: (405) 521-4994

OREGON

Ms. Louise Solliday
Director
Department of State Lands
775 Summer Street, Northeast
Suite 100
Salem, OR 97301
P: (503) 378-3805
F: (503) 378-4844
E: louise.c.solliday
    @state.or.us

Mr. Patrick Tate
Unclaimed Property Manager
Finance & Administration
Department of State Lands
775 Summer Street, Northeast,
Suite 100
Salem, OR 97301
P: (503) 986-5248
F: (503) 378-4844
E: patrick.tate@state.or.us

PENNSYLVANIA

Hon. Rob McCord (D)
State Treasurer
Treasury Department
Room 129, Finance Building
Harrisburg, PA 17120
P: (717) 787-2465
F: (717) 783-9760
E: rmm@patreasury.org

Mr. Frederick Stollsteimer
Deputy Chief Counsel
State Treasury
Room 127, Finance Building
Harrisburg, PA 17120
P: (717) 783-5926
F: (717) 772-0970
E: fstollsteimer
    @patreasury.org

PUERTO RICO

Ms. Hilda Enid Davila
Assistant Commissioner,
Administration
Office of the Commissioner of
Financial Institutions
P.O. Box 11855
San Juan, PR 00910
P: (787) 723-3131
F: (787) 723-4225
E: enidd@ocif.gobierno.pr

Mr. Alfredo Padilla
Commissioner of Financial
Institutions
Office of the Commissioner of
Financial Institutions
Commonwealth of Puerto Rico
P.O. Box 11855
San Juan, PR 00910
P: (787) 723-3131
F: (787) 723-4042
E: comisionado
    @ocif.gobierno.pr

RHODE ISLAND

Hon. Gina M. Raimondo (D)
General Treasurer
Office of the General Treasurer
State House, Room 102
Providence, RI 02903
P: (401) 222-2397
F: (401) 222-6140
E: generaltreasurer
    @treasury.ri.gov

Mr. David Salvatore
Unclaimed Property Manager
Unclaimed Property Division
P.O. Box 1435
Providence, RI 02901
P: (401) 222-6505
E: dsalvatore
    @treasury.ri.gov

SOUTH CAROLINA

Hon. Curtis Loftis (R)
State Treasurer
Office of the State Treasurer
P.O. Box 11778
Columbia, SC 29211
P: (803) 734-2101
F: (803) 734-2690
E: Linda.Champion-Gamble
    @sto.sc.gov

Ms. Barbara Rice
Assistant State Treasurer
State Treasury
P.O. Box 11778
Columbia, SC 29211
P: (803) 734-2682
F: (803) 734-2668
E: Barbara.Rice@sto.sc.gov

SOUTH DAKOTA

Ms. Lee DeJabet
Unclaimed Property
Administrator
State Treasury
State Capitol Building, Suite
212
500 East Capitol Avenue
Pierre, SD 57501
P: (605) 773-3900
F: (605) 773-3115
E: Lee.DeJabet@state.sd.us

Hon. Rich L. Sattgast (R)
State Treasurer
Office of the State Treasurer
State Capitol Building, Suite
212
500 East Capitol Avenue
Pierre, SD 57501
P: (605) 773-3378
F: (605) 773-3115
E: rich.sattgast
    @state.sd.us

TENNESSEE

Mr. John Gabriel
Director of Unclaimed Property
State Treasury
Andrew Jackson Building, 9th
Floor
502 Deaderick Street
Nashville, TN 37243
P: (615) 253-5354
F: (615) 734-6458
E: john.gabriel@tn.gov

Hon. David H. Lillard Jr.
State Treasurer
Department of Treasury
State Capitol, First Floor
Nashville, TN 37243
P: (615) 741-2956
F: (615) 253-1591
E: david.lillard
    @state.tn.us

TEXAS

Ms. Susan Combs
Comptroller of Public Accounts
Office of the Comptroller of
Public Accounts
111 East 17th
P.O.Box 13528
Austin, TX 78711
P: (512) 463-4444
F: (512) 463-4965
E: susan.combs
    @cpa.state.tx.us

Ms. Anna Presley-Burnham
Director, Unclaimed Property
Division
Comptroller of Public Accounts
LBJ State Office Building
111 East 17th Street
Austin, TX 78774
P: (512) 463-4759
E: Anna.Presley-Burnham
    @cpa.state.tx.us

UTAH

Mr. Kim Christensen
Deputy State Treasurer
Division of Unclaimed Property
P.O. Box 140530
Salt Lake City, UT 84114
P: (801) 715-3300
F: (801) 715-3309
E: kimchristensen@utah.gov

Hon. Richard K. Ellis (R)
State Treasurer
State Treasurer's Office
P.O. Box 142315
Salt Lake City, UT 84114
P: (801) 538-1042
F: (801) 538-1465
E: rellis@utah.gov

VERMONT
Mr. Albert LaPerle
Director of Unclaimed Property
State Treasury
109 State Street, 4th Floor
Montpelier, VT 05609
P: (802) 828-1452
F: (802) 828-2772
E: al.laperle@state.vt.us

Hon. Elizabeth Pearce
State Treasurer
Office of the State Treasurer
109 State Street, 4th Floor
Montpelier, VT 05609
P: (802) 828-1452
F: (802) 828-2772
E: Beth.Pearce@state.vt.us

VIRGINIA
Ms. Vicki D. Bridgeman
Director of Unclaimed Property
State Treasury
P.O. Box 2478
Richmond, VA 23218
P: (804) 225-3156
F: (804) 786-4653
E: vicki.bridgeman
   @trs.virgina.gov

Hon. Manju Ganeriwala
State Treasurer
Department of the Treasury
101 North 14th Street, 3rd Floor
James Monroe Building, P.O.
Box 1879
Richmond, VA 23218
P: (804) 371-6011
F: (804) 786-0833
E: Manju.Ganeriwala
   @trs.virginia.gov

WASHINGTON
Ms. Suzan DelBene
Director
Department of Revenue
P.O. Box 47454
Olympia, WA 98504
P: (360) 586-3462
F: (360) 586-2163

Ms. Celeste Monahan
Program Manager
Department of Revenue
P.O. Box 47454
Olympia, WA 98504
P: (360) 570-3201
F: (360) 664-8438
E: celestem@dor.wa.gov

WEST VIRGINIA
Ms. Carolyn Atkinson
Deputy Treasurer of Unclaimed
Property
State Treasury
One Player's Club Drive
Charleston, WV 25311
P: (304) 341-0703
F: (304) 558-5063
E: carolyn.atkinson
   @wvsto.com

Hon. John D. Perdue (D)
State Treasurer
State Treasurer's Office
Building 1, State Capitol
Complex
1900 Kanawha Boulevard, Suite
E-145
Charleston, WV 25305
P: (304) 558-5000
F: (304) 558-4097
E: john.perdue@wvsto.com

WISCONSIN
Ms. Mary Celentani
Administrator
Unclaimed Property Division
P.O. Box 2114
Madison, WI 53701
P: (608) 267-2208
F: (608) 261-6799
E: mary.celentani
   @wisconsin.gov

Hon. Kurt W. Schuller (R)
State Treasurer
Office of the State Treasurer
P.O. Box 7871
Madison, WI 53707
P: (608) 266-1714
F: (608) 266-2647
E: Kurt.Schuller
   @wisconsin.gov

WYOMING
Hon. Joe B. Meyer (R)
State Treasurer
Office of the State Treasurer
200 West 24th Street, Suite 122
Cheyenne, WY 82002
P: (307) 777-7408
F: (307) 777-5411
E: jmeyer3@state.wy.us

Ms. Nancy Russell
Director
Unclaimed Property Division
2515 Warren Avenue, Suite 502
Cheyenne, WY 82002
P: (307) 777-5590
F: (307) 777-5430
E: nrusse@state.wy.us

Veterans Affairs

Provides services and information to the state's veterans, their dependents and survivors.

ALABAMA
Mr. W. Clyde Marsh
Director
Department of Veterans Affairs
P.O. Box 1509
Montgomery, AL 36102
P: (334) 242-5077
F: (334) 242-5102
E: clyde.marsh
 @va.alabama.gov

ALASKA
Mr. Verdie Bowen
Administrator
Office of Veterans Affairs
Camp Danali, Building 49000
P.O. Box 5800
Ft. Richardson, AK 99505
P: (907) 428-6016
F: (907) 428-6019
E: verdie.bowen@alaska.gov

AMERICAN SAMOA
Mr. Paogofie Fiaigoa
Veterans Affairs Officer
Office of Veterans Affairs
American Samoa Government
P.O. Box 8586
Pago Pago, AS 96799
P: (684) 633-4206
F: (684) 633-2269

ARIZONA
Mr. Joey Strickland
Director
Department of Veterans' Affairs
3839 N. Third Street
Phoenix, AZ 85012
P: (602) 234-8415
F: (602) 255-1038
E: jstrickland@azdvs.gov

ARKANSAS
Mr. Dave Fletcher
Director
Department of Veterans Affairs
Building 65, Room 119
2200 Fort Roots Drive
North Little Rock, AR 72114
P: (501) 370-3820
F: (501) 370-3829
E: dave.fletcher
 @arkansas.gov

CALIFORNIA
Mr. Rocky Chavez
Acting Secretary
Department of Veterans Affairs
1227 O Street, Room 300
Sacramento, CA 95814
P: (916) 653-2158
F: (916) 653-2456
E: rocky.chavez@cdva.ca.gov

COLORADO
Mr. William Conroy
Director
Division of Veterans Affairs
7465 East 1st Avenue, Suite C
Denver, CO 80230
P: (303) 343-1268
F: (303) 343-7238
E: william.conroy
 @dmva.state.co.us

CONNECTICUT
Dr. Linda S. Schwartz
Commissioner
Department of Veterans Affairs
287 West Street
Rocky Hill, CT 06067
P: (860) 721-5891
F: (860) 721-5919
E: Linda.Schwartz
 @po.state.ct.us

DELAWARE
Mr. Antonio Davila
Executive Director
Commission of Veterans Affairs
Robbins Building
802 Silver Lake Boulevard
Dover, DE 19904
P: (302) 739-2792
F: (302) 739-2794
E: antonio.davila
 @state.de.us

DISTRICT OF COLUMBIA
Mr. Timothy J. Smith
Director
Office of Veterans Affairs
441 4th Street, Northwest
Suite 570, South
Washington, DC 20001
P: (202) 724-5454
F: (202) 724-7117
E: timothy.smith@dc.gov

FLORIDA
General Robert F.
 Milligan (R)
Interim Executive Director
Department of Veterans Affairs
4040 Esplanade Way, #180
Tallahassee, FL 32399
P: (850) 487-1533
F: (850) 488-4001
E: ExDir@fdva.state.fl.us

GEORGIA
Mr. Pete Wheeler
Commissioner
Department of Veterans Service
205 Butler Street
Suite E-970
Atlanta, GA 30334
P: (404) 656-2300
F: (404) 657-9738
E: gavetsvc@vs.state.ga.us

GUAM
Mr. Fred A. Gofigan
Administrator
Veterans Affairs Office
P.O. Box 5178
Hagatna, GU 96932
P: (671) 642-4114
F: (671) 642-4111
E: fred.gofigan
 @gvao.guam.gov

HAWAII
Mr. Gregory Jackson Jr.
Director
Office of Veterans Services
459 Patterson Road
E-Wing, Room 1-A103
Honolulu, HI 96819
P: (808) 433-0420
F: (808) 433-0385
E: gregory.jr.jackson
 @ovs.hawaii.gov

IDAHO
Mr. David Brasuell
Administrator
Division of Veterans Affairs
320 Collins Road
Boise, ID 83702
P: (208) 334-3513
F: (208) 334-2627
E: david.brasuell
 @veterans.idaho.gov

Mr. Donald G. Riegel
Chair
Veterans Affairs Commission
Division of Veterans Services
320 Collins Road
Boise, ID 83702
P: (208) 334-3513
F: (208) 334-2627
E: info@veterans.idaho.gov

ILLINOIS
Mr. Daniel Grant
Director
Department of Veterans Affairs
P.O. Box 19432
833 South Spring Street
Springfield, IL 62794
P: (217) 785-4114
F: (217) 524-0344
E: dan.grant@illinois.gov

INDIANA
Mr. Charles T. Applegate
Director
Department of Veterans Affairs
302 West Washington Street
Room E-120
Indianapolis, IN 46204
P: (317) 232-3910
F: (317) 232-7721
E: tapplegate@dva.in.gov

IOWA
Ms. Jodi Tymeson
Executive Director
Department of Veterans Affairs
Camp Dodge, Building 3663
7105 Northwest 70th Avenue
Johnston, IA 50131
P: (515) 242-5333
F: (515) 242-5659
E: Jodi.Tymeson@iowa.gov

KANSAS
Mr. Jack Fowler
Executive Director
Veterans Commission
Jayhawk Towers, Suite 701
700 Southwest Jackson Street
Topeka, KS 66603
P: (785) 296-3976
F: (785) 296-1462
E: jfowler@kcva.org

KENTUCKY
Mr. Ken Lucas
Commissioner
Department of Veterans Affairs
1111 Louisville Road (NGAKY
Building)
Frankfort, KY 40601
P: (502) 564-9203
F: (502) 564-9240
E: pamela.cypert@ky.gov

LOUISIANA
Mr. Lane Carson
Secretary
Department of Veterans Affairs
1885 Wooddale Blvd., 10th
Floor
P.O. Box 94095, Capitol Station
Baton Rouge, LA 70804
P: (225) 922-0500
F: (225) 922-0511
E: lane.carson
 @vetaffairs.la.gov

MAINE
Mr. Peter W. Ogden
Director
Bureau of Veterans Services
State House Station #117
Augusta, ME 04333
P: (207) 626-4464
F: (207) 626-4471
E: peter.w.ogden@maine.gov

MARYLAND

Mr. Edward Chow Jr.
Secretary
Department of Veterans Affairs
The Jeffrey Building, Fourth
Floor
16 Francis Street
Annapolis, MD 21401
P: (410) 260-3838
F: (410) 216-7928
E: mdveteransinfo
@mdva.state.md.us

MASSACHUSETTS

Mr. Coleman Nee
Secretary
Department of Veterans Services
600 Washington Street, Room
1100
Boston, MA 02111
P: (617) 210-5951
F: (617) 210-5755

MICHIGAN

Brig. Gen. Carol Ann
Fausone
Assistant Adjutant General for
Veterans
Department of Military &
Veterans Affairs
3423 N. Martin Luther King Jr.
Blvd.
Lansing, MI 48906
P: (517) 335-6523
F: (517) 241-0674
E: fausonec@michigan.gov

MINNESOTA

Maj. Gen. Larry W. Shellito
Commissioner
Department of Veterans Affairs
Veterans Services Building, 2nd
Floor
20 West 12th Street, Room 206
St. Paul, MN 55155
P: (651) 757-1555
F: (651) 296-3954
E: larry.shellito
@state.mn.us

MISSISSIPPI

Mr. Adrian Grice
Executive Director
Veterans Affairs Board
3466 Highway 80 East
P.O. Box 5947
Pearl, MS 39288
P: (601) 576-4850
F: (601) 576-4868
E: grice@vab.state.ms.us

MISSOURI

Mr. Larry D. Kay
Executive Director
Veterans Commission
P.O. Drawer 147
Jefferson City, MO 65102
P: (573) 522-1402
F: (573) 751-6836
E: larry.kay@mvc.dps.mo.gov

MONTANA

Mr. Joseph S. Foster
Administrator
Veterans Affairs Division
P.O. Box 5715
Helena, MT 59604
P: (406) 324-3740
F: (406) 324-3745
E: jofoster@mt.gov

NEBRASKA

Mr. John Hilgert
Director
Department of Veterans Affairs
P.O. Box 95083
Lincoln, NE 68509
P: (402) 471-2458
F: (402) 471-2491
E: john.hilgert
@nebraska.gov

NEVADA

Mr. Caleb Cage
Executive Director
Office of Veterans Affairs
5460 Reno Corporate Drive,
Suite 131
Reno, NV 89511
P: (775) 688-1653
F: (775) 688-1656

NEW HAMPSHIRE

Ms. Mary E. Morin
Director
State Veterans Council
275 Chestnut Street, #517
Manchester, NH 03101
P: (603) 624-9230
F: (603) 624-9236
E: mary.morin@vba.va.gov

NEW JERSEY

Mr. Raymond Zawacki
Deputy Commissioner for
Veterans Affairs
Department of Military &
Veterans Affairs
Eggerts Crossing Road
P.O. Box 340
Trenton, NJ 08625
P: (609) 530-7045
F: (609) 530-7075
E: raymond.zawacki
@njdmava.state.nj.us

NEW MEXICO

Mr. Timothy Hale
Secretary
Department of Veterans Services
407 Galisteo Street, Room 142
Santa Fe, NM 87504
P: (866) 433-8387

NEW YORK

Mr. William Kraus
Acting Director
Division of Veterans Affairs
Corning Tower, Suite 2836
5 Empire State Plaza
Albany, NY 12223
P: (518) 474-6114
F: (518) 474-6924

NORTH CAROLINA

Mr. Wayne Peedin
Interim Director
Division of Veterans Affairs
1315 Mail Service Center
325 North Salisbury Street
Raleigh, NC 27699
P: (919) 807-4250
F: (919) 807-4260

NORTH DAKOTA

Mr. Lonnie Wangen
Commissioner
Department of Veterans Affairs
P.O. Box 9003
Fargo, ND 58106
P: (701) 239-7165
F: (701) 239-7166
E: lwangen@nd.gov

NORTHERN MARIANA ISLANDS

Ms. Ruth Coleman
Director
Division of Veterans Affairs -
DC&CA
P.O. Box 503416 CK
Commonwealth of the N.
Mariana Islands
Saipan, MP 96950
P: (670) 664-2650
F: (670) 664-2660
E: veterans@gtepacifica.net

OHIO

Mr. Thomas N. Moe
Director
Department of Veterans Services
77 South High Street, 17th Floor
Columbus, OH 43215
P: (614) 644-0898
F: (614) 728-9498
E: thomas.moe@dvs.ohio.gov

OKLAHOMA

Ms. Martha Spear
Director
Department of Veterans Affairs
P.O. Box 53067
Oklahoma City, OK 73152
P: (405) 521-3684
F: (405) 521-6533
E: mspear@odva.state.ok.us

OREGON

Mr. Jim Willis
Director
Department of Veterans Affairs
Oregon Veterans' Building
700 Summer Street, Northeast
Salem, OR 97310
P: (503) 373-2388
F: (503) 373-2362
E: willisj@odva.state.or.us

PENNSYLVANIA

Mr. Scott D. Wagner
Deputy Adjutant General
Department of Military &
Veterans Affairs
Fort Indiantown Gap
Building S-O-47
Annville, PA 17003
P: (717) 861-8902
F: (717) 861-8589
E: scwagner@state.pa.us

PUERTO RICO

Mr. Jorge Mas
Public Advocate for Veterans
Affairs
P.O. Box 11737
San Juan, PR 00910
P: (787) 758-5760
F: (787) 758-5788
E: jorgelmas@hotmail.com

RHODE ISLAND

Mr. Daniel J. Evangelista
Director
Division of Veterans Affairs
480 Metacom Avenue
Bristol, RI 02809
P: (401) 254-8350
F: (401) 254-2320
E: devangelista@dhs.ri.gov

SOUTH CAROLINA

Mr. Howard Metcalf
Interim Director
Division of Veterans Affairs
1205 Pendleton Street, Suite 461
Columbia, SC 29201
P: (803) 734-0200
F: (803) 734-0197

Veterans Affairs

SOUTH DAKOTA
Maj. Gen. Tim Reisch
Adjutant General
Department of Military &
Veterans Affairs
Soliders & Sailors Memorial
Building
425 East Capitol Avenue
Pierre, SD 57501
P: (605) 773-3269
F: (605) 773-5380

Mr. George Summerside
Director
Division of Veterans Affairs
Soldiers & Sailors War
Memorial Building
500 East Capitol Avenue
Pierre, SD 57501
P: (605) 773-3518
F: (605) 773-5380
E: george.summerside
    @state.sd.us

TENNESSEE
Ms. Many-Bears Grinder
Commissioner
Department of Veterans Affairs
215 Rosa L. Parks Avenue
Nashville, TN 37243
P: (615) 741-2931
F: (615) 741-4785

TEXAS
Mr. James E. Nier
Executive Director
Veterans Commission
10th & Colorado, 6th Floor
P.O. Box 12277
Austin, TX 78711
P: (512) 463-5538
F: (512) 475-2395
E: info@tvc.state.tx.us

U.S. VIRGIN ISLANDS
Mr. Morris Moorehead
Director
Office of Veterans Affairs
1013 Estate Richmond
Christiansted
St. Croix, VI 00820
P: (340) 773-6663
F: (340) 692-9563
E: morrrisd5063@msn.com

UTAH
Mr. Terry Schow
Director
Department of Veterans Affairs
550 Foothill Boulevard, Room
202
Salt Lake City, UT 84108
P: (801) 326-2372
F: (801) 326-2369
E: tschow@utah.gov

VERMONT
Mr. Clayton A. Clark
Supervisor
State Veterans Affairs
118 State Street, Drawer 20
Montpelier, VT 05620
P: (802) 828-3379
F: (802) 828-5932
E: clayton.clark
    @state.vt.us

VIRGINIA
Mr. Paul Galanti
Commissioner
Department of Veterans Affairs
900 East Main Street
1st Floor, West Wing
Richmond, VA 23219
P: (804) 786-0286
F: (804) 786-0302
E: paul.galanti
    @dvs.virginia.gov

WASHINGTON
Mr. John E. Lee
Director
Department of Veterans Affairs
1011 Plum Street, Building 5,
2nd Floor
P.O. Box 41150
Olympia, WA 98504
P: (360) 725-2151
F: (360) 586-4393
E: john@dva.wa.gov

WEST VIRGINIA
Mr. Keith Gwinn
Director
Division of Veterans Affairs
1321 Plaza East, Suite 101
Charleston, WV 25301
P: (304) 558-3661
F: (304) 558-3662
E: kgwinn@state.wv.us

WISCONSIN
Ms. Donna Williams
Acting Secretary
Department of Veterans Affairs
P.O. Box 7843
30 West Mifflin Street
Madison, WI 53707
P: (608) 266-1315
F: (608) 264-7616
E: donna.williams
    @dva.state.wi.us

WYOMING
Mr. Larry Barttlebort
Executive Director
Veterans Commission
5500 Bishop Boulevard
Cheyenne, WY 82009
P: (307) 772-5145
F: (307) 772-5202
E: lbartt@state.wy.us

Vital Statistics

Maintains a statewide file of birth, death, marriage and divorce records, and issues certified copies of those records.

ALABAMA
Ms. Dorothy S. Harshbarger
Director
Center for Health Statistics
RSA Tower, 201 Monroe Street,
Suite 1150
P.O. Box 5625
Montgomery, AL 36103
P: (334) 206-5426
F: (334) 206-2659

ALASKA
Mr. Phillip Mitchell
Section Chief
Bureau of Vital Statistics
Department of Health & Social
Services
P.O. Box 110675
Juneau, AK 99801
P: (907) 465-3391
F: (907) 465-3618
E: phillip.mitchell
@alaska.gov

ARIZONA
Mr. Will Humble
Director
Department of Health Services
150 North 18th Avenue
Phoenix, AZ 85007
P: (602) 542-1025
F: (602) 542-1062

ARKANSAS
Mr. Michael Adams
Director
Division of Vital Records
4815 West Markham Street
Little Rock, AR 72205
P: (501) 661-2371
F: (501) 661-2717
E: mike.adams@arkansas.gov

CALIFORNIA
Ms. Janet McKee
Chief
Office of Vital Records
1616 Capitol Avenue, Suite 317,
MS 5000
P.O. Box 997377
Sacramento, CA 95899
P: (916) 552-8129
E: janet.mckee@cdph.ca.gov

COLORADO
Mr. Bob O'Doherty
Director and Chief Information
Officer
Center for Health and
Environmental Information &
Statistics
4300 Cherry Creek Drive South
Denver, CO 80246
P: (303) 692-2160
F: (303) 691-7704

CONNECTICUT
Ms. Jane Purtill
State Registrar of Vital Records
Health Information Systems &
Reporting
Department of Public Health
410 Capitol Avenue
Hartford, CT 06134
P: (860) 509-7895
F: (860) 509-7160
E: jane.purtill@ct.gov

DELAWARE
Ms. Judy Chaconas
Director
Bureau of Health Planning &
Resources Management
Jesse Cooper Building
417 Federal Street
Dover, DE 19901
P: (302) 744-4776
F: (302) 739-3313

DISTRICT OF COLUMBIA
Mr. David A. Berns
Director
Department of Human Services
64 New York Avenue, Northeast
6th Floor
Washington, DC 20002
P: (202) 671-4200
E: dhs@dc.gov

FLORIDA
Mr. Ken T. Jones
Deputy State Registrar
Department of Health
1217 Pearl Street
P.O. Box 210
Jacksonville, FL 32231
P: (904) 359-6900
F: (904) 359-6931
E: ken_jones
@doh.state.fl.us

GEORGIA
Dr. Brenda Fitzgerald
Director
Division of Public Health
Two Peachtree Street, Northwest
Atlanta, GA 30303
P: (404) 657-2700

HAWAII
Dr. Alvin T. Onaka
Chief & State Registrar
Office of Health Status
Monitoring
P.O. Box 3378
Honolulu, HI 96801
P: (808) 586-4600
F: (808) 586-4606

IDAHO
Ms. Jane S. Smith
Division Administrator for
Health
Bureau of Health Policy & Vital
Statistics
450 West State Street
4th Floor, Pete T. Cenarrusa
Building
Boise, ID 83720
P: (208) 334-5932
F: (208) 334-6581
E: smithj2@dhw.idaho.gov

ILLINOIS
Dr. Damon T. Arnold
Director
Department of Public Health
535 West Jefferson Street
Springfield, IL 62761
P: (217) 557-2556
F: (217) 785-3209

INDIANA
Ms. Erin Kellam
Director
Vital Records Division
2 North Meridian Street, Room
2NLL077
Indianapolis, IN 46204
P: (317) 233-7523
F: (317) 233-5956
E: ekellam@isdh.IN.gov

IOWA
Ms. Jill France
Bureau Chief
Bureau of Health Statistics
Lucas State Office Building
321 East 12th Street
Des Moines, IA 50319
P: (515) 281-4944
E: jill.france
@idph.iowa.gov

KANSAS
Dr. Elizabeth W. Saadi
Acting Bureau Director & State
Registrar
Office of Vital Statistics
Curtis State Office Building
1000 Southwest Jackson
Topeka, KS 66612
P: (785) 296-1400
F: (785) 296-8075
E: Vital.Records@kdheks.gov

KENTUCKY
Dr. William D. Hacker
Commissioner
Department for Public Health
275 East Main Street
Mailstop 4W-A
Frankfort, KY 40621
P: (502) 564-3970
F: (502) 564-3866

LOUISIANA
Ms. Darlene W. Smith
State Registrar & Center
Director
Vital Records & Statistics
Vital Records Registry
P.O. Box 60630
New Orleans, LA 70160
P: (504) 593-5100
F: (504) 568-8716
E: _dhh-vitalweb@la.gov

MAINE
Mr. Marty Henson
State Registrar & Director
Office of Data, Research &
Vital Statistics
11 State House Station
244 Water Street
Augusta, ME 04333
P: (207) 287-5500
F: (207) 287-5470
E: marty.henson@maine.gov

MARYLAND
Dr. Isabelle L. Horon
Director
Vital Statistics Administration
Department of Health & Mental
Hygiene
4201 Patterson Avenue
Baltimore, MD 21215
P: (410) 764-3513
F: (410) 767-6840
E: horoni@dhmh.state.md.us

MASSACHUSETTS
Mr. John Auerbach
Commissioner
Department of Public Health
250 Washington Street
Boston, MA 02108
P: (617) 624-6000

Vital Statistics

MICHIGAN
Mr. Glenn Copeland
State Registrar & Division
Director
Division for Vital Records &
Health Statistics
Capitol View Building, Second
Floor
201 Townsend Street
Lansing, MI 48913
P: (517) 335-8677
F: (517) 335-9264
E: CopelandG@michigan.gov

MINNESOTA
Dr. Edward Ehlinger
Commissioner
Department of Health
625 Robert Street North
Box 64975
St. Paul, MN 55164
P: (651) 201-5810
F: (651) 201-4986
E: edward.ehlinger
    @state.mn.us

MISSISSIPPI
Ms. Judy Moulder
State Registrar
Public Health Statistics
571 Stadium Drive
P.O. Box 1700
Jackson, MS 39216
P: (601) 576-7960
F: (601) 576-7505
E: jmoulder
    @msdh.state.ms.us

MISSOURI
Ms. Ivra J. Cross
State Registrar
Bureau of Vital Records
Department of Health & Senior
Services
930 Wildwood Drive, P.O. Box
570
Jefferson City, MO 65102
P: (573) 526-0348
F: (573) 526-3846
E: ivra.cross@dhss.mo.gov

MONTANA
Mr. Jim Edgar
Section Supervisor
Office of Vital Statistics
111 North Sanders, Room 205
Helena, MT 59604
P: (406) 444-4250
F: (406) 444-1803

NEBRASKA
Dr. Joann Schaefer
Director
Division of Public Health
Department of Health & Human
Services
P.O. Box 95007
Lincoln, NE 68509
P: (402) 471-8566
F: (402) 471-9449
E: joann.schaefer
    @nebraska.gov

NEVADA
Dr. Luana J. Ritch
Bureau Chief
Bureau of Health Statistics,
Planning & Emergency
Response
Department of Health & Human
Services
4150 Technology Way, Suite 200
Carson City, NV 89706
P: (775) 684-4242
F: (775) 684-4156
E: lritch@health.nv.gov

NEW HAMPSHIRE
Mr. Steven M. Wurtz
Supervisor
Division of Vital Records
Department of State
71 South Fruit Street
Concord, NH 03301
P: (603) 271-4655
F: (603) 271-3447
E: swurtz@sos.state.nh.us

NEW JERSEY
Ms. Mary E. O'Dowd
Acting Commissioner
Department of Health & Senior
Services
P.O. Box 360
Trenton, NJ 08625
P: (609) 292-7837
F: (609) 292-0053

NEW YORK
Mr. Peter Carucci
Director
Bureau of Production Systems
Management
800 North Pearl Street
Albany, NY 12204
P: (518) 474-5245

NORTH CAROLINA
Ms. Linda Brinkley
Director & State Registrar
Department of Health & Human
Services
Vital Records Division
1903 Mail Service Center
Raleigh, NC 27699
P: (919) 733-3000
F: (919) 733-1511

NORTH DAKOTA
Mr. Darin J. Meschke
State Registrar, Director
Division of Vital Records
600 East Boulevard Avenue
Department 301
Bismarck, ND 58505
P: (701) 328-2360
F: (701) 328-1850
E: dmeschke@nd.gov

**NORTHERN MARIANA
ISLANDS**
Mr. John G. Moore
Commonwealth Recorder
Vital Records Section
P.O. Box 500307
Saipan, MP 96950
P: (670) 236-9830
F: (670) 236-9831

OHIO
Mr. Robert J. Campbell
Deputy Director
Center for Public Health
Statistics & Informatics
Department of Health
246 North High Street
Columbus, OH 43215
P: (614) 995-5591
F: (614) 728-4638

OKLAHOMA
Ms. Kelly Baker
M.P.H. Director
Department of Health
Center for Health Statistics
1000 NE 10th Street
Oklahoma City, OK 73117
P: (405) 271-6225
F: (405) 270-9061
E: kellyb@health.ok.gov

OREGON
Ms. Jennifer Woodward
Program Manager/State
Registrar
Center for Health Statistics
Department Of Human Services
800 Northeast Oregon Street,
Suite 205
Portland, OR 97232
P: (971) 673-1190
F: (971) 673-1203
E: jennifer.a.woodward
    @state.or.us

PENNSYLVANIA
Ms. Linda Caniglia
Director
Division of Vital Records
101 South Mercer Street
P.O. Box 1528
New Castle, PA 16103
P: (724) 656-3286
F: (724) 656-3079

PUERTO RICO
Mr. Nicolas
    Fernandez-Cornier
Executive Director
Demographic Registry
P.O. Box 11854
San Juan, PR 00910
P: (787) 281-8867
F: (787) 751-5003

RHODE ISLAND
Ms. Colleen Fontana
Chief, State Registrar
Office of Vital Records
Department of Health
3 Capitol Hill, Room 101
Providence, RI 02908
P: (401) 222-7841
F: (401) 222-6548
E: colleen.fontana
    @health.ri.gov

SOUTH CAROLINA
Dr. Guang Zhao
Director & Assistant State
Registrar
Public Health Statistics &
Information Services
Dept. of Health &
Environmental Control
2600 Bull Street
Columbia, SC 29201
P: (803) 898-4144

SOUTH DAKOTA
Mr. Anthony Nelson
State Registrar
Vital Records
Hayes Building
600 East Capitol Avenue
Pierre, SD 57501
P: (605) 773-5303
F: (605) 773-5683
E: anthony.nelson
  @state.sd.us

TENNESSEE
Ms. Sharon Leinbach
State Registrar & Director
Vital Records
425 5th Avenue, North
Cordell Hull Building, 3rd Floor
Nashville, TN 37243
P: (615) 532-2600

TEXAS
Ms. Geraldine Harris
Vital Statistics
Department of State Health
Services
P.O. Box 12040
Austin, TX 78711
P: (888) 963-7111
F: (512) 458-7711

Dr. Yvonne Howze
Health Information & Vital
Statistics
1100 West 49th Street
P.O.Box 149347
Austin, TX 78714
P: (512) 458-7437
F: (512) 458-7711

U.S. VIRGIN ISLANDS
Ms. Fern P. Clarke
Acting Commissioner
Department of Health
1303 Hospital Grounds, Suite 10
Charlotte Amalie
St. Thomas, VI 00802
P: (340) 774-9000

UTAH
Ms. Janice Houston
Director
Office of Vital Records &
Statistics
288 North 1460 West
P.O. Box 141012
Salt Lake City, UT 84114
P: (801) 538-6262
F: (801) 538-7012
E: jlhouston@utah.gov

VERMONT
Dr. William K. Apao
Director
Division of Health Surveillance
Department of Health
108 Cherry Street
Burlington, VT 05402
P: (802) 863-7300
F: (802) 865-7754

VIRGINIA
Ms. Karen Remley
Commissioner
Department of Health
109 Governor Street, 13th Floor
Richmond, VA 23219
P: (804) 864-7009
F: (804) 864-7022
E: karen.remley
  @vdh.virginia.gov

WASHINGTON
Ms. Jennifer Tebaldi
Assistant Secretary
Epidemiology, Health Statistics
& Public Health Laboratories
Division
P.O. Box 47811
Olympia, WA 98504
P: (360) 236-4204
F: (360) 236-4245
E: jennifer.tebaldi
  @doh.wa.gov

WEST VIRGINIA
Mr. Gary L. Thompson
State Registrar
Health Statistics Center
350 Capitol Street, Room 165
Charleston, WV 25301
P: (304) 558-2931
F: (304) 558-1051
E: Gary.L.Thompson@wv.gov

WISCONSIN
Mr. Brett H. Davis
Medicaid Director
Division of Health Care
Financing
1 West Wilson Street, Room 350
Madison, WI 53701
P: (608) 266-1271
F: (608) 266-1096

WYOMING
Ms. Gladys Breeden
Manager
Vital Statistics Services
Rural & Frontier Health
Division
6101 Yellowstone Road, Suite
510
Cheyenne, WY 82002
P: (307) 777-7264
F: (307) 777-8545

Vocational Rehabilitation

Assists and encourages disabled persons to find suitable employment through training programs.

ALABAMA
Dr. Cary F. Boswell
Commissioner
Department of Rehabilitation Services
602 South Lawrence Street
Montgomery, AL 36104
P: (334) 293-7500
F: (334) 293-7383

ALASKA
Ms. Cheryl A. Walsh
Director
Department of Labor & Workforce Development
Division of Vocational Rehabilitation
801 West 10th Street, Suite A
Juneau, AK 99801
P: (907) 465-2814
F: (907) 465-2856
E: cheryl.walsh@alaska.gov

AMERICAN SAMOA
Mr. Pete Galea'i
Director
Vocational Rehabilitation
American Samoa Government
ASG Mail 3492
Pago Pago, AS 96799
P: (684) 699-1371
F: (864) 633-2393

ARIZONA
Ms. Katharine M. Levandowsky
Administrator
Rehabilitation Services Administration
1789 West Jefferson, 2nd Floor Northwest
Site Code 930A
Phoenix, AZ 85007
P: (602) 542-3332
F: (602) 542-3778

ARKANSAS
Ms. Katy Morris
Director
State Services for the Blind
Department of Human Services
P.O. Box 1437, Slot S101
Little Rock, AR 72201
P: (501) 682-0360
F: (501) 682-0366
E: katy.morris@arkansas.gov

Mr. Robert P. Trevino
Commissioner
Rehabilitation Services
Department of Workforce Education
1616 Brookwood Drive, P.O. Box 3781
Little Rock, AR 72203
P: (501) 296-1616
F: (501) 296-1141

CALIFORNIA
Mr. Anthony P. Sauer
Director
Department of Rehabilitation
721 Capitol Mall
P.O. Box 944222
Sacramento, CA 94244
P: (916) 558-5800
F: (916) 558-5806
E: asauer@dol.ca.gov

COLORADO
Ms. Nancy Smith
Director
Division of Vocational Rehabilitation
Administration Office
1575 Sherman Street, 4th Floor
Denver, CO 80203
P: (303) 866-4150
F: (303) 866-4905

CONNECTICUT
Ms. Amy Porter
Director
Bureau of Rehabilitation Services
Department of Social Services
25 Sigourney Street, 11th Floor
Hartford, CT 06106
P: (860) 424-4844
F: (860) 424-4850

Mr. Brian S. Sigman
Executive Director
Board of Education & Services for the Blind
184 Windsor Avenue
Windsor, CT 06095
P: (860) 602-4008
F: (860) 602-4020
E: brian.sigman@ct.gov

DELAWARE
Mr. Robert L. Doyle III
Director
Division for the Visually Impaired
Department of Health & Social Services
1901 North DuPont Highway
New Castle, DE 19720
P: (302) 255-9800
F: (302) 255-9964

Ms. Andrea Guest
Director
Division of Vocational Rehabilitation
Department of Labor
4425 North Market Street
Wilmington, DE 19802
P: (302) 761-8275
F: (302) 761-6611

DISTRICT OF COLUMBIA
Mr. Roy Albert
Administrator
Rehabilitation Services Administration
1125 15th Street, Northwest
Washington, DC 20005
P: (202) 442-8400
F: (202) 442-8742

FLORIDA
Ms. Joyce Hildreth
Director, Division of Blind Services
Department of Education
325 West Gaines Street
Turlington Building, Room 1114
Tallahassee, FL 32399
P: (850) 245-0300
F: (850) 245-0363
E: Joyce.Hildreth @dbs.fldoe.org

Mr. Bill Palmer
Director
Division of Vocational Rehabilitation
2002 Old St. Augustine Road, Building A
Tallahassee, FL 32301
P: (850) 245-3399
F: (850) 245-3316
E: Bill.Palmer@vr.fldoe.org

GEORGIA
Mr. Tim Evans
Deputy Commissioner, Rehabilitation Services
Department of Labor
148 Andrew Young International Boulevard
Suite 600
Atlanta, GA 30303
P: (404) 232-3922
F: (404) 292-3944

GUAM
Mr. Albert San Agustin
Director
Department of Vocational Rehabilitation
1313 Central Avenue
Tiyan, GU 96910
P: (671) 475-4637
F: (671) 477-2892

HAWAII
Mr. Joe Cordova
Administrator
Vocational Rehabilitation & Services for the Blind
Department of Human Services
601 Kamokila Boulevard, Room 515
Kapolei, HI 96707
P: (808) 692-7719
F: (808) 692-7727

IDAHO
Mr. Michael J. Graham
Administrator
Division of Vocational Rehabilitation
650 West State Street, Room 150
P.O. Box 83720-0096
Boise, ID 82720
P: (208) 287-6477
F: (208) 334-5305

Ms. Angela Jones
Administrator
Commission for the Blind & Visually Impaired
341 West Washington Street
P.O. Box 83720
Boise, ID 83720
P: (208) 334-3220
F: (208) 334-2963

ILLINOIS
Mr. Robert Kilbury
Director
Division of Rehabilitation Services
Department of Human Services
100 South Grand Avenue, 3rd Floor
Springfield, IL 62762
P: (217) 557-0401
F: (217) 558-4270

INDIANA
Mr. Greg McAloon
Director
Bureau of Rehabilitation Services
402 West Washington Street, Room W453
P.O. Box 7083
Indianapolis, IN 46207
P: (317) 232-1319
F: (317) 234-2099
E: Greg.Mcaloon@fssa.IN.gov

IOWA
Ms. Karen A. Keninger
Director
Department for the Blind
524 Fourth Street
Des Moines, IA 50309
P: (515) 281-1333
F: (515) 281-1263
E: karen.keninger
    @blind.state.ia.us

Mr. David Mitchell
Administrator
Vocational Rehabilitation
Services
Department of Education
510 East 12th Street
Des Moines, IA 50319
P: (515) 281-4703
F: (515) 281-6731
E: david.mitchell@iowa.gov

KANSAS
Mr. Michael Donnelly
Director, Rehabilitation Services
Department of Social &
Rehabilitation Services
915 Southwest Harrison, 9th
Floor North
Docking State Office Building
Topeka, KS 66612
P: (785) 368-8204
F: (785) 368-7467

KENTUCKY
Ms. Beth Smith
Executive Director
Office of Vocational
Rehabilitation
CHR Building
275 East Main Street, Mail Stop
2-EK
Frankfort, KY 40621
P: (502) 564-4440
F: (502) 564-4440
E: Beth.Smith@ky.gov

Mr. Christopher H. Smith
Executive Director
Office for the Blind
275 East Main Street
Mail Stop # 2-EJ
Frankfort, KY 40621
P: (502) 564-4754
F: (502) 564-2951
E: ChrisH.Smith@ky.gov

LOUISIANA
Mr. Ken York
Director
Rehabilitation Services
Department of Social Services
P.O. Box 91297
Baton Rouge, LA 70821
P: (225) 219-2225
F: (225) 219-2942
E: kyork@dss.state.la.us

MAINE
Ms. Betsy Hopkins
Director
Division of Vocational
Rehabilitation
150 State House Station
Augusta, ME 04333
P: (207) 623-6745
F: (207) 287-5292

Mr. John McMahon
Director
Division for the Blind &
Visually Impaired
150 State House Station
Augusta, ME 04333
P: (800) 698-4440
F: (207) 287-5292

MARYLAND
Ms. Suzanne Page
Assistant State Superintendent
Division of Rehabilitation
Services
Department of Education
2301 Argonne Drive
Baltimore, MD 21218
P: (410) 554-9385
F: (410) 554-9384

MASSACHUSETTS
Mr. Charlie Carr
Commissioner
Rehabilitation Commission
Fort Point Place
27-43 Wormwood Street
Boston, MA 00210
P: (617) 204-3600
F: (617) 727-1354

Ms. Janet LaBreck
Commissioner
Commission for the Blind
48 Boylston Street
Boston, MA 02116
P: (617) 727-5550
F: (617) 626-7685

MICHIGAN
Mr. Pat D. Cannon
Director
Commission for the Blind
Victor Building, Second Floor
201 North Washington Square
Lansing, MI 48913
P: (517) 335-4265
F: (517) 335-5140
E: cannonp@michigan.gov

Ms. Jaye N. Porter
Director
Rehabilitation Services
201 North Washington Square
P.O. Box 30010
Lansing, MI 48909
P: (517) 373-3390
F: (517) 335-7277

MINNESOTA
Ms. Kimberley T. Peck
Director
Rehabilitation Services Branch
First National Bank Building
332 Minnesota Street, Suite
#E200
St. Paul, MN 55101
P: (651) 259-7345
F: (651) 297-5159

Mr. Richard Strong
Director
State Services for the Blind
2200 University Avenue West,
Suite 240
St. Paul, MN 55114
P: (651) 649-5475
F: (651) 649-5927

MISSISSIPPI
Mr. H. S. Butch McMillan
Executive Director
Department of Rehabilitation
Services
1281 Highway 51
P.O. Box 1698
Jackson, MS 39215
P: (601) 853-5203
F: (601) 853-5205

MISSOURI
Mr. Mark Laird
Deputy Director
Rehabilitation Services for the
Blind
615 Howerton Court
P.O. Box 2320
Jefferson City, MO 65102
P: (573) 751-4249
F: (573) 751-4984
E: askrsb@dss.mo.gov

Dr. C. Jeanne Loyd
Assistant Commissioner
Division of Vocational
Rehabilitation
3024 Dupont Circle
Jefferson City, MO 65109
P: (573) 751-3251
F: (573) 751-1441
E: info@vr.dese.mo.gov

MONTANA
Mr. Jim Marks
Administrator, Vocational
Rehabilitation
Department of Public Health &
Human Services
P.O. Box 4210
Helena, MT 59604
P: (406) 444-2591
F: (406) 444-3632

NEBRASKA
Mr. Mark Schultz
Assistant Commissioner &
Director
Vocational Rehabilitation
6th Floor, 301 Centennial Mall
P.O. Box 94987
Lincoln, NE 68509
P: (402) 471-3649
F: (402) 471-0788

Ms. Pearl VanZandt
Director
Commission for the Blind &
Visually Impaired
4600 Valley Road, Suite 100
Lincoln, NE 68510
P: (402) 471-2891
F: (402) 471-3009

NEVADA
Ms. Maureen Cole
Administrator, Rehabilitation
Division
Department of Employment,
Training & Rehabilitation
1370 South Curry Street
Carson City, NV 89703
P: (775) 684-4040
F: (775) 684-4184

NEW HAMPSHIRE
Ms. Lisa Hatz
Interim Director
Bureau of Vocational
Rehabilitation
Department of Education
21 South Fruit Street, Suite 20
Concord, NH 03301
P: (603) 271-3471
F: (603) 271-7095
E: lhatz@ed.state.nh.us

Vocational Rehabilitation

NEW JERSEY
Mr. Vito J. De Santis
Executive Director
Commission for the Blind &
Visually Impaired
153 Halsey Street
P.O. Box 47017
Newark, NJ 07101
P: (973) 648-2324
F: (973) 648-7364

Ms. Alice Hunnicut
Director
Division of Vocational
Rehabilitation Services
135 East State Street
P.O. Box 398
Trenton, NJ 08625
P: (609) 292-7318
F: (609) 292-4033

NEW MEXICO
Mr. Greg Trapp
Executive Director
Commission for the Blind
2200 Yale Boulevard, Southeast
Albuquerque, NM 87106
P: (505) 827-4479
F: (505) 827-4475

Mr. Ralph Vigil
Director
Division of Vocational
Rehabilitation
Department of Education
435 St. Michael's Drive,
Building D
Santa Fe, NM 87505
P: (505) 954-8517
F: (505) 954-8562

NEW YORK
Ms. Debora Brown-Johnson
Assistant Commissioner
Vocational & Educational
Services for People with
Disabilities
One Commerce Plaza, Room
1601
Albany, NY 12234
P: (518) 473-1626

Mr. Brian Daniels
Director
Commission for the Blind &
Visually Handicapped
40 North Pearl Street
Albany, NY 12243
P: (518) 474-6812
F: (518) 486-5819

NORTH CAROLINA
Ms. Linda Harrington
Director
Division of Vocational
Rehabilitation Services
Department of Health & Human
Services
2801 Mail Service Center
Raleigh, NC 27699
P: (919) 855-3500
F: (919) 733-7968
E: linda.harrington
   @dhhs.nc.gov

Mr. Eddie Weaver
Director
Division of Services for the
Blind
309 Ashe Avenue, Fisher
Building
2601 Mail Service Center
Raleigh, NC 27699
P: (919) 733-9822
F: (919) 733-9769

NORTH DAKOTA
Mr. Russell Cusack
Director
Department of Vocational
Rehabilitation
Prairie Hills Plaza
1237 West Divide Avenue, Suite
1B
Bismarck, ND 58501
P: (701) 328-8926
F: (701) 328-8969

**NORTHERN MARIANA
ISLANDS**
Ms. Margarita R.
   Olopai-Taitano
Vocational Rehabilitation
Service
P.O. Box 501521
Commonwealth of the Northern
Marianas
Saipan, MP 96950
P: (670) 664-6448
F: (670) 322-6536

OHIO
Mr. Kevin Miller
Administrator
Rehabilitation Services
Commission
400 East Campus View
Boulevard
Columbus, OH 43235
P: (614) 438-1214
F: (614) 985-7906

OKLAHOMA
Dr. Mike O'Brien
Director
Department of Rehabilitation
Services
3535 Northwest 58th Street,
Suite 500
Oklahoma City, OK 73112
P: (405) 951-3400
F: (405) 951-3529

OREGON
Ms. Linda R. Mock
Administrator
State Commission for the Blind
535 Southeast 12th Avenue
Portland, OR 97214
P: (971) 673-1588 Ext. 31601
F: (971) 673-1570
E: linda.mock@state.or.us

Ms. Stephanie Parrish
   Taylor
Administrator
Office of Vocational
Rehabilitation Services
Department of Human Services
500 Summer Street, Northeast,
E-87
Salem, OR 97301
P: (503) 945-6201
F: (503) 947-5025
E: stephaine.taylor
   @state.or.us

PENNSYLVANIA
Mr. Tom Washic
Director
Office of Vocational
Rehabilitation
Department of Labor & Industry
1521 North 6th Street
Harrisburg, PA 17102
P: (717) 787-8187
F: (717) 712-1629

PUERTO RICO
Ms. Nydia Colon
Adminstrator
Vocational Rehabilitation
Administration
P.O. Box 191118
San Juan, PR 00919
P: (787) 727-0445
F: (787) 728-8070

RHODE ISLAND
Mr. Stephen Brunero
Administrator
Office of Rehabilitation
Services
Department of Human Services
40 Fountain Street
Providence, RI 02903
P: (401) 421-7005
F: (401) 222-3574

SOUTH CAROLINA
Ms. Barbara G. Hollis
Commissioner & Executive
Officer
Vocational Rehabilitation
Department
1410 Boston Avenue
P.O. Box 15
West Columbia, SC 29171
P: (803) 896-6503
F: (803) 896-6529

Mr. James Kirby
Commissioner
Commission for the Blind
1430 Confederate Avenue
P.O. Box 2467
Columbia, SC 29202
P: (803) 898-8822
F: (803) 898-8852

SOUTH DAKOTA
Mr. Grady Kickul
Director
Division of Rehabilitation
Services
C/o 500 East Capitol
Pierre, SD 57501
P: (605) 773-3195
F: (605) 773-5483

Ms. Gaye Mattke
Director
Services for the Blind
C/o 500 East Capitol
Pierre, SD 57501
P: (605) 773-4644
F: (605) 773-5483

TENNESSEE
Ms. Andrea L. Cooper
Assistant Commissioner
Division of Rehabilitation
Services
Department of Human Services
400 Deadrick Street, 15th Floor
Nashville, TN 37243
P: (615) 313-4714
F: (615) 741-4165

TEXAS

Mr. Jim Hanophy
Assistant Commissioner
Department of Assistive &
Rehabilitative Services
Division for Rehabilitation
Services
4800 North Lamar, Suite320
Austin, TX 78756
P: (512) 424-4220
F: (512) 424-4277

Ms. Barbara J. Madrigal
Assistant Commissioner
Department of Assistive &
Rehabilitative Services
Division for Blind Services
4800 North Lamar Boulevard,
Suite 320
Austin, TX 78756
P: (512) 377-0602
F: (512) 377-0551

U.S. VIRGIN ISLANDS

Mr. Vernon Finch
Director, Division of Disabilities
& Rehabilitation Services
Department of Human Services
Knud Hansen Complex,
Building A
1303 Hospital Ground
St. Thomas, VI 00802
P: (340) 774-0930
F: (340) 774-7773

UTAH

Mr. Donald R. Uchida
Executive Director
Office of Rehabilitation
250 East 500 South
P.O. Box 144200
Salt Lake City, UT 84114
P: (801) 538-7530
F: (801) 538-7522

VERMONT

Ms. Diane P. Dalmasse
Director
Department of Disabilities,
Aging & Independent Living
Vocational Rehabilitation
Division
03 South Main Street, Weeks 1A
Waterbury, VT 05671
P: (802) 241-2190
F: (802) 241-3359
E: Diane.Dalmasse
@ahs.state.vt.us

Mr. Fred Jones
Director
Divsion for the Blind &
Visually Impaired
Disabilities, Aging &
Independent Living
Weeks Building, 103 South Main
Street
Waterbury, VT 05671
P: (802) 241-2132
F: (802) 241-2210
E: Fred.Jones
@ahs.state.vt.us

VIRGINIA

Mr. Ray Hopkins
Commissioner
Department for the Blind &
Vision Impaired
397 Azalea Avenue
Richmond, VA 23227
P: (804) 371-3145
F: (804) 371-3157

Mr. James Rothrock
Commissioner
Department of Rehabilitation
Services
8004 Franklin Farms Drive
Richmond, VA 23229
P: (804) 662-7010
F: (804) 662-7644

WASHINGTON

Mr. Andres Aguirre
Interim Director
Division of Vocational
Rehabilitation
Department of Social & Health
Services
P.O. Box 45340
Olympia, WA 98504
P: (360) 725-3610
F: (360) 438-8011

Ms. Lou Oma Durand
Director
Department of Services for the
Blind
4565 7th Avenue, Southeast
Lacey, WA 98503
P: (360) 725-3835
F: (360) 407-0679
E: loudurand@dsb.wa.gov

WEST VIRGINIA

Ms. Deborah Lovely
Director
Division of Rehabilitation
Services
State Capitol
P.O. Box 50890
Charleston, WV 25305
P: (304) 766-4601
F: (304) 766-4905
E: Deborah.L.Lovely@wv.gov

WISCONSIN

Ms. Charlene Dwyer
Administrator, Division of
Vocational Rehabilitation
Department of Workforce
Development
201 East Washington Avenue,
Room A100
P.O. Box 7852
Madison, WI 53707
P: (608) 261-2126
F: (608) 260-3163

WYOMING

Mr. Jim McIntosh
Administrator
Division of Vocational
Rehabilitation
Department of Employment
1100 Herschler Building
Cheyenne, WY 82002
P: (307) 777-7389
F: (307) 777-5939

Waste Management

Develops and maintains a comprehensive waste management program in the state.

ALABAMA
Ms. Debi Thomas
Executive Assistant
Environmental Management
Commission
1400 Coliseum Boulevard
P.O. Box 301463
Montgomery, AL 36130
P: (334) 271-7706
F: (334) 279-3052

ARIZONA
Ms. Amanda Stone
Waste Programs Division
Director
Department of Environmental
Quality
ADEQ Central Office
1110 West Washington Street
Phoenix, AZ 85007
P: (602) 771-4567
F: (602) 771-2302
E: stone.amanda@azdeq.gov

ARKANSAS
Mr. Roger Lawrence
Chief
Solid Waste Division
P.O. Box 8913
Little Rock, AR 72209
P: (501) 682-0600
F: (501) 682-0611
E: lawrence
@adeq.state.ar.us

CALIFORNIA
Mr. Mark Leary
Acting Director
Department of Resources,
Recycling & Recovery
1001 I Street
P.O. Box 4025
Sacramento, CA 95812
P: (916) 341-6544
F: (916) 319-7319
E: Mark.Leary
@CalRecycle.ca.gov

COLORADO
Mr. Gary Baughman
Director
Hazardous Materials & Waste
Management Division
Dept. of Public Health &
Environment
Denver, CO 80246
P: (303) 692-3320
F: (303) 759-5355
E: comments.hmwnd
@state.co.us

CONNECTICUT
Mr. Robert Isner
Director
Waste Engineering &
Enforcement Division
Department of Environmental
Protection
79 Elm Street
Hartford, CT 06106
P: (860) 424-3023
F: (860) 424-4059
E: robert.isner@ct.gov

DELAWARE
Ms. Nancy C. Marker
Manager
Solid Waste & Hazardous
Management Branch
89 Kings Highway
Dover, DE 19901
P: (302) 739-9403
F: (302) 739-5060

DISTRICT OF COLUMBIA
Mr. William O. Howland Jr.
Director
Department of Public Works
2000 14th Street, Northwest, 6th
Floor
Washington, DC 20009
P: (202) 673-6833
F: (202) 671-0642
E: dpw@dc.gov

FLORIDA
Mr. Jorge Caspary
Director
Division of Waste Management
Department of Environmental
Protection
2600 Blairstone Road, MS 4500
Tallahassee, FL 32399
P: (850) 245-8693
E: jorge.caspary
@dep.state.fl.us

GEORGIA
Mr. Mark Smith
Branch Chief
Land Protection Branch
2 Martin Luther King, Jr. Drive,
SE
Suite 1154 East Tower
Atlanta, GA 30334
P: (404) 656-7802
F: (404) 651-9425

HAWAII
Mr. Steven Y.K. Chang
Branch Chief
Solid & Hazardous Waste
Branch
Department of Health
919 Ala Moana Boulevard, #212
Honolulu, HI 96814
P: (808) 586-4226
F: (808) 586-7509
E: schang
@eha.health.state.hi.us

IDAHO
Mr. Orville Green
Administrator
Waste Management &
Remediation Division
DEQ State Office
1410 North Hilton
Boise, ID 83706
P: (208) 373-0148
F: (208) 373-0154
E: orville.green
@deq.idaho.gov

ILLINOIS
Ms. Lisa Bonnett
Acting Director
Environmental Protection
Agency
1021 North Grand Avenue, East
P.O. Box 19276
Springfield, IL 62794
P: (217) 782-3397
F: (217) 782-9039

INDIANA
Mr. Bruce Palin
Assistant Commissioner, Office
of Land Quality
Department of Environmental
Management
100 North Senate Avenue
Room IGCN 1154
Indianapolis, IN 46204
P: (317) 233-6591
F: (317) 233-6647
E: bpalin@idem.in.gov

IOWA
Mr. Brian J. Tormey
Bureau Chief
Land Quality Bureau
Wallace Building
502 East 9th Street
Des Moines, IA 50319
P: (515) 281-8927
F: (515) 281-8895
E: brian.tormey
@dnr.iowa.gov

KANSAS
Mr. William L. Bider
Director
Bureau of Waste Management
1000 Southwest Jackson Street
Suite 320
Topeka, KS 66612
P: (785) 296-1600
F: (785) 296-8909

KENTUCKY
Mr. Anthony Hatton
Division Director
Division of Waste Management
Department for Environmental
Protection
200 Fair Oaks Lane
Frankfort, KY 40601
P: (502) 564-6716
F: (502) 564-4049
E: tony.hatton@ky.gov

LOUISIANA
Mr. Lourdes Iturralde
Administrator
Public Participation & Permits
Support Services
Department of Environmental
Quality
P.O. Box 4313
Baton Rouge, LA 70821
P: (225) 219-3180
F: (225) 219-3309

MAINE
Mr. Ron Dyer
Director
Bureau of Remediation & Waste
Management
Department of Environmental
Protection
17 State House Station
Augusta, ME 04333
P: (207) 287-7980
F: (207) 287-7826
E: ron.dyer@maine.gov

MARYLAND
Mr. Horacio Tablada
Director
Land Management
Administration
Department of Environment
1800 Washington Boulevard
Baltimore, MD 21230
P: (410) 631-3304
F: (410) 631-3321
E: htablada@mde.state.md.us

MASSACHUSETTS
Mr. Kenneth Kimmell
Commissioner
Department of Environmental
Protection
One Winter Street, #1022
Boston, MA 02108
P: (617) 292-5856
F: (617) 574-6880
E: ken.kimmell@state.ma.us

MINNESOTA
Mr. Paul Aasen
Commissioner
Pollution Control Agency
520 Lafayette Road North, 6th
Floor
St. Paul, MN 55155
P: (651) 757-2016
F: (651) 296-6334
E: paul.aasen@state.mn.us

MISSISSIPPI
Ms. Trudy H. Fisher
Executive Director
Department of Environmental
Quality
2380 Highway 80 West
P.O. Box 2369
Jackson, MS 39289
P: (601) 961-5001
F: (601) 961-5093
E: trudy_fisher
    @deq.state.ms.us

MISSOURI
Mr. Chris Nagel
Program Director
Solid Waste Management
Program
P.O. Box 176
Jefferson City, MO 65102
P: (573) 526-3900
F: (573) 526-3902
E: swmp@dnr.mo.gov

MONTANA
Mr. Richard H. Opper
Director
Department of Environmental
Quality
1520 East 6th Avenue
P.O. Box 200901
Helena, MT 59620
P: (406) 444-6815
F: (406) 444-4386
E: ropper@mt.gov

NEBRASKA
Mr. Michael J. Linder
Director
Department of Environmental
Quality
1200 N Street, Suite 400
P.O. Box 98922
Lincoln, NE 68509
P: (402) 471-3585
F: (402) 471-2909
E: mike.linder@nebraska.gov

NEVADA
Mr. Leo Drozdoff
Director
Department of Conservation &
Natural Resources
901 South Stewart, Suite 5001
Carson City, NV 89701
P: (775) 684-2710
F: (775) 684-2715
E: ldrozdoff@dcnr.nv.gov

Mr. Eric Noack
Bureau Chief
Bureau of Waste Management
Division of Environmental
Protection
901 South Stewart Street, Suite
4001
Carson City, NV 89701
P: (775) 687-9366
F: (775) 687-6396
E: enoack@ndep.nv.gov

NEW HAMPSHIRE
Mr. John Duclos
Bureau Administrator
Hazardous Waste Management
Bureau
29 Hazen Drive
P.O. Box 95
Concord, NH 03301
P: (603) 271-1998
F: (603) 271-0869
E: john.duclos@des.nh.gov

NEW MEXICO
Mr. Raj Solomon
Acting Director
Water & Waste Management
Division
1190 St. Francis Drive, Suite
N4050
Santa Fe, NM 87505
P: (505) 827-2855

NEW YORK
Mr. Joe Martens
Commissioner
Department of Environmental
Conservation
625 Broadway, 14th Floor
Albany, NY 12233
P: (518) 402-8540
F: (518) 402-8541
E: joemartens
    @gw.dec.state.ny.us

NORTH CAROLINA
Mr. Dexter Matthews
Director
Department of Environment &
Natural Resources
Division of Waste Management
1646 Mail Service Center
Raleigh, NC 27699
P: (919) 508-8400
F: (919) 733-4061
E: dexter.matthews
    @dcdenr.gov

NORTH DAKOTA
Mr. Scott Radig
Director
Division of Waste Management
Department of Health
918 East Divide Avenue, 3rd
Floor
Bismark, ND 58501
P: (701) 328-5166
F: (701) 328-5200
E: sradig@nd.gov

**NORTHERN MARIANA
ISLANDS**
Mr. Martin C. Sablan
Department of Public Works
Caller Box 10007, Capitol Hill
Saipan, MP
P: (670) 235-5827
F: (670) 235-6346

OHIO
Mr. David A. Sholtis
Acting Division Chief
Division of Hazardous Waste
Management
50 West Town Street, Suite 700
P.O. Box 1049
Columbus, OH 43216
P: (614) 644-3778
F: (614) 728-3898
E: dave.sholtis
    @epa.state.oh.us

OKLAHOMA
Mr. Scott Thompson
Director
Land Protection Division
Department of Environmental
Quality
P.O. Box 1677
Oklahoma City, OK 73101
P: (405) 702-5100
F: (405) 702-5101
E: scott.thompson
    @deq.state.ok.us

OREGON
Mr. Dick Pedersen
Director
Department of Environmental
Quality
811 Southwest 6th Avenue
Portland, OR 97204
P: (503) 229-5300
F: (503) 229-5850
E: pedersen.dick
    @deq.state.or.us

PENNSYLVANIA
Mr. Todd M. Wallace
Acting Bureau Director
Bureau of Waste Management
P.O. Box 8471
Harrisburg, PA 17105
P: (717) 783-2388
F: (717) 787-1904
E: ra-epwaste@state.pa.us

PUERTO RICO
Mr. Luis Bernal-Jimenez
Executive Director
Energy Affairs Administration
P.O. Box 41314
San Juan, PR 00940
P: (787) 999-2200 x2886
F: (787) 999-2246
E: lbernal@aae.gobierno.pr

Waste Management

Mr. Javier Quintana Mendez
Director
Solid Waste Management
Authority
P.O. Box 40285
San Juan, PR 00918
P: (787) 765-7575
F: (787) 753-2220

RHODE ISLAND
Ms. Janet Coit
Director
Department of Environmental
Management
235 Promenade Street, 4th Floor
Providence, RI 02908
P: (401) 222-2771
F: (401) 222-6802
E: janet.coit@dem.ri.gov

SOUTH CAROLINA
Ms. Daphne G. Neel
Bureau Chief
Bureau of Land & Waste
Management
Dept. of Health &
Environmental Control
2600 Bull Street
Columbia, SC 29201
P: (803) 896-4007
F: (803) 896-4001

SOUTH DAKOTA
Ms. Vonni Kallemeyn
Administrator
Department of Environment &
Natural Resources
Waste Management Program
523 East Capitol Avenue
Pierre, SD 57501
P: (605) 773-3153
F: (605) 773-6035

TENNESSEE
Mr. Mike Apple
Director
Division of Solid & Hazardous
Waste Management
5th Floor, L & C Tower
401 Church Street
Nashville, TN 37243
P: (615) 532-0780
F: (615) 532-0886

TEXAS
Mr. Earl Lott
Director
Waste Permits Division
12100 Park 35 Circle
P.O. Box 13087
Austin, TX 78711
P: (512) 239-2047
F: (512) 239-2007

U.S. VIRGIN ISLANDS
Mr. Darryl Smalls
Commissioner
Department of Public Works
6002 Estate Anna's Hope
Christiansted, VI 00820
P: (340) 773-1789
F: (340) 773-0670

UTAH
Mr. Scott Anderson
Director
Division of Solid & Hazardous
Waste
195 North 1950 West, 2nd Floor
P.O. Box 144880
Salt Lake City, UT 84114
P: (801) 536-0203
F: (801) 536-0222
E: standerson@utah.gov

VERMONT
Mr. George Desch
Director
Waste Management Division
103 South Main Street
West Office Building
Waterbury, VT 05671
P: (802) 241-3491
F: (802) 241-3296
E: george.desch@state.vt.us

VIRGINIA
Mr. David K. Paylor
Director
Department of Environmental
Quality
629 East Main Street
P.O. Box 1105
Richmond, VA 23218
P: (804) 698-4390
F: (804) 698-4019
E: dkpaylor
    @deq.virginia.gov

WASHINGTON
Mr. Ted L. Sturdevant
Director
Department of Ecology
P.O. Box 47600
Olympia, WA 98504
P: (360) 407-7001
F: (360) 407-6989
E: tstu461@ecy.wa.gov

WEST VIRGINIA
Ms. Mandirola Scott
Acting Division Director
Division of Water & Waste
Management
601 57th Street, Southeast
Charleston, WV 25304
P: (304) 926-0499
F: (304) 926-0463

WISCONSIN
Ms. Suzanne Bangert
Director
Waste Management Bureau
101 South Webster, 3rd Floor
Madison, WI 53707
P: (608) 266-0014
F: (608) 267-2768
E: suzanne.bangert
    @wisconsin.gov

WYOMING
Mr. John V. Corra
Director
Department of Environmental
Quality
Herschler Building
122 West 25th Street, 4th Floor,
West
Cheyenne, WY 82002
P: (307) 777-7937
F: (307) 777-7682
E: jcorra@wyo.gov

Water Resources

Responsible for water conservation, development, use and planning in the state.

ALABAMA
Mr. J. Brian Atkins
Division Director
Office of Water Resources
401 Adams Avenue, Suite 434
P.O. Box 5690
Montgomery, AL 36103
P: (334) 242-5499
F: (334) 242-0776
E: James.Atkins
   @adeca.alabama.gov

ALASKA
Mr. Gary Prokosch
Chief of the Water Resources
Section
Division of Mining, Land &
Water
Department of Natural
Resources
550 West 7th Avenue, Suite 1070
Anchorage, AK 99501
P: (907) 269-8645
F: (907) 269-8947
E: garyp@dnr.state.ak.us

AMERICAN SAMOA
Mr. John Marsh
Interim Chief Executive Officer
American Samoa Power
Authority
American Samoa Government
Pago Pago, AS 96799
P: (684) 644-2772
F: (684) 644-5005

ARIZONA
Ms. Sandra Fabritz-Whitney
Director
Department of Water Resources
3550 North Central Avenue,
Suite 442
Phoenix, AZ 85012
P: (602) 771-8426
F: (602) 771-8681
E: safabritz@azwater.gov

ARKANSAS
Mr. Randy Young
Executive Director
Soil & Water Conservation
Commission
101 East Capitol, Suite 350
Little Rock, AR 72201
P: (501) 682-1611
F: (501) 682-3991
E: randy.young@arkansas.gov

CALIFORNIA
Mr. Mark W. Cowin
Director
Department of Water Resources
1416 Ninth Street
P.O. Box 942836
Sacramento, CA 94236
P: (916) 653-7007
F: (916) 653-5028
E: mcowin@water.ca.gov

COLORADO
Mr. Dick Wolfe
Executive Director
Division of Water Resources
Department of Natural
Resources
1313 Sherman Street, Room 818
Denver, CO 80203
P: (303) 866-3581
F: (303) 866-3589
E: AskDWR@state.co.us

CONNECTICUT
Ms. Denise Ruzicka
Director
Inland Water Resources
Division
Department of Environmental
Protection
79 Elm Street
Hartford, CT 06106
P: (860) 424-3706
F: (860) 424-4075
E: denise.ruzicka@ct.gov

DELAWARE
Dr. Katherine E.
   Bunting-Howarth
Director
Division of Water Resources
89 Kings Highway
Dover, DE 19901
P: (302) 739-9949
F: (302) 739-7864
E: katherine.howarth
   @state.de.us

DISTRICT OF COLUMBIA
Mr. George S. Hawkins
General Manager
Water & Sewer Authority
5000 Overlook Avenue,
Southwest
Washington, DC 20032
P: (202) 787-2000
F: (202) 787-2333
E: info@dcwasa.com

FLORIDA
Mr. Mark Thomasson
Director
Water Resource Management
Department of Environmental
Protection
2600 Blairstone Road, MS 3500
Tallahassee, FL 32399
P: (850) 245-8336
F: (850) 245-8356
E: mark.thomasson
   @dep.state.fl.us

GEORGIA
Ms. Linda MacGregor
Branch Chief
Watershed Protection Branch
4220 International Parkway,
Suite 101
Atlanta, GA 30354
P: (404) 675-6232
F: (404) 675-6247

GUAM
Mr. Leonard Olive
General Manager
Waterworks Authority
P.O. Box 3010
Hagatna, GU 96910
P: (671) 647-7800

HAWAII
Mr. William Tam
Interim Deputy Director
Commission on Water Resource
Management
1151 Punchbowl Street, Room
227
P.O. Box 621
Honolulu, HI 96809
P: (808) 587-0214
F: (808) 587-0219
E: dlnr.cwrm@hawaii.gov

IDAHO
Mr. Gary Spackman
Interim Director
Department of Water Resources
P.O. Box 83720
Boise, ID 83720
P: (208) 287-4800
F: (208) 287-6700
E: gary.spackman
   @idwr.idaho.gov

ILLINOIS
Mr. Gary R. Clark
Director
Office of Water Resources
1 Natural Resources Way, 2nd
Floor
Springfield, IL 62702
P: (217) 785-3334
F: (217) 785-5014

INDIANA
Mr. Mike Neyer
Director
Division of Water
Department of Natural
Resources
402 West Washington Street,
Room W264
Indianapolis, IN 46204
P: (317) 232-4160
F: (317) 233-4579
E: mneyer@dnr.in.gov

IOWA
Mr. Bill Ehm
Water Policy Coordinator
Water Supply Section
Wallace Building
502 East 9th Street
Des Moines, IA 50319
P: (515) 281-4701
F: (515) 281-8895
E: william.ehm@dnr.iowa.gov

KANSAS
Mr. David W. Barfield
Chief Engineer
Division of Water Resources
109 Southwest 9th Street, 2nd
Floor
Topeka, KS 66612
P: (785) 296-3717
F: (785) 296-1176
E: David.Barfield
   @kda.ks.gov

Mr. Tracy D. Streeter
Director
Kansas Water Office
901 South Kansas Avenue
Topeka, KS 66612
P: (785) 296-3185
F: (785) 296-0878
E: tracy.streeter
   @kwo.ks.gov

KENTUCKY
Sandy Gruzesky
Director
Division of Water
Department for Environmental
Protection
200 Fair Oaks Lane, Fourth
Floor
Frankfort, KY 40601
P: (502) 564-3410
F: (502) 564-0111
E: water@ky.gov

Water Resources

LOUISIANA
Mr. Jim H. Welsh
Commissioner of Conservation
Office of Conservation
Department of Natural
Resources
P.O. Box 94275
Baton Rouge, LA 70804
P: (225) 342-5540
F: (225) 342-3705
E: Jim.Welsh@la.gov

MAINE
Mr. James Brooks
Acting Commissioner
Department of Environmental
Protection
17 State House Station
Augusta, ME 04333
P: (207) 287-2812
F: (207) 287-2814
E: james.p.brooks@maine.gov

MARYLAND
Mr. Frank W. Dawson
Assistant Secretary for Aquatic
Resources
Department of Natural
Resources
Tawes State Office Building, C4
580 Taylor Avenue
Annapolis, MD 21401
P: (410) 260-8110
F: (410) 260-8111
E: fdawson@dnr.state.md.us

MASSACHUSETTS
Mr. Rick Sullivan
Commissioner
Executive Office of Energy &
Environmental Affairs
100 Cambridge Street, Suite 900
Boston, MA 02114
P: (614) 626-1000
F: (614) 626-1181

MICHIGAN
Mr. Richard A. Powers
Chief
Water Bureau
P.O. Box 30273
Lansing, MI 48909
P: (517) 335-4176
F: (517) 373-2040

MINNESOTA
Mr. Paul Aasen
Commissioner
Pollution Control Agency
520 Lafayette Road North, 6th
Floor
St. Paul, MN 55155
P: (651) 757-2016
F: (651) 296-6334
E: paul.aasen@state.mn.us

MISSISSIPPI
Mr. Sam Mabry
Director
Office of Land & Water
Resources
P.O. Box 10631
Jackson, MS 39289
P: (601) 961-5200
F: (601) 354-6965

MISSOURI
Mr. Mike Wells
Deputy Department Director,
Chief of Water Resources
Water Resources Center
P.O. Box 176
Jefferson City, MO 65102
P: (573) 751-2867
F: (573) 751-7627
E: Mike.Wells@dnr.mo.gov

MONTANA
Ms. Mary Sexton
Director
Department of Natural
Resources & Conservation
1625 11th Avenue
P.O. Box 201601
Helena, MT 59620
P: (406) 444-2074
F: (406) 444-2684
E: msexton@mt.gov

NEBRASKA
Mr. Brian Dunnigan
Director
Department of Natural
Resources
P.O. Box 94676
Lincoln, NE 68509
P: (402) 471-2366
F: (402) 471-2900
E: brian.dunnigan
    @nebraska.gov

NEVADA
Mr. Jason King
State Engineer
Department of Conservation &
Natural Resources
Division of Water Resources
901 South Stewart, Suite 2002
Carson City, NV 89701
P: (775) 684-2800
F: (775) 684-2811
E: jking@water.nv.gov

NEW HAMPSHIRE
Mr. Harry T. Stewart
Director
Water Division - D.E.S.
29 Hazen Drive
P.O. Box 95
Concord, NH 03302
P: (603) 271-3308
F: (603) 271-2982
E: harry.stewart@des.nh.gov

NEW JERSEY
Ms. Michele Putnam
Director
Division of Water Supply
Department of Environmental
Protection
P.O. Box 402
Trenton, NJ 08625
P: (609) 292-7219
F: (609) 292-1654

NEW MEXICO
Mr. John R. D'Antonio
State Engineer/Secretary,
Interstate Stream Commission
Office of the State Engineer
130 South Capitol Street, NEA
Building
P.O. Box 25102
Santa Fe, NM 87504
P: (505) 827-6175
F: (505) 827-3806

NEW YORK
Mr. Mark Klotz
Director
Division of Water Resource
Management
625 Broadway
Albany, NY 12233
P: (518) 402-8233
F: (518) 402-9029
E: dowinfo
    @gw.dec.state.ny.us

NORTH CAROLINA
Mr. Tom Reeder
Director
Department of Environment &
Natural Resources
Division of Water Resources
1611 Mail Service Center
Raleigh, NC 27699
P: (919) 715-3045
F: (919) 733-3558
E: tom.reeder@ncdenr.gov

NORTH DAKOTA
Mr. Todd Sando
State Engineer
Water Commission
900 East Boulevard Avenue
Department 770
Bismarck, ND 58505
P: (701) 328-2750
F: (701) 328-3696
E: tsando@nd.gov

**NORTHERN MARIANA
ISLANDS**
Mr. Jesus B. Castro
Division Manager
Water Division
P.O. Box 501220
Saipan, MP 96950
P: (670) 235-7025
F: (670) 235-7053

OHIO
Mr. Steven J. Grossman
Executive Director
Water Development Authority
480 South High Street
Columbus, OH 43215
P: (614) 466-5822
F: (614) 644-9964

OKLAHOMA
Mr. J.D. Strong
Executive Director
Water Resources Board
3800 North Classen Boulevard
Oklahoma City, OK 73118
P: (405) 530-8800
F: (405) 530-8900

OREGON
Mr. Phillip C. Ward
Director
Water Resources Department
725 Summer Street, Northeast,
Suite A
Salem, OR 97301
P: (503) 986-0900
F: (503) 986-0904
E: Director@wrd.state.or.us

PENNSYLVANIA
Mr. Richard J. Allan
Acting Secretary
Department of Conservation &
Natural Resources
Rachel Carson State Office
Building
7th Floor, P.O. Box 8767
Harrisburg, PA 17105
P: (717) 772-9084
F: (717) 705-2832

PUERTO RICO
Mr. Daniel J. Galan Kercado
Secretary
Department of Natural &
Environmental Resources
P.O. Box 366147
San Juan, PR 00936
P: (787) 999-2000
F: (787) 999-2303

RHODE ISLAND
Ms. Alicia M. Good
Assistant Director of Water
Resources
Department of Environmental
Management
Office of Water Resources
235 Promenade Street
Providence, RI 02908
P: (401) 222-4700, Ext. 7214
F: (401) 222-3564
E: alicia.good@dem.ri.gov

SOUTH CAROLINA
Mr. Joe Gellici
Section Chief
Hydrology Section
Land, Water & Conservation
Division
1000 Assembly Street
Columbia, SC 29201
P: (803) 734-6428
F: (803) 734-9200
E: gellicij@dnr.sc.gov

SOUTH DAKOTA
Mr. Jim Feeney
Administrator
Department of Environment &
Natural Resources
Water Resources Assistance
Program
523 East Capitol Avenue
Pierre, SD 57501
P: (605) 773-4216
F: (605) 773-4068

TENNESSEE
Mr. John McClurkan
Administrator
Water Resources Program
440 Hogan Road
Nashville, TN 37220
P: (615) 837-5225
E: john.mcclurkan@tn.gov

TEXAS
Ms. Carolyn Brittin
Deputy Executive Administrator
Water Resources Planning &
Information
1700 North Congress Avenue
P.O. Box 13231
Austin, TX 78711
P: (512) 475-0933
F: (512) 936-0889

U.S. VIRGIN ISLANDS
Ms. Meliss C. McCall
Director
Division of Environmental
Protection
Cyril E. King Airport
Terminal Building, 2nd Floor
St. Thomas, VI 00802
P: (340) 774-3320
F: (340) 714-9549

UTAH
Mr. Dennis J. Strong
Director
Division of Water Resources
1594 West North Temple
P.O. Box 146201
Salt Lake City, UT 84114
P: (801) 538-7230
F: (801) 538-7279
E: dennisstrong@utah.gov

VERMONT
Mr. Peter LaFlamme
Director
Water Quality Division
103 South Main Street
Building 10, North
Waterbury, VT 05671
P: (802) 241-3765
F: (802) 241-3287
E: pete.laflamme
@state.vt.us

VIRGINIA
Mr. David K. Paylor
Director
Department of Environmental
Quality
629 East Main Street
P.O. Box 1105
Richmond, VA 23218
P: (804) 698-4390
F: (804) 698-4019
E: dkpaylor
@deq.virginia.gov

WASHINGTON
Mr. Ken Slattery
Program Manager
Water Resources Program
Department of Ecology
P.O. Box 47600
Olympia, WA 98504
P: (360) 407-6602
F: (360) 407-6574
E: kshw461@ecy.wa.gov

WEST VIRGINIA
Ms. Mandirola Scott
Acting Division Director
Division of Water & Waste
Management
601 57th Street, Southeast
Charleston, WV 25304
P: (304) 926-0499
F: (304) 926-0463

WISCONSIN
Mr. Bruce Baker
Administrator
Division of Water
101 South Webster
P.O. Box 7921
Madison, WI 53703
P: (608) 264-6278
F: (608) 267-2800
E: bruce.baker
@wisconsin.gov

Welfare

Administers the delivery of financial and medical benefits to low-income families and individuals.

ALABAMA
Ms. Nancy T. Buckner
Commissioner
Department of Human Resources
50 North Ripley Street
Montgomery, AL 36130
P: (334) 242-1160
F: (334) 242-0198
E: Nancy.Buckner
  @dhr.alabama.gov

ALASKA
Mr. Ron Kreher
Director
Division of Public Assistance
Department of Health & Social Services
P.O. Box 110640
Juneau, AK 99811
P: (907) 465-5847
F: (907) 465-5154
E: ron.kreher@alaska.gov

AMERICAN SAMOA
Ms. Leilua Stevenson
Director
Department of Human & Social Services
American Samoa Government
P.O. Box 997534
Pago Pago, AS
P: (684) 633-7506
F: (684) 633-7449

ARIZONA
Ms. Leona M. Hodges
Acting Director
Division of Benefits & Medical Eligibility
Department of Economic Security
1717 West Jefferson Street
Phoenix, AZ 85007
P: (602) 542-3596

ARKANSAS
Ms. Joni Jones
Director
Division of County Operations
P.O. Box 1437, Slot S301
Little Rock, AR 72203
P: (501) 682-8375
F: (501) 682-8367
E: joni.jones@arkansas.gov

CALIFORNIA
Mr. Will Lightbourne
Director
Department of Social Services
744 P Street
Sacramento, CA 95814
P: (916) 657-2598
F: (916) 651-6569

COLORADO
Mr. Reginald L. Bicha
Executive Director
Department of Human Services
1575 Sherman Street
Denver, CO 80203
P: (303) 866-5700
F: (303) 866-4740

CONNECTICUT
Mr. Roderick L. Bremby
Commissioner
Department of Social Services
25 Sigourney Street
Hartford, CT 06106
P: (860) 424-5053
E: roderick.bremby@ct.gov

DELAWARE
Ms. Elaine Archangelo
Director
Division of Social Services
Main Administration Bldg, 1st Fl. Annex
1901 North Dupont Highway
New Castle, DE 19720
P: (302) 255-9500
F: (302) 255-4433

DISTRICT OF COLUMBIA
Mr. David A. Berns
Director
Department of Human Services
64 New York Avenue, Northeast
6th Floor
Washington, DC 20002
P: (202) 671-4200
E: dhs@dc.gov

FLORIDA
Mr. David Wilkins
Secretary
Department of Children & Families
1317 Winewood Boulevard
Building 1, Room 202
Tallahassee, FL 32399
P: (850) 487-1111
F: (850) 922-2993
E: david_wilkins
  @dcf.state.fl.us

GEORGIA
Ms. Rachelle Carnesale
Director
Division of Family & Children Services
Two Peachtree Street, Northwest
Room 19-400
Atlanta, GA 30303
P: (404) 651-8409
F: (404) 657-5105

HAWAII
Ms. Patricia McManaman
Director
Department of Human Services
1390 Miller Street, Room 209
Honolulu, HI 96813
P: (808) 586-4997
F: (808) 586-4890
E: dhs@dhs.hawaii.gov

IDAHO
Mr. Russ Barron
Administrator
Division of Welfare
2nd & 6th Floors, Pete T. Cenarrusa Bldg
450 West State Street
Boise, ID 83720
P: (208) 332-7258
F: (208) 334-5571
E: barronr@dhw.idaho.gov

ILLINOIS
Ms. Julie Hamos
Director
Department of Healthcare & Family Services
201 South Grand Avenue, East
Springfield, IL 62763
P: (217) 782-1200

INDIANA
Ms. Pat Casanova
Director of Medicaid
Office of Medicaid Policy & Planning
402 West Washington Street, Room W461
P.O. Box 7083
Indianapolis, IN 46207
P: (317) 234-2407
F: (317) 233-4693
E: Pat.Casanova@fssa.in.gov

IOWA
Ms. Ann Wiebers
Administrator
Division of Financial, Health & Work Supports
Hoover State Office Building
1305 East Walnut Street
Des Moines, IA 50319
P: (515) 281-6080
F: (515) 281-7791
E: awieber@dhs.state.ia.us

KANSAS
Ms. Bobbi Mariani
Director
Economic & Employment Support
915 Southwest Harrison Street
Topeka, KS 66612
P: (785) 296-6750
F: (785) 296-6960

KENTUCKY
Ms. Patricia R. Wilson
Commissioner
Department for Community Based Services
275 East Main Street
Mail Stop 3W-A
Frankfort, KY 40621
P: (502) 564-3703
F: (502) 564-6907

MAINE
Ms. Stefanie Nadeau
Acting Director
Office of MaineCare Services
11 State House Station
Augusta, ME 04333
P: (207) 287-2093
F: (207) 287-2675
E: Stefanie.Nadeau
  @maine.gov

MASSACHUSETTS
Ms. Julia E. Kehoe
Commissioner
Department of Transitional Assistance
600 Washington Street
Boston, MA 02111
P: (617) 348-8500
F: (617) 348-8575

MICHIGAN
Ms. Maura D. Corrigan
Director
Department of Human Services
235 South Grand Avenue
P.O. Box 30037
Lansing, MI 48909
P: (517) 373-2035
F: (517) 335-6101
E: dhsweb@michigan.gov

MISSISSIPPI
Mr. Donald Thompson
Executive Director
Department of Human Services
750 North State Street
Jackson, MS 39202
P: (601) 359-4500

MISSOURI
Ms. Janel Luck
Director
Family Support Division
Department of Social Services
P.O. Box 2320
Jefferson City, MO 65102
P: (573) 751-3221

MONTANA
Ms. Anna Whiting Sorrell
Director
Department of Public Health &
Human Services
111 North Sanders, Room 301
P.O. Box 4210
Helena, MT 59604
P: (406) 444-5622
F: (406) 444-1970

NEVADA
Mr. Romaine E. Gilliland
Administrator
Division of Welfare & Social
Services
Department of Health & Human
Services
1470 College Parkway
Carson City, NV 89706
P: (775) 684-0500
F: (775) 684-0646
E: welfare@dwss.nv.gov

NEW HAMPSHIRE
Mr. Nicholas A. Toumpas
Commissioner
Department of Health & Human
Services
129 Pleasant Street
Concord, NH 03301
P: (603) 271-4331
F: (603) 271-4912
E: ntoumpas
@dhhs.state.nh.us

NEW JERSEY
Ms. Jeanette Page-Hawkins
Director
Division of Family
Development
P.O. Box 716
Trenton, NJ 08625
P: (609) 588-2400
F: (609) 584-4404

NEW MEXICO
Mr. Fred Sandoval
Director
Income Support Division
Human Services Department
2009 South Pacheco, Pollon
Plaza
Santa Fe, NM 87504
P: (505) 827-7250

NEW YORK
Ms. Elizabeth R. Berlin
Executive Deputy Secretary
Office of Temporary &
Disability Assistance
40 North Pearl Street
Albany, NY 12243
P: (518) 474-4152
F: (518) 486-9179

NORTH CAROLINA
Ms. Sherry S. Bradsher
Director
Division of Social Services
325 North Salisbury Street
2401 Mail Service Center
Raleigh, NC 27699
P: (919) 733-3055
F: (919) 733-9386
E: sherry.bradsher
@dhhs.nc.gov

NORTH DAKOTA
Ms. Carol K. Olson
Executive Director
Department of Human Services
State Capitol, Judicial Wing
600 East Boulevard Avenue,
Dept. 325
Bismarck, ND 58505
P: (701) 328-2538
F: (701) 328-1545
E: colson@nd.gov

**NORTHERN MARIANA
ISLANDS**
Ms. Eleanor S. Dela Cruz
Administrator
Nutrition Assistance Program
Caller Box 10007, Capital Hill
Saipan, MP 96950
P: (670) 235-9889
F: (670) 235-9250

OHIO
Mr. Michael B. Colbert
Director
Department of Job & Family
Services
30 East Broad Street, 32nd Floor
Columbus, OH 43215
P: (614) 466-6283
F: (614) 466-2815

OKLAHOMA
Ms. Mary Stalnaker
Director
Family Support Services
Division
Department of Human Services
P.O. Box 25352
Oklahoma City, OK 73125
P: (405) 521-3076
F: (405) 521-4158
E: fssinquiries@okdhs.org

OREGON
Ms. Erinn L. Kelley-Siel
Acting Director
Department of Human Services
500 Summer Street, Northeast,
E-62
Salem, OR 97301
P: (503) 945-5944
F: (503) 378-2897
E: erinn.kelley-siel
@state.or.us

PENNSYLVANIA
Mr. Gary D. Alexander
Acting Secretary
Department of Public Welfare
P.O. Box 2675
Harrisburg, PA 17105
P: (717) 787-2600
F: (717) 772-2062

PUERTO RICO
Ms. Yanitsia Irizarry
Mendez
Secretary
Department of the Family
P.O. Box 11398
San Juan, PR 00910
P: (787) 294-4900
F: (787) 294-0732

RHODE ISLAND
Ms. Sandra M. Powell
Director
Department of Human Services
Louis Pasteur Building
600 New London Avenue
Cranston, RI 02920
P: (401) 462-2121
F: (401) 462-3677
E: Director@dhs.ri.gov

SOUTH CAROLINA
Ms. Lillian B. Koller
Director
Department of Social Services
1535 Confederate Avenue
Extension
P.O. Box 1520
Columbia, SC 29202
P: (803) 898-7360
F: (803) 898-7277

SOUTH DAKOTA
Ms. Kim Malsam-Rysdon
Secretary
Department of Social Services
700 Governors Drive
Pierre, SD 57501
P: (605) 773-3165
F: (605) 773-4855
E: DSSInfo@state.sd.us

TENNESSEE
Dr. Raquel Hatter
Commissioner
Department of Human Services
400 Deaderick Street, 15th Floor
Nashville, TN 37243
P: (615) 313-4700
F: (615) 741-4165

TEXAS
Mr. Thomas Suehs
Executive Commissioner
Health & Human Services
Commission
4900 North Lamar
P.O. Box 13247
Austin, TX 78711
P: (512) 424-6502
F: (512) 424-6587

Mr. Chris Traylor
Commissioner
Department of Aging &
Disability Services
701 West 51st Street
P.O. Box 149030
Austin, TX 78714
P: (512) 438-3011
F: (512) 438-4220

U.S. VIRGIN ISLANDS
Mrs. Ermine Boschulte
Administrator
Division of Financial Programs
Knud Hansen Complex,
Building A
1303 Hospital Grounds
St. Thomas, VI 00802
P: (340) 774-2399
F: (340) 774-3466

UTAH
Ms. Kristen Cox
Executive Director
Department of Workforce
Services
P.O. Box 45249
Salt Lake City, UT 84145
P: (801) 526-9210
F: (801) 526-9211
E: kristencox@utah.gov

VERMONT
Mr. Dave Yacovone
Commissioner
Department for Children &
Families
103 South Main Street
Montpelier, VT 05671
P: (802) 241-2100
E: dave.yacovone
@ahs.state.vt.us

Welfare

VIRGINIA
Mr. Martin D. Brown
Commissioner
Department of Social Services
801 East Main Street
Richmond, VA 23219
P: (804) 726-7000
E: martin.brown
   @dss.virginia.gov

WASHINGTON
Ms. Susan N. Dreyfus
Secretary
Department of Social & Health
Services
P.O. Box 45130
Olympia, WA 98504
P: (360) 902-7800

WEST VIRGINIA
Mr. Michael J. Lewis
Cabinet Secretary
Department of Health & Human
Resources
One Davis Square, Suite 100
East
Charleston, WV 25301
P: (304) 558-0684
F: (304) 558-1130
E: DHHRSecretary@wv.gov

WISCONSIN
Ms. Jane Pawasarat
Administrator
Division of Employment &
Training
201 East Washington Avenue
Madison, WI 53707
P: (608) 266-3485
E: Jane.Pawasarat
   @dwd.wisconsin.gov

WYOMING
Mr. Steve Corsi
Director of Family Services
Department of Family Services
Hathaway Building, 3rd Floor
2300 Capitol Avenue
Cheyenne, WY 82002
P: (307) 777-7564
F: (307) 777-7747

Workers Compensation

Administers laws providing insurance and compensation for workers for job-related illnesses, injury or death.

ALABAMA
Mr. Scottie Spates
Director
Workers' Compensation
Division
649 Monroe Street
Montgomery, AL 36131
P: (334) 242-2868
F: (334) 353-8262
E: scottie.spates
@dir.alabama.gov

ALASKA
Mr. Michael Monagle
Director
Division of Workers'
Compensation
P.O. Box 115512
Juneau, AK 99811
P: (907) 465-2790
F: (907) 465-2797
E: michael.monagle
@alaska.gov

AMERICAN SAMOA
Lt. Col. Evelyn Vaiautolu
Langford
Director
Department of Human
Resources
American Samoa Government
Pago Pago, AS 96799
P: (684) 644-4485
F: (684) 633-1139

ARIZONA
Ms. Laura L. McGrory
Director
Industrial Commission
800 West Washington Street
Phoenix, AZ 85007
P: (602) 542-4411
F: (602) 542-7889
E: lmcgrory@ica.state.az.us

ARKANSAS
Mr. Alan McClain
CEO
Workers' Compensation
Commission
324 Spring Street
P.O. Box 950
Little Rock, AR 72203
P: (501) 682-3930
F: (501) 682-2777
E: amcclain
@awcc.state.ar.us

CALIFORNIA
Ms. Destie Overpeck
Chief Legal Counsel
Division of Workers'
Compensation
1515 Clay Street, 17th Floor
Oakland, CA 94612
P: (510) 286-0656
E: doverpeck@dir.ca.gov

COLORADO
Mr. Paul Tauriello
Director
Division of Workers
Compensation
633 17th Street, Suite 400
Denver, CO 80202
P: (303) 318-8700
F: (303) 318-8710

CONNECTICUT
Mr. John A. Mastropietro
Chair
Workers' Compensation
Commission
Capitol Place
21 Oak Street
Hartford, CT 06106
P: (860) 493-1500
F: (860) 247-1361
E: wcc.chairmansoffice
@po.state.ct.us

DELAWARE
Mr. John F. Kirk III
Administrator
Office of Workers'
Compensation
4425 North Market Street
Wilmington, DE 19802
P: (302) 761-8200
F: (302) 761-6601
E: jkirk@state.de.us

DISTRICT OF COLUMBIA
Ms. Lisa Maria Mallory
Acting Director
Department of Employment
Services
4058 Minnesota Avenue,
Northeast
Washington, DC 20019
P: (202) 724-7000
F: (202) 673-6993
E: does@dc.gov

FLORIDA
Mr. Tanner Holloman
Director
Division of Workers'
Compensation
200 East Gaines Street
Tallahassee, FL 32399
P: (850) 413-1600
E: Tanner.Holloman
@myfloridacfo.com

GEORGIA
Mr. Stan Carter
Executive Director/Chief
Operating Officer
State Board of Workers'
Compensation
270 Peachtree Street, Northwest
Atlanta, GA 30303
P: (404) 656-2048

GUAM
Ms. Leah Beth Naholowaa
Director
Department of Labor
Government of Guam
P.O. Box 9970
Tamuning, GU 96931
P: (671) 647-6510
F: (671) 674-6517

HAWAII
Mr. Gary S. Hamada
Administrator
Disability Compensation
Division
830 Punchbowl Street, Room
209
P.O. Box 3769
Honolulu, HI 96812
P: (808) 586-9151
F: (808) 586-9219
E: Gary.S.Hamada@hawaii.gov

IDAHO
Mr. R.D. Maynard
Chairman
Industrial Commission
700 Clearwater Lane
P.O. Box 83720
Boise, ID 83720
P: (208) 334-6000
F: (208) 334-2321
E: rmaynard@iic.idaho.gov

ILLINOIS
Mr. Mitch Weisz
Acting Chair
Workers' Compensation
Commission
100 West Randolph Street,
#8-200
Chicago, IL 60601
P: (312) 814-6560

INDIANA
Ms. Linda Hamilton
Chair
Worker's Compensation Board
402 West Washington Street,
Room W-196
Indianapolis, IN 46204
P: (317) 232-3809
F: (317) 233-5493
E: lhamilton@wcb.in.gov

IOWA
Mr. Christopher J. Godfrey
Commissioner
Division of Workers'
Compensation
Workforce Development
Organization
1000 East Grand Avenue
Des Moines, IA 50319
P: (515) 281-5387
F: (515) 281-6501
E: Christopher.Godfrey
@iwd.iowa.gov

KANSAS
Ms. Paula Greathouse
Director
Division of Workers
Compensation
800 Southwest Jackson Street,
7th Floor
Topeka, KS 66612
P: (785) 296-2996
F: (785) 296-0839
E: Paula.Greathouse
@hr.state.ks.us

KENTUCKY
Mr. Dwight T. Lovan
Commissioner
Department of Workers' Claims
657 Chamberlin Avenue
Frankfort, KY 40601
P: (502) 564-4439
F: (502) 564-5732

LOUISIANA
Mr. Jay Augustine
Deputy Executive Director
Workforce Commission
1001 North 23rd Street
Baton Rouge, LA 70802
P: (225) 342-3111
F: (225) 342-3778

Workers Compensation

MAINE
Mr. Phil Sighinolfi
Executive Director/Chair
Workers' Compensation Board
27 State House Station
Augusta, ME 04333
P: (207) 287-3751
F: (207) 287-7198
E: phil.sighinolfi
  @maine.gov

MARYLAND
Ms. Mary K. Ahearn
Executive Director of
Administration
Workers' Compensation
Commission
10 East Baltimore Street, 7th
Floor
Baltimore, MD 21202
P: (410) 864-5308
F: (410) 333-8122
E: Mahearn@Wcc.state.md.us

MASSACHUSETTS
Mr. Phillip Hillman
Department of Industrial
Accidents
1 Congress Street, Suite 100
Boston, MA 02114
P: (617) 727-4900
F: (617) 727-6477

MICHIGAN
Mr. Kevin Elsenheimer
Director
Workers' Compensation Agency
7150 Harris Drive
P.O. Box 30016
Lansing, MI 48909
P: (517) 322-1106
F: (517) 322-1808

MINNESOTA
Mr. Ken Peterson
Commissioner
Department of Labor & Industry
443 Lafayette Road North
St. Paul, MN 55155
P: (651) 284-5010
F: (651) 284-5721
E: dli.commissioner
  @state.mn.us

MISSISSIPPI
Mr. Liles Williams
Chair
Workers' Compensation
Commission
1428 Lakeland Drive
P.O. Box 5300
Jackson, MS 39296
P: (601) 987-4200

MISSOURI
Mr. Brian May
Acting Director
Division of Workers'
Compensation
3315 West Truman Boulevard,
Room 131
P.O. Box 58
Jefferson City, MO 65102
P: (573) 751-4231
F: (573) 751-2012
E: workerscomp@dolir.mo.gov

MONTANA
Mr. Keith Messmer
Bureau Chief
Workers' Compensation
Regulation Bureau
1805 Prospect Avenue
P.O. Box 8011
Helena, MT 59624
P: (406) 444-6541
F: (406) 444-1676

NEBRASKA
Mr. Glenn Morton
Administrator
Workers' Compensation Court
P.O. Box 98908
Lincoln, NE 68509
P: (402) 471-3602
F: (402) 471-2700
E: gmorton@wcc.state.ne.us

NEVADA
Mr. Donald E. Jayne
Administrator
Division of Industrial Relations
Department of Business &
Industry
400 West King Street, Suite 400
Carson City, NV 89703
P: (775) 684-7260
F: (775) 687-6305
E: djayne@business.nv.gov

NEW HAMPSHIRE
Ms. Kathryn J. Barger
Director
Workers' Compensation
Division
Department of Labor
95 Pleasant Street
Concord, NH 03301
P: (603) 271-2086
F: (603) 271-6194
E: kbarger
  @labor.state.nh.us

NEW JERSEY
Mr. Peter J. Calderone
Director/Chief Judge
Division of Workers'
Compensation
P.O. Box 381
Trenton, NJ 08625
P: (609) 292-2515
F: (609) 984-3924
E: dwc@dol.state.nj.us

NEW MEXICO
Mr. Ned S. Fuller
Director
Workers' Compensation
Administration
2410 Centre Avenue, Southeast
P.O. Box 27198
Albuquerque, NM 87125
P: (505) 841-6000
F: (505) 841-6009

NEW YORK
Mr. Robert E. Beloten
Chair
Workers' Compensation Board
20 Park Street
Albany, NY 12207
P: (518) 462-8880
F: (518) 473-1415

NORTH DAKOTA
Mr. Bryan Klipfel
Director
Workforce Safety & Insurance
1600 East Century Avenue,
Suite 1
P.O. Box 5585
Bismarck, ND 58506
P: (701) 328-3762
F: (701) 328-3820
E: bklipfel@nd.gov

**NORTHERN MARIANA
ISLANDS**
Mr. Frank Cabrera
Workers' Compensation
Commission
P.O. Box 501247
Capitol Hill
Saipan, MP 96950
P: (670) 664-8024
E: cabreraF
  @NMIretirement.com

OHIO
Mr. Steve Buehrer
Administrator/CEO
Bureau of Workers'
Compensation
William Green Building
30 West Spring Street
Columbus, OH 43215
P: (614) 466-5223
F: (877) 520-6446

OKLAHOMA
Mr. Michael Clingman
Administrator
Workers' Compensation Court
1915 North Stiles Avenue
Room 122
Oklahoma City, OK 73105
P: (405) 522-8600

OREGON
Mr. John L. Shilts
Division Administrator
Workers' Compensation
Division
P.O. Box 14480
350 Winter Street, Northeast
Salem, OR 97309
P: (503) 947-7810
F: (503) 947-7581
E: john.l.shilts
  @state.or.us

PENNSYLVANIA
Ms. Elizabeth A. Crum
Deputy Secretary for
Compensation & Insurance
Bureau of Workers'
Compensation
1700 Labor and Industry
Building
Harrisburg, PA 17121
P: (717) 787-5082
E: ecrum@state.pa.us

RHODE ISLAND
Mr. Matthew P. Carey III
Assistant Director
Workers Compensation Self
Insurance/Workers
Compensation Education
Department of Labor & Training
1511 Pontiac Avenue
Cranston, RI 02920
P: (401) 462-8127
F: (401) 462-8872
E: mcarey@dlt.ri.gov

SOUTH CAROLINA
Mr. Gary M. Cannon
Executive Director
Workers' Compensation
Commission
P.O. Box 1715
Columbia, SC 29202
P: (803) 737-5744
F: (803) 737-5764
E: gcannon@wcc.sc.gov

SOUTH DAKOTA
Mr. James E. Marsh
Director
Division of Human Rights
700 Governors Drive
Pierre, SD 57501
P: (605) 773-3681
F: (605) 773-4211
E: james.marsh@state.sd.us

TENNESSEE
Ms. Teresa Bullington
Assistant Administrator
Department of Labor &
Workforce Development
Workers' Compensation
Division
220 French Landing Drive
Nashville, TN 37243
P: (615) 741-2395
F: (615) 532-1468
E: wc.info@tn.gov

TEXAS
Mr. Rod Bordelon
Commissioner
Division of Workers'
Compensation
Department of Insurance
7551 Metro Center Drive, Suite
100
Austin, TX 78744
P: (512) 804-4400

UTAH
Mr. Ron Dressler
Acting Director
Industrial Accidents Division
160 East 300 South, 3rd Floor
P.O. Box 146610
Salt Lake City, UT 84114
P: (801) 530-6841
F: (801) 530-6804
E: rdressler@utah.gov

VERMONT
Mr. J. Stephen Monahan
Director
Workers' Compensation &
Safety Division
5 Green Mountain Drive
P.O. Box 488
Montpelier, VT 05601
P: (802) 828-2138
F: (802) 828-4022
E: stephen.monahan
   @state.vt.us

VIRGINIA
Ms. Virginia R. Diamond
Workers' Compensation
Commission
1000 DMV Drive
Richmond, VA 23220
P: (804) 367-8657
F: (804) 367-9740

WASHINGTON
Mr. Frank E. Fennerty Jr.
Labor Member
Board of Industrial Insurance
Appeals
2430 Chandler Court, Southwest
P.O. Box 42401
Olympia, WA 98504
P: (360) 753-6824
F: (360) 586-5611
E: fennerty@biia.wa.gov

WEST VIRGINIA
Ms. Jane L. Cline
Commissioner
Insurance Commission
1124 Smith Street
Charleston, WV 25301
P: (304) 558-3029
F: (304) 558-0412
E: jane.cline
   @wvinsurance.gov

WISCONSIN
Mr. John Metcalf
Division Administrator
Workers Compensation Division
201 East Washington Avenue
P.O. Box 7901
Madison, WI 53707
P: (608) 266-1340
F: (608) 267-0394
E: John.Metcalf
   @dwd.wisconsin.gov

Workforce Development

Administers job training and services for the unemployed, underemployed and economically disadvantaged in the state.

ALABAMA
Mr. Thomas Surtees
Director
Department of Industrial Relations
649 Monroe Street
Montgomery, AL 36131
P: (334) 242-8078
F: (334) 242-3960
E: tom.surtees
@dir.alabama.gov

ALASKA
Mr. Guy Bell
Director
Department of Labor & Workforce Development
Division of Administrative Services
P.O. Box 111149
Juneau, AK 99811
P: (907) 465-5980
F: (907) 465-2107
E: guy.bell@alaska.gov

Mr. Click Bishop
Commissioner
Department of Labor & Workforce Development
P.O. Box 21149
Juneau, AK 99802
P: (907) 465-2700
F: (907) 465-2784
E: commissioner.labor
@ak.gov

Mr. Thomas W. Nelson
Director
Department of Labor & Workforce Development
Division of Employment Security
P.O. Box 115509
Juneau, AK 99811
P: (907) 465-2712
F: (907) 465-4537
E: esd.director@alaska.gov

AMERICAN SAMOA
Lt. Col. Evelyn Vaiautolu Langford
Director
Department of Human Resources
American Samoa Government
Pago Pago, AS 96799
P: (684) 644-4485
F: (684) 633-1139

ARIZONA
Mr. James Apperson
Assistant Director
Divison of Employment & Rehabilitation Services
Department of Economic Security
1717 West Jefferson Street
Phoenix, AZ 85007
P: (602) 542-4910
E: japperson@azdes.gov

ARKANSAS
Mr. Artee Williams
Director
Department of Workforce Services
#2 Capitol Mall
Little Rock, AR 72201
P: (501) 682-2121
E: artee.williams
@arkansas.gov

CALIFORNIA
Mr. Jaime Fall
Deputy Secretary of Workforce & Development
Labor & Workforce Development Agency
801 K Street, Suite 2101
Sacramento, CA 95814
P: (916) 327-9064

Ms. Pam Harris
Chief Deputy Director
Employment Development Department
P.O. Box 826880, MIC 83
Sacramento, CA 94280
P: (916) 654-8210
E: pharris@edd.ca.gov

COLORADO
Ms. Ellen Golombek
Executive Director
Department of Labor & Employment
633 17th Street, Suite 201
Denver, CO 80202
P: (303) 318-8000
F: (303) 318-8048
E: egolombek@state.co.us

Ms. Stephanie Steffens
Director
Workforce Development Council
633 17th Street, 12th Floor
Denver, CO 80202
P: (303) 318-8113
E: stephanie.steffens
@state.co.us

CONNECTICUT
Mr. Glenn Marshall
Commissioner
Department of Labor
200 Folly Brook Boulevard
Wethersfield, CT 06109
P: (860) 263-6505
F: (860) 263-6529
E: glenn.marshall@ct.gov

DELAWARE
Mr. John McMahon
Secretary of Labor
Department of Labor
4425 North Market Street, 4th Floor
Wilmington, DE 19802
P: (302) 761-8000
F: (302) 761-6621
E: john.mcmahon@state.de.us

Ms. Lori Reeder
Director
Department of Labor
Division of Employment & Training
4425 North Market Street
Wilmington, DE 19802
P: (302) 761-8110
E: lori.reeder@state.de.us

DISTRICT OF COLUMBIA
Ms. Lisa Maria Mallory
Acting Director
Department of Employment Services
4058 Minnesota Avenue, Northeast
Washington, DC 20019
P: (202) 724-7000
F: (202) 673-6993
E: does@dc.gov

FLORIDA
Ms. Cynthia R. Lorenzo
Director
Agency for Workforce Innovation
107 East Madison Street
MSC 110, Caldwell Building
Tallahassee, FL 32399
P: (850) 245-7298
F: (850) 921-3223
E: cynthia.lorenzo
@flaawi.com

GEORGIA
Hon. Mark Butler (R)
Commissioner
Department of Labor
148 International Boulevard Northeast
Atlanta, GA 30303
P: (404) 232-7300
F: (404) 656-2683
E: mark.butler
@dol.state.ga.us

HAWAII
Mr. Dwight Y. Takamine
Director
Department of Labor & Industrial Relations
830 Punchbowl Stree, Room 321
Honolulu, HI 96813
P: (808) 586-8865
F: (808) 586-9099

IDAHO
Mr. Roger B. Madsen
Director
Department of Labor
317 West Main Street
Boise, ID 83735
P: (208) 332-3579
F: (208) 334-6430
E: rmadsen@cl.idaho.gov

ILLINOIS
Ms. Therese McMahon
Deputy Director
Department of Commerce & Economic Opportunity
Office of Employment & Training
620 E. Adams, 5th Floor
Springfield, IL 62701
P: (217) 785-6006

Mr. Warren Ribley
Director
Department of Commerce & Economic Opportunity
James R. Thompson Center
100 West Randolph
Chicago, IL 60601
P: (312) 814-7179

INDIANA
Mr. Mark W. Everson
Commissioner
Department of Workforce Development
10 North Senate Avenue
Indianapolis, IN 46204
P: (317) 232-7676
E: MEverson@dwd.IN.gov

Workforce Development

IOWA
Ms. Teresa Wahlert
Agency Director
Workforce Development
Organization
1000 East Grand Avenue
Des Moines, IA 50319
P: (515) 281-5364
E: teresa.wahlert
   @iwd.iowa.gov

KANSAS
Ms. Karin Brownlee
Secretary
Department of Labor
401 Southwest Topeka
Boulevard
Topeka, KS 66603
P: (785) 296-5058
F: (785) 368-5286
E: karin.brownlee
   @dol.ks.gov

Mr. Pat George
Secretary
Department of Commerce
1000 Southwest Jackson Street,
Suite 100
Topeka, KS 66612
P: (785) 296-3481
F: (785) 296-5055
E: pgeorge
   @kansascommerce.com

KENTUCKY
Ms. Linda Prewitt
Division Director
Division of Workforce &
Employment Services
Office of Employment &
Training
275 East Main Street
Frankfort, KY 40621
P: (502) 564-3906
F: (502) 564-7459

LOUISIANA
Mr. Curt Eysink
Executive Director
Workforce Commission
1001 North 23rd Street
Baton Rouge, LA 70802
P: (225) 342-3111
F: (225) 342-3778
E: ceysink@lwc.la.gov

Mr. John Riley
Director
Workforce Commission
Office of Workforce
Development
1001 North 23rd Street
Baton Rouge, LA 70802
P: (225) 342-3111

MAINE
Ms. Laura Boyett
Acting Commissioner
Department of Labor
P.O. Box 259
Augusta, ME 04332
P: (207) 287-3787
F: (207) 623-7934
E: luara.l.boyett@maine.gov

MARYLAND
Ms. Paulette Francois
Assistant Secretary
Division of Workforce
Development & Adult Learning
1100 North Eutaw Street, Room
616
Baltimore, MD 21201
P: (410) 767-2997
E: pfrancois
   @dllr.state.md.us

MASSACHUSETTS
Ms. Tamika N. Correia
Director
Workforce Investment Board
Charles F. Hurley Building
19 Staniford Street
Boston, MA 02114
P: (617) 626-5680
F: (617) 727-8671

Ms. Joanne F. Goldstein
Secretary
Executive Office of Labor &
Workforce Development
One Ashburton Place
Suite 2112
Boston, MA 02108
P: (617) 626-7122
F: (617) 727-1090
E: joanne.goldstein
   @state.ma.us

MICHIGAN
Ms. Janet Howard
Deputy Director
Bureau of Workforce Programs
Victor Office Center
201 N. Washington Square, 5th
Floor
Lansing, MI 48911
P: (517) 335-5858
F: (517) 241-8217

Mr. Andrew S. Levin
Acting Director
Department of Energy, Labor &
Economic Growth
P.O. Box 30004
Lansing, MI 48909
P: (517) 373-7230
F: (517) 373-2129
E: LevinA@michigan.gov

MINNESOTA
Ms. Bonnie Elsey
Director
Department of Employment &
Economic Development
Workforce Development
332 Minnesota Street, Suite
E200
St. Paul, MN 55101
P: (651) 259-7563
E: bonnie.elsey@state.mn.us

MISSISSIPPI
Mr. Les Range
Executive Director
Department of Employment
Security
1235 Echelon Parkway
P.O. Box 1699
Jackson, MS 39215
P: (601) 321-6100
F: (601) 321-6104
E: lrange@mdes.ms.gov

MISSOURI
Ms. Julie Gibson
Director
Department of Economic
Development
Division of Workforce
Development
P.O. Box 1157
Jefferson City, MO 65102
P: (573) 751-3349
F: (573) 751-8162
E: dwdsupport@ded.mo.gov

Mr. Lawrence G. Rebman
Director
Department of Labor &
Industrial Relations
P.O. Box 504
Jefferson City, MO 65102
P: (573) 751-4091
F: (573) 751-4945
E: larry.rebman
   @labor.mo.gov

MONTANA
Mr. Mike Cooney
Administrator
Workforce Services Division
Department of Labor & Industry
P.O. Box 1728
Helena, MT 59624
P: (406) 444-2648
F: (406) 444-3037

Mr. Keith Kelly
Commissioner
Department of Labor & Industry
P.O. Box 1728
Helena, MT 59624
P: (406) 444-9091
F: (406) 444-1394
E: dliquestions@mt.gov

NEBRASKA
Ms. Catherine D. Lang
Commissioner of Labor
Department of Labor
P.O. Box 94600
Lincoln, NE 68509
P: (402) 471-9000
F: (402) 471-2318
E: catherine.lang
   @nebraska.gov

Ms. Joan Modrell
Director
Department of Labor
Office of Workforce Programs
550 S. 16th Street
Lincoln, NE 68509
P: (402) 471-5919

NEVADA
Ms. Cindy A. Jones
Deputy Director/Administrator
for the Employment Security
Division
Department of Employment,
Training & Rehabilitation
Employment Security Division
500 East Third Street
Carson City, NV 89713
P: (775) 684-3909
F: (775) 684-3850
E: cajones@nvdetr.org

Mr. Larry J. Mosley
Director
Department of Employment,
Training & Rehabilitation
500 East Third Street
Carson City, NV 89713
P: (702) 486-7923
F: (775) 684-3850

NEW HAMPSHIRE
Mr. Darrell L. Gates
Deputy Commissioner
Department of Employment
Security
32 South Main Street
Concord, NH 03301
P: (603) 228-4064
E: darrell.l.gates
   @nhes.nh.gov

Workforce Development

NEW JERSEY
Mr. Harold Wirths
Commissioner
Department of Labor &
Workforce Development
P.O. Box 110
Trenton, NJ 08625
P: (609) 292-2323
F: (609) 633-9271
E: hal.wirths
    @dol.state.nj.us

NEW MEXICO
Ms. Celina Bussey
Secretary
Department of Workforce
Solutions
401 Broadway Northeast
Albuquerque, NM 87103
P: (505) 841-8405
F: (505) 841-8491

NEW YORK
Ms. Karen Coleman
Director
Department of Labor
Employment & Workforce
Solutions
State Campus, Building 12
Albany, NY 12240
P: (518) 457-9000

Ms. Colleen C. Gardner
Commissioner
Department of Labor
W. Averell Harriman State
Office Campus
Building 12
Albany, NY 12240
P: (518) 457-9000
F: (518) 485-6297
E: colleen.gardner
    @labor.state.ny.us

NORTH CAROLINA
Ms. Lynn Holmes
Chair
Employment Security
Commission
P.O. Box 25903
Raleigh, NC 27
P: (919) 733-4329
F: (919) 733-9420

Mr. Roger Shackleford
Executive Director of Workforce
Development
Department of Commerce
313 Chapanoke Road, Suite 120
4316 Mail Service Center
Raleigh, NC 27699
P: (919) 329-5230
F: (919) 662-4770

NORTH DAKOTA
Ms. Maren L. Daley
Executive Director
Job Service North Dakota
P.O. Box 5507
Bismarck, ND 58506
P: (701) 328-2825
F: (701) 328-4000
E: mdaley@nd.gov

OHIO
Mr. Michael B. Colbert
Director
Department of Job & Family
Services
30 East Broad Street, 32nd Floor
Columbus, OH 43215
P: (614) 466-6283
F: (614) 466-2815

Ms. Susan Crotty
Deputy Director
Department of Job & Family
Services
Office of Workforce
Development
30 East Broad Street, 32nd Floor
Columbus, OH 43215
P: (614) 466-7609
F: (614) 466-2815

OKLAHOMA
Mr. Richard McPherson
Executive Director
Employment Security
Commission
2401 North Lincoln Boulevard
Will Rogers Memorial Office
Building
Oklahoma City, OK 73105
P: (405) 557-7201

OREGON
Ms. Camille Preus
Commissioner
Department of Community
Colleges & Workforce
Development
255 Capitol Street, Northeast
Salem, OR 97310
P: (503) 947-2433
F: (503) 378-3365
E: camille.preus
    @state.or.us

Ms. Laurie A. Warner
Director
Employment Department
875 Union Street, NE
Salem, OR 97311
P: (503) 947-1477
F: (503) 947-1472
E: laurie.a.warner
    @state.or.us

PENNSYLVANIA
Ms. Julia Hearthway
Acting Secretary
Department of Labor & Industry
651 Boas Street, Room 1700
Harrisburg, PA 17121
P: (717) 787-5279
F: (717) 787-8826

PUERTO RICO
Mr. Miguel Romero
Director
Department of Labor & Human
Resources
P.O. Box 191020
San Juan, PR 00919
P: (787) 754-5353
F: (787) 756-1149

RHODE ISLAND
Mr. Charles J. Fogarty
Director
Department of Labor & Training
1511 Pontiac Avenue
Cranston, RI 02920
P: (401) 462-8000
F: (401) 462-8872
E: director-dlt@dlt.ri.gov

SOUTH CAROLINA
Mr. John L. Finan
Executive Director
Employment Security
Commission
1550 Gadsden Street
P.O. Box 995
Columbia, SC 29202
P: (803) 737-2617

SOUTH DAKOTA
Ms. Marcia Hultman
Deputy Secretary of Labor
Division of Workforce Services
Division of Workforce Services
700 Governors Drive
Pierre, SD 57501
P: (605) 773-3101
F: (605) 773-6184

Ms. Pamela S. Roberts
Secretary
Department of Labor
700 Governors Drive
Pierre, SD 57501
P: (605) 773-3101
F: (605) 773-4211
E: pamela.roberts
    @state.sd.us

TENNESSEE
Ms. Susan Cowden
Administrator
Department of Labor &
Workforce Development
Workforce Development
Division
220 French Landing Drive
Nashville, TN 37243
P: (615) 741-1031
F: (615) 741-5078
E: susan.cowden@tn.gov

Ms. Karla Davis
Commissioner
Department of Labor &
Workforce Development
Andrew Johnson Tower
710 James Robertson Parkway
Nashville, TN 37243
P: (615) 741-6642
F: (615) 741-5078
E: karla.davis@state.tn.us

TEXAS
Mr. Larry Jones
Director of Workforce
Development
Workforce Commission
Workforce Development
Division
101 East 15th Street
Austin, TX 78778
P: (512) 936-0697
E: larry.jones
    @twc.state.tx.us

Mr. Larry E. Temple
Executive Director
Workforce Commission
101 East 15th Street
Austin, TX 78778
P: (512) 463-0735
F: (512) 475-2321
E: larry.temple
    @twc.state.tx.us

UTAH
Ms. Kristen Cox
Executive Director
Department of Workforce
Services
P.O. Box 45249
Salt Lake City, UT 84145
P: (801) 526-9210
F: (801) 526-9211
E: kristencox@utah.gov

VERMONT
Ms. Annie Noonan
Commissioner
Department of Labor
P.O. Box 488
Montpelier, VT 05602
P: (802) 828-4301
F: (802) 828-4022
E: annie.noonan@state.vt.us

VIRGINIA
Mr. John R. Broadway
Commissioner
Employment Commission
703 East Main Street
Richmond, VA 23219
P: (804) 786-1485
E: john.broadway
    @vec.virginia.gov

Mr. Nicholas Kessler
Deputy Commissioner
Employment Commission
703 East Main Street
Richmond, VA 12119
P: (804) 786-1485
E: nicholas.kessler
    @vec.virginia.gov

WASHINGTON
Mr. Paul Trause
Commissioner
Employment Security
Department
212 Maple Park Avenue,
Southeast
P.O. Box 9046
Olympia, WA 98507
P: (360) 902-9301
E: ptrause@esd.wa.gov

WISCONSIN
Mr. Manny Perez
Secretary
Department of Workforce
Development
P.O. Box 7946
Madison, WI 53707
P: (608) 267-9692
F: (608) 266-1784
E: manuel.perez
    @dwd.wisconsin.gov

WYOMING
Ms. Joan Evans
Director
Department of Workforce
Services
122 West 25th Street
Herschler Building, 2 East
Cheyenne, WY 82002
P: (307) 777-8650
E: jevans1@state.wy.us